NIGHTJARS

A GUIDE TO NIGHTJARS
AND RELATED NIGHTBIRDS

NIGHTJARS

A GUIDE TO NIGHTJARS
AND RELATED NIGHTBIRDS

NIGEL CLEERE

ILLUSTRATED BY DAVE NURNEY

PICA PRESS
SUSSEX

Pica Press
(an imprint of Helm Information Ltd.)
The Banks, Mountfield,
Nr. Robertsbridge,
East Sussex TN32 5JY

ISBN 1-873403-48-8

A catalogue record for this book is available from the British Library.

Published in the Netherlands and Belgium as *Dutch Birding Vogelgids 10* by
Ger Meesters Boekprodukties
Vrijheidsweg 86,
2033 CE Haarlem,
The Netherlands

ISBN 90-74345-18-2
(Netherlands and Belgium only)

Distributed in Southern Africa by
Russel Friedman Books CC
PO Box 73,
Halfway House,
1685,
South Africa.

Edited by Nigel Collar
Series Editor: Nigel Redman

Production and design by Fluke Art, Bexhill on Sea, East Sussex
Colour separation by The Scanning Gallery, Tonbridge, Kent
Printed by Midas Printing, Hong Kong

CONTENTS

INTRODUCTION

The hours of darkness conceal the activities of a group of nocturnal birds which, despite their almost global distribution, generally remain little known, unstudied and difficult to observe. Nightjars and their relatives are secretive birds of the night, generally appearing in the fading light of dusk, and vanishing again before the following sunrise.

In many countries, they have long been the subject of local folklore, and one of the oldest and most widespread beliefs concerns the European Nightjar, which was thought to visit livestock during the night, and suckle milk from goats and other animals. First mentioned thousands of years ago by Aristotle, this belief became widespread throughout much of Europe and gave rise to the colloquial name 'goatsucker', a term still often used for many nightjars to this day. It is also reflected by the scientific name of the largest genus within the group, *Caprimulgus*, meaning a milker of goats.

Four other bird families (potoos, frogmouths, owlet-nightjars and oilbird) are closely related to nightjars, and together they form a distinct avian grouping, the order Caprimulgiformes. These remarkable birds offer many exciting challenges in all aspects of ornithological study, including real potential to discover species new to science. Prigogine's Nightjar (1990), Bahian Nighthawk (1994) and Nechisar Nightjar (1995) have only recently been described, and unidentified birds continue to be sighted, photographed and tape-recorded in many parts of the world. In addition, several elusive species that have not been seen for many years await possible rediscovery, e.g. New Caledonian Owlet-nightjar (known only from the type specimen taken in 1880), Jamaican Poorwill (last seen in about 1860), Cayenne Nightjar (known only from the type specimen taken in 1920) and the very distinctive New Caledonian subspecies of White-throated Nightjar (known only from the type specimen taken in 1939).

This book is the first comprehensive guide to include and illustrate all the known Caprimulgiformes, and it hopefully summarises much of what is currently known about these fascinating birds. The author recognises that this work is only a beginning, and invites anyone with new information on caprimulgiform biology to contact him, c/o Pica Press, The Banks, Mountfield, Robertsbridge, East Sussex TN32 5JY, U.K.

ACKNOWLEDGEMENTS

During the five years that it has taken me to research and write this book, I have been assisted by many people in many ways and to all those who have willingly shared their time and knowledge I offer my deepest thanks.

The foundation for all the work that has gone into preparing this volume has been the many months spent examining and measuring museum specimens. For allowing me access to the collections in their care and for their assistance and advice whilst I was working in those collections, I would firstly like to thank Robert Prŷs-Jones, Peter Colston, Michael Walters, Cyril Walker and Mark Adams at the Natural History Museum (BMNH), Tring; Clem Fisher (Merseyside County Museums, Liverpool); René Dekker (Rijksmuseum voor Natuurhistorisch Historie, Leiden, Netherlands); Michel Louette (Koninklijk Museum voor Midden-Afrika, Tervuren, Belgium); Ernst Bauernfeind (Naturhistorisches Museum, Vienna); Giuliano Doria (Museo Civico di Storia Naturale, Genova); Leon Bennun (National Museums of Kenya, Nairobi, Kenya); George Barrowclough, Mary LeCroy and Paul Sweet (American Museum of Natural History, New York); James Dean (National Museum of Natural History, Washington, D.C.); Kenneth Parkes (Carnegie Museum of Natural History, Pittsburgh) and David Agro (Academy of Natural Sciences, Philadelphia). For the loan of additional material and for supplying information on other specimens, I again thank all those mentioned above and also Robert Dickerman (AMNH); David Willard (Field Museum of Natural History, Chicago); Dr R. A. Paynter (Museum of Comparative Zoology, Cambridge, Massachusetts); Ned Johnson (Museum of Vertebrate Zoology, California); Jon Fisher (Western Foundation of Vertebrate Zoology, California); Miguel Lentino (Colección Ornitológica Phelps, Caracas, Venezuela); Dante Teixeira (Museu Nacional, Rio de Janeiro, Brazil); Michele Blair (Museo National de Historia Natural, La Paz, Bolivia); Dr P. A. Clancey (Durban Museum, Durban, South Africa) and Walter Boles (Australian Museum, Sydney, Australia).

For helping me to gather together the relevant literature, I am indebted to Effie Warr at the Natural History Museum, Tring; Linda Birch at the Alexander Library, Edward Grey Institute, Oxford; Dante Teixeira at the Museu Nacional, Rio de Janeiro, Brazil; Walter Boles at the Australian Museum, Sydney; and all the staff at BirdLife International, Cambridge, U.K.

Valuable information, ranging from scientific papers to personal field observations, was received from a great many people, and in particular thanks are due to David Agro, Clive Barlow (D. Smart), Mark Brigham, Paul Bühler, Phil Chantler, Claude Chappuis, Rob Clay, Miles Coverdale, Brian Cresswell, Jared Diamond, Françoise Dowsett-Lemaire, Richard Fuller, Johan Ingels, Des Jackson, Niels Krabbe, Carl Larsen, Durwyn Liley, James Lowen, Clive Mann, Juan Mazar Barnett, Bob Medland, Camilla Myers, Eddie Myers, David Pearson, George Reynard, Robert Ridgely, Mark Robbins, Steve Rooke, Phil Round, Andy Swash, Peter Symens, Roberto de Urioste, Bas van Balen, Francisco Vilella and Rob Williams.

Numerous high-quality photographs were willingly sent to me and for their kindness (and photographic skills!) I thank Ian Andrews, George Armstrong, Chris Balchin, Clive Barlow, Eustace Barnes, Roger Barnes, Bob Behrstock, K. David Bishop, Mark Bolton, Nik Borrow, Stuart Butchart, Phil Chantler, Hugh Chittenden, Simon Cook, David Cottridge, John Cudworth, Susan Davis, Greg and Yvonne Dean, Françoise Dowsett-Lemaire, Peter Ellis, Kay Fuhrmann, Michael Gallagher, David Gibbs, Steve Goodman, Jon Hornbuckle, Simon Harrap, David Holmes, Johan Ingels, Colin Jackson, Des Jackson, Ian Lewis, Tim Loseby, James Lowen, Clive Mann, David Massie, Bob Medland, Pete Morris, Phil Palmer, Mark Pearman, David Pearson, Michael Poulsen, Robert Prŷs-Jones, Romulo Ribon, Robert Ridgely, Hadoram Shirihai, Andrew Silcocks, Chris Smeenk, Steve Smith, Andy Swash, Peter Symens, Barry Trevis, Arnoud B. van den Berg, Martin Wadewitz, Richard Webb, Rob Williams and Gordon Wilson. Many slides were also obtained from VIREO, Philadelphia, and the Fitzpatrick Library, Transvaal Museum, South Africa.

Richard Ranft at the British Library of Wildlife Sounds (National Sound Archive), London, and Greg Budney and Steve Pantle at the Library of Natural Sounds, New York, supplied many recordings of caprimulgiform vocalisations, and I thank all those who have deposited their material at these institutions and who gave their permission for copies to be sent to me. Additional recordings were received from David Bishop, Tom Butynski, Rob Clay, John Corbett, Miles Coverdale, Ron Demey, Françoise Dowsett-Lemaire, David Gibbs, J. W. Hardy, Simon Harrap, Niels Krabbe, Joe Marshall, Juan Mazar Barnett, Ken Mitchell, David Pearson, Nigel Redman, Romulo Ribon, Mark Robbins, Phil Round, Roberto Straneck, John Wilsher and Hans Winkler.

I am especially grateful to David Christie, Mark Pearman and Glenis Vowles for translating papers, documents and correspondence and to Mark Brigham, Hugh Buck, Brian Cresswell, Brian Hickey, Johan Ingels, Bas van Balen and David Wells for reviewing and improving some of the draft species accounts.

Dave Nurney would like to thank David Christie, Jon Dunn, Ian Dawson, Roy and Moira Hargreaves, Robert Prys-Jones, Richard Webb and especially Jackie for much help and encouragement.

Finally, special thanks are owed to Christopher Helm, Nigel Redman and Amanda Helm at Pica Press for all their help, encouragement and patience throughout this project, to Claire Medland for typing much of the manuscript and to Richard Andrews and Ian Hunter.

EXPLANATION OF THE SPECIES ACCOUNTS

SPECIES SEQUENCE AND NOMENCLATURE

Each species has been given a reference number to act as a guide throughout the book. These numbers appear in the species headings, throughout the text and opposite the plates. The order in which the species are treated generally follows that given by Peters (1940), although there are a few alterations, especially within the Caprimulgidae.

The most widely accepted vernacular names are generally used for each species and these also appear throughout the text. Included in the species account headings are the commonest alternative names, the scientific name and the author and year of published description. Beneath each species account heading is listed the abbreviated reference for all subspecies currently recognised for that species.

IDENTIFICATION

The length of each species, measured from the tip of the bill to the tip of the tail, is given in centimetres. This is then followed by the general size of the species, which is based on length rather than wingspan. The scale I have chosen to use for size is: up to 20cm 'small', 20–28cm 'medium' and over 28cm 'large' or 'very large'. General coloration and breeding range are also given and, where applicable, mention is made of sexual dimorphism. Key identification features are then listed in two sections, at rest and in flight. For birds at rest, the upperparts, hind collar, wing-coverts, scapulars, facial and throat markings, and underparts are described. For birds in flight, the general flight actions are given where known, followed by the wing and tail markings for each sex. It should be noted here that the white throat, wing and tail markings of most nightjars are generally not visible on birds at rest. Finally, similar species (usually within the same range) and their major differences are described.

VOICE

All vocalisations are discussed where known. The territorial song or call of the male is usually described first, followed by the periods when it is most likely to be heard and a summary of the typical song-perches. Other calls of the adults (both sexes) are then given, including flight calls, courtship and breeding calls, alarm calls, defence and threat calls and calls to the young. The vocalisations of the chicks are described at the end of the section.

HABITAT

The preferred breeding habitats are described first, followed by all other known habitats, including atypical ones in which birds may appear during migration. At the end of the section, the altitudinal breeding range is given in metres above sea level.

HABITS

All known habits, apart from breeding behaviour, are summarised in full. This section includes activity periods, roosting sites and habits, relationships with other birds, predation, migration, flocking habits and feeding methods.

FOOD

A full list of all food items eaten by each species is given where known. Most data have been extracted from the published results of contents found and identified during stomach and gizzard examinations.

BREEDING

In this section, breeding biology is discussed in full. The known breeding seasons, month to month, are given for each region or country. Where a month is followed by a question mark, this suggests that the actual breeding season is probably, or possibly, longer than stated.

Territorial and courtship behaviour is described first, followed by nest-site location and construction, behaviour at the nest, timing of egg-laying, egg descriptions and measurements, nest defence and distraction displays, and incubation periods. Finally, the care of the young, the behaviour of the chicks and the fledging periods are also described.

DESCRIPTION

A detailed description, including all feather tracts, markings and significant variations, is given for the commonest colour morph of the adult male. For polytypic species, the nominate race is described in this section. For those species known only from single specimens of females or immatures, descriptions of these are given in full. Summaries of the female, immature and juvenile plumages are then given, followed by a brief description of the chick.

The bare parts described are usually those of a typical adult. A full range of adult bird measurements, usually taken from museum specimens, is given at the end of each section, with all but one species (Bahian Nighthawk) having been personally examined and measured by the author. For those species where fewer than five specimens have been available, the number of specimens examined is given in brackets. The measurements given, in millimetres, are the 'outer' wing length (i.e. the maximum or flattened wing length from the carpal joint to the tip of the longest primary), the tail length (measured from the base of the central pair of tail feathers to the tip of the longest tail feather, unless stated otherwise), the bill length (bill-tip to skull) and the tarsus length (measured from the rear of the intertarsal joint to the lower edge of the last scale before the toes). Weights, in grams, are also given.

MOULT

Full moult data, including timings and sequence, are given where known.

GEOGRAPHICAL VARIATION

For each species, the main variations within the nominate race are discussed (including the occurrence of colour phases where appropriate), followed by brief descriptions of each currently recognised subspecies (museum specimens of most races having been personally examined and measured by the author). Size (length), in centimetres, is given where the subspecies differs significantly from the nominate race, and wing lengths, tail lengths and weights of adult males and females are given where known.

DISTRIBUTION AND MOVEMENTS

After a general summary of the species' range, the known breeding range of each subspecies is listed. If migratory, the timings, routes and wintering grounds are given where known.

STATUS

The status of each species is summarised where known.

REFERENCES

To allow the species accounts to be more readable, references are not cited within the text. Major references used in the compilation of each account are listed by author and year of publication, in a separate section at the end of the account. In addition, all references used in the preparation of this book are given in full in the Bibliography at the rear of the volume.

MAPS

Within the text of each species account is a map showing the known (or probable) breeding range of each subspecies. A question mark has been used to express uncertain status during the breeding season. For migratory species, the non-breeding (wintering) range is also shown. Vagrant records are marked with a cross.

PLATES

Thirty-six colour plates are included in a separate section before the species accounts. With the exception of the recently described Nechisar Nightjar, all species and major subspecies are depicted, many being illustrated here for the first time. All species (generally males) are depicted at rest, and most nightjars (both sexes) are also shown in flight. Exceptions to this are the Asian (*Batrachostomus*) frogmouths, where both sexes are shown at rest, and those species where only females are currently known. The figures on each plate are painted to scale, although the scale may differ slightly from plate to plate. A scale bar is given at the foot of each plate.

14

Taxonomy and Relationships

The nightjars (including nighthawks, poorwills and pauraques), potoos, frogmouths, owlet-nightjars and oilbird are generally regarded as being closely related to each other, and members of this group are placed in the order Caprimulgiformes. However, the classification of the Caprimulgiformes has long been the subject of debate amongst avian systematists, and it could be argued that their true affinities have yet to be fully resolved.

Historically, two schools of thought appear to have predominated, one considering all Caprimulgiformes to be closely related to owls, the other considering them to be more closely related to swifts and hummingbirds. A third, less commonly held opinion is that some of the Caprimulgiformes (oilbird, frogmouths and owlet-nightjars) are related to the owls, whilst the others (nightjars and potoos) are relatives of the swifts; within such treatment these two groups tended to be separated by other families including the rollers, kingfishers, hornbills, bee-eaters and todies. Other systems and relationships have also been put forward and an historical review of caprimulgiform classification can be found in Sibley and Ahlquist (1990).

In recent times, the generally accepted view has been to place the Caprimulgiformes between the owls Strigiformes and the swifts Apodiformes. Under this classification, the following sequence became established.

> Order Caprimulgiformes
>> Suborder Steatornithes
>>> Family Steatornithidae Oilbird
>> Suborder Caprimulgi
>>> Family Podargidae Frogmouths
>>> Family Nyctibiidae Potoos
>>> Family Aegothelidae Owlet-nightjars
>>> Family Caprimulgidae Nightjars
>>>> Subfamily Chordeilinae (Nighthawks)
>>>> Subfamily Caprimulginae (Nightjars)

In 1988, Sibley, Ahlquist and Monroe published the results of their DNA-DNA hybridisation studies and, from the evidence of their work, they presented a new classification of the living birds of the world. Under their treatment, the proposed sequence of caprimulgiform taxonomy became:

> Order Strigiformes
>> Suborder Aegotheli
>>> Family Aegothelidae Owlet-nightjars
>> Suborder Caprimulgi
>>> Infraorder Podargides
>>>> Family Podargidae Australasian Frogmouths
>>>> Family Batrachostomidae Asian Frogmouths
>>> Infraorder Caprimulgides
>>>> Parvorder Steatornithida
>>>>> Superfamily Steatornithoidea
>>>>>> Family Steatornithidae Oilbird
>>>>> Superfamily Nyctibioidea
>>>>>> Family Nyctibiidae Potoos
>>>> Parvorder Caprimulgida
>>>>> Superfamily Eurostopodoidea
>>>>>> Family Eurostopodidae Eared-nightjars
>>>>> Superfamily Caprimulgoidea
>>>>>> Family Caprimulgidae Nightjars
>>>>>>> Subfamily Chordeilinae (Nighthawks)
>>>>>>> Subfamily Caprimulginae (Nightjars)

(Note: Only the Caprimulgiformes have been listed above. For the full classification, see Sibley *et al.* 1988, Sibley and Ahlquist 1990, Sibley and Monroe 1990).

Several significant changes are immediately apparent in this new work. Firstly, nightjars and owls are considered to be closely related, and as a result the order Caprimulgiformes is deleted and all its families are placed within the Strigiformes. Secondly, different relationships are now suggested between the Caprimulgiformes and accordingly, the subdivisions of caprimulgiform taxonomy are redefined as follows. The oilbird, previously placed in its own suborder, is thought to be closely related to the potoos and both families are now placed in a separate superfamily within a new parvorder. The two frogmouth genera are considered so divergent from each other as to merit separate families within a new infraorder. The owlet-nightjars might not be allied to the frogmouths and are elevated to subordinal rank, whilst the so called 'eared-nightjars' are separated from the other nightjars, with each group being placed in a different superfamily under a new parvorder.

Such a monumental revision has yet to be undertaken for the lower taxonomic categories and, for the time being, our understanding of caprimulgiform genera, species and subspecies remains largely unchanged, with workers at the specific and subspecific level continuing to use morphological and vocal criteria to establish true affinities.

Recent studies by Mariaux and Braun (1996) apparently support some of the earlier taxonomic views put forward by ornithologists, whilst their results also suggest that the treatment of *Batrachostomus* and *Eurostopodus* as separate families is also justified. However, for the purposes of this book, I have chosen to follow the accepted classification prior to the DNA-DNA hybridisation studies, simply because this has been the established taxonomy in recent times.

Davis (1962 & 1978) discussed the acoustic evidence of relationships in the potoos and nightjars and he reclassified many of the genera and species that he examined. He proposed three new genera of Caprimulgidae: *Allasma* (type species *Caprimulgus clarus*); *Diaphorasma* (type species *Caprimulgus donaldsoni*) and *Annamornus* (type species *Caprimulgus rufus*), and he also resurrected several genera that have long been synonymised with *Caprimulgus*, i.e. *Antrostomus*, *Setochalcis*, *Systellura* and *Setopagis*. Two potoos, *Nyctibius abbotti* and *Nyctibius cornutus*, were considered to be valid species and a new species of nightjar was described within the genus *Allasma*. Given the name Kenya Nightjar *Allasma northi*, this new species was apparently based on a recording of *Caprimulgus pectoralis*, made by S. Keith. To date, this work appears to have been largely ignored by ornithologists.

DISTRIBUTION

The order Caprimulgiformes is cosmopolitan, occurring on every continent except Antarctica but with a distinct bias towards the warmer regions of the world. They occupy a wide range of habitats and are absent only from extreme environments which are unable to support sufficient insects, such as polar regions, barren waterless deserts and mountains above the snow line.

Of the five families of Caprimulgiformes, the nightjars themselves (Caprimulgidae) are by far the most widespread. The remaining four families have a much more restricted distribution: the potoos and Oilbird occur in the northern Neotropical region, the frogmouths are found in southern Asia (*Batrachostomus*) and Australasia (*Podargus*), and the owlet-nightjars are largely Australasian (extending marginally outside into Wallacea and the South-West Pacific).

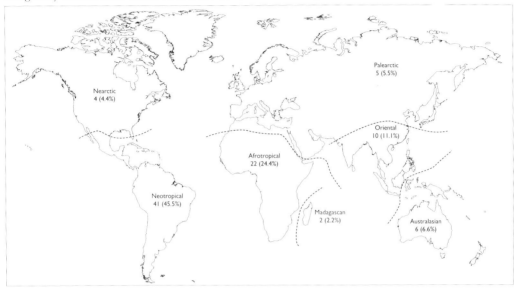

Distribution of nightjars Caprimulgidae according to main breeding range. The number and percentage of the world's species are given for each faunal zone. Species with a breeding range spanning more than one zone are counted only once, and therefore the number of species breeding in each zone may be higher.

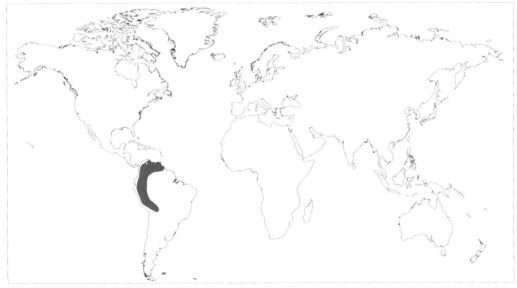

Distribution of Oilbird Steatornithidae.

17

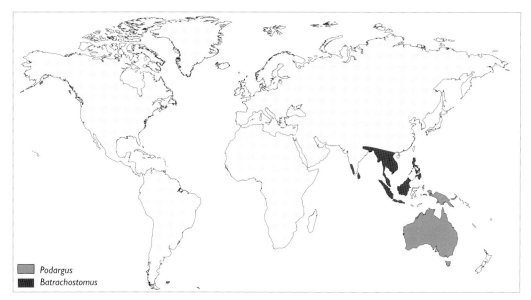

Podargus
Batrachostomus

Distribution of frogmouths Podargidae.

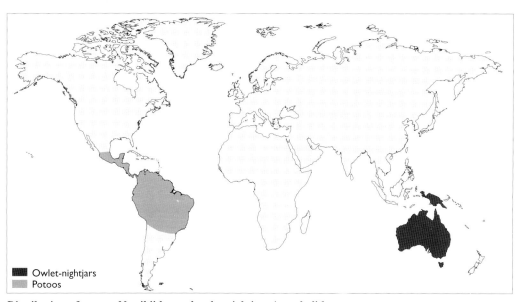

Owlet-nightjars
Potoos

Distribution of potoos Nyctibiidae and owlet-nightjars Aegothelidae.

TOPOGRAPHY AND MORPHOLOGY

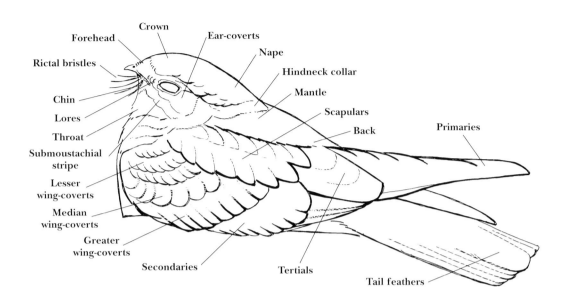

Crown
Forehead
Ear-coverts
Nape
Rictal bristles
Hindneck collar
Chin
Mantle
Lores
Scapulars
Throat
Back
Submoustachial stripe
Primaries
Lesser wing-coverts
Median wing-coverts
Greater wing-coverts
Secondaries
Tertials
Tail feathers

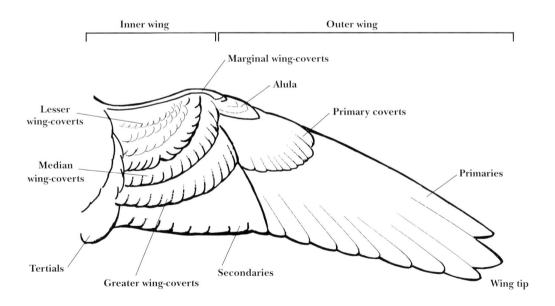

Inner wing
Outer wing
Marginal wing-coverts
Alula
Lesser wing-coverts
Primary coverts
Median wing-coverts
Primaries
Tertials
Greater wing-coverts
Secondaries
Wing tip

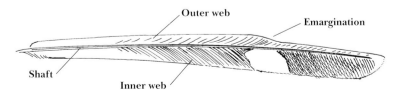

Outer web
Emargination
Shaft
Inner web

Nightjar Primary

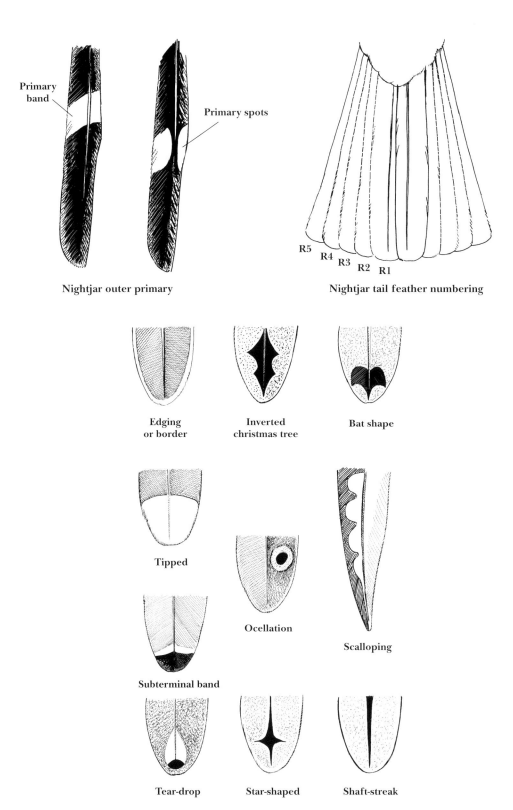

Primary band

Primary spots

Nightjar outer primary

R5 R4 R3 R2 R1

Nightjar tail feather numbering

Edging
or border

Inverted
christmas tree

Bat shape

Tipped

Ocellation

Scalloping

Subterminal band

Tear-drop

Star-shaped

Shaft-streak

Nightjar feather patterning

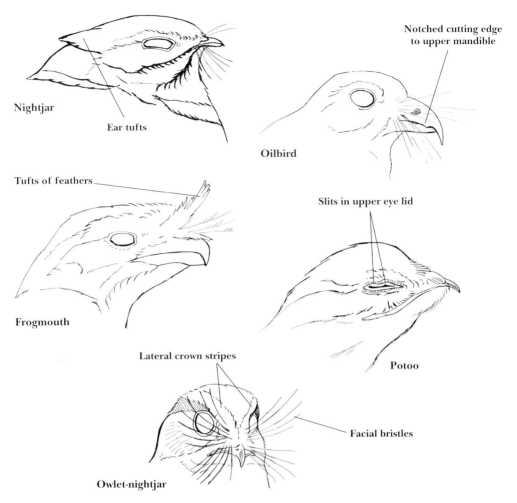

Heads of the five families of Caprimulgiformes.

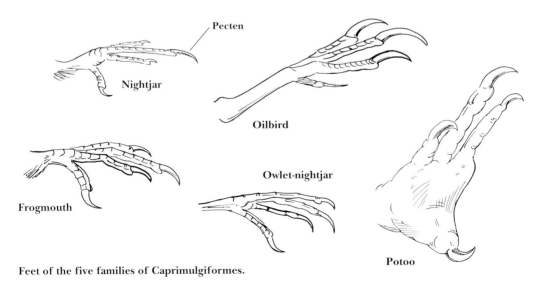

Feet of the five families of Caprimulgiformes.

STRUCTURE AND MECHANICS

The physiology of some Caprimulgiformes has been well studied, and this chapter briefly examines the adaptations of form and function in these remarkable birds.

Steatornithidae (Oilbird)

The oilbird has a strongly hooked bill with a subterminal tooth on the upper mandible, and this serves as an efficient tool for plucking fruits from trees. It has a hard corneous rhamphotheca covering to the palate, which lacks a transpalatine canal (Cowles 1967), and the bill is surrounded by long rictal bristles. It has been suggested that these bristles might be highly sensitive and, if so, they could be used as a tactile organ in places with little or no light, e.g. at the nest in darkened breeding caves (Ingram 1958).

An oilbird's eyes are extremely sensitive to light, and sight is probably used whenever possible (Snow 1961), but oilbirds also spend much of their time in very dark caves, where there is little or no light available. To move around safely when flying in this environment, oilbirds use a form of echolocation, and they are one of only a very few species of birds (and the only nocturnal one) that is known to have developed this capability. However, echolocation is probably employed only when light levels fall below a certain point (Snow 1961). When echolocating, oilbirds emit short bursts of loud, sharp clicks produced by the syrinx, of a lower frequency than similar sounds emitted by bats. Each click consists of a few sound waves, has a frequency of 6,100–8,750 clicks per second and lasts 0.3-1.5msec; two or more clicks may be emitted in a burst, with gaps of 1.7-4.4msec between each click (Griffin 1953). Oilbirds seem unable to detect small obstacles when echolocating. Their hearing is restricted to fairly low frequencies, and their greatest sensitivity to sound is at about 2kHz, after which it declines rapidly, with little or no sensitivity above 6kHz (Konishi and Knudsen 1979). Oilbirds also have a large, heavily innervated olfactory organ, with one of the thickest mucous membranes of all birds and a large respiratory concha, and it is possible that they may sometimes use the sense of smell to locate the aromatic fruits on which they feed (Snow 1961).

For a large bird, the oilbird has surprisingly small legs and the feet are anisodactyl and synpelmous. When resting on a flat surface, three toes point forwards and the hallux points inwards towards the body, but, when clinging, the toes are spread out so that the inner two point forwards, the outermost is held outwards and the hallux points inwards or occasionally backwards (Ingram 1958, Snow 1961). Oilbirds do not appear to be able to cling to vertical surfaces, however, as their feet are usually held back (not forwards as in other birds, e.g. woodpeckers), their claws are not strongly hooked and their tail feathers are not stiffened (Snow 1961).

The only information available on temperature regulation concerns young chicks, which are unable to maintain their own body temperature until they are about three weeks of age, after which they begin to put on large deposits of fat and grow thick down (Snow 1961).

Structure Palate desmognathous; pelvic formula XY; coracoids separated; basipterygoid processes small; flexor tendons Type 5a; feet anisodactyl, synpelmous; hypotarsus complex; syrinx bronchial; nares holorhinal, impervious; aftershaft small; primaries 10, secondaries 11-13, diastataxic, rectrices 10; adult down restricted to apteria; cervical vertebrae 15; caeca large; intestinal convolutions Type 6.

Podargidae (frogmouths)

Podargus frogmouths have large, heavily ossified bills with hooked tips, the lower mandibles are supported by thick mandibular rami, and the upper mandibles have a large premaxillary plate extending back to the flanges of the palatines to cover the palatal bones with a bony shield (Schodde and Mason 1980). *Batrachostomus* frogmouths have smaller jaws and shorter, wider, more rounded bills. The longer, straighter bills of *Podargus* frogmouths are adapted for taking prey from the ground, whilst the smaller bills of *Batrachostomus* are better suited for taking prey in flight (Serventy 1936). Frogmouths have slit-like nostrils near the base of the bill which are protected by operculum overhung with feathers, have a hard corneous rhamphotheca covering to their palates and lack transpalatine canals.

To waterproof their plumage during preening, frogmouths use their bills to take fats from the powderdowns and distribute them amongst the feathers. Frogmouths have two large powderdowns, one on either side of the rump, and each consists of about 50 short plumose feathers on the femoral tract that continuously exude fats from the quill or calamus. However, the oil (uropygial) gland has atrophied, at least in the *Podargus* frogmouths (Schodde and Mason 1980).

To aid silent flight when hunting, frogmouths have frayed trailing edges to the flight and tail feathers (Schodde and Mason 1980), but the *Podargus* species have a heavier wing loading and are faster, more powerful flyers, whilst the *Batrachostomus* species have larger tails in relation to body size, for greater manoeuvrability (Serventy 1936).

Frogmouths have short tarsi and weak, anisodactylous feet. Their side toes are semizygodactylous and can be splayed out at rightangles to produce a better grip. They have five phalanges in the outer toe and the middle toe is not pectinate.

In hot weather, temperature regulation appears to be accomplished by panting, rather than gular-fluttering. During a study of captive Tawny Frogmouths, it was found that when sitting in shade a female had a breathing rate of 19-21 breaths per minute, and her breathing rate increased as her body temperature rose, until a maximum rate of 100 breaths per minute was reached. When her breathing rate rose above 60 breaths per minute, she opened her mouth, lowered her gular area and increased the blood flow to the mouth. When her body temperature reached 42.5°C she also lowered and slightly spread her wings, and compressed her body feathers (Lasiewski and Bartholomew 1966). A captive Marbled Frogmouth also panted when it became too hot (Lasiewski *et al.* 1970).

Structure Palate desmognathous; no crop; pelvic muscle formula AXY; carotids left only; coracoids separated; basipterygoid processes absent; flexor tendons Type 5a; feet anisodactyl, synpelmous; hypotarsus complex; nares holorhinal, impervious; aftershaft small; primaries 10 with vestigial 11th (remicle), secondaries 11-13, diastataxic, rectrices 10; cervical vertebrae 13; caeca large; intestinal convolutions Type 6; metasternum with two notches on each side.

Nyctibiidae (potoos)

Potoos have a hooked bill, with flexible mandibles and a toothed maxilla. All species except the Rufous Potoo lack rictal bristles or vibrissae around the gape, and this may have something to do with their feeding habits, most potoos hunting in more open places such as above the canopy or along forest edges, whilst Rufous prefers to hunt within forests (Sick 1993).

Potoos are unique amongst the Caprimulgiformes, in having two (sometimes three) notches in the upper eyelid (Borrero 1974). Although the function of these eyelid notches is not fully understood, they may enable a potoo to keep watch on potential danger whilst it is 'frozen' in its cryptic alarm posture. Another adaptation which may support this function is that both eyelids can open and close independently, so that the notches can be moved to allow a different field of view, without the bird having to move its head (Borrero 1974).

For plumage maintenance, potoos have a powderdown on either side of the rump, and a large oil (uropygial) gland.

Potoos have short tarsi, long fleshy toes, and a thick pad of skin between the innermost toe and hallux, which are adaptations for long periods of perching. They have five phalanges in the outer toe, three phalanges in the hallux and the middle toe is not pectinate.

Thermoregulation by potoos is similar to that of frogmouths, i.e. when hot, birds open their mouths, which have highly vascularised skin, and pant.

Structure Palate schizognathous; pelvic muscle formula AXY; carotids left only; coracoids separated; basipterygoid processes small; flexor tendons Type 5a; feet anisodactyl, synpelmous; hypotarsus complex; syrinx bronchial; nares holorhinal, impervious; aftershaft small; primaries 10, secondaries 11-13, diastataxic, rectrices 10; caeca large; intestinal convolutions Type 6; metasternum with two notches on each side.

Aegothelidae (owlet-nightjars)

Owlet-nightjars have small broad bills surrounded by long facial bristles and a wide gape, a soft coriaceous covering to the palate and no transpalatine canals. The nostrils are situated near the tip of the bill. Owlet-nightjars have a large oil gland at the base of the tail, and all species have relatively long tarsi with five phalanges in the outer toe; the middle toe is not pectinate.

Structure Palate schizognathous; pelvic muscle formula AXY; coracoids separated; basipterygoid processes absent; flexor tendons Type 5a; feet anisodactyl, synpelmous; hypotarsus complex; nares holorhinal, impervious; aftershaft small; primaries 10 and remicle; secondaries 11-14, diastataxic; rectrices 10; cervical vertebrae 13; caeca absent; intestinal convolutions Type 6; metasternum with two notches on each side.

Caprimulgidae (nightjars)

Nightjars have small weak bills, but have a very large gape. A study of the skull morphology and jaw mechanics of four species of Caprimulgidae (1 *Chordeiles*, 1 *Nyctidromus* and 2 *Caprimulgus*), has revealed that nightjars have an extremely specialised spreading mechanism of the lower jaw. They are able to open their mouths both vertically and horizontally, and this is probably an adaptation for catching insects in reduced visibility at night (Bühler 1970). In an earlier study of several species (1 *Podager*, 1 *Eurostopodus*, 1 *Nyctidromus*, 7 *Caprimulgus* and 1 *Macrodipteryx*), it was found that nightjars have vascular, membranous and highly sensitive palates with well-marked transpalatine canals, and this might also be an adaptation for nocturnal aerial feeding (Cowles 1967). Many nightjars have long rictal bristles around the gape, although they are generally absent or extremely short in nighthawks (i.e. all genera within the subfamily Chordeilinae) and *Eurostopodus* nightjars. Rictal bristles are modified contour feathers that have strong shafts and no barbs, and they are attached to special muscles in skin rich in Herbst corpuscles. These specialised feathers may be highly tactile and, if so, this may be another adaptation to aerial feeding at night.

Although nightjars have good hearing, eyesight is probably their most highly developed sense. Their eyes are relatively large, and are situated laterally on the head to offer a good field of view when hunting. Nightjars (and indeed perhaps all Caprimulgiformes) are most unusual amongst birds in having a tapetum in the retina. A tapetum is a reflective surface at the back of the eye, and sits behind a layer of photoreceptors in the retina: it increases the detection rate of light entering the eye, by reflecting any unabsorbed light passing through the retina to the photoreceptors. In artificial light, it is the tapetum which shows as the distinctive eye-shine in these birds (Nicol and Arnott 1974, Martin 1990).

All species have a low wing-loading, i.e. a very large wing area in proportion to weight, and as a result they are powerful and accomplished flyers.

Nightjars water-proof their plumage during preening, by using their bills to transfer oils from down feathers on the breast and above the tail. The oil (uropygial) gland at the base of the tail is often vestigial and atrophied (Schodde and Mason 1980).

Nightjars have short tarsi, small, weak feet and toes that are partly webbed at the base. The outermost toe has four phalanges, the hallux two, and the middle toe is pectinate, the pecten being situated on the inner side of the claw. Although the exact purpose of the pecten remains unclear, it has been suggested that it might be used as a comb for removing parasites during preening, or to straighten out the rictal bristles. During one study, a captive Common Poorwill was often seen to scratch its head, including the bill and rictal bristles, by turning its foot outwards so that the pecten engaged the feathers and, after scratching, the pecten usually contained fragments of feather and down. Also, the rictal bristles often became tangled during preening, and they were frequently scratched with the pecten immediately afterwards (Brauner 1953).

In hot weather a nightjar can regulate its body temperature by gular-fluttering, during which it opens its mouth and rapidly vibrates the gular area, whilst at the same time the heart rate increases and the flow of blood to the buccal area rises. Unlike panting, the lungs, air sacs and trachea are not used during gular-fluttering. Studies of a captive Common Poorwill showed that the rate of gular-flutter varies between 590 and 690 per minute (Lasiewski and Bartholomew 1966). Similar flutter rates have been recorded in a captive Common Nighthawk (Lasiewski and Dawson 1964). Studies of the Lesser Nighthawk show that it can also maintain a brain temperature of about 1.28°C below that of body temperature, this being achieved by having a highly vascularised area in the temples, which allows a heat exchange between warm blood flowing into the brain and cooler blood flowing from it. (Kilgore *et al.* 1976).

Some species are occasionally subjected to cold weather and reduced prey availability, and the study of physiological responses to these conditions by caprimulgids probably began when a Common Poorwill was discovered hibernating in California in December 1946 (Jaeger 1948), although a much earlier report of a torpid Common Poorwill dates back to 1890 (Brauner 1952). Studies of the Californian bird suggested that the same site was possibly used by the same individual during three winters; the longest period of hibernation documented was late November 1947 to late February 1948, and body temperature during hibernation ranged from 18.0 to 19.8°C while body weight ranged from 44.56 to 52.68g (Jaeger 1948, 1949). Since this discovery, the Common Poorwill has been studied in captivity and in the wild, and has been shown to be a truly remarkable species with several unique qualities. It is the only species of bird known to hibernate, although some authorities have suggested that it enters a state of prolonged torpor rather than true hibernation, torpor being an energy-saving strategy by which a bird can lower its body temperature and reduce its metabolism, to enable it to survive periods of low temperatures and poor feeding conditions. On the Canadian breeding grounds, in the north of the species' range, poorwills can enter periods of short-term hibernation (called daily torpor) lasting 1-2 days. On cold spring nights during one study, torpid Poorwills were recorded with body temperatures of less than 5°C (i.e. more than 35°C below normal), and this constitutes the lowest body temperature ever recorded for any species of wild bird (Brigham 1994). Torpidity during the breeding season is probably rarer, although there is one instance of an adult male and its offspring both entering short-term torpor (Kissner and Brigham 1993). When conditions improve, Poorwills can bring themselves out of torpor by shivering, rocking from side to side and fluffing out their feathers to increase their body heat (Austin and Bradley 1969, Bartholomew *et al.* 1962). Studies of captive birds have shown that Poorwills can fly when their body temperature is as low as 27.4°C, the lowest recorded for any species of bird (Austin and Bradley 1969). Another study examined the relationship of food and torpidity in this species, and showed that beetles, which form a large part of a Poorwill's diet, are very high in unsaturated fats, whilst moths are very low in unsaturated fats. Unsaturated fats remain liquid at low temperatures and would therefore be metabolically available to a torpid poorwill, whilst saturated fats solidify at low temperatures and would not (Brigham 1994).

Captive Common Nighthawks are also physiologically capable of entering and arousing from torpor (Lasiewski and Dawson 1964), but studies of birds in the wild have suggested that they are unlikely, or physiologically unable, to enter torpor under normal conditions (Firman *et al.* 1993). However, subsequent field observations of two apparently dormant birds suggest that under certain adverse conditions this species can lower its body temperature to below normal levels (Brigham *et al.* 1995). Lesser Nighthawks have also been studied in captivity, and although this species did not enter torpor it was thought that it might have the capacity to do so (Marshall 1955). Field tests in Ontario showed that Whip-poor-wills did not enter torpor in periods of cold weather, and were probably incapable of doing so (Hickey 1993).

There is one report from Denmark of a European Nightjar being found in a torpid state in May, when the temperature was below freezing (Peiponen and Bosley 1964). Studies of captive birds show that the body temperature of this species has two peaks during foraging periods, the highest at sunset and another just before sunrise, and two lows during periods of rest, one at midnight and the other at midday. In cool weather conditions with poor prey availability, birds may enter light torpor (body temperature above 15°C) or deep torpor (body temperature below 14-15°C), the depth of torpidity perhaps being determined by the ambient temperature. Results also suggest that this species cannot enter prolonged torpor, and birds must therefore migrate to escape the northern winters (Peiponen 1965, 1966, 1970).

Structure Palate schizognathous (desmognathous in *Chordeiles*); no crop; pelvic muscle formula AXY; carotids 2; coracoids separated; basipterygoid processes small; flexor tendons Type 5a; feet anisodactyl, synpelmous; hypotarsus complex; syrinx tracheo-bronchial; nares schizorhinal-holorhinal, impervious; aftershaft small; primaries 10, *Eurostopodus* with remicle, secondaries 11-14, diastataxic; rectrices 10; cervical vertebrae 14; caeca large and club-shaped; intestinal convolutions Type 6; metasternum with one notch on each side.

Plumages and Moult

The development and maintenance of feathers are vital to a bird's well being, and the problems of feather loss, accidental damage and general wear, are overcome by the replacement of some or all of the plumage during annual moults. The timing and sequence of moult may be governed by factors such as feeding methods, nesting habits or periods of migration, so each species or group of species has evolved a moult strategy best suited to its particular life cycle.

Although moult within the Caprimulgiformes has been poorly studied to date, this section includes summaries of work published on the Oilbird (Snow 1962), the frogmouths (Stresemann and Stresemann 1966), Common Nighthawk (Oberholser 1914, Selander 1954), Chuck-will's-widow (Rohwer 1971, Mengel 1976), Whip-poor-will (Sutton 1941), Red-necked Nightjar (Gargallo 1994), Long-tailed Nightjar (Herremans and Stevens 1983) and Standard-winged and Pennant-winged Nightjars (Stresemann and Stresemann 1966). Moult details of all species, where known, are also included in the systematic section.

Although the terms for plumages and moult in this volume are widely used, alternative terminologies proposed by Humphrey and Parkes (1959) are also in popular usage, especially in North America. A simple comparison of terminologies, based on *Eurostopodus* nightjar moult, is listed below (Humphrey and Parkes names are listed in the two right-hand columns):

Plumage	Moult	Plumage	Molt
Juvenile	post-breeding (partial)	Juvenal	1st prebasic
Immature	pre-breeding (partial)	1st basic	1st prealternate
Immature	post-breeding (complete)	1st alternate	2nd prebasic
Adult	pre-breeding (partial)	Definitive basic	2nd prealternate
Adult	post-breeding (complete)	Definitive alternate	3rd prebasic
	etc.		etc.

It should be noted, however, that many *Caprimulgus* nightjars replace all of their plumage during one annual moult, and this may be compared as follows:

Plumage	Moult	Plumage	Molt
Juvenile	post-breeding (complete)	Juvenal	1st prebasic
Adult	post-breeding (complete)	Definitive basic	2nd prebasic
	etc.		etc.

Steatornithidae (Oilbird)

At hatching, the chick is generally naked, with only a few down feathers, usually on the underparts. Whilst in the nest, the chick grows a second set of down feathers and these are then replaced, over a long period of time, by feathers of the juvenile plumage. The timing and sequence of moult during the change from juvenile to adult plumage is not known, but primary moult in adult birds can be quite variable and is sometimes rather irregular, with two different moult strategies having been recorded (Snow 1962). In one strategy, the primaries are replaced descendantly, usually commencing with the innermost (P1) and finishing with the outermost (P10), although on some birds one wing may be further advanced in its moult than the other, or one wing may be in moult whilst the other is not! In the other strategy, the primaries may be replaced in a serially descendant moult, with two or three moult centres having been recorded, e.g. P1, P6 and P9 (Snow 1962).

Podargidae (frogmouths)

At hatching, the chick is covered in down, which is white in all *Podargus* and at least one *Batrachostomus* species. *Podargus* frogmouths grow a second set of down feathers, which are usually greyish, whilst still in the nest and these begin to be replaced almost immediately by feathers of the juvenile plumage. The timing and sequence of moult from juvenile to immature plumage is poorly documented, but the change from immature to adult plumage appears to take place at the end of the second summer. The primary moult in adult birds of both frogmouth genera is serially descendant, although some birds may occasionally moult their primaries descendantly. No further data are available.

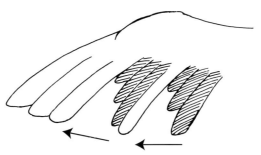

Serially descendant moult, as shown by frogmouths and potoos.

Nyctibiidae (potoos)

At hatching, the chick is covered in white down and this is quickly replaced by feathers of the juvenile plumage. Details of the moult into adult plumage are not known, but adults replace their primaries in a serially descendant sequence. No further data are available.

Aegothelidae (owlet-nightjars)

The following is based on Australian Owlet-nightjar *Aegotheles cristatus* only. At hatching, the chick is covered in white down and this is briefly replaced by a second, greyish down, before the juvenile feathers appear. The timing and sequence of the transition from juvenile to adult plumage is poorly known. Adults moult their primaries descendantly. No further data are available.

Caprimulgidae (nightjars)

At hatching, the chick is covered in down (which in most species is generally buffish), and before fledging the down feathers are replaced by feathers of the juvenile plumage. The change from juvenile to immature plumage often begins during the fledging period and involves a partial moult, during which the body feathers and wing-coverts are replaced. The timing and sequence of the moult from immature to adult plumage varies, however, and several different moult strategies have so far been identified (see table on p.28). Some species complete their moult by replacing their primaries, secondaries, tertials and tail feathers during the non-breeding or winter period, and thereby attain adult plumage before their second summer. Other species retain their immature plumage through to the end of their second summer, then undertake a complete moult, during which all their feathers are replaced. Less commonly, some immature birds undergo a second partial moult during the non-breeding season, and retain this 'second-year' plumage through to the end of the following breeding season, after which they have a complete moult. Others may undergo a complete moult during their first winter. Some migratory species may interrupt or suspend their moult, whilst they are moving between the breeding and non-breeding areas.

During the wing moult of most species, the primaries are usually replaced descendantly. The secondaries may be replaced ascendantly, but in some species, e.g. Red-necked Nightjar, European Nightjar and Pennant-winged Nightjar, the secondary moult appears to be centripetal with two moult centres, one commencing with the outermost feather (S1) and proceeding ascendantly, the other commencing with the innermost feather (S12) and proceeding descendantly, the moult converging on S7 or S8.

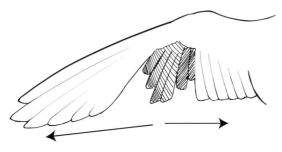

Typical wing moult strategy in Caprimulgidae species.

	YEAR ONE BREEDING				YEAR TWO BREEDING				YEAR THREE BREEDING		
	SPRING	SUMMER	AUTUMN	WINTER	SPRING	SUMMER	AUTUMN	WINTER	SPRING	SUMMER	AUTUMN

Chuck-will's-widow — Immature / First winter — Adult
Whip-poor-will — Immature / First winter — Adult
Red-necked Nightjar 1 — Immature — Imm./2nd summer — Sub-adult? — Adult
Red-necked Nightjar 2 — Immature — Adult
European Nightjar 1 — Immature — Adult
European Nightjar 2 — Adult
European Nightjar 3 — Adult
Rufous-cheeked Nightjar — Immature — Adult
Common Nighthawk 1 — Immature — Adult
Common Nighthawk 2 — Immature — Second year — Adult
Pennant-winged Nightjar — Immature — Adult — Adult
Standard-winged Nightjar — Immature — Adult? (♂ without 'standard') — Adult (♂ without 'standard')
Spotted Nightjar — Immature — Adult
White-throated Nightjar — Immature — Adult

☐ Partial moult   ■ Complete moult   ▨ Completion of a previously started moult

▨ Continuation of a previously started moult, but which is suspended before completion

General moult strategies as shown by some Caprimulgidae species. Note that different populations in some species (e.g. European Nightjar) appear to have different moult strategies.

The Chuck-will's-widow of North America replaces its wing feathers in a slightly different sequence. It moults its primaries descendantly, similar to many other species, but its secondary moult is serially ascendant, and has two moult centres, one commencing with the outermost feather (S1) and the other beginning at either S6, S7, S8 or S9 (see figure below), although the inner sequence on each wing does not always start with the same feather. The inner sequence appears to start before the outer sequence and usually begins when the primary moult has reached P6 or P7 (Rohwer 1971).

Two species of *Eurostopodus* nightjar, Spotted Nightjar and White-throated Nightjar, also replace their secondaries in a serially ascendant sequence, although the moult centres are usually S1 and S10.

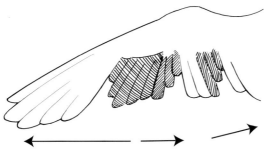

Wing moult in Chuck-will's-widow.

The Red-necked Nightjar has an unusual wing moult strategy, in that although it tends to replace its primaries descendantly, they are not moulted in the sequence P1 to P10 in the same cycle, i.e. immature birds renew some primaries during their first winter and the moult is then suspended. During the next annual moult, birds replace all of their primaries, commencing at the point of suspension the previous year. This cycle of moult appears to continue from year to year (Gargallo 1994).

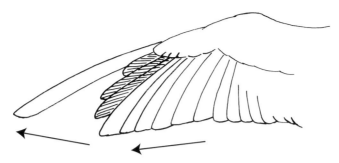

Wing moult in Red-necked Nightjar.

One Afrotropical species, the Long-tailed Nightjar, replaces its primaries descendantly, but generally moults its secondaries in an unusual sequence in which there are two moult centres. One commences with the outermost feather (S1) and proceeds ascendantly towards S5, the other often commences with S9 and is centrifugal (Herremans and Stevens 1983).

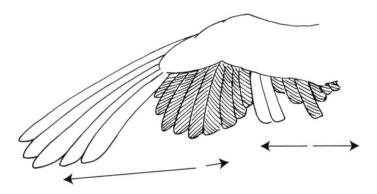

Wing moult in Long-tailed Nightjar.

The two species within the genus *Macrodipteryx* have different wing moult strategies, and the breeding males of both are exceptional in having extremely elongated second primaries. The Standard-winged Nightjar generally replaces its primaries descendantly, although young males do not attain the 'standards' until their third calendar year, i.e. following completion of their second annual moult. Until then, the second primary usually resembles a juvenile-type feather (Stresemann and Stresemann 1966). The Pennant-winged Nightjar has a very different wing-shape and replaces its primaries in an unusual sequence. The innermost primary (P1) is moulted first, followed by P5 and P6. P7 and P8 are replaced at the same time as P4, P3 and P2, and the moult ends with P9 and P10 (Stresemann and Stresemann 1966). The primaries are therefore mainly replaced in a descendant sequence, with P4-P2 moulting ascendantly (although P2 may occasionally appear before or after P4). Females do not have this unusual wing moult and replace their primaries descendantly.

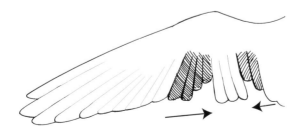

Typical wing moult strategy of male Pennant-winged Nightjar.

The replacement of the tail feathers in most species is generally centrifugal, i.e. starting at the central pair (R1) and proceeding outwards (see figure below), although the outermost feather (R5) is often replaced before R4. The Chuck-will's-widow is known to moult its tail quite rapidly, replacing almost all the feathers at the same time (Mengel 1976). The Red-necked Nightjar often replaces R1, R2 and R5 during its first winter and commences with R3 and R4 in the following moult cycle.

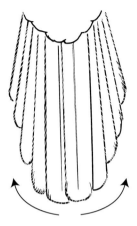

Centrifugal tail moult, typical of many Caprimulgidae.

Glossary (based on Ginn & Melville 1983, Baker 1993)

Arrested moult A moult cycle which stops before it has been completed. Any remaining 'old' feathers are then retained until the next complete moult, when they are replaced in the normal sequence, i.e. if primary moult is arrested at P8, then P9 and P10 are not renewed until P1-P8 have been replaced again during the next moult.

Ascendant moult A moult cycle in the wing which proceeds inwards towards the body.

Centrifugal A moult cycle which proceeds in two directions from one moult centre.

Centripetal A moult cycle which commences at two moult centres and converges.

Complete moult A moult in which all feathers are replaced.

Descendant moult A moult cycle in the wing which proceeds outwards from the body.

Moult centre A point where a moult cycle commences.

Moult cycle A sequence in which all feathers of a particular tract are replaced, e.g. primaries, secondaries, or tail feathers.

Partial moult A moult in which not all feathers are replaced.

Serially descendant or ascendant moult A moult cycle with two or more active moult centres which have commenced at the same time and are proceeding in the same direction. Also known as 'stepwise' or Staffelmauser moult.

Suspended moult A moult cycle which is temporarily halted and is completed later, recommencing at the point where it was halted, i.e. if descendant primary moult is suspended at P6, the moult will resume at P7 and P7-P10 will be replaced in sequence.

BEHAVIOUR

Most Caprimulgiformes are generally considered to be crepuscular and/or nocturnal, especially when there is plenty of moonlight or when they have young to feed. During the day, their behaviour, and in most species their plumage, is adapted to enable them to remain hidden and undetected by potential predators, although a few species of nightjar, most notably some of the New World nighthawks, may also be active at this time.

The Caprimulgiformes are an extremely diverse group of bird families, yet within each family species often exhibit behavioural similarities in particular stages of their life cycles.

ROOSTING

As mentioned above, the Caprimulgiformes need to remain safely hidden when diurnal predators are alert and actively seeking their prey. Many species achieve this by camouflage, their plumage and behaviour being adapted to suit their choice of roost-site, whilst others simply hide away in caves, tree-holes or tangles of vegetation.

The Oilbird usually roosts in inaccessible places deep inside caves and crevices, and so has no real need of the cryptic plumage or specialised roosting behaviour that is important to most other Caprimulgiformes. It tends to roost on flat surfaces such as ledges, and rests in a top-heavy horizontal posture, with its head low, feet well forward and tail slightly up in the air. Owlet-nightjars also hide away during the day, and tend to roost in tree-holes and hollows or clumps of vegetation above ground. Some species have also taken to using artificial sites such as buildings. As with the Oilbird, roosting owlet-nightjars do not need to rely on camouflage for their safety. Potoos and frogmouths roost in trees, often high above ground. They rest in an upright posture on branches (sometimes close to tree-trunks), snags and stumps, often in such a way that they look like an extension of whatever they are roosting on, and the colour and patterning of their plumage further enables them to blend in with their surroundings. This is their first line of defence. If relaxed, roosting birds tend to face forwards and from time to time they may shift their position, preen, or open their eyes and look around. If danger approaches, roosting birds very slowly adopt an alarm posture, their second line of defence, by closing their eyes, stretching up their neck and head, pointing their head and bill upwards, compressing all of their feathers to the body and then remaining motionless. Such behaviour further enhances their appearance of being part of a tree or branch. Whilst in this alarm posture, the roosting bird has a third line of defence in that it is able to keep watch on the intruder through the smallest of gaps between the eyelids, and it may even slowly turn its head in order to be able to do this. If the danger approaches too closely, the final defence is for the roosting bird to flush and fly away.

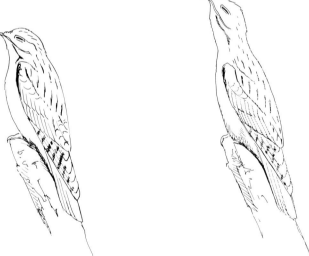

A roosting potoo in relaxed posture (left) and alarm posture (right). Similar behaviour is also adopted by breeding potoos, and by roosting or breeding frogmouths.

Nightjars generally roost on the ground, on rocks or on branches in trees, and rest in a horizontal posture. Their plumages are highly cryptic, with colours and patterns enabling them to blend in completely with their immediate surroundings. As with potoos and frogmouths, this is their first line of defence against predators. If relaxed, roosting birds may sit upright, open their eyes, preen, stretch their wings, gape (yawn?), or move around, e.g. out of direct sunlight. If danger approaches, a roosting bird adopts a flattened posture by lowering its head and bill towards the ground, closing its eyes and compressing all of its feathers to the body. This is its second line of defence. Although its eyes may appear closed whilst in this posture, it is able to keep watch on the intruder through tiny gaps between the eyelids, and should the danger approach too closely it will employ the last line of defence, the escape, by flushing, flying away and alighting out of sight.

A roosting nightjar in relaxed posture (left) and 'threatened' posture (right).

FEEDING AND DRINKING

With the exception of the Oilbird and the larger *Podargus* frogmouths, many Caprimulgiformes feed almost entirely on insects, with moths and beetles perhaps forming the greater part of their diets.

The Oilbird is a frugivore and feeds exclusively on the fruits of trees such as palms and laurels. To obtain its food, an Oilbird usually hovers close to a tree and plucks a fruit in its bill, although some birds may also alight in order to eat. The main hunting technique of the frogmouths is to fly from perch to perch, search the area beneath them and pounce onto prey that comes within range. They often take their food from the ground, but will also take prey from branches, tree-trunks or vegetation. Large prey items are usually beaten against a hard surface before being swallowed. The larger frogmouths of the genus *Podargus* may also take insects attracted to lights, feed on carrion, or even adopt a 'wait and see' policy by perching with their bills open and snapping at passing insects. It has also been suggested that when frogmouths are sitting with their bills open, insects may be attracted to a sticky paste discharged from the birds' palate (Diamond 1994), although this has yet to be proved. Some *Batrachostomus* frogmouths may also hawk for insects in flight. Potoos are generally aerial feeders, although they will also take prey from branches, rotten wood, vegetation or the ground. In flight, a foraging bird generally keeps its bill closed and snaps at individual prey items. They may also hawk for food by making sallies from a perch, a term often referred to as 'flycatching'. Owlet-nightjars generally hunt in flight, but their long legs also enable them to run about after prey on the ground.

Nightjars generally hunt on the wing, their extremely agile and buoyant foraging flights being full of twists, turns, climbs and dives, interspersed with frequent glides. Many species also 'flycatch' by making sallies from perches or from the ground. Occasionally, some species may also hover in order to take prey from vegetation, some may hover before swooping after insects in flight and some may take food whilst they are on the ground. Nightjars often feed on insects attracted to lights.

Scientific data on feeding nightjars is rather scarce, but studies have shown that in British Columbia foraging Common Nighthawks may fly at speeds of up to 5.3m per second, pursue up to 18-19 items of prey per minute, take more than one prey item at a time and spend up to 5.3% of each 24-hour period foraging (Aldridge and Brigham 1991, Brigham and Fenton 1991). Also in Canada, studies have shown that Whip-poor-wills are 'lunarphilic', i.e. their activity and feeding levels are highest during periods of twilight and bright moonlight (Mills 1986), and this probably applies to most species of caprimulgiform. The same study also states that although many insects are 'lunarphobic', i.e. they are less active during periods of twilight and bright moonlight, the greater amount of light probably improves a Whip-poor-wills foraging success despite the reduced prey availability (see also Structure and Mechanics). Foraging European Nightjars may take up to 12 prey items per minute, and if 'flycatching' they may take up to 31 items of prey in 28 sallies, over a c. 15 minute period (Cramp 1985).

Small stones and pebbles, grit, sand and even small molluscs have been found in the stomachs of many species of caprimulgiform. Although these items may sometimes be swallowed accidentally, they are also often taken deliberately, and their ingestion is thought to aid the grinding up of food. Chuck-will's-widows frequently pick up small stones in the tip of their bill, raise their heads and swallow (Jenkinson and Mengel 1970). Small pieces of bark and wood, twigs and pieces of vegetation are also ingested by some caprimulgiforms, but these items are probably taken at the same time as normal prey.

Drinking by caprimulgiforms has been poorly studied, and there appear to be few or no data available for many species, especially the frogmouths and potoos. The Oilbird possibly obtains much of its water from the fruits that it eats, and owlet-nightjars may alight and drink from the water's edge. Observations on nightjars drinking are commoner, however, with many species usually gliding or fluttering low over water with their wings and tail raised, and dipping or trawling their bill into the surface to drink. Some species may occasionally descend to the surface in a series of hovers, whilst others may alight at the water's edge and drink from there.

Male European Nightjar drinking in flight.

BREEDING

Although all caprimulgiforms are territorial during the breeding season, some species are colonial nesters, some are partially or semi-colonial, and the remainder choose to nest alone.

The Oilbird breeds in small to large colonies, often deep inside caves and crevices. It builds a nest of rotten fruit, regurgitated seeds, mud and faeces, usually on a high ledge, lays 1-4 white eggs, and its territory consists of the nest and its immediate surroundings. Frogmouths usually breed in forested or wooded country, build their nests in trees, lay 1-3 whitish eggs, and their territories may be as large as 80 hectares. *Podargus* frogmouths build large, untidy nests that are platforms of sticks, twigs and vegetation. *Batrachostomus* frogmouths build small, neat nests composed of bark, cobwebs, hair, moss, lichen and other vegetation. The potoos also nest in forested or wooded habitats, but do not build nests, and lay a single white, marked egg in a small depression in a branch or on top of a snag or stump. There is no information on territory sizes. Owlet-nightjars breed in forests and woodlands, but again there are no data on territory sizes; they nest in holes and hollows, usually in trees, often line their nests with vegetation and feathers and lay clutches of 4-5 whitish eggs. Nightjars breed in a range of different habitats, from deserts, semi-deserts and open country, to forests, wood-lands and suburban areas. Most species usually nest alone, in territories ranging up to 40 hectares, but some species may nest in loose, semi-colonial groups, others in colonies. Nightjars usually nest on the ground, although a few species do so on rocks, a few in palms or ferns, at least one in trees and several on the roofs of buildings. They do not build, and lay clutches of 1-2 white eggs, which are either plain or marked with browns, reds and greys.

Several studies have been undertaken to establish whether nightjars synchronise their breeding with the lunar cycle. In Canada, Common Nighthawks did not, but Whip-poor-wills were often found to do so, with chicks hatching and growing during periods when their parents had the maximum amount of moonlight for foraging, and young birds becoming independent during the following lunar period when there was the maximum amount of moonlight for them to forage (Mills 1986). In another study in Canada, Poorwills were found not to synchronise their breeding attempts with the lunar cycle (Brigham and Barclay 1992). European Nightjars possibly synchronise their nesting with the lunar cycle, but only if a full moon period occurs when they would normally commence laying (Cresswell 1996). In Africa, four Afrotropical species (3 *Caprimulgus* and 1 *Macrodipteryx*) were studied at a site in Zimbabwe, and the results showed that all four species often, but not always, synchronised their breeding with the lunar cycle (Jackson 1985a). It would appear that many factors, such as the experience of the parents, failed clutches, weather and, in the case of migratory species, time avail-able for breeding, may affect an attempt to synchronise breeding with a particular phase of the moon.

For many years, nightjars were thought to move their eggs or chicks away from potential danger, by deliberately carrying them out of harm's way, and reports on such behaviour have been published on species in North America, Europe and Africa. It has now been suggested, however, that there is no satisfactory evidence to support this view, and where cases could be investigated properly it has been found that eggshells, eggs or chicks appear to have become stuck on feet, legs or parts of the plumage, presumably by albumen from a hatched or broken egg (Jackson 1985c). Until recently, this behaviour had only been documented in nightjars, but it has now also been described for a *Batrachostomus* frogmouth (Mann 1991). Nightjars may occasionally move an egg a short distance by pushing it with its bill, e.g. if an egg becomes dislodged from the nest-site, but usually move their chicks by alighting nearby and calling to them, the chicks responding by walking, running or hop-ping towards their parent.

Defence display by a juvenile European Nightjar.

With the exception of the cave-nesting Oil-bird, members of the Caprimulgiformes defend their nests and young in a variety of ways. If danger approaches its nest, an adult *Podargus* frogmouth first assumes an alarm posture (see Roosting, above), relying on camouflage to escape detection. If the danger continues, it may then perform a defence display, intended to in-timidate and frighten off the intruder. Elements of such displays include spreading the wings and tail, fluffing out plumage, making circular move-ments with the head, gaping and staring, bill-snapping and producing clucking and hissing sounds. It may also flutter at the intruder. After the eggs have hatched, both adults and young may adopt the alarm posture when threatened. Older, unattended chicks may also perform a defence display by employing some of the tactics described above. The *Batrachostomus* frogmouths also adopt the alarm posture when first threat-ened, but as yet there is no published data on other behaviour. Owlet-nightjars usually just sit tight in their nesting chambers, or flush and fly away, although brooding adults with young may perform a defence display by fluffing up their plumage, gaping and hissing. The potoos of South America exhibit remarkably similar behaviour to the Australasian *Podargus* frogmouths (see above). Nightjars also rely on camouflage and, to a lesser degree, defence displays for nest protection, but they also perform a distraction display, during which they frequently gape and produce hissing sounds or other vocalisations. The commonest form of display is possibly the injured or broken-wing display, in which an adult flutters along the ground or across low vegetation, tail fanned and one or both wings outstretched. If a predator follows it, it will lead it away from the nest before flying off.

Typical distraction display by a Common Nighthawk on the ground.

This type of display may also be performed in the air, during which an adult appears to have difficulty in flying, often landing repeatedly between bouts of laboured fluttering flight. A third type of display takes place on a perch above ground, with the adult fanning its tail, and drooping and fluttering its wings.

Nightjars may also fly around, or at, an intruder to deter it. During a defence display, an adult may stand up, spread its wings and tail, fluff up its plumage, gape and hiss, and occasionally flap its wings at the intruder or back away from the nest. Older, feathered chicks perform a similar display by standing up, extending their wings, stretching up their neck, gaping and hissing.

Typical distraction display by a perched European Nightjar.

FOSSIL RECORD

Although the origin of the Caprimulgiformes is unknown, it would seem likely that the order is probably derived from ancient landbirds (Feduccia 1996). Fossil remains have so far been discovered for relatively few species, but the examination of these remains can still provide an insight into the natural history and evolution of this group of birds.

The nightjars can be considered to have been the most successful of the Caprimulgiformes, and they now occur in many parts of the world, although they are generally absent from the coldest regions. The other members of the order do not appear to have fared so well. The fossil evidence suggests that oilbirds, potoos, frogmouths and owlet-nightjars may also once have been found worldwide, but today each family has a rather limited, possibly relictual, distribution.

Era	Period	Epoch			Million years before present day
CENOZOIC (65)	QUATERNARY (1.64)	Recent (Holocene) (0.01) Plesistocene (1.63)			1.64
	TERTIARY		Neogene (22)	Pliocene (3.5)	5.2
				Miocene (18.3)	23.5
				Oligocene (12.0)	35.5
			Paleogene (42)	Eocene (21.0)	56.5
				Paleocene (8.5)	65
MESOZOIC (180)	CRETACEOUS (81)	Late (32)			97
		Early (49)			146
	JURASSIC (62)	Late (12)			157
		Middle (21)			178
		Early (30)			208
	TRIASSIC (37)				245

Geological periods up to the present. Figures quoted are millions of years (from Feduccia 1996).

SUMMARY OF CAPRIMULGIFORM FOSSIL REMAINS

Archaeotrogonidae

An extinct family of birds, containing a single genus *Archaeotrogon* comprised of four species, from the late Eocene to late Oligocene, France. Originally considered to be fossil trogons, even though the bones lacked the heterodactyl foot, characteristic of living trogons. In a review of *Archaeotrogon*, Mourer-Chauviré (1980) noted that the humeri and other bones showed similarities to those of the nightjar genera *Caprimulgus* and *Chordeiles*; after further study, it was considered that it indeed represented an extinct family of Caprimulgiformes.

Steatornithidae

An extinct genus *Prefica* containing one extinct species, from the early Eocene, Wyoming, North America, and a possible undescribed genus and species from the late Oligocene, France.

Podargidae

Fossil remains from the Quaternary, Australia. There is also a single undescribed species from the middle Eocene, Europe, and an extinct genus *Quercypodargus*, represented by one species, from the late Eocene to late Oligocene, France.

36

Nyctibiidae

Fossil remains of *Nyctibius griseus* from the Pleistocene, Brazil, and possibly *N. jamaicensis* from the Pleistocene, Jamaica. There is also an extinct genus *Euronyctibius*, containing one species, from the late Eocene to late Oligocene, France.

Aegothelidae

Fossil remains of *Aegotheles savesi* from the late quaternary, New Caledonia, and *Aegotheles cristatus* from the Holocene and Pleistocene, Australia. There is also an extinct species (previously placed in a new genus *Megaegotheles*) from the Pleistocene to sub-recent, South Island, New Zealand, an extinct genus *Quipollornis* containing one species, from the early to middle Miocene, Australia, and a possible undescribed genus and species, from the late Oligocene, France.

Caprimulgidae

Fossil remains of *Chordeiles minor*, *Eurostopodus mystacalis*, *Nyctidromus albicollis*, *Phalaenoptilus nuttallii*, *Siphonorhis brewsteri* ?, *Siphonorhis americana* (now extinct?), *Caprimulgus noctitherus*, *C. europaeus*, *Hydropsalis brasiliana* and *Eleothreptus anomalus*, all from Pleistocene or prehistoric sites. There is also an undescribed species from the middle Eocene, Europe, an extinct *Siphonorhis* poorwill from the quaternary (probably Holocene), Cuba, and an extinct genus *Ventivorus* containing one species, from the upper Eocene, France.

EXTINCT SPECIES

Order Caprimulgiformes
        Family Archaeotrogonidae
                Genus *Archaeotrogon* Milne-Edwards 1892
                (type species *Archaeotrogon venustus* Milne-Edwards 1892).

                        Archaeotrogon venustus Milne-Edwards 1892
                        Late Eocene to late Oligocene, Phosphorites du Quercy, France.
                        The smallest species within the genus and the commonest, at least in terms of recently collected material (Mourer-Chauviré 1980).

                        Archaeotrogon zitteli Gaillard 1908
                        Late Eocene to late Oligocene, Phosphorites du Quercy, France.
                        A larger species than *A. venustus*.

                        Archaeotrogon cayluxensis Gaillard 1908
                        Late Eocene to late Oligocene, Phosphorites du Quercy, France.
                        The largest species within the genus.

                        Archaeotrogon hoffstetteri Mourer-Chauviré 1980
                        Late Eocene to late Oligocene, Phosphorites du Quercy, France.
                        Intermediate? in size between *A. venustus* and *A. zitteli*.

        Family Steatornithidae
            Subfamily Preficinae
                Genus *Prefica* Olson 1985
                (type species *Prefica nivea* Olson 1985)

                        Prefica nivea Olson 1985
                        Early Eocene, Wyoming, North America.
                        A smaller species than the living Oilbird, it was probably incapable of hovering flight and therefore not adapted for life in caves (Olson 1985).

Family Podargidae

Genus *Quercypodargus* Mourer-Chauviré 1989
(type species *Quercypodargus olsoni* Mourer-Chauviré 1989)

Quercypodargus olsoni Mourer-Chauviré 1989
Upper Eocene, Phosphorites du Quercy, France.
The fossil evidence shows the tarsometatarsus to be short and thick, and close to that of modern *Podargus* frogmouths (Mourer-Chauviré 1989).

Family Nyctibiidae

Genus *Euronyctibius* Mourer-Chauviré 1989
(type species *Euronyctibius kurochkini* Mourer-Chauviré 1989)

Euronyctibius kurochkini Mourer-Chauviré 1989
Upper Eocene, Phosphorites du Quercy, France.
The fossil evidence reveals that the proximal section of the humerus resembles that of modern potoos *Nyctibius* sp., but it has the internal tuberosity less well developed on the inner side and the narrowing at the base is more marked (Mourer-Chauviré 1989).

Family Aegothelidae

Genus *Aegotheles* Vigors and Horsfield 1826
(type species *Aegotheles novae-hollandiae*)

Aegotheles novaezealandiae (Scarlett 1968)
Pleistocene to sub-recent, South Island, New Zealand.
A large owlet-nightjar, originally place in a new genus *Megaegotheles*. The fossil remains show a general increase in body size from North Island to South Island, in accordance with Bergman's Rule. Its large hindlimb and small forelimb, pectoral girdle and sternal keel suggest that it was, or was almost, a flightless species (Scarlett 1968).

Genus *Quipollornis* Rich and McEvey 1977
(type species *Quipollornis koniberi* Rich and McEvey 1977)

Quipollornis koniberi Rich and McEvey 1977
Early to middle Miocene, New South Wales, Australia.
This species had a rather elongate forelimb in relation to its hindlimb, suggesting that it was more of an aerial forager than the living owlet-nightjars (Rich and McEvey 1977).

Family Caprimulgidae

Genus *Ventivorus* Mourer-Chauviré 1988
(type species *Ventivorus ragei* Mourer-Chauviré 1988)

Ventivorus ragei Mourer-Chauviré 1988
Upper Eocene, Phosphorites du Quercy, France.

Genus *Siphonorhis* Sclater 1861
(type species *Siphonorhis americanus* (Linnaeus 1758))

Siphonorhis daiquiri Olson 1985
Quaternary, probably Holocene, Cuba.
Intermediate in size between Jamaican Poorwill *S. americana* and Least Poorwill *S. brewsteri* (Olson 1985).

Note: *Siphonorhis americana* Linnaeus 1758 has not been recorded since 1860 and is considered to be extinct by some authorities (see systematic section).

PLATES
1-36

PLATE 1: *PODARGUS* FROGMOUTHS

2   Tawny Frogmouth *Podargus strigoides*   Text and map page 116

A chiefly Australian species, found also on Tasmania and many offshore islands, including Fraser Island and larger islands in the Torres Strait; recently reported from southern New Guinea. All populations possibly sedentary. Inhabits open forests and woodlands, and also occurs in cleared farmland and towns, but avoids treeless areas and dense rainforest.

Sexes differ slightly, females being slightly smaller, paler and plainer than males. Racial differences also slight (see Text).

> **2**   **Adult** (nominate grey phase) A large, greyish frogmouth. Upperparts greyish, speckled and spotted white, and streaked blackish; wing-coverts greyish, speckled brown and boldly spotted white; scapulars whitish, mottled and speckled brown. Often shows a whitish supercilium. Submoustachial stripe blackish, edged chestnut-brown. Underparts greyish streaked blackish, boldly spotted white. At night, generally shows a reddish eyeshine in artificial light.

3   Papuan Frogmouth *Podargus papuensis*   Text and map page 119

Occurs throughout New Guinea and many of its islands, including the Aru Islands, and range extends south across north-eastern Australia to Townsville region in north-eastern Queensland. All populations probably sedentary. Generally inhabits the edges of forests and woodlands, but also occurs in other wooded habitats including gardens and mangroves.

Sexes differ slightly, females often being paler, plainer and buffier than males, with buffish scapulars. Races vary mainly in size (see Text).

> **3**   **Adult** (nominate) A very large, greyish-brown frogmouth. Upperparts greyish-brown, speckled buff, cinnamon and white, streaked and spotted blackish; wing-coverts greyish-brown mottled buff, tawny and white, streaked and spotted blackish and often boldly spotted white; scapulars whitish, speckled brown. Buffish supercilium extending around front of forehead, buff submoustachial stripe often streaked blackish-brown. Underparts greyish-brown, barred and streaked brown, becoming whitish on belly and flanks.

4   Marbled Frogmouth *Podargus ocellatus*   Text and map page 121

An Australasian species, occurring throughout New Guinea, the Aru Islands, the Trobriand, D'Entrecasteaux and Louisiade archipelagos, and the Solomon Islands, with two separate populations in north-eastern and central-eastern Australia. All races probably sedentary. Generally inhabits dense, lowland forests.

Sexes differ slightly, females often being plainer than males. Racial differences mainly involve size, although coloration and markings occasionally relevant (see Text).

> **4**   **Adult** (nominate) A large, brownish frogmouth. Upperparts rufescent-brown, speckled brown and buff; spotted and streaked blackish-brown; wing-coverts rufescent-brown, speckled and spotted blackish, boldly spotted whitish; scapulars buffish, distinctly spotted blackish-brown. Buffish supercilium extending around front of forehead above bill. Underparts greyish-brown, barred brown and boldly spotted whitish or pale buff. At night, generally shows an orange eyeshine in artificial light.

8 Gould's Frogmouth *Batrachostomus stellatus*   Text and map page 127

A South-East Asian species, occurring from the Thai Peninsula south to Natuna Besar Island, Borneo and Sumatra, including the Riau and Lingga archipelagos. Sedentary. Inhabits lowland and hill forests.

Monotypic.

8a   **Adult male** A medium-sized frogmouth. Upperparts tawny, chestnut or chestnut-brown, with a narrow white or buffish-white nuchal collar barred or edged blackish-brown, and a buffish supercilium; wing- coverts tawny, chestnut or chestnut-brown, boldly spotted whitish; scapulars boldly marked with white or greyish-white oval-shaped spots. Under parts tawny, boldly marked with buffish oval-shaped spots.

8b   **Adult female** Similar to male but generally darker and more reddish.

6 Dulit Frogmouth *Batrachostomus harterti*   Text and map page 125

A little-known species, endemic to the forests of central Borneo. Sedentary. Inhabits hill and submontane forests, including second growth.

Sexes similar. Monotypic.

6   **Adult** A large darkish frogmouth. Upperparts chestnut-brown, distinctly barred buffish on crown, with a narrow buffish nuchal collar; wing-coverts chestnut-brown boldly spotted buffish-white, spots bordered blackish; scapulars tawny, barred brown and spotted blackish, the black spots usually tipped buffish-white. Underparts chestnut-brown barred buffish, becoming pale brown boldly spotted greyish- or cinnamon-buff on belly and flanks, markings often T-shaped.

5 Large Frogmouth *Batrachostomus auritus*   Text and map page 124

A little-known South-East Asian species, occurring from the Thai Peninsula, south to Sumatra and Borneo. Sedentary. Inhabits the interior of lowland forests.

Sexes similar. Monotypic.

5   **Adult** A large, darkish frogmouth. Upperparts chestnut-brown or light brown, distinctly spotted or vermiculated buffish on crown, with a pale buffish brown-barred nuchalcollar extending around lower throat, pale buffish stripe along side of crown from in front of eye down side of nape, and a pale buffish submoustachial stripe; wing-coverts chestnut-brown or light brown, boldly spotted white or buffish-white, spots edged blackish and often 'tear-drop' shaped; scapulars chestnut-brown or light brown, with pale bars and blackish buff-tipped spots. Underparts rufescent-brown speckled brown, often spotted buffish.

8b

8a

6

5

100mm

PLATE 3: *BATRACHOSTOMUS* FROGMOUTHS (2)

11 Pale-headed Frogmouth *Batrachostomus poliolophus* Text and map page 130

A very poorly known species, endemic to Sumatra. Sedentary. Apparently confined to submontane primary forest.

Monotypic.

11a **Adult male** A small, brownish frogmouth. Upperparts rufescent-brown, with a buffish-white nuchal collar; wing-coverts rufescent-brown, boldly spotted buffish-white on greater and median coverts; scapulars very boldly spotted whitish. Underparts rufescent-brown boldly scalloped white on breast, generally buffish-white on belly and flanks, feathers edged brown or tawny.

11b **Adult female** Brighter, more rufescent-tawny than male, with fewer and smaller whitish spots on wing-coverts, scapulars and underparts. Often has a narrower nuchal collar.

12 Bornean Frogmouth *Batrachostomus mixtus* Text and map page 131

A little-known species, endemic to Borneo. Sedentary. Inhabits submontane and montane forests.

Monotypic.

12a **Adult male** A small, brownish frogmouth. Upperparts brown or light brown, with a narrow white nuchal collar; wing-coverts brown or light brown, boldly spotted whitish on greater coverts and some median coverts; scapulars very boldly spotted whitish. Under parts light brown, boldly scalloped and spotted white.

12b **Adult female** Brighter, more rufescent-tawny than male, with fewer, smaller white spots on wing-coverts, scapulars and underparts; narrower white nuchal collar.

7 Philippine Frogmouth *Batrachostomus septimus* Text and map page 125

A little-known species endemic to the Philippine Islands, although absent from Palawan. Sedentary. Inhabits forests from sea-level to 2,500m.

Races differ mainly in size (but see Text).

7a **Adult male** (nominate) A medium-sized brownish or rufescent frogmouth. Upperparts rufescent-brown tinged chestnut, barred tawny or buff on crown, with distinct buffish or buffish-white nuchal collar and pale cinnamon-buff supercilium; wing-coverts rufescent-brown tinged chestnut, boldly spotted pale buff; scapulars generally pale buff, speckled and vermiculated brown. Underparts rufescent-brown, tawny or buffish, speckled, spotted and barred pale buff and brown; broad pale buff band around lower throat, another around lower breast.

7b **Adult female** (nominate) Similar to male but may average darker and plainer.

9 Ceylon Frogmouth *Batrachostomus moniliger* Text and map page 128

Confined to Sri Lanka and the Western Ghats of south-western India, where it is the only species of frogmouth present. Sedentary. Inhabits lowland, hill and submontane forests, but tends to avoids disturbed areas and plantations.

Monotypic.

9a **Adult male** A medium-sized, greyish-brown frogmouth. Upperparts greyish-brown or brownish, spotted blackish, with a narrow greyish-white or buffish nuchal collar, and buffish supercilium; wing-coverts greyish-brown or brownish, boldly spotted greyish-white or buffish; scapulars whitish, speckled and vermiculated brown, boldly spotted blackish. Row of white or pale buff spots around throat. Underparts greyish-brown or brownish, boldly spotted white or pale buff on belly and flanks.

9b **Adult female** Tawnier, browner or more chestnut than male and often plainer, with fewer, smaller blackish spots on upperparts. Often lacks whitish nuchal collar, and has smaller whitish spots on median and greater coverts, buffier scapulars, and smaller and fewer whitish spots around lower throat.

11a

12b

12a

11b

7a

7b

9b

9a

100mm

14   Sunda Frogmouth *Batrachostomus cornutus*   Text and map page 134

A little-known species, currently known from Borneo, Sumatra and the Kangean Islands, but not Java. Sedentary. Inhabits the edges of lowland and hill forest, but also occurs in mangroves and gardens, occasionally near towns and villages.

Races differ slightly in plumage, tail length and bill size (see Text).

> **14a**   **Adult male** (nominate) A medium-sized brownish frogmouth. Upperparts and wing-coverts brown, speckled and spotted buff, white and blackish; scapulars boldly marked with whitish, oval-shaped spots. Whitish nuchal collar and broad whitish supercilium. Underparts brown, speckled and spotted buff, white and cinnamon, becoming generally whitish, streaked, spotted and barred brown, on belly and flanks.

> **14b**   **Adult female** (nominate) Brighter, tawnier and plainer than male, with smaller whitish spots on the scapulars.

13   Javan Frogmouth *Batrachostomus javensis*   Text and map page 132

A poorly understood Asian frogmouth, comprising four subspecies. Situation complex, and currently treated as one species. Occurs from central Burma south-east to S Laos and C Vietnam, south to Sumatra and Java, and east to Borneo, Palawan and the Calamian Islands. All populations probably sedentary. Inhabits lowland and hill forest, especially where there is a thick understorey. Race *affinis* also occurs in submontane forests to 1,600m.

Females are brighter, plainer and tawnier than males, with smaller whitish spots on the scapulars and less white on the underparts. Races differ in size, boldness of markings and vocalisations (see Text).

> **13a**   **Adult male** (nominate) A small to medium-sized brownish frogmouth. Upperparts and wing-coverts brown, speckled and spotted buff and white, distinctly spotted blackish; scapulars boldly marked with whitish oval-shaped spots. Whitish nuchal collar and distinct whitish supercilium. Underparts brown, speckled and spotted buff, cinnamon and white, becoming generally whitish, barred brown and spotted brown and black, on belly and flanks.

> **13b**   **Adult male** (*affinis*) Similar to the nominate but smaller and often less boldly marked.

> **13c**   **Adult male** (*continentalis*) Smaller, paler and less boldly marked than the nominate and often has a less distinct nuchal collar.

10   Hodgson's Frogmouth *Batrachostomus hodgsoni*   Text and map page 129

Range extends from north-eastern India east to southern China and south to central Burma, north-western Thailand, Laos and central Vietnam. Sedentary. Generally inhabits hill, submontane and montane forests, but may occasionally stray to lower altitudes.

Races differ slightly in size and tail length.

> **10a**   **Adult male** (nominate) A medium-sized brownish frogmouth. Upperparts and wing-coverts greyish-brown tinged tawny or buff, heavily spotted blackish; scapulars whitish, edged and spotted blackish. Narrow white or pale buff nuchal collar; buffish supercilium. Underparts greyish-brown tinged tawny or buff, boldly spotted creamy-white or buffish and speckled blackish.

> **10b**   **Adult female** (nominate) More rufescent-tawny than male, and plainer.

14b

14a

13a

13c

13b

10b

10a

100mm

PLATE 5: OILBIRD AND NEOTROPICAL POTOOS

17 Northern Potoo *Nyctibius jamaicensis*

Text and map page 138

The northern counterpart of Grey Potoo, with range confined to the northern and central parts of Central America, and islands in the Greater Antilles. Occurs from central Mexico south to north-western Costa Rica, and in the Greater Antilles it is found on Jamaica and Hispaniola. Probably sedentary in all regions. Shows a preference for lowland forests and woodlands, but is also found in open and semi-open country with scattered trees and hedges.

Sexes similar. Racial differences often slight, and mainly involve size (see Text).

17   **Adult** (nominate grey phase) A large, greyish-brown potoo. Upperparts greyish-brown streaked blackish-brown, mottled greyish-white, buff and tawny. Underparts greyish-brown, streaked blackish-brown; boldly spotted blackish-brown on centre of throat and across upper breast. At night, generally shows a reddish-orange or orange eyeshine in artificial light.

18 Grey Potoo *Nyctibius griseus*

Text and map page 140

The southern counterpart of Northern Potoo, and widely distributed from southern Central America to the central parts of South America. Occurs from eastern Nicaragua, south to northern Argentina. All populations probably sedentary. Chiefly a species of woodlands and forests, but may also be found in other habitats, including cerrado, plantations, mangroves and open fields.

Sexes similar. Racial differences often rather slight (see Text).

18a   **Adult** (nominate grey phase) A large, greyish-brown potoo. Upperparts greyish-brown streaked blackish-brown, mottled greyish-white, buff and tawny. Underparts greyish-brown streaked blackish-brown, boldly spotted blackish-brown on centre of throat and across upper breast. At night, generally shows a reddish-orange or orange eyeshine in artificial light.

18b   **Adult** (nominate rufous phase) Similar to the greyish form, but browner and more rufous.

15 Great Potoo *Nyctibius grandis*

Text and map page 136

Widely distributed throughout Central and South America, occurring in lowland woods and forests from southern Mexico, south to central Bolivia. Sedentary. Also inhabits areas of second growth, savannas, plantations, cultivation, gardens and coastal sand-ridges.

Sexes similar. Monotypic.

15   **Adult** A large, greyish-white potoo. Upperparts and wing-coverts greyish-white, speckled and mottled black, brown, tawny and buff. Underparts greyish-white, barred and speck led buff, brown and blackish-brown. At night, shows a reddish-orange eyeshine in artificial light.

1 Oilbird *Steatornis caripennis*

Text and map page 113

A unique South American species, occurring in Colombia, Venezuela, Trinidad, Guyana, Ecuador, Peru and central Bolivia. Inhabits forests and woodlands, but needs large caves and deep crevices to roost and breed in. Also occasionally found in scrubland, secondary forest and coffee plantations interspersed with mature fruit trees. Tends to avoid disturbed forest, urban and suburban areas, and villages. Partially and seasonally migratory, moving away from breeding sites in search of fruiting trees.

Sexes similar. Monotypic.

1   **Adult** Mainly rufescent-brown, spotted whitish on the crown, rump, uppertail-coverts and median coverts. Also shows white spots along the outer primaries, secondaries, and outermost tail feathers. Underparts rufescent-brown, boldly spotted whitish.

PLATE 6: SOUTH AMERICAN POTOOS

19 Andean Potoo *Nyctibius maculosus* Text and map page 142

A highland forest species, endemic to the Andes of north-western and west-central South America. Occurs from western Venezuela, south to western Bolivia. Possibly sedentary throughout its range.

Sexes differ slightly, females averaging buffier or tawnier than males, with a buffier white patch on the wing-coverts. Monotypic.

> **19** **Adult** A large, brownish potoo. Upperparts brown, streaked white, buff, tawny and blackish-brown. Shows a large white wing-panel. Throat whitish; rest of underparts brown spotted black and buff, becoming buff barred brown with blackish-brown spots on belly and flanks.

16 Long-tailed Potoo *Nyctibius aethereus* Text and map page 137

A widely distributed but surprisingly poorly known South American species. Occurs from western and south-eastern Colombia east to Brazil and south to north-eastern Argentina. All populations are probably sedentary. Confined to lowland forests, and usually inhabits forest interiors.

Sexes similar. Racial differences involve size and overall coloration.

> **16** **Adult** (nominate) A large, long-tailed, brownish potoo. Often appears dark-crowned. Upperparts and wing-coverts brownish, mottled and spotted buff and brown, spotted and streaked blackish-brown, with a distinct buffish panel across the shoulders, buffish supercilium, and a buff submoustachial stripe that broadens along sides of throat. Underparts brownish, speckled, streaked and spotted buff and blackish-brown.

20 White-winged Potoo *Nyctibius leucopterus* Text and map page 143

A rare and little-known South American species, so far recorded only from central and south-western Guyana, and northern and eastern Brazil. Probably sedentary. Appears to prefer undisturbed primary forest, and often found near rivers or streams.

Sexes similar, although males often have a slightly larger white wing-patch. Monotypic.

> **20** **Adult** Upperparts greyish-brown streaked blackish-brown. Lower lesser coverts, median coverts and greater coverts whitish, forming a broad white wing-panel, although this may often be obscured by scapulars. Indistinct greyish-white or pale buffish nuchal collar. Throat pale buffish or greyish-white; rest of underparts greyish-brown, streaked and spotted blackish-brown.

21 Rufous Potoo *Nyctibius bracteatus* Text and map page 144

A poorly known South American species, recorded from the western parts of central Colombia south to eastern Peru and east to north-western Brazil and Guyana. Probably sedentary through-out its range, and apparently confined to lowland forest interiors.

Sexes similar. Monotypic.

> **21** **Adult** The smallest, most brightly coloured potoo, and unmistakable. Upperparts rufescent-tawny, barred and spotted blackish, especially on head. Wing-coverts rufescent-tawny, speckled dark brown; scapulars boldly spotted whitish. Underparts rufescent-tawny, boldly spotted whitish.

19

16

20

21

100mm

24 Australian Owlet-nightjar *Aegotheles cristatus*   Text and map page 147

Most common and widespread owlet-nightjar, extending from southern and south-eastern Papua New Guinea across all Australia and many of its islands to Tasmania. Sedentary. Generally inhabits forests and woodlands, but avoids rainforests, mangroves and treeless plains.

Sexes similar. Racial differences slight, involving size and coloration (see Text).

24a/b Adult A small to medium-sized, variable owlet-nightjar, birds ranging from grey to rufous. Upperparts and wing-coverts generally greyish, speckled greyish-white. Distinct greyish-white lateral crown-stripes, greyish-white band around rear of crown, and greyish-white nuchal collar. Underparts pale buffish-white, narrowly barred or vermiculated brown.

22 Moluccan Owlet-nightjar *Aegotheles crinifrons*   Text and map page 145

A little-known species endemic to the northern Moluccas, and recorded only from Halmahera, Bacan and Kasiruta. Sedentary. Inhabits forests, woodlands and well wooded areas. Also occurs in coconut plantations and cultivated areas.

Sexes possibly similar (see Text). Monotypic.

22a   **Adult** (brown phase) A large owlet-nightjar. Upperparts brown, finely barred greyish-brown, with buffish lateral crown-stripes; wing coverts brown finely barred greyish-brown, spotted pale buff on the median and greater coverts. Underparts buffish-brown speckled and spotted dark brown on breast, becoming buff spotted brown on belly and flanks.

22b   **Adult** (rufous phase) Paler, plainer and more rufescent-tawny on the upperparts and breast.

25 New Caledonian Owlet-nightjar *Aegotheles savesi*   Text and map page 149

The rarest and least-known owlet-nightjar, endemic to New Caledonia. Known from a single male specimen taken near Nouméa in 1880.

Monotypic.

25a/b Adult male A large brownish owlet-nightjar. Upperparts and wing-coverts brown, thinly barred greyish-white. Underparts also brown densely barred greyish-white.

23 Large Owlet-nightjar *Aegotheles insignis*   Text and map page 146

Endemic to New Guinea, and the largest owlet-nightjar there. Sedentary. Widely distributed and generally confined to montane forests and woodlands, although south-eastern race *tatei* is a lowland form.

Sexes similar. Races differ mainly in size, and head and underparts markings (see Text).

23a/b Adult (rufous phase) A large owlet-nightjar. Upperparts and wing-coverts rufescent-tawny, lightly spotted or speckled white or buff; scapulars boldly spotted white or buff, the spots being broadly bordered blackish-brown. Bold whitish or buffish lateral crown-stripes. Underparts rufescent-tawny, but chin and throat whitish or buff, and centre of breast, flanks and lower belly boldly spotted white.

23c   **Adult** (brown phase) Similar to the rufous phase, but more rufescent-brown on the upperparts and breast.

24b

24a

22b

22a

25b

25a

23b

23a

23c

100mm

26   Barred Owlet-nightjar *Aegotheles bennettii*   **Text and map page 150**

Endemic to New Guinea, the Aru Islands and the D'Entrecasteaux Archipelago, where it is generally confined to lowland and hill forest. Sedentary.

Sexes similar. Races differ mainly in size and shade of plumage (see Text).

26a/b Adult (nominate) A small to medium-sized, greyish-brown owlet-nightjar. Upperparts and wing-coverts brownish or blackish, finely barred and vermiculated greyish-white. Broad, buffish lateral crown-stripes and a distinct buffish or whitish nuchal collar. Underparts buffish to greyish-white, spotted, speckled and vermiculated brown.

27   Wallace's Owlet-nightjar *Aegotheles wallacii*   **Text and map page 151**

Endemic to New Guinea and the Aru Islands, where generally found in lowland and hill forest. Also occurs in wooded gardens. Sedentary.

Sexes similar. Races differ in size and general coloration (see Text).

27a/b Adult (nominate) A small to medium-sized, greyish-brown owlet-nightjar. Upperparts dark brown or blackish-brown, finely speckled and vermiculated greyish- or buffish-white, sometimes with indistinct lateral crown-stripes. Wing-coverts dark brown, speckled greyish-white and spotted buffish-white. Throat buffish, breast dark brown, rest of underparts buffish- or greyish-white, boldly spotted or vermiculated brown.

29   Archbold's Owlet-nightjar *Aegotheles archboldi*   **Text and map page 153**

A poorly known central New Guinea endemic, generally found in montane forest. Sedentary.

Sexes similar. Monotypic.

29a/b Adult A small, dark, heavily spotted owlet-nightjar. Upperparts and wing-coverts dark brown tinged rufous, boldly spotted whitish. Pale buffish lateral crown-stripes, a thin but distinct whitish nuchal collar; sides of neck and throat mottled brown. Underparts pale buff tinged tawny, boldly blotched and spotted dark brown.

28   Mountain Owlet-nightjar *Aegotheles albertisi*   **Text and map page 152**

A little-known species endemic to New Guinea, where it is usually found in submontane or montane forests. Also occurs in alpine tree-fern savannas and gardens. Sedentary.

Sexes similar. Racial differences slight (see Text).

28a/b Adult (nominate) A small, darkish, spotted owlet-nightjar. Upperparts and wing-coverts brown or rufous-brown, spotted greyish-white. Buffish lateral crown-stripes, a prominent tawny patch behind the eyes, narrow greyish-white or pale buff nuchal collar; and sides of neck and throat finely speckled and barred brown. Underparts pale buff or whitish, streaked, spotted and blotched brown, markings often forming a bold V-shaped pattern down the breast and belly.

26b

27b

26a

27a

29b

28b

29a

28a

100mm

PLATE 9: NIGHTHAWKS (1)

30   Semi-collared Nighthawk *Lurocalis semitorquatus*   **Text and map page 154**

A widely distributed, but poorly known, Central and South American species. Range extends from south-eastern Mexico, south to northern and eastern Bolivia, Paraguay and northern Argentina. Movements not fully understood. Southern populations migratory, wintering as far north as Venezuela. Generally inhabits forests, woodlands or partly wooded country, but also occurs in plantations, scrubland, open countryside and at the edges of marshes and watercourses.

Sexes similar. Racial variation often slight, and involves size and coloration (see Text).

   30a   Adult (nominate) A dark medium-sized nighthawk. At rest, wing-tips project well beyond tail. Upperparts and wing-coverts dark brown, speckled and spotted rufous, tawny and buff. No nuchal collar; white throat-patch.

   30b/c Adult (nominate) In flight, lacks white markings on wings and tail.

31   Rufous-bellied Nighthawk *Lurocalis rufiventris*   **Text and map page 155**

A highland forest species endemic to the Andes of western South America. Range extends from western Venezuela and western Colombia, south along the Andes of central Ecuador and western and southern Peru to western Bolivia. Generally sedentary, but may also be partly nomadic. Inhabits montane forests and woodlands at 1,650–3,000m.

Sexes similar. Monotypic.

   31a   Adult A dark medium-sized nighthawk. At rest, wing-tips project well beyond tail. Upperparts and wing-coverts dark brown, speckled and spotted rufous, tawny and buff. No nuchal collar; white throat-patch.

   31b/c Adult In flight, lacks white markings on wings and tail.

39   Nacunda Nighthawk *Podager nacunda*   **Text and map page 172**

A widely distributed South American species, extending from northern and central Colombia east to Guyana, Surinam and northern Brazil, south to Bolivia, Paraguay, Uruguay and northern and central Argentina. Migratory in parts of range, but movements poorly understood, i.e. visitor to southern regions from mid-August to mid-May, casual visitor to Patagonia. A lowland species, inhabiting savannas, grasslands, marshy areas and forest edge. Also found near rivers and seashores.

Sexes differ slightly, females having more heavily barred underparts and smaller white spots on the outer primaries. Racial differences also slight (see Text).

   39a   Adult male (nominate) A stocky, medium-sized to large brownish nighthawk. Wing-coverts and scapulars heavily spotted blackish. No nuchal collar; large white throat-patch (may show only as a white band).

   39b/c Adult (nominate) In flight shows a white band towards the wing-tip across the outer five or six primaries, and broad white tips to all but the central pair of tail feathers. Underparts quite striking, the dark head and breast contrasting with the white belly, flanks and underwing-coverts. Brown trailing edge to wing and darkish wing-tips.

34   Sand-coloured Nighthawk *Chordeiles rupestris*   **Text and map page 159**

A South American species, found in suitable lowland habitat from eastern Ecuador south to central Bolivia east to northern and central Brazil. Sedentary and partially migratory, some populations undertaking local movements. Entirely restricted to rivers and marshes within forests, where it occurs on rocky islands, beaches and sandbars. Also frequents open spaces close to rivers such as airstrips and village streets.

Sexes similar. Racial differences slight (see Text).

   34a   Adult A small to medium-sized, pale, greyish-brown nighthawk. Wing-coverts and scapulars boldly spotted with blackish, star-shaped markings. No nuchal collar; white throat-patch.

   34b   Adult In flight, shows large white patch across rear of wings, with brownish trailing edge and wing-tips. All but the central pair of tail feathers are white, broadly tipped brown.

30b

31b

30c

31c

30a

31a

39b

39a

39c

34a

34b

100mm

32 Least Nighthawk *Chordeiles pusillus*　　　　**Text and map page 157**

A South American species, with a discontinuous range extending from eastern Colombia east to eastern Brazil, south to north-eastern Bolivia, north-eastern Argentina and south-eastern Brazil. Some populations possibly sedentary, others migratory, but movements poorly understood. Generally a species of lowland savanna and grassland with scattered trees and scrub.

Races vary mainly in size and coloration (see Text).

32a **Adult male** (nominate) A small, brownish, heavily mottled nighthawk, quite variable in colour; wing-coverts heavily spotted buff and pale buff. No nuchal collar; small white throat-patch.

32b **Adult male** (nominate) In flight shows a white band towards the wing-tip across the four outer primaries, white trailing edge to inner wing, and white tips to innerwebs of all but the central pair of tail feathers.

32c **Adult female** (nominate) Similar to male, but with a thinner white band across the outer primaries, a duller, buffier trailing edge to inner wing, and no white tips to some or all tail feathers.

38 Band-tailed Nighthawk *Nyctiprogne leucopyga*　　　　**Text and map page 170**

A little-known species widely distributed throughout much of tropical lowland South America from eastern Colombia, east to Guyana, Surinam, French Guiana and northern Brazil, south to northern and eastern Bolivia. Most populations possibly resident. Inhabits forests and savannas, usually close to water.

Sexes similar. Racial variation often slight (see Text).

38a **Adult** (nominate) A small, brown, variegated nighthawk. Wing-coverts speckled and spotted pale brown, greyish-brown and cinnamon, with a buffish line along scapulars. No nuchal collar; small white patch on either side of lower throat.

38b **Adult** (nominate) In flight, lacks white markings on wings, but shows a prominent white band across middle of three outer tail feathers.

33 Bahian Nighthawk *Chordeiles vielliardi*　　　　**Text and map page 158**

A recently described and still little-known lowland species of north-eastern South America. So far recorded only from dry caatinga areas along riverbanks in eastern Brazil. Presumably sedentary. Female undescribed. Monotypic.

33a **Adult male** A small chestnut-brown nighthawk. Wing-coverts spotted buffish; tawny or buff line along scapulars. No nuchal collar or white on throat.

33b **Adult male** In flight, lacks white markings on wings and tail.

32b

32c

32a

38b

38a

33b

33a

100mm

36   Common Nighthawk *Chordeiles minor*   Text and map page 164

A highly migratory species, breeding throughout much of North and Central America, and wintering in South America as far south as northern Patagonia. Generally inhabits arid, open or semi-open country, and occurs in a wide variety of habitats. In many areas it penetrates towns and cities, often breeding on flat roofs.

Races mainly separated by coloration of plumage and markings (see Text). In both sexes, the white band across the outer primaries becomes broader towards trailing edge of wing, and above the band the inner primaries appear blackish and unmarked.

36a   **Adult male** (nominate) A medium-sized, greyish-brown nighthawk. At rest, wing-tips usually extend well beyond the tail. Lesser coverts darkish brown, often giving a dark-shouldered appearance; rest of wing-coverts speckled and spotted greyish-white, white or pale buff, often with a white patch on the marginal coverts. No nuchal collar; greyish-white supercilium and large white throat-patch.

36b   **Adult male** (nominate) In flight shows a broad white band, almost midway along the outer wing, across the five outer primaries, and a broad white subterminal band across all but the central pair of tail feathers.

36c   **Adult female** (nominate) Differs from male in having a buffish throat-patch and, in flight, a thinner, less distinct white band across outer primaries, and no white on tail.

37   Antillean Nighthawk *Chordeiles gundlachii*   Text and map page 168

Breeds throughout much of the Caribbean, including the Bahamas, Cuba, Cayman Islands, Jamaica, Hispaniola, Puerto Rico and Virgin Islands, plus Florida. Migratory, possibly wintering in South America. Prefers open or semi-open arid habitats.

Racial differences slight, mainly involving size. In both sexes, above the white patch, the inner primaries appear blackish and unmarked.

37a   **Adult male** (nominate) A medium-sized, greyish-brown nighthawk, not easily separable from Common Nighthawk except by voice. At rest, wing-tips occasionally fall short of tip of tail. Lesser coverts dark brown, often giving a dark-shouldered appearance; rest of wing-coverts speckled and spotted greyish-white and cinnamon, often showing white patch on marginal coverts. No nuchal collar; greyish-white supercilium and large white throat-patch.

37b   **Adult male** (nominate) In flight shows a broad white band, almost midway along the outer wing, across the five outer primaries, and a broad white subterminal band across all but the central pair of tail feathers.

37c   **Adult female** (nominate) Differs from male in having buffish or buffish-white throat-patch and, in flight, a less distinct white band across outer primaries, and no white on tail.

35   Lesser Nighthawk *Chordeiles acutipennis*   Text and map page 160

Widely distributed over much of South America, breeding range extending northwards to south-west North America. Possibly resident throughout much of range, but northern populations migratory, moving south after breeding to winter throughout Central America. Occurs in a great variety of habitats, including deserts, semi-deserts, scrubland, savanna and farmland.

Racial variation complex (see Text). In both sexes, the band across the outer primaries becomes narrower towards trailing edge of wing, and above the band the inner primaries are spotted buffish.

35a   **Adult male** (nominate) A medium-sized, brownish or greyish-brown nighthawk. At rest, wing-tips reach tip of tail; wing-coverts spotted buffish, with a white patch on the marginal coverts and a buffish line along scapulars. Often has an indistinct buffish or greyish-white nuchal collar; large white throat-patch.

35b   **Adult male** (nominate) In flight shows a white band towards the wing-tip across the four outer primaries, and a narrow white subterminal band across all but the central pair of tail feathers.

35c   **Adult female** (nominate) Differs from male in having a buffish throat-patch and, in flight, a buffish or buffish-white band across outer primaries, and no white on tail.

36c

36b

36a

37c

37b

37a

35c

35b

35a

100mm

PLATE 12: POORWILLS AND PAURAQUE

49   Jamaican Poorwill *Siphonorhis americana*   Text and map page 190

Endemic to Jamaica, but not reliably recorded since about 1860 and often now considered extinct. Habitat unknown; possibly a bird of semi-arid woodland or open country.

Sexes differ, but not greatly (see Text). Monotypic.

> **49a**   **Adult** A medium-sized brownish and variegated nightjar. Wing-coverts spotted blackish-brown and pale buff; may show a buffish line along the scapulars. Indistinct rufous or rufous-buff nuchal collar; large white throat-patch.
>
> **49b**   **Adult** In flight lacks white markings on wings, but has all except the central pair of tail feathers narrowly tipped white or yellowish-buff.

---

50   Least Poorwill *Siphonorhis brewsteri*   Text and map page 190

A little-known species, endemic to Hispaniola. Resident. Favours arid or semi-arid lowlands, especially where there are woodlands.

Sexes similar. Monotypic.

> **50a**   **Adult** A small, greyish-brown, variegated nightjar. Wing-coverts boldly spotted white; may show a pale buffish line along scapulars. Broad buff nuchal collar; white throat-patch.
>
> **50b**   **Adult** In flight lacks white markings on wings, but has all except the central pair of tail feathers narrowly tipped white or pale buff.

---

48   Common Poorwill *Phalaenoptilus nuttallii*   Text and map page 187

Breeding range extends from south-eastern Canada, south through the western and central parts of North America to northern Mexico. Northern populations are migratory and winter in southern parts of the range; in southern regions, some birds may move to lower altitudes after breeding. Generally inhabits arid or semi-arid country such as deserts, open prairie, grassy hillsides with scattered trees or scrub, rocky country with scattered vegetation, and chaparral.

Colour variation in races often slight (see Text).

> **48a**   **Adult male** (nominate) A small, pale, short-tailed nightjar. Wing-coverts spotted buffish; scapulars with large, almost star-shaped markings. No nuchal collar; sides of throat white; thin white submoustachial stripe.
>
> **48b**   **Adult male** (nominate) In flight lacks white markings on wings, but has all except the central pair of tail feathers narrowly tipped white.
>
> **48c**   **Adult female** (nominate) Differs from male in having a buffish submoustachial stripe, and less white in tail.

---

47   Pauraque *Nyctidromus albicollis*   Text and map page 184

A widespread Neotropical species, ranging from southern Texas south as far as northern Argentina. Most populations probably resident, although the race breeding in southern Texas possibly winters in eastern Mexico. Prefers forested or wooded habitats, but also occurs in scrubland, areas of cultivation, semi-arid regions, llanos, marshy areas and mangroves.

Racial variation complex, some populations being larger and greyer than others (see Text).

> **47a**   **Adult male** (nominate) A medium-sized, long-tailed nightjar with two distinct colour phases, greyish-brown (illustrated) and reddish-brown or tawny. At rest, wing-tips reach about half-way along tail. Lesser coverts chestnut; rest of wing-coverts greyish-brown boldly spotted buff, with a buffish line along scapulars. Head distinctive, with buffish eye-ring and submoustachial stripe contrasting with rufous or chestnut lores and ear-coverts. No nuchal collar but a white throat-patch.
>
> **47b**   **Adult male** (nominate) In flight shows a broad white band near the wing-tip across the five outer primaries, and the three outer tail feathers are largely white.
>
> **47c**   **Adult female** (nominate) Differs from male in having a thinner white band across the outer primaries, and narrow white tips to second and third outermost tail feathers.

49b

49a

50b

50a

48c

48b

48a

47c

47a

47b

100mm

PLATE 13: *NYCTIPHRYNUS* POORWILLS

51 Eared Poorwill *Nyctiphrynus mcleodii*   Text and map page 191

A little-known species confined to western Mexico. Mainly resident, but sometimes undertakes local movements. Generally a woodland species, but also occurs in other wooded habitats such as overgrown fields with scattered trees.

Sexes similar. Two races within limited range, but differences slight.

51a   **Adult** (nominate) A small, rather plain, greyish or rufescent-brown nightjar; may show small 'ear-tufts' at rear of crown. Large blackish spots on scapulars, smaller white spots on wing-coverts. Narrow buffish-white nuchal collar; conspicuous white band around throat.

51b   **Adult** (nominate) In flight lacks white markings on wings, but has all except the central pair of tail feathers narrowly tipped white.

52 Yucatan Poorwill *Nyctiphrynus yucatanicus*   Text and map page 192

A poorly known species endemic to Central America in south-east Mexico, northern Guatemala and northern Belize. Probably resident. Inhabits arid and semi-arid lowlands, preferring scrubland, deciduous forest and open woodland; also found in farmland and cultivation.

Sexes similar. Monotypic.

52a   **Adult** A small, brownish nightjar, with wing-coverts lightly spotted buffish-white. Narrow indistinct buffish nuchal collar; large white throat-patch.

52b   **Adult** In flight lacks white markings on wings, but has all except the central pair of tail feathers narrowly tipped white.

53 Ocellated Poorwill *Nyctiphrynus ocellatus*   Text and map page 193

A South American species, with a separate population in Central America. Main range extends from south-west Colombia, south to north-east Argentina and east to eastern Brazil. In Central America found in north-east Nicaragua, north-west Costa Rica and possibly Panama. Sedentary. Generally inhabits forest clearings.

The Central American race is smaller than the nominate, with narrower white tips to the tail feathers.

53a   **Adult male** (nominate) A small, dark, greyish-brown and rather plain nightjar. Scapulars and some wing-coverts boldly spotted blackish-brown, the spots bordered rufous or buffish; white band around throat.

53b   **Adult male** (nominate) In flight lacks white markings on wings, but the outer three or four tail feathers are narrowly tipped white.

53c   **Adult female** (nominate) Similar to male but generally paler and rather rufous.

54 Chocó Poorwill *Nyctiphrynus rosenbergi*   Text and map page 194

A little-known species, generally restricted to the Chocó faunal region in north-western South America, i.e. only in western Colombia and north-west Ecuador. Resident. Mainly inhabits primary forest, although sometimes found in adjacent secondary forest.

Sexes similar. Monotypic.

54a   **Adult** A small, darkish, cinnamon-brown nightjar. Wing-coverts and scapulars rather heavily spotted blackish-brown; two or three large white spots on inner greater coverts; large white throat-patch.

54b   **Adult** In flight lacks white markings on wings, but all the tail feathers are narrowly tipped white.

51b

51a

52a

52b

53a

53b

53c

54a

54b

100mm

63   Whip-poor-will *Caprimulgus vociferus*   **Text and map page 205**

Widely distributed throughout much of North and Central America from southern Canada south to Honduras and El Salvador. Bulk of population migratory, generally wintering south of main breeding range. Central American populations probably resident. Inhabits forests and woodlands.

Races differ mainly in size and coloration (see Text).

63a   Adult male (nominate) A medium-sized, greyish-brown, variegated nightjar. Row of large blackish spots along scapulars and across upper forewing. Indistinct tawny-buff nuchal collar; thin buffish moustachial stripe; indistinct white malar stripe; white or buffish-white band around lower throat.

63b   Adult male (nominate) In flight lacks white markings on wings, but has broad white tips to the three outer tail feathers.

63c   Adult female (nominate) Differs from male in having narrow buff tips to the outer tail feathers.

64   Puerto Rican Nightjar *Caprimulgus noctitherus*   **Text and map page 208**

Endemic to Puerto Rico in the West Indies, where now restricted to the arid south-west. Resident. Inhabits forest, woodland and scrub.

Females (not illustrated) are similar to males, but have narrower, buffish tips to the outer tail feathers. Monotypic.

64a   Adult male A medium-sized, brownish, variegated nightjar. Shows a row of large blackish spots across the upper forewing and along the scapulars. Indistinct, tawny-buff nuchal collar; white or buffish-white band around lower throat.

64b   Adult male In flight lacks white markings on wings, but has broad white tips to the three outer tail feathers.

65   Dusky Nightjar *Caprimulgus saturatus*   **Text and map page 210**

Endemic to Costa Rica and western Panama in Central America. Resident. Generally confined to montane forest and woodland, but also occurs in highland pastures with scattered trees.

Monotypic.

65a   Adult male A small to medium-sized, dark nightjar, heavily spotted tawny and buff. Indistinct pale buffish band around lower throat.

65b   Adult male In flight lacks white markings on wings, but has broad white tips to the three outer tail feathers.

65c   Adult female Often paler than male, sometimes much more rufous; narrower tawny-buff tips to the outer tail feathers.

62   Buff-collared Nightjar *Caprimulgus ridgwayi*   **Text and map page 204**

A surprisingly poorly known species, generally restricted to Central America, from extreme south-west North America through western Mexico to central parts of Guatemala, Honduras and Nicaragua. Mainly resident; northern population partially migratory. Inhabits arid or semi-arid open woodland, scrubland and rocky places with scattered vegetation.

Races differ slightly in size.

62a   Adult male (nominate) A medium-sized, greyish-brown, variegated nightjar. Wing-coverts and scapulars boldly spotted blackish-brown and buff. Broad tawny or buff nuchal collar; narrow buffish-white supercilium and moustachial stripe; broad buffish-white band around lower throat.

62b   Adult male (nominate) In flight lacks white markings on wings, but has broad white tips to the three outer tail feathers.

62c   Adult female (nominate) Similar to male but with narrower, buffish tips to the tail feathers.

63b

63c

63a

64b

64a

65c

65a

65b

62c

62b

62a

100mm

55 Chuck-will's-widow *Caprimulgus carolinensis* Text and map page 196

A North American species, breeding across many central and eastern states. Migratory, wintering from south-eastern Texas and Louisiana south through Central America to northern South America; and from northern Florida south through the Bahamas to the Greater Antilles. Inhabits woodland, forest and wooded country.

Monotypic.

55a **Adult male** A large, brown or greyish-brown, variegated nightjar. Wing-coverts heavily spotted buff and buffish-white; scapulars boldly spotted blackish. Narrow indistinct tawny-buff nuchal collar; narrow white or buffish-white band around lower throat.

55b **Adult male** In flight lacks white markings on wings, but has white innerwebs to the three outer tail feathers, outerwebs being tawny, speckled or barred blackish.

55c **Adult female** Similar to male, but lacks white on tail.

56 Rufous Nightjar *Caprimulgus rufus* Text and map page 198

A widespread South American species extending into the southern parts of Central America, from southern Costa Rica south to northern Argentina and east to eastern Brazil; also on Trinidad and in the Lesser Antilles. Resident throughout much of range, but southern populations move north in post-breeding period. Mainly a forest or woodland species, but also often found in other habitats such as scrubland.

Races differ mainly in tone of rufescent coloration (see Text).

56a **Adult male** (nominate) A large, reddish-brown or brownish, variegated nightjar. Wing-coverts and scapulars boldly spotted blackish-brown. Narrow indistinct tawny-buff nuchal collar; narrow white or buffish-white band around lower throat.

56b **Adult male** (nominate) In flight lacks white markings on wings, but has large white spots on innerwebs of the three outer tail feathers, outerwebs being tawny and generally unmarked.

56c **Adult female** (nominate) Similar to male, but lacks white on tail.

57 Cuban Nightjar *Caprimulgus cubanensis* Text and map page 199

A little-known species endemic to Cuba and the Isle of Pines. Resident. Generally inhabits woodland but also found in scrub and the edge of swamps.

Sexes similar, but females (not illustrated) have narrower, buffish tips to the outer tail feathers.

Racial variation is clinal, with smaller, darker birds occurring on the Isle of Pines.

57a **Adult male** (nominate) A large, dark nightjar. Wing-coverts speckled and spotted pale buff, scapulars buffish-white, boldly spotted blackish-brown. Buffish-white submoustachial stripe, broad, pale buff band around the lower throat.

57b **Adult male** (nominate) In flight lacks white markings on wings, but has white tips to the three outer tail feathers.

58 Hispaniolan Nightjar *Caprimulgus ekmani* Text and map page 200

A poorly known Caribbean species, endemic to Hispaniola. Resident; possibly confined to pine forest.

Sexes similar, but females (not illustrated) have buffish tips to the outer tail feathers. Monotypic.

58a **Adult male** A large, dark nightjar. Wing-coverts speckled greyish-white and -brown and spotted buffish, scapulars spotted blackish-brown. Narrow indistinct band of cinnamon-buff spots around lower throat.

58b **Adult male** In flight lacks white markings on wings, but has very broad white tips to the three outer tail feathers.

55b

55a

55c

56b

56a

56c

57a

57b

58a

58b

100mm

61 Silky-tailed Nightjar *Caprimulgus sericocaudatus*   Text and map page 203

A little-known South American species. Two populations, one in south-east Brazil, eastern Paraguay and extreme north-east Argentina, the other in northern Brazil, northern Peru and north-west Bolivia. Sedentary. Inhabits forest edge and clearings.

Races differ in size and coloration (see Text).

61a **Adult male** (nominate) A large, dark nightjar. Wing-coverts spotted buff and cinnamon; scapulars boldly spotted blackish-brown. Very broad but indistinct tawny-buff nuchal collar; large buff or buffish-white patch on lower throat.

61b **Adult male** (nominate) In flight lacks white markings on wings, but has whitish tips to the three outer tail feathers.

61c **Adult female** (nominate) Similar to male, but has narrower buffish tips to the outer tail feathers.

59 Tawny-collared Nightjar *Caprimulgus salvini*   Text and map page 201

A little-known species, generally confined to the lowlands of eastern Mexico. Mainly resident but may undertake southward post-breeding movements. Occurs in semi-desert, open woodland, scrub, fields and thickets, forest edge and clearings.

Sexes similar, but females (not illustrated) have narrower white or buffish tips to the outer tail feathers. Monotypic.

59a **Adult male** A dark, medium-sized nightjar. Wing-coverts lightly spotted and speckled cinnamon, scapulars boldly spotted blackish. Tawny or buff nuchal collar; narrow white or buffish-white band around lower throat.

59b **Adult male** In flight lacks white markings on wings, but has broad white tips to the three outer tail feathers.

60 Yucatan Nightjar *Caprimulgus badius*   Text and map page 202

Mainly resident on the Yucatan Peninsula in south-eastern Mexico, but some birds move south in winter, e.g. recorded in the non-breeding season in Belize, Guatemala?, northern Nicaragua and Half Moon Cay. A lowland species, preferring open woodland and forest edge.

Monotypic.

60a **Adult male** A generally dark, medium-sized nightjar. Wing-coverts spotted and speckled greyish-white, cinnamon, buff and tawny, scapulars spotted blackish-brown. Broad tawny or tawny-buff nuchal collar; broad buffish-white band around lower throat.

60b **Adult male** In flight lacks white markings on wings, but has broad white tips to the three outer tail feathers.

60c **Adult female** Similar to male, but has narrow tawny-buff tips to the outer tail feathers.

61b

61c

61a

59a

59b

60b

60a

60c

100mm

PLATE 17: NEOTROPICAL NIGHTJARS (3)

73 Blackish Nightjar *Caprimulgus nigrescens*   **Text and map page 222**

A widespread South American species, occurring throughout the Amazon Basin from eastern Colombia south to Bolivia and east to northern Brazil. Resident. Inhabits forest and savanna, preferring stony country, granite outcrops and stony areas in and along rivers.

Monotypic.

73a **Adult male** A small, blackish nightjar, heavily spotted or mottled tawny, cinnamon, buff and greyish-white. Small white patch on either side of lower throat.

73b **Adult male** In flight shows a small white spot towards the wing-tip on the second, third and fourth outermost primaries, and white tips to the second and third outermost tail feathers.

73c **Adult female** Differs from male in lacking white on wings and tail.

74 Roraiman Nightjar *Caprimulgus whitelyi*   **Text and map page 224**

An extremely uncommon species, endemic to the Pantepui of south-east Venezuela, possibly ranging into adjacent areas of Guyana and northern Brazil. Resident. Confined to slopes and summits of the tabletop mountains, where it inhabits clearings and openings in humid forests.

Sexes differ, females (not illustrated) having a thin tawny bar on the outer primaries and smaller white spots on the tail. Monotypic.

74a **Adult male** A small, blackish nightjar, heavily spotted cinnamon, buff, greyish-white and tawny. White patch on either side of lower throat, or large white patch across whole of throat.

74b **Adult male** In flight shows a thin white bar towards the wing-tip across the three outer primaries, and large white spots on the innerwebs tips of the second and third outermost tail feathers.

66 Band-winged Nightjar *Caprimulgus longirostris*   **Text and map page 211**

A common and widespread South American species (see also Plate 18). Race illustrated here is confined to the Pantepui of southern Venezuela. Probably resident.

66a **Adult male** (*roraimae*) A medium-sized, blackish but spotted nightjar, with a tawny nuchal collar and large white patch around lower throat.

66b **Adult male** (*roraimae*) In flight shows a narrow white band towards the wing-tip across the three or four outer primaries, white tips to the three or four outer tail feathers, and white bar across middle of tail, although markings restricted to innerwebs of the three or four outer tail feathers and not always visible.

66c **Adult female** (*roraimae*) Differs from male in having a buffish throat-patch, narrow tawny or buffish band across the four outer primaries, and usually no white on tail.

72 Cayenne Nightjar *Caprimulgus maculosus*   **Text and map page 221**

An extremely rare and almost completely unknown South American species, not recorded with certainty since the type specimen was taken in French Guiana in 1917. Possibly a resident forest species.

Female unknown. Monotypic.

72a **Adult male** A small, brown, variegated nightjar. Wing-coverts heavily spotted buff; buffish line along the scapulars. Narrow indistinct tawny nuchal collar; large white patch on either side of lower throat.

72b **Adult male** In flight shows a small white spot towards the wing-tip on the four outer primaries, and broad white tips to the three outer tail feathers.

73c

73b

73a

74b

74a

66b

66a

66c

72b

72a

100mm

PLATE 18: NEOTROPICAL NIGHTJARS (4)

67 **White-tailed Nightjar** *Caprimulgus cayennensis* **Text and map page 214**

A reasonably common South American and southern Central American species, extending from Costa Rica south to N Ecuador and east to the Guianas and northern Brazil, plus the Caribbean islands of Margarita, Curaçao, Aruba, Bonaire, Trinidad, Tobago, the Bocas, Little Tobago and Martinique. Generally resident, inhabiting open grassland, savanna, scrub and forest edge.

Racial differences often rather subtle (see Text).

67a **Adult male** (nominate) A small, greyish-brown, variegated nightjar. Wing-coverts heavily spotted white, buff and pale buff, with a thin whitish line across forewing. Broad tawny-buff nuchal collar; buffish or white supercilium and submoustachial stripe; large white throat-patch. Breast buffish heavily spotted white; rest of underparts white.

67b **Adult male** (nominate) In flight shows a well-defined white band towards the wing-tip across the four outer primaries, and a largely white tail.

67c **Adult female** (nominate) Differs from male in having a buffish throat-patch, darker, buffier underparts, no white on wings or tail.

66 **Band-winged Nightjar** *Caprimulgus longirostris* **Text and map page 211**

A widespread, fairly common South American species (see also Plate 17). Possibly resident in many parts of its range, but southern populations are migratory, moving north after breeding. Generally in forest or woodland, but also shrubby páramo, puna grassland, deserts and stony semi-deserts, steppe country and grassy areas.

There are seven races which may be separated into blackish, spotted forms or the greyish, streaked forms, although all races are extremely variable in coloration and markings (see Text).

66d **Adult male** (nominate) A medium-sized greyish-brown nightjar. Wing-coverts boldly spotted buff, pale buff or greyish-buff. Broad tawny or buffish nuchal collar; large white patch around lower throat.

66e **Adult male** (nominate) In flight shows a white patch on marginal coverts, white band towards the wing-tip across the four outer primaries, and broad white tips to the three or four outer tail feathers; also a white bar across the middle of the tail, although markings restricted to innerwebs of the three or four outer tail feathers and may not always be visible.

66f **Adult female** (nominate) Differs from male in having a buffish patch around lower throat, narrow buffish or buffish-white band across the four outer primaries, and either no white on tail or an indistinct whitish spot on innerwebs of the outer one or two tail feathers.

66g **Adult male** (*ruficervix*) Darker and more heavily spotted than the nominate, and occasionally more rufous.

66h **Adult male** (*ruficervix*) In flight often shows a narrower white band across the outer primaries, and less white on tail.

66i **Adult female** (*ruficervix*) Differences similar to those of female nominate.

66j **Adult male** (*atripunctatus*) Paler and greyer than *ruficervix*.

66k **Adult male** (*atripunctatus*) Broader white band across the outer primaries.

67b

67c

67a

66e

66d

66f

66h

66g

66i

66k

66j

100mm

119 Sickle-winged Nightjar *Eleothreptus anomalus*   Text and map page 294

An uncommon and poorly known species from central, eastern and south-east Brazil, eastern Paraguay and north-east Argentina. Migratory, at least in the south of its range, whence birds move north during the austral winter. Inhabits chaco-type woodland, forest edge, savanna, grassland and marshy areas.

Monotypic.

> **119a** **Adult male** A small, pale, greyish-brown nightjar. Large-headed and short-tailed, with curved outer primaries. Pale buffish-white stripe above eye, distinct cinnamon patch on primary coverts, and sometimes an indistinct buffish nuchal collar.

> **119b** **Adult male** In flight shows a distinctive wing-shape and (often inconspicuous) white tips to the five outermost primaries. All but the central pair of tail feathers are broadly tipped white or buffish-white.

> **119c** **Adult female** Browner than male, with paler, browner wings and buffish tips to the tail feathers.

> **119d** **Adult female** Shows distinctive wing-shape, but wings browner and less contrasting than male.

68 White-winged Nightjar *Caprimulgus candicans*   Text and map page 215

A rare and little-known South American lowland species, occurring in central and south-west Brazil, eastern Paraguay and northern Bolivia. Possibly migratory in parts of its range. Inhabits open grassland and savanna with scattered trees and bushes.

Monotypic.

> **68a** **Adult male** A small, pale, greyish-brown nightjar, often tinged cinnamon. Outer wing-coverts white, edged brown and boldly spotted blackish. Broad pale buff submoustachial stripe and a ring of buffish spots around lower throat. Breast greyish-brown tinged chestnut and tawny; rest of underparts white.

> **68b** **Adult male** In flight the wings are largely whitish, outer primaries broadly tipped brown, and all but the central pair of tail feathers mainly white.

> **68c** **Immature female?** Differs from the adult male in lacking white in the plumage; buffish underparts.

> **68d** **Immature female?** Lacks striking wing pattern of male in flight.

119b

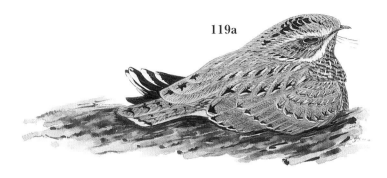

119a

119d

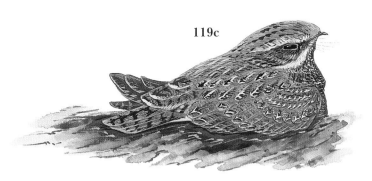

119c

68b

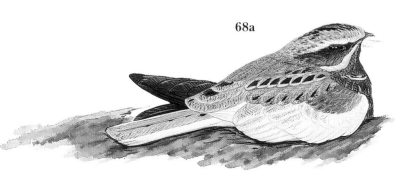

68a

68d

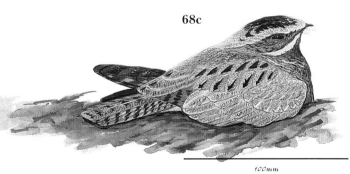

68c

100mm

70 Little Nightjar *Caprimulgus parvulus* Text and map page 218

A widely distributed and fairly common South American species, mainly found from south of the Amazon to northern Argentina but with a separate population in northern Colombia and northern and central Venezuela. Mainly resident, but migratory in the south of its main range. Generally inhabits open woodland, lightly wooded country, savanna, thickets, pastures and weedy fields.

Races differ mainly in the amount of white on wings and tail. Vocalisations also appear to differ.

70a **Adult male** (nominate) A small, variegated, greyish-brown nightjar. Wing-coverts spotted buff, tawny and white, with a buffish line along scapulars. Broad but indistinct buff or tawny-buff nuchal collar; large white throat-patch.

70b **Adult male** (nominate) In flight shows large white spots towards the wing-tip on the four outer primaries, and white tips to all but the central pair of tail feathers.

70c **Adult female** (nominate) Differs from male in generally lacking white on wings and tail, but may rarely show some white on tips of the three outer tail feathers.

71 Scrub Nightjar *Caprimulgus anthonyi* Text and map page 220

A poorly known South American species, restricted to the lowlands and adjacent foothills of western Ecuador and north-west Peru. May be partially nomadic, seasonal movements possibly being triggered by rains. Inhabits arid scrubland, open grassy country with scattered vegetation, and woodland edges. Also occurs in farmland, wet pastures and damp grassy meadows.

71a **Adult male** A small, variegated, greyish-brown nightjar. Wing-coverts boldly spotted buff, with a buffish line along scapulars. Broad but indistinct tawny-buff nuchal collar; white patch across lower throat.

71b **Adult male** In flight shows a white band towards the wing-tip across the five outer primaries, and white innerwebs to the two outer tail feathers.

71c **Adult female** Differs from male in having a thinner, less well-defined white band across the outer primaries, and much less white in tail.

69 Spot-tailed Nightjar *Caprimulgus maculicaudus* Text and map page 217

Fairly widespread in Central and South America from south-east Mexico south to central Bolivia and east to Brazil. Generally resident, but migratory in Central America. Usually in lowland savanna and grassland with scattered trees and thickets.

69a **Adult male** A small, variegated or occasionally heavily spotted nightjar. Three rows of large buff or cinnamon spots on wing-coverts, broad buffish line along scapulars. Crown dark, with a distinct buff or tawny nuchal collar, thickish buff supercilium, thin buff sub-moustachial stripe, very broad triangular blackish malar stripe, and small buff or cinnamon-buff throat-patch. Distinct cinnamon-rufous band on lower breast and upper belly.

69b **Adult male** In flight lacks white on wings, but may show a thinnish buff trailing edge to inner wing. All but the central pair of tail feathers are tipped white. There are also three widely spaced white spots along the innerwebs of the four outer tail feathers.

69c **Adult female** Similar to male, but lacks white markings on tail.

75 Pygmy Nightjar *Caprimulgus hirundinaceus* Text and map page 225

A poorly known species found only in north-east Brazil. Resident. Generally considered endemic to the caatinga region. Occurs in woodland and cleared areas.

Races vary in coloration, and by the amount of white on the outer primaries (see Text).

75a **Adult male** (nominate) A small, greyish, rather speckled nightjar, often appearing rather pale, small-headed and large-eyed. Thin indistinct whitish supercilium and buff sub-moustachial stripe, large white throat-patch, and sometimes a buffish nuchal collar.

75b **Adult male** (nominate) In flight shows white spots towards the wing-tip on the four outer primaries, and white tips to the two outer tail feathers.

75c **Adult female** (nominate) Similar to male, but has smaller white spots on the outer primaries, and lacks white on tail.

70b

70c

70a

71c

71b

71a

69b

69a

69c

75c

75b

75a

Dawes 96.

100mm

116 Swallow-tailed Nightjar *Uropsalis segmentata*   Text and map page 290

An Andean endemic, confined to montane forest in Colombia, Ecuador and central Peru. Resident. Inhabits forest edge, clearings and glades, páramo and open shrubby slopes.

Main difference between races concerns tail length of males (see Text).

116a   **Adult male** (nominate) A small to medium-sized, dark, spotted nightjar, with extremely elongated outer tail feathers.

116b   **Adult male** (nominate) In flight lacks white markings on wings. The elongated outer tail feathers have very narrow white outerwebs and very broad dark brown innerwebs.

116c   **Adult female** (nominate) Similar to male, but shorter- and darker-tailed.

115 Scissor-tailed Nightjar *Hydropsalis brasiliana*   Text and map page 289

Widely distributed over much of central South America, from southern Surinam, south to central Argentina, with an isolated population in central Peru. Southern populations are migratory, moving north during the austral winter. Occurs in forest, woodland, cerrado, grassland with scattered vegetation, and urban parks.

Races differ in size; the colour of the nuchal collar also tends to be different.

115a   **Adult male** (nominate) A medium to large, variegated, brownish nightjar, with elongate outermost tail feathers extending beyond the central pair. Wing-coverts heavily spotted buff and greyish-white, with a distinct buffish line along scapulars. Broad tawny or buff nuchal collar; thin whitish submoustachial stripe.

115b   **Adult male** (nominate) In flight lacks white markings on wings; tips and innerwebs of the outermost tail feathers whitish, and the second to fourth outer tail feathers broadly tipped whitish.

115c   **Adult female** Similar to male, but with a shorter, darker tail.

114 Ladder-tailed Nightjar *Hydropsalis climacocerca*   Text and map page 287

A widely distributed species, occurring throughout much of central South America from eastern Colombia south to central Bolivia and east to the Guianas and Amazonian Brazil. Resident. Mainly inhabits lowland forest and woodland, often occurring close to or along rivers and waterways.

Racial variation often slight, and not fully understood (see Text).

114a   **Adult male** (nominate) A medium-sized, variegated, greyish-brown nightjar. Wing-coverts boldly spotted buffish; buffish line along scapulars. Buffish nuchal collar (often indistinct), white submoustachial stripe, white throat-patch.

114b   **Adult male** (nominate) In flight shows a broad white band towards the wing-tip across the four outer primaries, and a largely white tail.

114c   **Adult female** (nominate) Differs from male in having a buffish throat-patch, narrower white band across the outer primaries, and usually no white in tail.

114d   **Adult male** (*schomburgki*) Darker and browner than the nominate and slightly smaller.

114e   **Adult male** (*schomburgki*) Darker and browner than the nominate.

116c

116b

116a

115b

115c

115a

114b

114a

114c

114e

114d

100mm

117 Lyre-tailed Nightjar *Uropsalis lyra*   Text and map page 291

An Andean endemic, locally distributed in western Venezuela, western Colombia, central Ecuador, Peru, western, central and southern Bolivia, and north-west Argentina. Possibly sedentary throughout range. Generally inhabits forest edges, clearings and glades, often near cliffs, rocky ravines or cave entrances.

Races differ mainly in size (see Text).

117a/b Adult male (nominate) A medium-sized brownish variegated nightjar with extremely elongated outer tail feathers. Wing-coverts boldly spotted tawny and buff; but no obvious scapular pattern. Broad tawny or tawny-buff nuchal collar; tawny or buff band around lower throat.

117c Adult male (nominate) In flight lacks white markings on wings, and the elongated outer tail feathers are very broad and dark, with white tips.

117d Adult female (nominate) Similar to male, but shorter- and darker-tailed.

118 Long-trained Nightjar *Macropsalis creagra*   Text and map page 293

An uncommon South American species with a highly restricted range in south-east Brazil and north-east Argentina. Sedentary. Generally inhabits forest edge, second growth and woodland, often close to water, and in the more northerly parts of its range, it occurs in more mountainous regions.

Monotypic.

118a/b Adult male A medium-sized brownish variegated nightjar with elongated outer tail feathers. Wing-coverts boldly spotted tawny and buff, with a buffish line along the scapulars. Broad tawny or tawny-buff nuchal collar.

118c Adult male In flight lacks white markings on wings. Innerwebs of the two outer tail feathers are broadly edged whitish, those of the inner three pairs entirely greyish- or brownish-white.

118d Adult female Similar to male, but darker- and shorter-tailed.

117d

117b

117a

117c

118c

118d

118b

118a

100mm

PLATE 23: EURASIAN AND AFRICAN NIGHTJARS (1)

79   European Nightjar *Caprimulgus europaeus*   **Text and map page 232**

Breeds over large parts of Europe, Asia east to northern China and Mongolia, and north-west Africa. Migratory. Most populations winter in Africa, although some Asian birds may overwinter in north-west India and Pakistan. Generally inhabits dry, open country with scattered trees and bushes, woodland clearings and edges, open woodland and young forestry plantations.

Racial differences appear to be clinal, becoming smaller and paler eastwards and southwards.

79a   Adult male (nominate) A medium-sized, greyish-brown, variegated nightjar. Lesser coverts brown; rest of wing-coverts spotted buffish, with a distinct buff line across forewing and a buff line along scapulars. Indistinct pale buff nuchal collar; broad buffish-white submoustachial stripe, white throat-patches.

79b   Adult male (nominate) In flight shows white spots towards the wing-tip on the three (rarely four) outer primaries, and white tips to the two outer tail feathers.

79c   Adult female (nominate) Differs from male in lacking white markings on wings and tail.

79d   Adult male (*unwini*) Paler, greyer and plainer, upperparts more narrowly streaked.

77   Red-necked Nightjar *Caprimulgus ruficollis*   **Text and map page 227**

Has restricted breeding range in Spain, Portugal and the northern parts of Morocco, Algeria and Tunisia. Migratory. Winters in western Africa. Generally inhabits lowlands and hillsides with relatively open vegetation such as pine woodland, coastal forest, coastal dunes, plantations and scrub.

Races differ in coloration (see Text).

77a   Adult male (nominate) A large, variegated, greyish-brown nightjar. Wing-coverts boldly spotted buff, with a buffish line along scapulars. Broad buff or tawny-buff nuchal collar; prominent white or buffish-white submoustachial stripe, large white throat-patch.

77b   Adult male (nominate) In flight shows large white spots towards the wing-tip on the three outer primaries, and broad white tips to the two outer tail feathers.

77c   Adult female (nominate) Similar to male, but with smaller whitish spots on the outer primaries and smaller, dirtier white tips to the two outer tail feathers.

77d   Adult male (*desertorum*) Much paler, more sandy-buff and often heavily tinged rufous.

81   Rufous-cheeked Nightjar *Caprimulgus rufigena*   **Text and map page 239**

A southern African breeding species. Migratory, moving north to winter in parts of central Africa. Inhabits open wooded savannas, miombo woodland, scrub, plantations and gravelly semi-deserts.

Races differ mainly in coloration (see Text).

81a   Adult male (nominate) A medium-sized, greyish-brown, variegated nightjar. Wing-coverts heavily spotted tawny and buff, with a broad buffish line along scapulars. Narrow buff or tawny-buff nuchal collar; white throat-patch.

81b   Adult male (nominate) In flight shows large white spots towards the wing-tip on the four outer primaries, and white tips to the two outer tail feathers.

81c   Adult female (nominate) Similar to male, but has smaller white spots, usually tinged tawny, on the outer primaries, and pale buff tips to the two outer tail feathers.

80   Sombre Nightjar *Caprimulgus fraenatus*   **Text and map page 238**

Range restricted to East Africa, where generally a Rift Valley species, occurring discontinuously from northern Ethiopia south to northern Tanzania. Sedentary and locally migratory. Inhabits open bush and scrub country, usually on stony or rocky ground; also grasslands and plantations.

80a   Adult male A medium-sized, darkish nightjar. Wing-coverts heavily spotted tawny and buff, with a distinct row of large blackish spots along scapulars. Broad buff or tawny-buff nuchal collar; white submoustachial stripe; white throat-patch.

80b   Adult male In flight shows large white spots towards the wing-tip on the four outer primaries, and very broad white tips to the two outer tail feathers.

80c   Adult female Differs from male in having smaller white spots, usually tinged buffish, on the outer primaries, and pale buff tips to the two outer tail feathers.

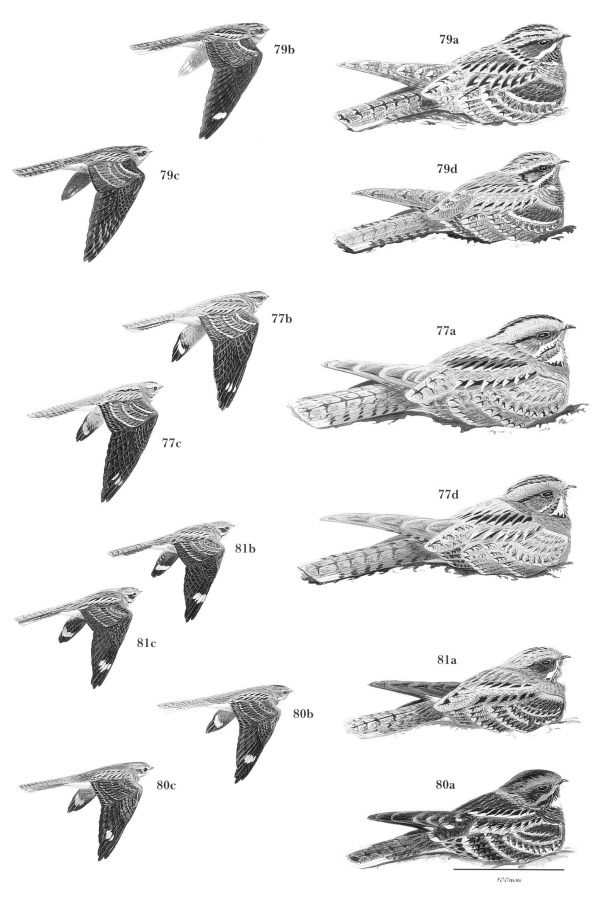

79b

79a

79c

79d

77b

77a

77c

81b

77d

81c

80b

81a

80c

80a

100mm

83   Sykes's Nightjar *Caprimulgus mahrattensis*   **Text and map page 243**

An Asian species with a limited breeding range in the lowlands of south-east Iran, southern Afghanistan and Pakistan. Resident and partially migratory, dispersing widely in winter throughout western and central India. Generally inhabits semi-deserts, scrub and sparsely vegetated stony country.

    83a   **Adult male** A medium-sized, rather uniform, sandy-grey nightjar. Wing-coverts boldly spotted buff and pale buff; scapulars spotted blackish-brown. Indistinct buffish nuchal collar; whitish submoustachial stripe; white throat-patch.

    83b   **Adult male** In flight shows a broad white band towards the wing-tip across the three outer primaries, and broad white tips to the two outer tail feathers.

    83c   **Adult female** Similar to male, but smaller buffish-white tips to two outer tail feathers.

82   Egyptian Nightjar *Caprimulgus aegyptius*   **Text and map page 241**

A Palearctic species with two distinct breeding populations, one in the Middle East and southern Asia, the other in north-west Africa. Both populations are migratory, wintering mainly in the sahelian zone of Africa, although small numbers may overwinter in the Arabian Peninsula. Generally inhabits deserts and semi-deserts.

Sexes similar, although females (not illustrated) have pale buffish tips to the outer tail feathers. African breeding birds are smaller and sandier than Asian birds.

    82a   **Adult male** (nominate) A medium to large-sized, rather uniform, sandy-grey nightjar. Wing-coverts boldly spotted buff; scapulars spotted blackish-brown. Indistinct buff nuchal collar; buffish-white submoustachial stripe; white throat-patch.

    82b   **Adult male** (nominate) In flight generally has dark brownish wing-tips, but underwings largely white. Narrow whitish tips to the two outer tail feathers.

    82c   **Adult** (nominate) Showing small white spot towards wing-tip on the outer primaries.

86   Golden Nightjar *Caprimulgus eximius*   **Text and map page 246**

An African species mainly confined to the sahelian zone, where it occurs discontinuously from southern Mauritania and northern Senegal east to central Sudan. Mainly resident. Generally inhabits sandy or stony semi-deserts sparsely vegetated with scrub and grass.

Racial differences slight (see Text).

    86a   **Adult male** (nominate) A small to medium-sized, uniquely coloured nightjar. Generally tawny or tawny-buff, covered with greyish-white rectangular spots edged and densely speckled dark brown. Large white throat-patch.

    86b   **Adult male** (nominate) In flight shows large white spots towards the wing-tip on the four outer primaries, and broad white tips to the two outer tail feathers.

    86c   **Adult female** (nominate) Similar to male, but the white spots on the outer primaries are narrowly edged tawny-buff, and the white tips to the two outer-tail feathers are fractionally smaller and often washed buff or pale tawny.

84   Vaurie's Nightjar *Caprimulgus centralasicus*   **Text and map page 244**

Rare and almost completely unknown. The only known specimen was taken in south-west Xinjiang, western China, in 1929. Possibly occurs on arid plains and sandy foothills in the southern Tarim basin along the Kun Lun.

Male unknown. Monotypic (see Text).

    84a   **Female** A small, fairly uniform, sandy-buff nightjar, with no obvious nuchal collar or scapular pattern. Wing-coverts spotted pale buff.

    84b   **Female** In flight lacks white markings on wings; underwing buffish. The two outer tail feathers are narrowly tipped pale buffish-white.

83b

83c

83a

82b

82a

82c

86b

86a

86c

84a

84b

100mm

103 Freckled Nightjar *Caprimulgus tristigma*   Text and map page 271

A widely distributed, fairly common African species. Mainly resident, although some populations may move locally in poor weather. Prefers rocky habitats such as outcrops, boulder-strewn hillsides, kopjes, inselbergs and ravines. Races differ mainly in size and coloration (see Text).

103a **Adult male** (nominate) A large, greyish-black nightjar, with upperparts and wing-coverts profusely spotted and speckled white, pale buff and cinnamon; white throat-patch.

103b **Adult male** (nominate) In flight shows small white spots towards the wing-tip on the four outer primaries and broad white tips to the two outer tail feathers.

103c **Adult female** (nominate) Differs from male in having smaller white spots on the outer primaries, and lacks white in the tail.

108 Bates's Nightjar *Caprimulgus batesi*   Text and map page 277

An African rainforest species, occurring in western and southern Cameroon, Gabon, southern Central African Republic, north-east and western Congo, Zaire, and western Uganda. Resident. Usually found in lowland primary forest, where it inhabits clearings and forest edges

108a **Adult male** A large, very dark nightjar. Buff or tawny nuchal collar; white throat-patch.

108b **Adult male** In flight shows very small white spots towards the wing-tip on the four outer primaries, and white tips to the two outer tail feathers.

108c **Adult female** Generally paler than male, and lacks white markings on wings and tail.

76 Brown Nightjar *Caprimulgus binotatus*   Text and map page 226

A poorly known species, confined to lowland rainforest in West and Central Africa. Probably resident. Generally found in areas of primary forest with an open canopy and a thick understorey.

76a **Adult** A small to medium-sized, darkish brown nightjar, with upperparts and wing-coverts densely mottled and flecked tawny and chestnut-brown; often buffish markings on scapulars. Small but distinctive white spot on either side of lower throat.

76b **Adult** In flight lacks white markings on wings and tail.

98 Swamp Nightjar *Caprimulgus natalensis*   Text and map page 264

A widely distributed African species ranging discontinuously from eastern Gambia east to central Sudan and south to eastern South Africa. Generally resident; local movements occur after rains or fires. Inhabits a variety of damp habitats, including grassland, meadows, swamps, marshes, bogs, dambos, floodplains and vleis. Racial differences often rather slight (see Text).

98a **Adult male** (nominate) A medium-sized, short-tailed, greyish-brown nightjar. Wing-coverts, scapulars and tertials heavily spotted with large, irregularly shaped blackish-brown marks. Indistinct buffish nuchal collar; white throat-patch.

98b **Adult male** (nominate) In flight shows large white spots towards the wing-tip on the four outer primaries, and very broad white tips to the two outer tail feathers, the outermost usually being entirely white on the outerweb.

98c **Adult female** (nominate) Differs from male in having buffish or pale tawny spots on the outer primaries and narrow, buffish-white tips to the two outer tail feathers, the outer most usually being entirely buff on the outerweb.

106 Prigogine's Nightjar *Caprimulgus prigoginei*   Text and map page 275

An African species, currently known only from one female specimen taken in the Itombwe mountains in eastern Zaire in 1955. Possibly a forest species. Male unknown. Monotypic.

106a **Female** A small, darkish nightjar, with upperparts and wing-coverts heavily speckled and spotted dark brown, tawny and buff.

106b **Female** In flight shows small tawny spots towards the wing-tip on the second, third and fourth outermost primaries, and has narrow whitish tips to the outermost tail feathers, and narrower buffish or tawny tips to the remainder.

103a

103b

103c

108a

108b

108c

76a

76b

98a

98b

98c

106a

106b

100mm

85 Nubian Nightjar *Caprimulgus nubicus*   Text and map page 245

Range confined to north-east Africa, south-west and southern Yemen, Socotra Island, south-west Saudi Arabia, Israel and Jordan. Resident and partially migratory, i.e. part of the Middle Eastern population may winter in the coastal lowlands of north-east Africa. Often inhabits dry, open scrubland, sparsely vegetated with tamarisk or acacia.

85a   **Adult male** (nominate) A small, greyish or buffish nightjar; wing-coverts and scapulars lightly spotted buff or heavily spotted tawny and buff. Broad tawny-buff nuchal collar; white throat-patch.

85b   **Adult male** (nominate) In flight shows large white spots towards the wing-tip on the four outer primaries, and broad white tips to the two outer-tail feathers.

85c   **Adult female** Differs from male in having smaller white spots, edged buffish, on the outer primaries and, occasionally, smaller white tips to the two outer tail feathers.

85d   **Adult male** (*torridus*) Greyer and slightly larger than the nominate, and more heavily spotted rufous, buff and tawny. Also has smaller white tips to the two outer tails feathers.

91 Donaldson-Smith's Nightjar *Caprimulgus donaldsoni*   Text and map page 254

Range limited to East Africa, largely east of the Rift Valley. Mainly resident. Occurs in dry scrublands, bush country and wooded wadis.

91a   **Adult male** A small, richly coloured nightjar, the upperparts and wing-coverts generally being rather chestnut or rufous, with buffish line along scapulars. Broad rufous, tawny and buff nuchal collar; white throat-patch.

91b   **Adult male** In flight shows white spots towards the wing-tip on the four outer primaries, and broad white tips to the two outer tail feathers.

91c   **Adult female** Differs from male in having smaller white spots on the outer primaries, and narrower white tips to the two outer tail feathers.

100 Plain Nightjar *Caprimulgus inornatus*   Text and map page 266

An African species breeding throughout the Sahelian savannas, with a small population in south-west Arabia. Generally migratory. After breeding, many populations withdraw southwards to winter in wooded savannas from Senegal and Liberia east to Ethiopia and south to Tanzania.

Monotypic, but extremely variable in colour, ranging from blackish-brown, brown or greyish-brown to deep vinaceous, pale tawny-buff and sandy-buff.

100a   **Adult male** A small to medium-sized, rather plain nightjar, with blackish-brown markings generally restricted to head and scapulars. Sometimes shows lines of buffish spots across wing-coverts.

100b   **Adult male** In flight shows white spots towards the wing-tip on the four outer primaries, and broad white tips to the two outer tail feathers.

100c   **Adult female** Differs from male in having tawny spots on the outer primaries, and lacks white in the tail.

101 Star-spotted Nightjar *Caprimulgus stellatus*   Text and map page 268

A poorly known species, with range confined to East Africa. Resident. Inhabits dry, open bush country, bushy grasslands and stony semi-deserts.

101a   **Adult male** A small to medium-sized, generally dark greyish-brown nightjar. Rather uniform, with blackish streaks or spidery, star-shaped spots on crown and scapulars. Small white patch on either side of lower throat.

101b   **Adult male** In flight shows white spots towards the wing-tip on the four outer primaries, and narrow white tips to the two outer tail feathers.

101c   **Adult female** Similar to male.

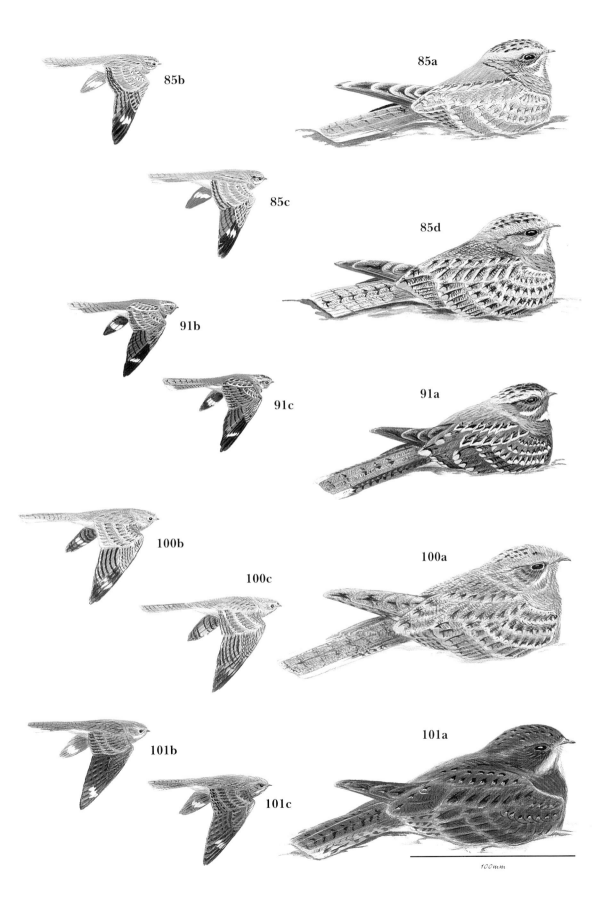

85b

85a

85c

85d

91b

91a

91c

100b

100a

100c

101b

101a

101c

100mm

92 **Black-shouldered Nightjar** *Caprimulgus nigriscapularis* **Text and map page 255**

Range lies in West and Central Africa. Possibly resident in lowland forest, woodland, wooded country, grassy or stony hillsides and mossy thickets.

92a **Adult male** A small to medium-sized, variegated, brownish or rufescent nightjar. Lesser coverts blackish-brown, giving distinct 'dark-shouldered' appearance. Rest of wing-coverts spotted buffish, with a buffish line along scapulars. Broad tawny-buff nuchal collar; white throat-patch.

92b **Adult male** In flight shows small white spots towards the wing-tip on the four outer primaries, and broad white tips to the two outer tail feathers.

92c **Adult female** Similar to male, but has slightly smaller white spots on the outer primaries, and narrower white tips to the two outer tail feathers.

93 **Fiery-necked Nightjar** *Caprimulgus pectoralis* **Text and map page 256**

A southern African species extending north to south-east Kenya. Many populations appear to be partially migratory. Found in lowland woods, but also scrubland, plantations and gardens. Racial differences and colour variation often complex (see Text).

93a **Adult male** (nominate) A small to medium-sized, brown or greyish-brown variegated nightjar. Two or three distinctive rows of pale spots across wing-coverts; scapulars boldly spotted blackish. Broad buff or tawny-buff nuchal collar; white submoustachial stripe; large white throat-patch.

93b **Adult male** (nominate) In flight shows large white spots towards the wing-tip on the four outer primaries, and broad white tips to the two outer tail feathers.

93c **Adult female** (nominate) Similar to male, but has smaller white or buffish spots on the outer primaries, and smaller white tips to the two outer tail feathers, often smudged buff or brown on outerwebs.

93d/e Adult male (*fervidus*) Paler, browner, and often tawnier than the nominate.

93f **Adult female** (*fervidus*) Differences similar to those of the nominate (see above).

94 **Abyssinian Nightjar** *Caprimulgus poliocephalus* **Text and map page 258**

Generally confined to East Africa, although a small population exists in south-west Arabia. African populations possibly resident; Arabian birds may move to lower altitudes in winter. Inhabits montane forests, woodlands and wooded country, including large suburban gardens.

94a **Adult male** A medium-sized, greyish-brown nightjar. Wing-coverts spotted buff; buffish line along scapulars. Broad buff or tawny-buff nuchal collar; whitish submoustachial stripe; white throat-patch.

94b **Adult male** In flight shows large white spots towards the wing-tip on the four outer primaries, and the two outer tail feathers are largely white.

94c **Adult female** Generally darker than male, and often lacks white on throat. In flight shows smaller white spots on the outer primaries, and has less white in tail.

95 **Montane Nightjar** *Caprimulgus ruwenzorii* **Text and map page 260**

An African species, resident in a fairly narrow belt from south-west Uganda south to northern Malawi, with populations in western Angola and Tanzania's Usambara Mountains. Inhabits montane woodland and forest.

Sexes similar, but females (not illustrated) have the white primary spots tinged buffish, and less white on the tail. Races differ clinally in amount of white on the two outer tail feathers.

95a **Adult male** (nominate) A medium-sized, dark greyish-brown nightjar. Wing-coverts spotted pale buff, with a buffish line along scapulars. Broad buff or tawny-buff nuchal collar; whitish submoustachial stripe; white throat-patch.

95b **Adult male** (nominate) In flight shows small white spots towards the wing-tip on the four outer primaries, and very broad white tips to the two outer tail feathers.

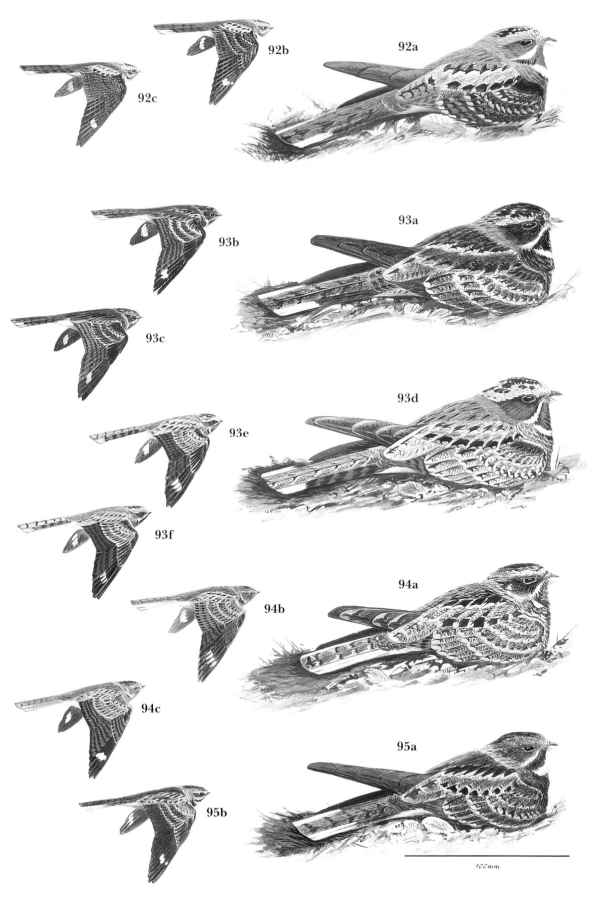

92c

92b

92a

93b

93a

93c

93d

93e

93f

94b

94a

94c

95b

95a

100mm

109 Long-tailed Nightjar *Caprimulgus climacurus* Text and map page 278

A fairly common and widespread species, breeding in many parts of Africa. Northern populations partially migratory, wintering south of their main breeding range; southern populations possibly mainly resident. Habitats include arid semi-desert, woodland, forest, clearings, grassland and cultivated areas.

Three races, differing mainly in overall coloration (but see Text).

109a **Adult male** (nominate) A long-tailed nightjar, extremely variable in colour, generally greyish-brown but ranging from pale brown, brown and greyish-brown to sandy-buff. Usually a bold white line across wing-coverts. Broad tawny or buff nuchal collar; a white throat-patch. Tail gradated, central feathers much longer than the outer pair.

109b **Adult male** (nominate) In flight shows a broad white band towards the wing-tip across the five outer primaries, and a white trailing edge to the inner wing. The outer tail feathers are generally edged and tipped white, the second outermost tail feathers tipped white.

109c **Adult female** (nominate) At rest shows a buffish-white line across wing-coverts; shorter-tailed. In flight shows the white band across the outer primaries washed buff, a buff or buffish-white trailing edge to the inner wing, and buff on the two outer tail feathers.

109d **Adult male** (*nigricans*) Differs from other races and colour morphs by being blackish or very dark grey. Often longer-tailed than the nominate.

110 Slender-tailed Nightjar *Caprimulgus clarus* Text and map page 280

A common and widespread East Africa species. Mainly resident, although local movements may be triggered by rains. Inhabits thorny bush country, scrub, lightly wooded grassland and open woodland.

Monotypic.

110a **Adult male** A small, greyish-brown nightjar. White line across wing-coverts; buffish line along scapulars. Broad tawny or buff nuchal collar; white throat-patch.

110b **Adult male** In flight shows a broad white band towards the wing-tip across the six outer primaries and a white trailing edge to the inner wing. Tail gradated and wedge-shaped, with central pair slightly longer than outer pair, which are edged and broadly tipped white.

110c **Adult female** At rest shows a buff line across wing-coverts. In flight shows a narrower white band across outer primaries, washed buff or tawny on outerwebs, and a buff or buffish-white trailing edge to the inner wing. Tail less gradated; outer feathers edged and tipped buff.

111 Mozambique Nightjar *Caprimulgus fossii* Text and map page 281

A common and widely distributed species, breeding throughout much of Central and southern Africa. Mainly resident, but partially migratory in some regions. Habitats include open woodland and edge, wooded grassland and hillsides, scrub, thorn and bush country, plantations, edges of cultivation, and gardens.

Three races (see Text).

111a **Adult male** (*welwitschii*) A small, dark, rather spotted nightjar. White or sometimes buffish band across wing-coverts; buffish line along scapulars. Broad buff or tawny-buff nuchal collar; prominent buffish-white submoustachial stripe; white throat-patch. Tail square-ended.

111b **Adult male** (*welwitschii*) In flight shows a broad white band towards the wing-tip across the five outer primaries, a white trailing edge to the inner wing, and the outermost tail feathers are broadly edged and tipped white.

111c **Adult female** (*welwitschii*) At rest shows a buff band across wing-coverts. In flight shows a narrower, whitish band across the five outer primaries, a buff trailing edge to the inner wing, and the outermost tail feathers are broadly edged and tipped buffish.

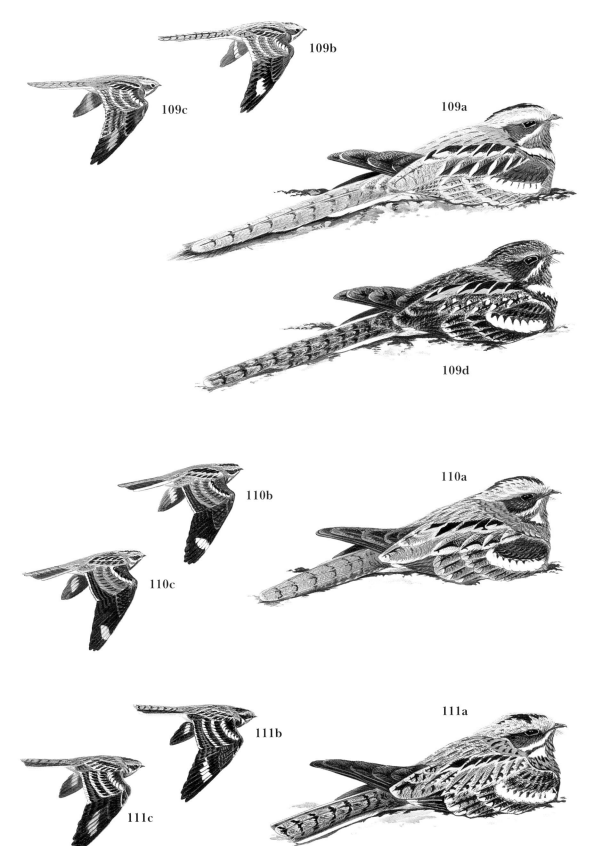

109b

109c

109a

109d

110a

110b

110c

111a

111b

111c

100mm

97 Madagascar Nightjar *Caprimulgus madagascariensis*   Text and map page 263

Resident on Madagascar and Aldabra. The more widespread of only two species found on Madagascar, found in open or lightly wooded country, forest edge and clearings, savanna, heath, scrub, eucalyptus plantations, cultivation and gardens. Only nightjar on Aldabra, inhabiting open sandhills and casuarina woods.

Racial differences slight (see Text).

97a **Adult male** (nominate) A small to medium-sized, greyish-brown, variegated nightjar. Wing-coverts heavily spotted buff with brown centres; buffish line along scapulars. Sometimes an indistinct tawny-buff nuchal collar; whitish submoustachial stripe; small white patch on either side of lower throat.

97b **Adult male** (nominate) In flight shows white spots towards the wing-tip on the four outer primaries, and white tips to the two outer tail feathers.

97c **Adult female** (nominate) Differs from male in having small buffish spots on the outer primaries, and smaller white tips to the outer tail feathers.

97d **Juvenile** Generally greyish-brown.

107 Collared Nightjar *Caprimulgus enarratus*   Text and map page 276

Endemic to Madagascar. Uncommon and little-known resident of primary lowland forest, but also found in adjacent second growth, dry deciduous forest and mangroves.

Monotypic.

107a **Adult male** A medium-sized brownish nightjar. Wing-coverts and scapulars boldly spotted blackish-brown, the spots broadly bordered chestnut or pale buff. Very broad rufous nuchal collar bordered above by a thin, well-defined buff band; tawny-buff band around lower throat.

107b **Adult male** In flight lacks white markings on wings, but has narrow white tips to the outer one or two tail feathers.

107c **Adult female** Similar to male.

107d **Juvenile** Generally darkish brown, spotted buffish on wing-coverts.

97c

97b

97d

97a

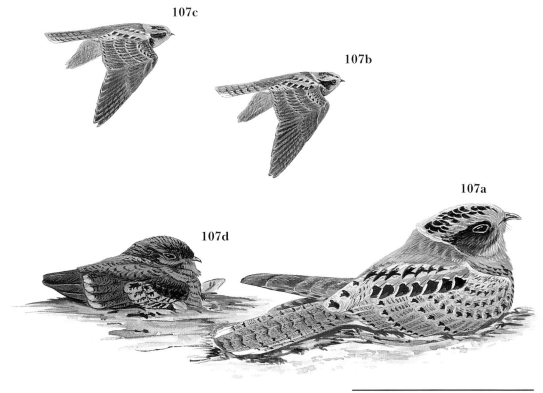

107c

107b

107a

107d

100mm

112 Standard-winged Nightjar *Macrodipteryx longipennis*   Text and map page 283

Breeds across the southern savannas of West and Central Africa, from southern Senegal and Liberia east to south-west Sudan and north-west Kenya. Migratory, generally moving north to spend the wet season in the sahelian and sudanese savannas. Inhabits scrub and wooded savanna, also farmland, open grassland, stony hillsides with scattered vegetation, and coastal plains.

Monotypic.

> **112a** **Adult male** (breeding) A medium-sized, greyish or greyish-brown nightjar. Wing-coverts heavily spotted buff, with buffish line along scapulars. Broad tawny or tawny-buff nuchal collar; short buff supercilium; buffish throat-patch. The second innermost primaries (the 'standards') have extremely elongated shafts and large webs at the tips, with innerweb much broader than outerweb.
>
> **112b** **Adult male** (breeding) In flight lacks white markings on wings and tail. The 'standards' generally trail upwards from the centre of the wing.
>
> **112c** **Adult male** (non-breeding) Similar to the breeding male, but without the 'standards'.
>
> **112d** **Adult female** Similar to but sometimes paler than the non-breeding male.
>
> **112e** **Adult female** Similar to the non-breeding male.

113 Pennant-winged Nightjar *Macrodipteryx vexillarius*   Text and map page 285

A fairly common and widespread southern African species, breeding from Angola to south-west Tanzania south to north-east South Africa. Non-breeding migrant to a central belt stretching from south-east Nigeria to southern Sudan and Uganda.

During migration, often occurs outside the breeding or non-breeding ranges. Inhabits woodlands, especially miombo or mopane, but also other wooded habitats including suburban areas, cultivation and plantations.

Monotypic.

> **113a** **Adult male** (breeding) A medium to large, brownish nightjar. Wing-coverts spotted tawny, with a buffish line along scapulars. Broad tawny nuchal collar; longish buff supercilium; white throat-patch. Belly and flanks white. Second innermost primaries extremely elongated, forming the 'pennants'.
>
> **113b** **Adult male** (breeding) In flight shows broad, blackish wings, with narrow white tips to the four outer primaries, white trailing edge to the inner wing, and a broad, bow-shaped white band towards the wing-tip across the eight outer primaries. The fifth to second innermost primaries are longer than the preceding feather, with the second innermost primary, the 'pennant', whitish in colour.
>
> **113c** **Adult male** (non-breeding) Similar to the breeding male, but without the 'pennants'.
>
> **113d** **Adult female** Differs from the non-breeding male in having buffish underparts and no white in wings and tail.
>
> **113e** **Adult female** No white in wings and tail.

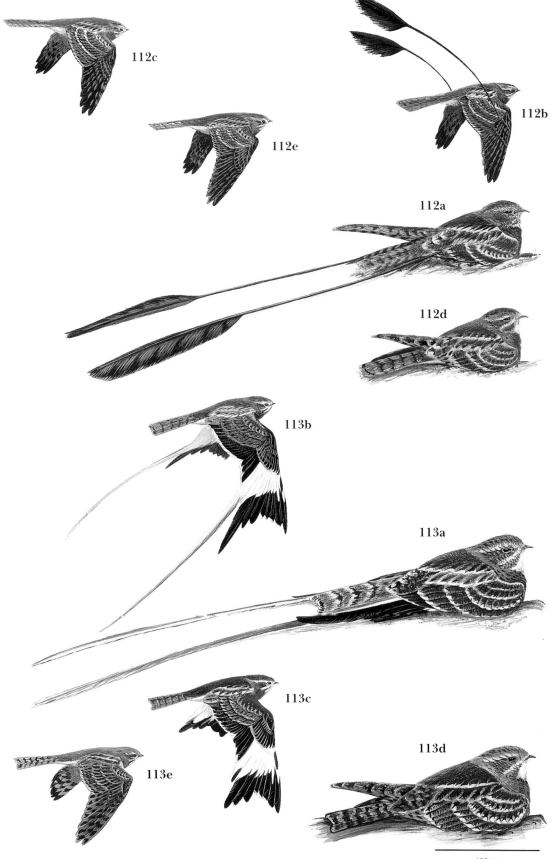

112c

112e

112b

112a

112d

113b

113a

113c

113d

113e

100mm

102 Savanna Nightjar *Caprimulgus affinis* Text and map page 269

A widespread and not uncommon Oriental species, ranging from India to central Indonesia. Mainly resident. Inhabits grassland, open woodland, stony or sparsely vegetated hillsides, swamp and mangrove edges, sandy or shingle beaches, riverbanks, coastal scrub and urban greenery.

Races are separated into two distinct groups, northern populations being larger and browner than southern forms (see Text).

102a **Adult male** (nominate) A small to medium-sized, generally greyish, rather uniform nightjar. Lesser coverts brown, other coverts paler and boldly spotted pale buff. Buffish or whitish line along scapulars. Indistinct buffish, cinnamon or whitish nuchal collar; buffish submoustachial stripe; small white patch on either side of lower throat.

102b **Adult male** (nominate) In flight shows large white spots towards the wing-tip on the four outer primaries, and the two outer tail feathers are generally white, tipped or edged brownish.

102c **Adult female** (nominate) In flight, differs from male in having buffish spots on outer primaries and no white on tail.

102d **Adult male** (*monticolus*) Larger and generally browner than the nominate.

102e **Adult male** (*monticolus*) In flight, larger white spots on the outer primaries.

102f **Adult female** (*monticolus*) Differences similar to those of the nominate (see above).

96 Indian Nightjar *Caprimulgus asiaticus* Text and map page 261

A common Asian species, found throughout India and southern Indochina. Generally resident, but may be locally migratory. Habitats include woodland, scrub, cultivation, plantations and gardens.

Racial differences very slight (see Text).

96a **Adult male** (nominate) A medium-sized, greyish-brown, variegated nightjar. Lesser coverts greyish-brown, other coverts boldly spotted buff, with a buffish line along scapulars. Broad buff or tawny nuchal collar; whitish submoustachial stripe; large white patch on either side of lower throat.

96b **Adult male** (nominate) In flight shows white spots towards the wing-tip on the four outer primaries, and broad white tips to the two outer tail feathers.

96c **Adult female** (nominate) Differs from male in having smaller white spots, tinged or edged buff, on the outer primaries, and narrower white tips to the outer tail feathers.

78 Jungle Nightjar *Caprimulgus indicus* Text and map page 230

A widespread Oriental and eastern Palearctic species, found from south-east Siberia, eastern China and Japan west to India and south to Sri Lanka. Some populations locally migratory, with post-breeding movements possibly being altitudinal. Eastern Palearctic breeding population migratory, wintering in S China, Indochina, Malaysia, Sumatra, Java, Borneo and the Philippines. Inhabits forests, woodlands, wooded country, open scrub, farmland and cultivation.

Races differ mainly in size and darkness of plumage (see Text).

78a **Adult male** (nominate) A large, greyish-brown, variegated nightjar. Lesser coverts brown, other coverts boldly spotted greyish-white, pale buff or pale tawny, spots distinctly smudged or vermiculated brown. Indistinct pale buff or tawny-buff nuchal collar; buffish-white submoustachial stripe; large white patch either side of lower throat.

78b **Adult male** (nominate) In flight shows large white spots towards the wing-tip on the four outer primaries, and white tips (distally washed brown) to all but the central pair of tail feathers.

78c **Adult female** (nominate) Differs from male in having brownish-tawny or tawny spots on outer primaries, and brownish-white or brownish- buff tips to tail feathers.

78d **Adult male** (*jotaka*) Larger and darker than all other races.

102b

102c

102a

102d

102e

102f

96a

96b

96c

78a

78b

78d

78c

100mm

87 Large-tailed Nightjar *Caprimulgus macrurus*   Text and map page 247

A widely distributed, fairly common Asian species, extending from north-east India south-east through Indochina and Indonesia to northern Australia. Mainly resident with some local movements, and in Pakistan it is a summer breeding visitor only. Wide variety of habitats includes forest, woodland, plantations, scrub, grassland, gardens, mangroves, beaches, sandbanks and swamps.

Seven races (see Text).

87a **Adult male** (nominate) A generally large, greyish-brown, variegated nightjar. Lesser coverts dark brown, contrasting with other buff-spotted coverts. Buff line along scapulars. Indistinct buff or tawny-buff nuchal collar; white submoustachial stripe; large white throat-patch.

87b **Adult male** (nominate) In flight shows large white spots towards the wing-tip on the four outer primaries, and broad white tips to the two outer tail feathers.

87c **Adult female** (nominate) Differs from male in having buff spots on outer primaries and narrow buff or buffish-white tips to outer tail feathers.

88 Jerdon's Nightjar *Caprimulgus atripennis*   Text and map page 250

Resident in southern and eastern India, and Sri Lanka, mainly in forested or wooded country.

Racial differences slight (see Text).

88a **Adult male** (nominate) A large, greyish-brown, variegated nightjar, often appearing rather pale-headed. Lesser coverts dark brown; other coverts speckled and spotted buff. Ill-defined rufous nuchal collar; white throat-patch.

88b **Adult male** (nominate) In flight shows white spots towards the wing-tip on the four outer primaries, and broad white tips to the two outer tail feathers.

88c **Adult female** (nominate) Differs from male in having small, buffish spots on outer primaries, and narrow buff or buffish-white tips to outer tail feathers.

90 Sulawesi Nightjar *Caprimulgus celebensis*   Text and map page 253

Endemic to Sulawesi (to date only known from the northern and central-eastern parts) and the Sula Islands, in secondary forest, coastal bush and mangrove edge.

Sexes similar. Races differ slightly in the size of their white tail-spots.

90a **Adult male** (nominate) A medium to large-sized, greyish-brown, variegated nightjar. Lesser coverts dark brown; other coverts boldly spotted buff, pale buff and tawny. Buffish line along scapulars; white throat-patch.

90b **Adult male** (nominate) In flight shows white spots towards the wing-tip on the second, third and fourth outer primaries, and white tips to the two outer tail feathers.

89 Philippine Nightjar *Caprimulgus manillensis*   Text and map page 251

A Philippine endemic, but absent from the Palawan group. Resident in forest, woodland, scrub, open wooded country, mangroves, edges of towns, agricultural land and near rocky beaches.

Monotypic.

89a **Adult male** A large, greyish-brown, variegated nightjar. Lesser coverts dark brown; other coverts spotted blackish-brown, tawny, buff and pale buff. Buffish line across forewing and along scapulars. White band around throat.

89b **Adult male** In flight shows white spots towards the wing-tip on the second, third and fourth outer primaries, and white tips to the two outer tail feathers (outerweb of the outermost often wholly or partly brown).

89c **Adult female** Similar to male.

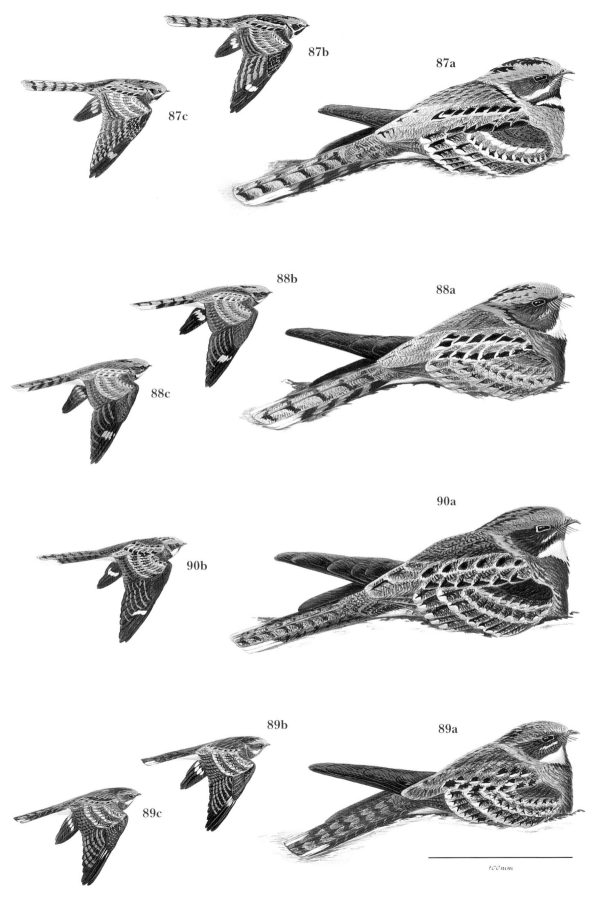

87a

87b

87c

88a

88b

88c

90a

90b

89a

89b

89c

100mm

PLATE 33: INDONESIAN NIGHTJARS

104 Bonaparte's Nightjar *Caprimulgus concretus*   Text and map page 273

A poorly known species, resident on Sumatra, Belitung (Billiton) and Borneo. Inhabits lowland forests, but often found in clearings and open spaces.

Monotypic.

104a Adult male A small to medium-sized brown nightjar. Wing-coverts spotted chestnut and cinnamon; scapulars blackish-brown edged pale buff. White submoustachial stripe; large white throat-patch.

104b Adult male In flight lacks white on wings, but has white tips to the two outer tail feathers.

104c Adult female Similar to male, but either lacks white on tail or has the two outer tail feathers very narrowly tipped white.

105 Salvadori's Nightjar *Caprimulgus pulchellus*   Text and map page 274

A little-known Indonesian species, restricted to submontane and montane forests in Sumatra and Java. Probably resident. Often occurs near cliffs, and may also sometimes be found in small, marshy areas.

Two races, although taxonomic status unclear (see Text).

105a Adult male (nominate) A small, darkish nightjar. Wing-coverts spotted and barred tawny, cinnamon and buff, with a thin buffish line along scapulars. Indistinct tawny-buff nuchal collar; tawny submoustachial stripe; large white patch on either side of lower throat.

105b Adult male (nominate) In flight shows a small white spot or bar towards the wing-tip on the second to fifth outermost primaries, and a white spot on the tips of the two outer most tail feathers.

105c Adult male (*bartelsi*) Similar to the nominate but slightly smaller, with a large white throat-patch.

105d Adult male (*bartelsi*) In flight, small white marks on the outer four primaries, and white tips to the two outer tail feathers.

105e Adult female (*bartelsi*) Differs from male in having a small tawny spot on the second and third outer primaries, and white or buff tips to the outer tail feathers.

104c

104b

104a

105b

105a

105d

105c

105e

100mm

45   Malaysian Eared-nightjar *Eurostopodus temminckii*   **Text and map page 181**

A Greater Sunda species from the Thai Peninsula to Sumatra and Borneo. Probably resident. Inhabits lowland and hill forest and edge, open country, open woodland, scrub, grassland, grassy swamp and coastal vegetation.

Sexes similar. Monotypic.

45a   Adult A large brown nightjar which may show 'ear-tufts' at rear of crown. Wing-coverts speckled and spotted buff, pale buff, buffish-white, tawny and cinnamon; scapulars boldly spotted blackish-brown. Thin buff nuchal collar; white throat-patch.

45b   Adult In flight lacks white markings on wings and tail.

46   Great Eared-nightjar *Eurostopodus macrotis*   **Text and map page 182**

The largest nightjar, range generally extending from south-west and north-east India east to southern China and south-east to central Sulawesi. Mainly resident, but locally migratory in north-east India. Lives in forests, scrub, wooded grassland and open country.

Sexes similar. Races differ in size and coloration (see Text).

46a   Adult (nominate) A very large brownish nightjar which may show 'ear-tufts' at rear of crown. Wing-coverts speckled and spotted tawny, buff and cinnamon; scapulars boldly spotted blackish-brown. Broad tawny-buff or buff nuchal collar; large white spot, sometimes tinged buffish, on either side of lower throat.

46b   Adult (nominate) In flight lacks white markings on wings and tail.

46c   Adult (*cerviniceps*) Paler, more buffish-brown, and longer-winged and longer-tailed than the nominate.

45b

45a

46b

46a

46c

100mm

42   **Heinrich's Nightjar** *Eurostopodus diabolicus*   Text and map page 178

A little-known Sulawesi endemic, until recently known only from a female specimen taken in the north-east in 1931, but now recorded from Lore Lindu National Park in the northern-central part of the island. Resident in primary forest, where it may be found in clearings and edges.

Male not described. Monotypic.

> **42a**   **Adult female** A medium-sized to large dark nightjar. Wing-coverts spotted and ocellated cinnamon-tawny; scapulars blackish, ocellated cinnamon on feather-tips. Buffish band around throat.
>
> **42b**   **Adult female** In flight shows a small whitish spot on the third and fourth outermost primaries, and all tail feathers are very narrowly tipped buffish.

44   **Archbold's Nightjar** *Eurostopodus archboldi*   Text and map page 180

A little-known montane forest species, endemic to New Guinea. Resident in forest clearings and open areas of heath.

Monotypic.

> **44a**   **Adult male** A large, dark, rather spotted nightjar. Wing-coverts spotted cinnamon, buff and tawny; scapulars blackish-brown distally, spotted cinnamon or buff. Indistinct, light greyish-brown nuchal collar.
>
> **44b**   **Adult male** In flight lacks white markings on wings, but has extremely narrow, greyish-white tips to the tail feathers.
>
> **44c**   **Adult female** Similar to male, although perhaps more densely spotted cinnamon and tawny on upperparts and breast.
>
> **44d**   **Adult female** In flight, tail feathers very narrowly tipped buffish.

43   **Papuan Nightjar** *Eurostopodus papuensis*   Text and map page 179

A lowland forest species, endemic to New Guinea. Resident. Typically inhabits clearings, tree-fall openings and glades, with good ground vegetation.

Sexes similar. Monotypic.

> **43a**   **Adult** A medium-sized to large dark variegated nightjar. Wing-coverts speckled, spotted and tipped tawny and buff; scapulars cinnamon-buff, boldly spotted blackish-brown. Large white throat-patch.
>
> **43b**   **Adult** In flight lacks white markings on wings and tail.

42b

42a

44b

44a

44c

44d

43a

43b

100mm

40 Spotted Nightjar *Eurostopodus argus*   Text and map page 174

Breeds in Australia, but generally absent from eastern and south-eastern coastal areas. Northern populations are locally nomadic, southern populations migratory and partly resident. Wintering birds also occur on islands in the Banda Sea and on the Aru Islands. Inhabits open forest, woodland, savanna, grassland, scrub and mangroves.

Sexes similar. Monotypic.

40a **Adult** A large, greyish-brown, heavily spotted nightjar. Wing-coverts boldly spotted buff or pale buff, with a prominent buffish line along scapulars. Broad buffish nuchal collar; buff submoustachial stripe; large white throat-patch.

40b **Adult** In flight shows large white spots towards the wing-tip on the four outer primaries, but lacks white on the tail.

41 White-throated Nightjar *Eurostopodus mystacalis*   Text and map page 176

Endemic to the Australasian region, breeding in eastern Australia, the Solomon Islands and New Caledonia. Australian population partially migratory, and during the non-breeding season also occurs in New Guinea. Populations on the Solomons and New Caledonia probably resident. Inhabits forest and woodland, but also savanna, scrub, open grassland, gardens, marsh and near mangroves. On the Solomons often occurs on or near beaches and on offshore islets.

Sexes similar. Three races, although the taxonomic status of each is unclear (see Text).

41a **Adult** (nominate) A large, dark, variegated nightjar. Wing-coverts spotted buff; scapulars greyish-white or -brown, broadly edged blackish-brown. Buff or tawny-buff nuchal collar; large white patch on either side of throat.

41b **Adult** (nominate) In flight the wings are spotted and barred buff, with a white distal spot on the outer four primaries. No white on tail.

41c **Adult** (*nigripennis*) Smaller and slightly paler than the nominate, with a tawnier, more distinct nuchal collar.

41d **Adult** (*nigripennis*) In flight shows a very small white mark towards the wing-tip on the third outermost primary, and a white band on the fourth outermost.

41e **Adult female** (*exul*) An extremely distinct, pale greyish form, currently known only from one museum specimen.

41f **Adult female** (*exul*) In flight may show white bars towards the wing-tip on the second, third and fourth outermost primaries.

40b

40a

41a

41b

41c

41d

41f

41e

100mm

OILBIRD STEATORNITHIDAE

STEATORNIS

Steatornis Humboldt, in Humboldt and Bonpland, 1814, Voy. Intér. Am., 1, p. 416. Type by monotypy, "Guacharo" = *Steatornis caripensis* Humboldt, 1817

One large Neotropical species. The unique Oilbird has a strongly hooked bill, clawed feet and stiff, graduated tail feathers. Gregarious in its habits, it breeds and roosts in caves and is able to move around easily in total darkness, by using echo-location. Feeds outside caves, on fruits located by both smell and sight and is the only nocturnal, frugivorous bird currently known to science.

---

1   OILBIRD
Steatornis caripensis   Plate 5

Steatornis caripensis Humboldt, 1817, *Bull. Sci. Soc. Philom. Paris* p.52 (Caverns of Caripe, Cumaná, Venezuela)

IDENTIFICATION Length 41-48cm. A very large, unique, frugivorous Neotropical nightjar, with a strong, hawk-like, hooked bill. Sexes similar. **At rest** Upperparts rufescent-brown, spotted whitish on the crown, rump and uppertail-coverts. Wing-coverts rufescent-brown, with a distinctive row of white spots along the median coverts. No obvious scapular pattern and no collar around the hindneck. Also shows a row of white spots along the four outer primaries, the first or first and second outer secondaries and the outermost tail feathers. Tail 'tented' and held in an inverted V-shape. Underparts rufescent-brown, boldly spotted whitish. **In flight** Normally flies with rapid, shallow wingbeats. Long-winged and round-tailed. Shows white spots along the outer primaries, secondaries and tail feathers (see above). **Similar species** None.

VOICE Utters a variety of harsh screams, snarls, shrieks and snoring sounds, especially whilst inside caves. When flying inside caves, emits bursts of 2-6 or more rapid, high-pitched clicks or clucks, which are used for echolocation. When leaving a cave, utters a continuous and rapid series of loud, sharp clicks. Very occasionally makes similar sounds when outside caves, i.e. when flying below dark forest canopies. Also gives *cree, cree, crrree* or *crrau* call notes. During courtship, utters low, clucking calls or a long, harsh *karrr.* At the nest, intruding Oilbirds are greeted with loud, harsh calls. The alarm call is a shrill scream or a loud shriek. Young nestlings utter high-pitched cheeps. At c. 20 days of age, chicks give loud, rather hoarse squeaks, which become louder with age. When begging for food, these squeaks become quite shrill. Outside the caves, the contact call of flying adults is a double-noted *karr-karr* or treble-noted *kuk kuk kuk.*

HABITAT Prefers forest and woodland, with caves and cave-like crevices in which to roost and breed. Occurs in primary forest, seasonally dry, mountainous forest, tropical forest and occasionally scrubland. Prefers to feed over primary forest, but will also visit secondary growth and coffee plantations with tall shading fruit trees. Avoids disturbed forest, towns and villages. 0–3,000m.

HABITS Nocturnal and crepuscular. Roosts in caves and cave-like crevices. During the breeding season, pairs roost side-by-side at the nest. Occasionally, a few birds roost out in the open, often in palm trees. Gregarious at colonies and in feeding areas. Inside caves, can fly slowly with deep wingbeats, hover, and twist and turn with great agility, using echolocation (see Voice) to move around with ease. Leaves caves to feed at or just after dusk and returns just before dawn. Birds often leave in groups of up to several hundred at a time and fly straight to a feeding area, each bird having a favourite site so that not all birds fly off in the same direction. At caves with vertical entrances, birds tend to leave singly, circling up through the entrance shaft. Outside caves, flies swiftly with rapid, shallow wingbeats, and can increase speed by holding wings in a more swept-back position. In forested areas, usually flies above the canopy. Occasionally stoops like a falcon, with wings half-closed. Sometimes perches in trees at night, especially when cloudy, alighting on bare, often slender, branches and woody vines. In foggy weather, disorientated birds may be attracted to bright lights.

Often flies up to 40-50km to a foraging area, occasionally up to 100km. Birds may visit more than one foraging area during the night, with distances of up to c. 150km between sites. Birds will revisit the same feeding area and the same fruiting tree several times during a (breeding) season. Usually forages over mountainous forests but also visits adjacent lowlands, especially outside the breeding season. Possibly locates fruiting trees by smell, especially those producing aromatic fruits. Once a fruiting tree has been discovered, individual fruit is probably located by sight. Forages in groups, with 3-5 birds at one tree, circling the tree and taking turns to pluck a fruit. Feeding birds either fly up to a tree, hover, pluck off a fruit and swoop away, or dive down from above to take a fruit. Fruits are swallowed whole and the seeds regurgitated undigested. Occasionally, birds cling briefly to bunches of fruit, beating their wings as they do so. They usually consume single-seeded black or purplish-brown fruits, generally 4-60 x 5-30mm. Breeding birds are able to carry large quantities of fruit back to their caves.

FOOD Fruits of laurels (including *Ocotea floribunda, O.* aff. *austini, O. wachenheimii, O. caracasana, O. oblonga, O. canaliculata, Persea coerulea, P. rigens, Phoebe cinnamonifolia, Nectandra* aff. *laurel, N. turbacensis, N. membranacea, N. martinicensis, N. kaburiensis, N. pichurium, Beilschmiedia sulcata, Cinnamomum elongatum, Aniba firmula, A. trinitatus, Aiouea schomburgkii, Pleurothyrium costanense* and *Licaria guianensis*), palms (including *Bactris setulosa, B. cuesa, Jessenia bataua, J. oligocarpa, Geonoma densa, G. vaga, Euterpe precatoria, E. langloisii, E. oleracea, E. edulis, Morenia caudata, Prestoea acuminata, Mauritia aculeata, M. subinermis, Livistona chinensis, Roystonea oleracea, Desmoncus* sp. and *Aiphanes* sp.), Burseraceae (including *Dacryodes trinitensis, Trattinnickia rhoifolia* and *Protium heptaphylum*), Araliaceae, Oleaceae (including *Linociera caribaea*), Myristicaceae (including *Virola surinamensis*), Anacardiaceae (including

Tapirira guianensis), Sapotaceae (including *Pouteria minutiflora*), Boraginaceae (including *Cordia bicolor*), Malpighiaceae (including *Byrsonima spicata*), Annonaceae and Polygonaceae.

BREEDING Breeding season is December to late June in Colombia, March–October in Venezuela, December–September (mainly December–May) in Trinidad and March?–September? in Ecuador. No published data are available from elsewhere. In northern Venezuela, studies have shown that although the majority of clutches are started between mid-March and early May, a few may be laid any time up to early September, thereby extending the overall breeding season.

Monogamous. During courtship, 2-3 birds circle around each other in a swift, swooping flight, calling (see Voice). After a pair-bond has been established, one of the pair (perhaps the male) often preens its mate's head whilst roosting, usually prior to or during the egg-laying period. Breeds in colonies, colony sizes ranging from around 20 to 5,000 pairs. Nests in mountainous regions, in caves and cave systems, on cliffs outside caves (especially at larger colonies where there is a shortage of nest-sites inside the caves), in deep, narrow, dark ravines and in natural cavities of canyon walls. Nesting caves may be up to 820m from the cave system entrance, up to 55m high and 30m or more wide. Nesting caves often have a stream running through them and are warm inside, c. 19°C, with 100% humidity. The entrances to nesting caves are often horizontal, although some may be vertical and up to 75m deep. The nest is a rim, mound or platform, constructed with regurgitated fruit seeds, rotten fruits, fecal matter or mud, c. 37cm in diameter. Nest-sites in caves are usually on high, narrow ledges close to the cave roof, up to c. 50m above the cave floor. As many as 10-40 pairs nest on some ledges, often with several nests close together, while single pairs nest on others. Pairs may use the same nest-sites year after year, with additional nesting material being added in subsequent breeding seasons. Pairs defend their nest area against neighbouring or intruding birds by calling (see Voice), bill grappling and twisting, and tugging their opponents. Clutch 1-4. Eggs oval and white, staining brown during the incubation period, 38.1-43.7 x 29.7-33.5mm. The eggs are laid at 2-9 day intervals.

Incubation begins with the first egg. During the day, both members of the pair incubate, sitting side-by-side on the nest. At night, they take turns in incubating. The changeover is silent, one bird getting up off the eggs and shuffling to one side whilst the other takes its place. Eggs are occasionally dislodged from the nest but, if less than four inches away, will often be retrieved by the adult. The adults often regurgitate fruit seeds whilst incubating. Smaller seeds are moved outside the nest, larger seeds are occasionally left where they are among the eggs. Rodents (i.e. *Proechimys urichi*) occasionally raid nests on accessible ledges and steal eggs. The incubation period is c. 32-35 days. The eggs hatch asynchronously, the egg shells not being cleared away from the nest promptly. The altricial young are mostly naked at hatching, weigh 12-15.5g and are unable to regulate their own body temperature for up to c. 3 weeks. They are brooded by both adults, usually by one at a time but sometimes by both together sitting side-by-side, for c. 25 days. The chicks lie with their heads beneath an adult's wing or breast and often point their heads upwards. Chicks in the nest (e.g. in Trinidad) are occasionally predated by crabs

Pseudothelphusia garmani. Some chicks may fall from the nest to the cave floor, and are then abandoned by their parents and may be preyed on by rats. The young are fed at night by both adults, which forage in areas closest to the nesting cave for the first 6-8 weeks and then move to more distant areas, presumably when the availability of ripe fruit is depleted. In Venezuela, the home range of an individual bird is around 85–96km . For a colony as a whole, the home range may be 230km at the start of the breeding season, expanding rapidly to c. 1,350km as the season progresses. The adults may feed their young 2-3 times a night during the first c. 30 days. For the first 12 days or so the young are probably fed on semi-digested fruit, thereafter gradually changing to partly or wholly undigested fruit. When begging for food, the chick cranes its head upwards, calls (see Voice), half-turns its head and grabs the adult's bill. The adult then partially opens its bill and regurgitates food with short, quick jerks of the head. Feeding visits decrease to one per night towards the end of the breeding season. Young chicks defecate at the edge of the nest with their backs pointing towards the nest rim. When they are older, they defecate clear of the nest, as the adults do. Older chicks can clamber up quite steep slopes by using their feet, digging in the leading edge of their wings and pulling themselves up with their bills. The maximum growth rate of the chicks occurs in the first 30 days, during which they gain an average 260g in weight. After this their weight increases at a slower rate until they weigh about 560g at c. 60 days and about 600-650g at 70-80 days. At this time, they weigh half as much again as their parents. After this, they lose weight until they fledge, at 88-125 days of age, weighing c. 400g.

Generally single-brooded, although birds will often lay replacement clutches if the first fails. If failure occurs late into the breeding season, birds may not lay again, and usually wait until the following breeding season. Some pairs that breed successfully may be double-brooded every second or third year. At some colonies (e.g. in Trinidad), birds remain in their caves throughout the year. At others, some or all birds move to another cave system after breeding, taking 2-4 months to abandon the breeding cave. Both adults and immatures roost in the new cave and adopt new foraging areas during the non-breeding season. Birds usually return to their breeding caves at the start of the following breeding season, although non-breeding birds often commute between the two (perhaps more) caves.

DESCRIPTION Adult male Forehead, crown and nape rufescent-brown, lightly spotted or vermiculated white or greyish-white, markings bordered brown. No collar around hindneck. Mantle and back brown or rufescent-brown barred brown, bars widely spaced. Rump and uppertail-coverts rufescent-brown or chestnut-brown speckled and barred brown, boldly spotted white or greyish-white, markings bordered brown. Lesser coverts rufescent-brown faintly speckled brown, often with small whitish spots along the lower row. Median coverts rufescent-brown boldly spotted whitish in the centres, spots bordered brown. Greater coverts rufescent-brown speckled and thinly barred brown, bars widely spaced. Primary coverts rufescent-brown faintly speckled brown. Marginal wing-coverts white or creamy white, lightly vermiculated brown. Scapulars rufescent-brown, speckled and barred brown. Primaries brown tinged rufous, more so on outerwebs; P10-P7 boldly spotted whitish along the outerwebs, markings bordered brown. Secondaries rufescent-brown, speckled and barred brown on outerwebs, brown on innerwebs, barred pale buffish-brown along inner edges; S1, and often S2, boldly spotted whitish along the outerwebs, markings bordered brown. Tertials rufescent-brown, speckled and barred brown. Tail chestnut-brown, speckled and thinly barred brown, very narrowly (c. 1mm) tipped greyish-white or buffish; R5 boldly spotted greyish-white along the outerwebs, markings bordered brown. Tail rounded, central pair (R1) longest, R2 c. 10-15mm shorter, R3 c. 20-30mm shorter, R4 c. 30-45mm shorter and R5 c. 60-75mm shorter. Chin rufescent-brown tinged greyish. Throat, breast, belly and flanks rufescent-brown boldly spotted greyish-white, spots variable in shape and bordered brown. Undertail-coverts rufescent-brown, boldly spotted and barred greyish-white, markings bordered brown. Underwing-coverts rufescent-brown and either plain or lightly spotted greyish-white, markings bordered brown. **Adult female** Similar to the male, although occasionally paler or more rufous. **Immature** Similar to the adults. **Juvenile** Darker than the adults. Upperparts blackish-brown, wings and tail dark brown, underparts slaty-brown. Lesser coverts rufescent-brown edged whitish. **Chick** At hatching, naked except for some sparse down, usually on the underparts. First down feathers are short and pale grey. Second down feathers are darker grey and much longer. **Bare parts** Iris dark brown or dull yellow; bill reddish-brown; legs and feet reddish-brown or pinkish-flesh.

MEASUREMENTS Wing (male) 285-335, (female) 286-331; tail (male) 181-232, (female) 176-217; bill (male) 31-36, (female) 30-33; tarsus (male) 17.5-27.6, (female) 17.4-22.4. Weight (male) 360-480g, (female) 273-395g.

MOULT Moult has been recorded in every month of the year but is generally undertaken from June to November. Some birds may moult whilst breeding. The primaries are generally moulted descendantly, although serially descendant moult has also been recorded, and can be quite protracted, taking up to 10 months to complete. Irregular moult may also occur, with one wing being moulted and not the other. No further published data available.

GEOGRAPHICAL VARIATION Monotypic.

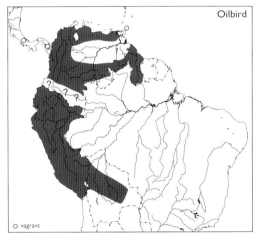

DISTRIBUTION AND MOVEMENTS North-western and west-central South America. Colombia (Magdalena south to Cauca, east to Vaupés), Venezuela (NW Zulia, Falcón,

Trujillo, Mérida (possibly Táchira), Cojedes, Aragua, Miranda, Monagas, S, SE and E Bolívar and C Amazonas), Trinidad, Guyana, Ecuador, Peru and C Bolivia (La Paz, Cochabamba and Santa Cruz). Partially and/or seasonally migratory. Can move long distances from the breeding caves, presumably in search of food. Presumed vagrants recorded from Tobago (group, September), eastern Panama (possibly only one record, E Darién, March) and eastern Costa Rica (corpse, January).

STATUS Throughout its range, this species is suffering severe reductions in numbers and is extremely vulnerable to human activities. It is locally distributed in Colombia, where several colonies are currently threatened. Some colonies in Bolivia are also threatened. No further data available.

REFERENCES Bosque & Ramirez (1988), Bosque *et al.* (1995), de Bellard-Pietri (1953), Fjeldså and Krabbe (1990), Griffin (1953), Hilty & Brown (1986), Roca (1994), Snow, B. K. (1979), Snow, D. W. (1961, 1962), Stresemann & Stresemann (1966).

FROGMOUTHS PODARGIDAE

PODARGUS

Podargus Vieillot, 1818, Nouv. Dict. Hist. Nat., 27, p. 151. Type by monotypy, *Podargus cinereus* Vieillot 1818.

Three large species, confined to Australia and New Guinea. Frogmouths of this genus have large heads, partly forward-facing eyes, massive bills that are broad, flat and slightly hooked at the tip and tufts of feathers across the front of the forehead. They also have a large powder-down patch on either side of the rump, short tarsi, weak feet with semizygodactylous side toes and an elongated middle toe that is not pectinated. All species are extremely variable in size and coloration and show sexual dimorphism. Arboreal. Nests are loose platforms of mainly sticks and twigs and the eggs are white and unmarked. They generally feed by pouncing onto prey from a perch.

2 TAWNY FROGMOUTH
Podargus strigoides Plate 1

Caprimulgus strigoides Latham, 1802, *Index Orn. Suppl.* p.lviii (New Holland = Sidney, New South Wales, *apud* Mathews)
Podargus strigoides brachypterus Gould, 1841, *Proc. Zool. Soc. London* p.163 (Swan River, West Australia)
Podargus strigoides phalaenoides Gould, 1840, *Proc. Zool. Soc. London* p.142 (north-west coast of Australia)
Podargus strigoides lilae Deignan, 1951, *Emu* p.72 (Ambukwamba = 'Umbakumba', Groote Eylandt, Gulf of Carpentaria)
For dates of publication, see Schodde and Mason 1997, pp.305-312

IDENTIFICATION Length 34-53cm. A large to very large, greyish frogmouth, endemic to Australia and its islands. Sexually dimorphic, males having only a grey morph, females having grey, rufous or chestnut morphs (see Geographical Variation). **At rest** Upperparts greyish, speckled and spotted white and streaked blackish. No collar around hindneck. Wing-coverts greyish, speckled brown and boldly spotted white. Scapulars whitish, mottled and speckled brown. Whitish supercilium often weak or even absent. Blackish submoustachial stripe edged chestnut-brown. Underparts greyish streaked blackish, boldly spotted white. At night, generally shows a reddish eyeshine in artificial light. **In flight** Appears longer-winged and shorter-tailed than other *Podargus* frogmouths. Wings rather pointed. Both sexes lack white markings on wings and tail. **Similar species** Papuan Frogmouth (3) is slightly larger, longer-tailed, heavier-billed and often less greyish, has whiter (male) or buffier (female) scapulars, is less boldly streaked blackish along the submoustachial stripe and has paler, more spotted underparts; at night generally shows an orange eyeshine in artificial light, and in flight wings appear more rounded. Marbled Frogmouth (4) is similar to rufous-phased birds but is generally smaller, slimmer and less streaked, appears longer-tailed, has bolder whitish spots on the wing-coverts and a more conspicuous supercilium; at night, generally shows an orange eyeshine in artificial light.

VOICE The song (or call), given by both sexes, is a deep, continuous booming *oom... oom... oom... oom*, which may last for up to several minutes and is either even or slightly rising in pitch. Each note is repeated at regular intervals, although notes are occasionally delivered at a faster rate. Sings with head stretched forward and upward and bill closed. With each note, the bird moves its body from side to side, shifting its weight from one leg to the other. May be heard at dusk and dawn and throughout the night during the breeding season. Sings from regular perches, such as branches in trees up to 15m above ground.

Males occasionally call to females with a rapid series of slurred, low-pitched, drumming *did-did-do* or *t-toom* notes, the females responding with a single-note reply (apparently not described). An adult sitting on its nest sometimes utters a rapid rattling sound, which may also be given by its mate nearby. The (apparent flight) call is a deep harsh crow-like *kaah* note, which can be heard from a small group hawking for food. If alarmed during the day, adults give a rapid, guttural *oo-oo oo-oo* or *too-took* call. At night, a variation of this call appears to be a loud *maw-pawk*. If disturbed, utters a loud *gree-er*, and a harsh scream in fright. Screams are also given by two birds fighting. When annoyed, often makes croaking or grunting sounds. During threat displays, the adult growls at potential danger and during defence displays at the nest, adults cluck, hiss and snap their bills. Young birds sometimes make owl-like hissing sounds. When active and hungry, chicks make soft, groaning, rasping, gurgling or squeaking sounds, and when alarmed they screech. Chicks almost old enough to fledge give deep barks when begging for food. At this age, they may also utter a series of soft *a-woo* notes, which may be an early attempt at singing.

HABITAT Prefers open forests and woodlands, and woodland clearings and edges. Occurs in *Eucalyptus* woods and forests, mixed or deciduous woodlands, *Acacia* and *Eucalyptus* shrublands, and along riverside groves of *Eucalyptus*. It also frequents vegetated dunes, heathlands, grassy plains, vegetated sandplains, saltmarshes, cleared farmland, towns, parkland, suburban gardens, orchards, and plantations. Occasionally inhabits mangroves. In Tasmania, also inhabits sclerophyll forest and savanna woodland. Generally avoids rainforest, although quickly colonizes openings such as roadways. Also avoids treeless deserts.

HABITS Crepuscular and nocturnal. Usually roosts on branches in trees, often in rather open situations, 1-25m above ground. Occasionally roosts on the ground, where roost-sites may be at the base of a tree or beneath a fallen dead branch or an open shrub or bush. Also roosts in artifical situations such as on a stable roof, a water pipe in the branches of a tree, or a windlass over a well shaft, although such occurrences may be quite rare. Up to 5-8 roost-sites may be used regularly throughout the territory, with each site being used for up to several months, although some birds may change roost-site daily. Roosting birds sit upright, perching across or along a branch, with heads pointing forwards and eyes almost closed. Occasionally birds open their eyes and look around, move about and scratch and preen themselves. If danger approaches, a roosting bird assumes an alarm position, by stretching up its body at an angle to the branch on which it is roosting, often with its tail lying along the branch, its head and bill held upwards, its eyes almost closed and its feathers compressed. In this posture, it 'freezes', keeping watch on the intruder and only relaxing once the danger has passed. Roosts singly, in pairs or in family groups of up to five birds. Birds may roost close to one another in adjacent trees or on adjacent branches, or may roost side-by-side on the same branch. If two birds are together, one may roost with its feathers fluffed out whilst the other adopts a more normal upright posture (see above). Both birds occasionally wake, move about and scratch and preen themselves or each other. If disturbed or discovered during the day, roosting birds may be mobbed by other species of birds, such as Restless Flycatcher *Miagra inquieta*, friarbirds *Philemon* sp., Yellow-throated Miner *Manorina flavigula*, White-plumed Honeyeater *Lichenostomus pencillatus*, Figbird *Sphecotheres viridis*, Red Wattlebird *Anthochaera carunculata*, Apostlebird *Struthidea cinerea*, Grey Butcherbird *Cracticus torquatus* or Pied Currawong *Strepera graculina*. Ground- (and tree-) roosting birds occasionally sunbathe by ruffling their feathers and stretching out their wings. Ground-roosting birds often fall prey to feral cats, dogs and foxes. At night, birds may be preyed on by Powerful Owls *Ninox strenua*, and may possibly be attacked by Boobook Owls *Ninox novaeseelandiae*.

Hunts from low perches, such as bare branches, tree-stumps and posts, flying from perch to perch throughout its territory. From a perch, it scans the ground below by turning its head or moving about on the perch. It then glides down or pounces, snaps up the prey and flies back up to the same or another perch, where the food is eaten. Larger prey is beaten against a hard surface before being swallowed. Food is also taken from branches and birds may hover to feed in this way. Birds may also adopt a wait-and-see technique, by perching for long periods with their bills open, quickly snapping up any passing insects. Clearings and roadsides are favoured hunting areas. Occasionally chases insects in flight, or takes insects attracted to artificial lights, including from windows of buildings. Forages after dusk and before dawn, spending the middle part of the night sitting about, dozing and digesting. Indigestible matter is regurgitated in pellets.

FOOD Snails, slugs, worms, cockroaches (including Blattidae and Blaberidae), earwigs (including Labiduridae), centipedes (including Scolopendridae), millipedes, mantids, Orthoptera (including Stenopelmatidae, Gryllacrididae, Tettigoniidae, Eumastacidae, Rhaphidophoridae, Gryllidae, Gryllotalpidae and Acrididae), dragonflies, stick insects, bugs (including Cicadidae and Coreidae), antlions, moths (including Cossidae, Geometridae, Arctiidae, Hepialidae, Lasiocampidae, Thaumetopoeidae, Noctuidae and Saturniidae), moth larvae, sawfly larvae, beetles (including Silphidae, Staphylinidae, Carabidae, Dytiscidae, Hydrophilidae, Lucanidae, Trogidae, Scarabaeidae, Elateridae, Tenebrionidae, Cerambycidae, Chrysomelidae and

Curculionidae), ants, Crustacea, scorpions (including Scorpionidae and Bothriuridae) and spiders (including Agelenidae, Araneidae, Deinopidae, Heteropodidae, Hexathelidae, Gnaphosidae, Lycosidae, Nicodamidae, Dipluridae, Salticidae and Sparassidae). Occasionally also takes frogs (including Hylidae and Myobatrachidae), lizards and small snakes, small birds (including Climacteridae and Passeridae) and small mammals (including Muridae). Plant material, twigs, feathers, grit and soil may also be ingested, perhaps sometimes accidentally. Does not feed on carrion.

BREEDING Breeding season August–December, with peak egg-laying in September–October, although in dry inland areas often breeds following the rains.

Permanently territorial, territory sizes ranging from 20-80ha. A favoured song post is often chosen as the nest-site. Prior to and during nest building, both sexes sing (see Voice) with increasing frequency from the nest-site. One adult roosts on the nest, the other nearby. Both sexes help build, which may take 2-4 weeks; some nests may be built but not used during the year of building. Nest material is taken from trees and bushes, by diving down and breaking off twigs and shoots with the bills. Sticks and twigs are also picked up from the ground. The nest is a rather flimsy platform, c. 10-30cm in diameter and c. 3-12cm deep, made of twigs, sticks, bark, grass and cobwebs and often lined with green leaves, plants, thistle heads, feathers or wool. Birds continue to add material during the first week after the eggs have been laid, and constantly rearrange pieces of the nest throughout the incubation period. The nest is usually built in the fork of a bare, horizontal, sloping or sometimes upright branch, c. 2-20m or more above ground. The nest-site is usually in open situations beneath the shelter of overhanging foliage, but is seldom actually amongst foliage. Favoured trees for nesting are eucalypts, casuarinas, tea trees (*Melaleuca*) and wattles, preferably in forest, scrubland or bush country, sometimes in strips of scrub along roads. Occasionally nests on the tops of tall tree-stumps, in the crowns of grass trees (*Xanthorrhoea*), in the entrances to hollow tree sprouts, or in the disused nests of other birds, i.e. Apostlebird *Struthidea cinerea*, White-winged Chough *Corcorax melanorhamphos*, crows *Corvus* sp., cormorants *Phalacrocorax* sp., Black Kite *Milvus migrans*, Australian Magpie *Gymnorhina tibicen*, Black-faced Cuckoo-shrike *Coracina novaehollandiae* or Magpie Lark *Grallina cyanoleuca*. Has also been known to build a nest on a house roof gutter. The same nest-site may be used year after year, for up to 21 years in succession. Clutch 1-3, occasionally 4, rarely 5, the eggs laid at 1-3 day intervals. Eggs elliptical, white, and slightly glossy, 36.0-51.7 x 25.0-34.3mm. Eggs vary greatly in size but tend to average smaller in the north and west of the species's range.

The eggs are generally laid on successive days. Incubation begins when the first egg is laid, and is done by the male during the day, the female roosting close by in the same or an adjacent tree, and by both sexes during the night. At night, the incubating bird is regularly fed by its mate. At the start of the incubation period, the adults incubate in a rather upright position but adopt a flatter, more relaxed posture as the incubation period progresses. During the day, the incubating bird sits tight and rarely moves, with its tail resting along one of the branches on which the nest is built, its body and head facing forwards. The eggs are turned only c. 4 times every 24 hours. If danger approaches, the incubating bird assumes the alarm posture (see Habits). In the face of persistent danger it may perform a defence display (see below), make circular movements with its head and repeatedly bill-snap, or flush from the nest. Unattended eggs may be taken by crows or currawongs. At night, both sexes may sing or call from the nest (see Voice), during which they bend their heads forward and sway from side to side. The incubation period is 28-32 days, and the eggs hatch asynchronously.

The chicks are semi-altricial and nidicolous, and tend to be brooded by the male during the day and alternately by both sexes at night, at least during the first 2-3 weeks. Both parents may assist the hatchlings out of their eggs and remove their droppings from the nest during the first 10-11 days. Adults may also eject infertile eggs from the nest. The chicks are possibly fed only by the female for the first 2-3 weeks, although this has not been properly documented. If danger approaches, the brooding adult assumes the alarm posture (see Habits), then (if danger persists) performs a defence display by spreading its wings and tail, fluffing up its feathers, gaping and glaring at the intruder and bill-snapping, clucking and hissing (see Voice). At 11-12 days of age, the chicks defecate over the side of the nest. At 3-4 weeks they are fed simultaneously by both parents, who hold up food for their offspring to reach up and take. If food is short, the younger, smaller chicks may succumb. The chicks fledge at 25-35 days of age, although they often fall or get blown from the nest before then. One of the adults usually roosts with a fallen chick but mortality can be high and the success rate from each clutch is usually 1-2 fledged young. Fledglings remain dependent on their parents for food for a further 1-2 weeks after leaving the nest and usually roost with one or both of the adults. If danger approaches, both adults and juveniles assume the alarm posture (see Habits). The young may be left unattended after c. 6 weeks but remain with or near their parents for at least several months. For a month or so, the family party roosts in or near the nest-tree but will then move to another roost-site within the territory.

Single- or occasionally double-brooded, especially in southern Australia. Second clutches may be started in the same nest, c. 21 days after the first brood has fledged.

DESCRIPTION *P. s. strigoides* **Adult male** Forehead, crown and nape greyish-brown, speckled and spotted whitish, broadly streaked blackish-brown with chestnut-brown edges. No collar around hindneck. Mantle, back, rump and uppertail-coverts greyish-brown, speckled and spotted with greyish-white, white and brown, and broadly streaked blackish-brown, the streaks edged chestnut-brown. Scapulars whitish, mottled and vermiculated brown. Wing-coverts greyish-brown, often heavily tinged chestnut-brown, speckled brown and boldly spotted whitish. Primaries brown, boldly spotted buff or pale buff along outerwebs, barred and mottled buffish along innerwebs. Secondaries brown, barred and speckled greyish-white or buffish. Tertials greyish-brown, mottled greyish-white and brown and streaked blackish-brown. Tail greyish-brown, broadly barred and mottled with greyish-white or greyish-buff, with narrower blackish-brown bars or vermiculations. Whitish supercilium around front of forehead above bill is often indistinct or even absent. Lores and ear-coverts greyish or greyish-buff, often tinged chestnut, rufous or cinnamon, speckled brown. Line of blackish-brown

feathers, edged chestnut-brown, along submoustachial stripe. Chin and throat greyish-brown, speckled brown and thinly streaked blackish-brown. Breast greyish-brown, speckled and vermiculated brown, streaked blackish-brown and boldly spotted whitish. Belly, flanks and undertail-coverts greyish-brown, often tinged buffish, barred and vermiculated brown, streaked dark brown. Underwing-coverts greyish-white, barred or vermiculated brown. **Adult female** Smaller, paler and plainer than the male, often tinged chestnut, and smaller-billed. **Immature** Similar to adults. **Juvenile** Upperparts grey, finely speckled white, spotted and blotched blackish, becoming barred grey and white on rump. Underparts pale grey, faintly barred white and blackish. **Chick** At hatching, covered in white protoptile down; at c. 7 days, covered in a greyer mesoptile down. **Bare parts** Iris yellow to orange-yellow; bill blackish or brownish; legs and feet pale olive-brown to blackish-brown.

MEASUREMENTS Wing (male) 248-295, (female) 220-281; tail (male) 183-229, (female) 167-225; bill (male) 30.5-50.0, (female) 29.0-47.2; tarsus (male) 23.1-35.0, (female) 23.2-34.0. Weight (male) 178-680g, (female) 157-555g.

MOULT Adults undergo a post-breeding moult, although the moult is often suspended, and it may take up to two years before all feathers are renewed. The primary moult is serially descendant with as few as 1-2 primaries being replaced in each series, so that following each suspension, there may be several generations of feathers in the wing. The sequence of secondary moult has yet to be fully understood. Tail moult appears to be asymmetrical and irregular. Juveniles possibly undertake a partial post-breeding moult, during which only body feathers are replaced; immatures undertake a complete post-breeding moult, possibly in their second year, the moult being simpler than in subsequent years (see above).

GEOGRAPHICAL VARIATION Four races are currently recognised.

P. s. strigoides Described above. The largest and darkest race. Males have only a grey morph, females have grey and chestnut morphs. Variation in body size is clinal, birds becoming larger southwards. Birds on Tasmania are slightly smaller, and appear plainer as a result of narrower streaking on the upperparts. Intergrades with *P. s. brachypterus* in the west of its range.

P. s. brachypterus A pale race, with only a grey morph. Wing of male 214-289, of female 209-266; tail of male 160-222, of female 165-212. Weight of male 205-416g, of female 185-327g. Intergrades with *P. s. strigoides* in the east of its range, and possibly intergrades with *P. s. phalaenoides* in the north of its range.

P. s. phalaenoides A small, pale race, the palest birds occurring in the west of its range. Males have only a grey morph, females have grey and rufous morphs. Wing of male 198-248, of female 193-250; tail of male 149-200, of female 148-198. Weight of male 180-283g, of female 123-230g. Intergrades with *P. s. strigoides* in the southeast of its range, and possibly intergrades with *P. s. brachypterus* in the south of its range.

P. s. lilae A pale, silvery-grey race, and rather plain, being less boldly marked than other subspecies. Wing of male (three) 195-202, of female (two) 195-206; tail of male (two) 160-167, of female (two) 157-169. Weight no data.

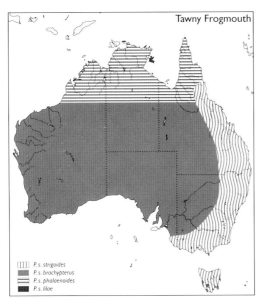

Tawny Frogmouth

P. s. strigoides
P. s. brachypterus
P. s. phalaenoides
P. s. lilae

IDENTIFICATION Length 46-60cm. A very large, greyish-brown Australasian frogmouth (with a very rare rufous phase). Sexually dimorphic. **At rest** Upperparts greyish-brown, speckled buff, cinnamon and white, streaked and spotted blackish. No collar around hindneck. Wing-coverts greyish-brown mottled buff, tawny and white, streaked and spotted blackish and often boldly spotted white. Scapulars whitish, speckled brown. Buffish supercilium extends around front of forehead, submoustachial stripe often streaked blackish-brown. Underparts greyish-brown, barred and streaked brown, becoming whitish on belly and flanks. Females are generally paler, plainer and buffier with buffish scapulars, and are smaller-billed. At night, generally shows an orange eyeshine in artificial light. **In flight** Wings appear rather short with rounded tips. The tail is long and graduated. Both sexes lack white markings on wings and tail. **Similar species** Tawny Frogmouth (2) is slightly smaller, shorter-tailed, less heavy-billed and often greyer, is more boldly streaked blackish along the submoustachial stripe, and has darker, less spotted underparts; at night, generally shows a reddish eyeshine in artificial light.

VOICE The song (or perhaps contact call) is a low, resonant drumming or booming, composed of a monotonously repeated series of *ooom*, *uum* or *woo* notes either even or slightly rising in pitch. Both sexes boom, although the calls of the male are deeper. Although it may occur throughout the year, booming is greatest at the start of the breeding season, when both sexes call antiphonally for up to 30 minutes at a time. Sings from branches in trees. May be heard predominantly at night. During threat/defence displays, the presumed male utters a rapid series of deep, muffled, bubbling notes that ends with a sudden (perhaps bill-) snapping sound, i.e. *bu-bu-bu-bu-klik* or *hoo-hoo-hoo-hoo-klik*. If threatened, disturbed or flushed, utters a loud, harsh, croaking scream, usually with its bill open. Also when threatened, it may give a mournful, drawn-out, double-noted *maw-pork* call, the first note rising in pitch, the second trailing away.

At the nest, adults utter low screeches and twitterings to each other. During threat/defence displays at the nest, adults hiss at intruders. If agitated at the nest, the adult female and its chick call to each other with loud hisses. When handled, an adult bird makes a long, drawn-out, harsh hissing sound.

DISTRIBUTION AND MOVEMENTS Endemic to Australia and Tasmania, and recently reported from southern New Guinea.

P. s. strigoides Eastern Australia, east of the Great Dividing Range, from Burdekin River, Townsville south to Victoria, and southern Australia, south of the Great Dividing Range, west to SE South Australia and Tasmania. Intergrades with *P. s. brachypterus* along the western edge of the Great Dividing Range. Sedentary.
P. s. brachypterus Most of mainland Australia, west of the Great Dividing Range, and south of latitude 20°S. Intergrades with *P. s. strigoides* along the western edge of the Great Dividing Range, and possibly intergrades with *P. s. phalaenoides* along latitude 20°S. Sedentary.
P. s. phalaenoides Northern Australia, north of latitude 20°S. Probably intergrades with *P. s. strigoides* in the region of the Einasleigh Uplands and the Burdekin-Lynd Divide, and possibly intergrades with *P. s. brachypterus* along latitude 20°S. Recently reported from southern New Guinea. Sedentary.
P. s. lilae Occurs only on Groote Eylandt in the Gulf of Carpentaria, northern Australia. Sedentary.

STATUS Abundant in many parts of Australia, common in Tasmania. The loss of habitat, or the use of pesticides, are potential threats in some regions, and birds are often killed by traffic on roads.

REFERENCES Barker & Vestjens (1989), Beruldsen (1980), Blakers *et al.* (1984), Higgins (in press); Rose & Eldridge (1997), Schodde & Mason (1981, 1997), Stresemann & Stresemann (1966), Tarr (1985).

HABITAT Prefers forest and woodland edges, avoiding the interior of dense forests, but occurring in a wide range of habitats including rainforest, monsoon forest, pockets and edges of vine forest, open woodland, dense savanna, paperbark and other gallery woodland, riparian jungle, groves, secondary growth, gardens and mangroves. Also frequents mature mangroves along tidal creeks. 0–2,200m.

HABITS Nocturnal and crepuscular. Roosts on branches in trees, 10-30m above ground, often sitting close to the trunk and either upright or at an angle, especially along sloping branches or at the bend of a thick bough. Often roosts in pairs or family parties, two birds sometimes roosting side-by-side or two or more birds roosting close to each other, either in the same or neighbouring trees. Also roosts in mangroves, often as low as a few metres above the high-water mark; occasionally roosts on the ground at the base of a tree or beneath a large log. If danger approaches, the roosting bird assumes an alarm posture by stretching its neck and head up, pointing its head and bill upwards, compacting its feathers and often raising its

3   PAPUAN FROGMOUTH
Podargus papuensis   **Plate 1**

Other name: Great Papuan Frogmouth

Podargus papuensis Quoy and Gaimard, 1830, *Voy. 'Astrolabe', Zool.* p.207, *Atlas, Ois.* pl.13 (Dorey [i.e. Manokwari] Harbour, New Guinea)

crest forward over its bill. It then 'freezes' in this position until the danger has passed. If the danger persists, the bird may perform a threat/defence display by lowering and thrusting forward its head, gaping and calling (see Voice), or fluffing out its feathers, spreading out its wings, gaping and calling (see Voice). If flushed from its roost, it often calls (see Voice) and flies off, alighting high in trees some distance away. At night, it often sits out in the open on bare branches, tree stumps or roadside posts. Has few enemies but may be preyed on by Rufous Owls *Ninox rufa*, feathers having been found below owl roosts.

Both sexes forage over a range of 20-30ha, methodically flying from perch to perch throughout their territory, especially in open woodland and clearings. Hunting birds alight on low perches such as branches, tree-stumps, stakes and fence-posts and scan the ground or vegetation below them. If prey is sighted, they glide down, snap it up and either swallow it on the spot or, if it is larger item, fly back up to a perch and batter it against a hard surface before eating it. Also feeds on insects attracted to street lights and lights outside buildings, and has been known to take prey from window gratings. Will also chase insects during sallying flights, take carrion from roadkills, occasionally steal prey from other birds, i.e. Helmeted Friarbird *Philemon buceroides*, or take small fish from the surface of water. Most hunting and feeding probably occurs in the early evening, or just before dawn.

FOOD Moths, beetles, grasshoppers, locusts, caterpillars, spiders, snails, myriapods, frogs, toads (including *Bufo marinus*), lizards, small birds, small mammals, and possibly small fish. Gravel may be ingested accidentally.

BREEDING Breeding season throughout its range August–January or February, peaking in October–November in the austral spring and early summer.

Permanently territorial. In north-eastern Australia, territories may be as small as 5-7ha. No published information available on courtship and pair-bonding. Both sexes help build the nest, which takes up to four weeks to construct. It is a loose, shallow, saucer-shaped construction of dry sticks and twigs, 10-35cm in diameter, 6-15cm deep and lined with leaves. One bird dives at a twig, grabs it in its bill, snaps it off in flight and returns to the nest-site, passing it to its mate to weave into the nest. One or other of the adults sits at the nest-site from the moment building begins, with the other roosting close by. At night, the adults regularly 'drum' (see Voice) from the nest-site. The nest is built in a fork in a horizontal branch or at the junction of a branch and a tree trunk, 6-36m above ground. Paperbarks *Melaleuca* are favoured nesting trees in north-eastern Australia. Also nests low down in mangroves, often only 2-3m above the tidal water. In north-eastern Australia, pairs nesting in mangroves may build as close as c. 100m to a neighbouring pair. Clutch 1-2. Eggs elliptical, slightly glossy and white, 43.0-55.0 x 31.0-35.5mm.

Incubation is by the male during the day and probably by the female, or both sexes, at night. If danger approaches the nest, the incubating adult assumes an alarm posture (see Habits). If the danger persists, the adult performs a threat/defence display by gaping, hissing (see Voice) and bill-snapping. It may also flutter towards the intruder, bill-snapping. At night, the incubating adult is constantly visited and fed by its mate. From c. 13 days after laying, the eggs may be left unattended at night for short periods. The incubation period is c. 40 days.

Both sexes appear to take turns in brooding their offspring during the first few weeks. Chicks semi-altricial and nidicolous. Chicks leave the nest at c. 26-30 days of age but remain close by and often return to the nest during the next seven days or so. Chicks can make adult-like calls at c. 30 days of age (see Voice) and fend for themselves shortly afterwards, although they may remain with their parents until the beginning of the next breeding season. Possibly double-brooded.

DESCRIPTION Adult male Forehead, crown and nape greyish-brown, speckled and vermiculated buff, cinnamon, greyish-white and white, boldly spotted or streaked blackish-brown. No collar around hindneck. Mantle, back, rump and uppertail-coverts greyish-brown, mottled and vermiculated buff, cinnamon, greyish-white and white, and boldly spotted or streaked blackish-brown. Wing-coverts greyish-brown, mottled and vermiculated buff, tawny, cinnamon and greyish-white, boldly spotted and streaked blackish-brown and often very boldly spotted whitish, the white spots speckled brown or buff. Scapulars whitish, speckled and vermiculated brown. Primaries brown, boldly spotted buff along outerwebs, barred and speckled buff along innerwebs; P5-P1 broadly tipped buff or whitish. Secondaries brown mottled buff, broadly tipped buff or whitish. Tertials greyish-brown, mottled and speckled buff, cinnamon, greyish-white and white. Tail greyish-brown, speckled and mottled blackish-brown, broadly barred greyish-white or greyish-buff, bars edged and speckled dark brown. Supercilium buffish speckled brown, extending around front of forehead above bill. Lores and ear-coverts buff or tawny, barred or vermiculated brown. Often streaked blackish-brown along sub-moustachial stripe. Chin, throat and breast greyish-brown, often tinged buff, tawny or cinnamon, barred, streaked and vermiculated brown. Belly, flanks and undertail-coverts whitish, mottled, streaked or vermiculated brown and blackish-brown. Underwing-coverts buffish, speckled and barred brown. **Adult female** Similar to the male but upperparts often slightly paler and buffier and less heavily mottled. Scapulars greyish-buff, tinged buff and speckled brown on outerwebs, buff and fairly plain on innerwebs and spotted blackish towards feather-tips. Underparts often less boldly patterned, with less white and often tinged buffish. Often less heavy-billed. **Immature** Similar to the adults but iris yellow. **Juvenile** Possibly similar to the immature. **Chick** At hatching, covered in white protoptile down. This is later replaced (age uncertain) by fawnish-white mesoptile down with faint brownish bars. **Bare parts** Iris red, orange-red or reddish-brown; bill horn, greyish or brownish; legs and feet brownish.

MEASUREMENTS Wing (male) 252-325, (female) 228-310; tail (male) 238-294, (female) 219-286, unsexed (one) 302; bill (male) 44.4-59.6, (female) 44.0-55.5; tarsus (male) 21-39, (female) 26.2-38.4. Weight (male) 290-599.2g, (female) 300-445g, unsexed 290-570g.

MOULT Adults undertake a post-breeding moult, although the moult is often suspended, and it may take up to two years before all feathers are renewed. The primary moult is serially descendant with as few as 1-2 primaries being replaced in each series, so that following each suspension there may be several generations of feathers in the wing. The sequence of secondary moult has yet to be documented; tail moult appears to be asymmetrical and irregular. Juveniles undergo a partial post-breeding moult during which only body feathers appear to be renewed, immatures undertake a complete post breeding moult, possibly in their second year, the moult being simpler than in subsequent years (see above).

GEOGRAPHICAL VARIATION Monotypic. Variable in ground colour, although no colour morphs are recognised, males ranging from pale grey or greyish-brown, to brownish or dark brown. Females are generally more rufous. In Australian populations, individual and sexual variation is much greater than geographical variation, although southern birds are often darker, with the variation being clinal.

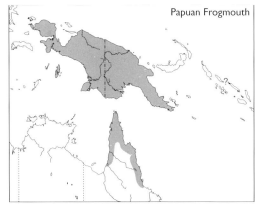

Papuan Frogmouth

DISTRIBUTION AND MOVEMENTS Widespread in New Guinea, extending south into northeastern Australia. West Papuan Islands (Waigeo, Batanta, Salawati and Misool), Irian Jaya (including the islands of Biak, Numfor and Yapen in Geelvink Bay), Aru Islands, Papua New Guinea, and NE Australia (Cape York Peninsula, south to the Staaten River on the western coast and to the Cooktown region in the east, and NE Queensland, north to Mt Finnegan – Bloomfield River and south to at least Townsville). Sedentary. Possibly also occurs on the Solomon Islands.

STATUS Fairly common locally throughout New Guinea, common to moderately abundant in north-eastern Australia.

REFERENCES Beehler *et al.* (1986), Bell (1986), Beruldsen (1980), Coates (1985), Condon (1975), Higgins (in press), Rand & Gilliard (1967), Schodde & Mason (1981, 1997), Tolhurst (1993).

---

4 MARBLED FROGMOUTH
Podargus ocellatus Plate 1

Other name: Little Papuan Frogmouth

Podargus ocellatus Quoy and Gaimard, 1830, *Voy. 'Astrolabe' Zool.* 1, p.208, *Atlas, Ois.* pl.14 (Dorey [i.e. Manokwari] Harbour, New Guinea)
Podargus ocellatus marmoratus Gould, 1855, *Bds. Austr., Suppl.* pt. 2, pl.[8] (Cape York Peninsula)
Podargus ocellatus plumiferus Gould, 1846, *Proc. Zool. Soc. London* p.104 (Clarence and MacLeay rivers, New South Wales)
Podargus ocellatus intermedius Hartert, 1895, *Bull. Brit. Orn. Club* 5, p.x (Kirivina, Trobriand Islands)

Podargus ocellatus meeki Hartert, 1898, *Bull. Brit. Orn. Club* 8, p.8 (Sudest Island)
Podargus ocellatus inexpectatus Hartert, 1901, *Bull. Brit. Orn. Club* 12, p.24 (Ysabel Island, Solomon Islands)

IDENTIFICATION Length 32-48cm. A large, brownish Australasian frogmouth. Slightly sexually dimorphic. **At rest** Upperparts rufescent-brown, speckled brown and buff, spotted and streaked blackish-brown. No collar around hindneck. Wing-coverts rufescent-brown, speckled and spotted blackish, boldly spotted whitish. Scapulars buffish, distinctly spotted blackish-brown. Buffish supercilium extends around front of forehead above the bill. No submoustachial stripe. Underparts greyish-brown, barred brown and boldly spotted whitish or pale buff. At night, generally shows an orange eyeshine in artificial light. **In flight** Tail long and pointed. Both sexes lack white markings on wings and tail. **Similar species** Rufous-phase Tawny Frogmouth (2) is generally large, bulkier and more streaked, less boldly spotted whitish on the wing-coverts with a weaker or no supercilium, and appears shorter-tailed; at night, generally shows a reddish eyeshine in artificial light.

VOICE The song (perhaps call) of the male is a series of up to nine mournful *kooo* notes (possibly nominate race only), reminiscent of a distant train whistle, or a series of liquid *koor-loo, koo-loo, koo-look* or *whoor-loop* notes, usually even but occasionally rising slightly in pitch. The song is often given in short bursts, but during the breeding season it may continue monotonously for long periods. The female has a similar but harsher song (call). Sings from perches such as branches in trees and low hanging vines. May be heard predominantly at dusk and dawn but throughout the night during the breeding season.

Another call frequently given by both sexes, mainly during the breeding season, is an accelerating series of c. 10 'gobbling' notes, either rising in pitch and becoming jumbled at the end, or descending in pitch and trailing away. This gobbling is occasionally preceded or succeeded by rapid *woolook, kook* or *coop* notes, and may function as a warning of territory or nest-site occupancy; it also occasionally ends with bill-snaps.

The birds also give a liquid *woo-woo-woo-woo-wooa* (male) or *wa-wa-wa-wa-wa* (female) that descends slightly in pitch and ends with bill-snapping. These calls may be similar to, or the same as, one of the above. In New Guinea, another vocalisation is described as a hoarse, mournful *u-woa-woa*.

Other calls include a monotonous, liquid trill, a shorter, loud and high-pitched trill or *brrrr* and short barking *chuck* notes. In response to the playback of its song, the presumed male gives slow, high-pitched *oom-oom-oom* notes.

At the nest, males and females feeding each other make soft, squeaking, hissing and rasping sounds. Adults also make hissing sounds when alarmed or whilst performing a threat/defence display. Whilst contact-calling ('dual singing') with its fledged offspring, an adult gives a low-pitched growl and the fledgling utters a monotonous series of *awhoo, kooo* or *koo-loooo* notes.

HABITAT Prefers dense, closed, lowland rainforest, but also occurs in isolated areas of such forest and in monsoon forest and scrub, tall secondary forest and forest edge. In Papua New Guinea it also inhabits eucalypt savanna and in northern Australia riverine or coastal, semi-deciduous mesophyll vine forest and notophyll vine forest. 0–1,600m.

In eastern Australia it occurs in tall to medium

subtropical rainforest with thick canopy cover, and often prefers areas containing steep gullies and running water. Occasionally found in open, sclerophyll forest, or in plantations. 0–800m.

HABITS Crepuscular and nocturnal. Roosts inside dense, closed forest on the ground, on branches on or near the ground, on roots and fallen trees, amidst vines and low ferns or other epiphytes on horizontal branches, or on twigs or projections from a tree trunk a few metres above ground level, often tucking itself up against the trunk. Usually roosts singly but may occasionally roost in pairs or small family parties. Two or more birds roost shoulder-to-shoulder, chicks roosting in-between their parents. Roost-sites may be used for up to several days. If danger approaches, the roosting bird assumes an alarm posture by compressing its feathers, stretching its neck and head up and pointing head and bill upwards. Birds roosting close to a tree trunk press body and tail close to the trunk. If flushed from its roost, it flies up to a higher perch and sits lengthways along a branch, often in full view. After alighting it is often harassed or mobbed by other birds such as honeyeaters *Meliphaga*; when this happens, the bird assumes the alarm posture (see above) but with its mouth wide open.

Outside the breeding season, territories may be 8-18ha in size. Main activity is from dusk until mid-evening and just before dawn. During the middle part of the night it often keeps to the upper canopy. During the breeding season, however, or when there is a full moon, birds are usually active all night. Frequently perches across branches and occasionally sits on roadside posts. If threatened, performs a threat/defence display by spreading its wings. Hunts from low perches such as branches, stumps, posts, bare stems of hanging vines and emergent rocks. Foraging birds fly from perch to perch throughout their territory. Hunting birds glide down from a perch in a shallow dive and snap up their prey from the ground, tree-trunks, branches or foliage. Smaller food is eaten on the spot, while larger prey is carried back to a perch to be battered against a hard surface before being eaten. Occasionally hunts close to artificial lights, i.e. spotlight beams and gas lanterns.

FOOD Stoneflies, cockroaches (including Blattidae), earwigs, Orthoptera (including Gryllacrididae, Tettigoniidae and Stenopalmatidae), moths, moth larvae (e.g. Anthelidae), beetles (including Cerambycidae), spiders, bugs (including Cicadidae) and frogs. May also occasionally try to take micro-chiropterans and small birds (e.g. Pale-yellow Robin *Tregellasia capito*) caught in mist-nets.

BREEDING The breeding season is August–December throughout its range, covering the austral spring.

Permanently territorial. Breeding territories may be as small as a few hectares. Territorial birds may fall silent and be temporarily displaced by calling Tawny Frogmouths. Both sexes build the nest, collecting material by diving down and snapping off twigs and sticks, or by breaking off sticks above the nest-site. At night the adults regularly call (see Voice) from the nest-site. The nest is a small, shallow platform, c. 8-20cm in diameter and 2-4cm deep, constructed with twigs, sticks, vine tendrils, grasses, lichens and moss. There is a very shallow depression in which to lay the eggs. Nest-sites are usually in the forks of branches in trees, c. 3-40m above ground, and may be used for several years. Also nests in the crowns of epiphytes and once recorded building a nest of tiny twigs on the ground. Clutch 1-2, occasionally 3. Eggs elliptical, dull white, 32.0-55.0 x 25.4-35.0mm.

Incubation is by the male during the day, the female roosting up to 50m or more from the nest-site. Both sexes probably share duties during the night. The incubating (or brooding) bird is visited and fed every c. 15 minutes throughout the night. The incubation period is not known. Chicks semi-altricial and nidicolous; may possibly be fed several times after dusk, and again just before dawn. The fledging period is about 31 days. In northern Australia (Cape York Peninsula), it is normal for only one chick to fledge successfully. No further information available.

DESCRIPTION *P. o. ocellatus* **Adult male** Forehead, crown and nape rufescent-brown spotted blackish-brown, spots with buff tips. No collar around hindneck. Mantle, back, rump and uppertail-coverts rufescent-brown, speckled brown and buff, streaked or spotted blackish-brown, markings often tipped buffish. Primary coverts dark brown, barred or spotted tawny. Rest of wing-coverts rufescent-brown, speckled and spotted blackish. Occasionally greater coverts, median coverts and lower row of lesser coverts boldly spotted creamy white on tips of outerwebs. Scapulars buffish, speckled, barred or vermiculated brown and spotted blackish-brown at feather tips. Primaries brown, boldly spotted buff or tawny along outerwebs, plain or indistinctly barred buff or pale tawny along innerwebs. Secondaries brown, indistinctly mottled pale tawny or buff, especially along the outerwebs. Tertials rufescent-brown, mottled brown and spotted blackish-brown, spots tipped buffish. Tail rufescent-brown, mottled, barred and vermiculated blackish-brown. Supercilium white, or buff speckled brown, extending around front of forehead above the bill. Lores and ear-coverts rufous, plain or barred brown. Chin, throat and upper breast pale buff or greyish-white, narrowly barred brown. Breast greyish-brown barred brown, boldly spotted pale buff or creamy white, streaked and spotted blackish-brown. Often has rufescent-brown markings extending along the submoustachial stripe, sides of throat and breast and across the lower breast. Belly and flanks speckled and barred brown, boldly spotted pale buff or creamy white. Undertail-coverts pale buff or creamy white, vermiculated brown. Underwing-coverts buffish, marginal coverts barred brown. **Adult female** Similar to the male but plainer on the upperparts, with smaller blackish-brown spotting and plainer, browner or buffier-brown underparts, often showing very little pale buff or creamy white spotting. **Immature** Similar to the adults. **Juvenile** Upperparts rufous-brown, faintly barred white and blackish, underparts whitish, finely barred brown. **Chick** At hatching, covered in white down. **Bare parts** Iris red, reddish-brown, brown, yellow or orange; bill brownish-horn; legs and feet flesh or pinkish-brown.

MEASUREMENTS Wing (male) 170-232, (female) 168-198; tail (male) 144-166, (female) 136-181; bill (male) 30.2-34.2, (female) 29.8-33.5; tarsus (male) c. 18-26.8, (female) c. 18-23.5. Weight (male, two) 137-156g, (female) 132-141g.

MOULT Adults undertake a complete post-breeding moult. The primary moult is serially descendant, and is often suspended, frequently resulting in several overlapping sequences being active at the same time. The pattern of secondary moult has not been documented, and the tail moult appears to be irregular. Juveniles possibly have a partial post-breeding moult, immatures probably undergo a complete post-breeding moult, possibly in their second year.

GEOGRAPHICAL VARIATION Six races are currently recognised.

P. o. ocellatus Length 32-35.5cm. Described above. Some individuals (both sexes) are browner than others.

P. o. marmoratus Length 38-41cm. Similar to the nominate race but longer-tailed. Also has longer facial bristles and yellower irides. Some males often have the underparts more boldly spotted whitish. Wing (male) 178-191, (female) 173-189; tail (male) 175-207, (female) 168-207. Weight (male, one) 163g, (female) 131-142g.

P. o. plumiferus (Plumed Frogmouth) Length 45-48cm. The largest race. Wing (male) 230-243, (female) 200-229; tail (male) 229-250, (female) 202-251. Weight (male) 217-286g, (female) 147-238g. Some authorities consider this form to be a colour variation of the nominate race of Tawny Frogmouth, others consider it to be a full species.

P. o. intermedius Length 40-42.5cm. Similar to the nominate race but larger. Males (perhaps Fergusson Island only) are occasionally paler than the nominate race, being greyer on the upperparts and whiter on the underparts. Wing (male) 208-243, (female) (three) 195-207; tail (male) 189-202, (female, two) 195. Weight no data.

P. o. meeki Intermediate in size between the nominate race and *intermedius*. Females are always brownish and never tinged rufous. Wing (male) (one) 197, (female) 179-185, unsexed 190-195; tail (male, one) 173, (female, one) 158, unsexed 167-180. Weight no data.

P. o. inexpectatus Similar to *intermedius* but has rounder white spots on the wing-coverts. Males are also darker and plainer. Larger than the nominate race. One female (perhaps immature) taken from Bougainville in January is heavily tinged chestnut, especially on the upperparts. Wing (male) 202-235, (female) 196-220; tail (male) 165-192, (female) 150-190. Weight no data.

DISTRIBUTION AND MOVEMENTS An Australasian species, ranging from New Guinea to the Solomon Islands, south to north-eastern and eastern Australia.

P. o. ocellatus Western New Guinea islands (Waigeo, Salawati and Misool), Irian Jaya (including Yapen and Meos Num Islands in Geelvink Bay), Aru Islands and Papua New Guinea. Sedentary.

P. o. marmoratus Extreme NE Australia (N Queensland, on the eastern side of the Cape York Peninsula,

south to the McIlwraith Range). Sedentary.

P. o. plumiferus CE Australia (coastal forests of SE Queensland and NE New South Wales, from Gympie south to the MacLeay River, although habitat there now largely unsuitable, and inland to the eastern scarp of the Great Dividing Range). Sedentary.

P. o. intermedius Trobriand Islands and the D'Entrecasteaux Archipelago (Goodenough Island, Fergusson Island and Normanby Island). Sedentary.

P. o. meeki Louisiade Archipelago (Tagula Island = Sudest Island). Sedentary.

P. o. inexpectatus Solomon Islands (Bougainville Island, Choiseul Island and Isabel Island). Sedentary.

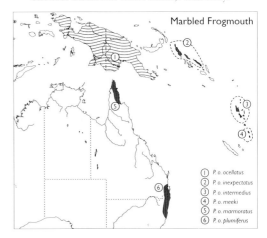

Marbled Frogmouth

1 P. o. ocellatus
2 P. o. inexpectatus
3 P. o. intermedius
4 P. o. meeki
5 P. o. marmoratus
6 P. o. plumiferus

STATUS Not uncommon in Papua New Guinea, uncommon on the Solomon Islands (Bougainville Island), moderately abundant in north-eastern Australia and rare in central-eastern Australia. Australian populations may be susceptible to loss of habitat through logging and forest clearance. No data available from other regions.

REFERENCES Atherton *et al.* (1980), Beehler *et al.* (1986), Beruldsen (1980, 1993), Coates (1985), Davis & Beehler (1993), Higgins (in press), Holmes (1981), McAllan (1995), Meggs (1993), Rand & Gilliard (1967), Schodde & Mason (1981, 1997), Smith *et al.* (1993, 1994).

BATRACHOSTOMUS

Batrachostomus Gould, 1838, Icones Av. pt. 2, pl. [17] and text. Type by monotypy, *Podargus auritus* J.E.Gray 1829.

Ten species, occurring from southwestern India and Sri Lanka, through South-East Asia to the Philippines, Borneo, Sumatra and Java. They are replaced in New Guinea and Australia by the larger frogmouths of the genus *Podargus*. Sibley, Ahlquist and Monroe (1988) consider species in *Batrachostomus* to be distantly related to the *Podargus* frogmouths, and suggest that they be placed in a separate family, the Batrachostomidae. This view is supported by Mariaux and Braun (1996). Features that differentiate the *Batrachostomus* frogmouths include their smaller, rounder bills, their more rounded tails and their tufts of conspicuous bristles in front of the eyes and at the base of the bill. All species show sexual dimorphism with, in most, the females being brighter and the males duller. Arboreal. In some species, territorial calls are thought to be given by females rather than males. Nests are generally small pads of down, vegetation and other materials, often built out in the open on small branches. They usually feed by pouncing onto prey from a perch or by picking off food from branches and other surfaces.

5 LARGE FROGMOUTH
Batrachostomus auritus   **Plate 2**

Podargus auritus 'Vigors and Horsfield' J. E. Gray, 1829, in Griffith's *Anim. Kingd.* 7, p.114 and pl. (No locality = Sumatra)

IDENTIFICATION Length 39-42cm. A large, darkish frogmouth of South-East Asia. Sexes similar. **At rest** Upperparts chestnut-brown or light brown, distinctly spotted or vermiculated buffish on crown. Pale buffish collar around hindneck is barred brown and extends around lower throat. Wing-coverts chestnut-brown or light brown, boldly spotted white or buffish-white, spots edged blackish and often 'tear-drop' shaped. Scapulars chestnut-brown or light brown, with pale bars and blackish buff-tipped spots. Pale buffish stripe extends along side of crown from front of eye down side of nape. Pale buffish submoustachial stripe. Underparts rufescent-brown speckled brown, plain or spotted (sometimes boldly) buffish. **In flight** No information. Both sexes lack white markings on wings and tail. **Similar species** None except in Borneo, where Dulit Frogmouth (6) is smaller, darker and more chestnut in coloration: the crown is barred rather than spotted or vermiculated, the wing-coverts are less heavily spotted and the underparts are darker, more boldly marked.

VOICE The song is a series of 4-8 loud liquid trills, usually rising but occasionally even in pitch. Sings from perches in trees, up to c. 20m above ground. May be heard mainly at night. No further information available.

HABITAT Prefers the interiors of lowland forests. Occurs in primary forest, tall secondary forest, often with a dense and tangled middle and upper storey of creepers and vines, dipterocarp forest and alluvial forest. Occasionally frequents low bushes along rivers. 0-100m, occasionally at c. 250m. In Borneo, calling birds apparently tape-recorded at c. 1,000m may be worthy of further investigation.

HABITS Nocturnal. Roosts on branches in the forest canopy. Hunts from a perch by pouncing onto prey on the ground, or taking food from branches in trees. No further information available.

FOOD Cicadas and grasshoppers. No further data available.

BREEDING Breeding season December?–January in C Borneo. No published data available from other regions.
   The nest is constructed by matting together fine down into a thick, round pad. It is built on a slender branch of a shrub or small tree, up to 1.3m above ground. Clutch 1. Incubation is by the male during the day and generally by the female at night. No further information available.

DESCRIPTION Adult male Forehead, crown and nape chestnut-brown or light brown, spotted or vermiculated buffish, markings bordered dark brown. Collar around hindneck pale buff or buffish-white, barred brown. Mantle and back chestnut-brown or light brown, finely speckled brown. Rump and uppertail-coverts chestnut-brown or light brown, barred pale chestnut-brown or brown, bars bordered dark brown. Alula brown, barred pale tawny along outerweb, primary coverts brown, washed chestnut at tips. Rest of wing-coverts chestnut-brown or light brown, speckled brown. Greater coverts, median coverts and lower row of lesser coverts boldly spotted white or buffish-white at tips, spots edged blackish and often 'tear-drop' shaped. Scapulars broad with pointed tips, chestnut-brown or light brown, with pale bars bordered brown, ends spotted blackish tipped buff, although buff often disappears with wear. Primaries brown, washed tawny at tips and spotted tawny-buff or tawny-brown along outerwebs. Secondaries brown on innerwebs, tawny speckled and barred brown on outerwebs and tips. Tertials chestnut-brown or light brown, with pale bars bordered brown. Tail brown or tawny-brown, with distinct pale bars bordered brown or blackish-brown. Sides of crown from front of eye to side of nape pale buffish, often speckled brown. Submoustachial stripe pale buffish, often speckled brown. Lores and ear-coverts chestnut-brown or pale brown. Centre of chin buff tinged chestnut or brown, sides of chin and whole of throat rufescent-brown. On lower throat 1-4 pale buffish bands are a continuation of the hindneck collar. Breast rufescent-brown speckled brown, occasionally boldly spotted pale buff. Belly and flanks pale rufescent-brown or buffish-brown, speckled brown, feathers often narrowly tipped buff. Undertail-coverts pale buff tinged brown or cinnamon, plain or barred brownish. Underwing-coverts brownish spotted cinnamon-white. **Adult female** Similar to the male but often duller and plainer. **Immature** Presumably similar to the adults. **Juvenile** Paler and plainer than the adults, with no collar around the hindneck and no spotting on the upperparts, wing-coverts and scapulars. **Chick** Not described. **Bare parts** Iris white? or brown; bill horn; legs and feet yellowish.

MEASUREMENTS Wing (male) 247-279, (female) 247-279; tail (male) 185-213, (female) 185-213; bill (male) 35.5-37.4, (female) 35.5-37.3; tarsus (male) 23.4-25.3, (female) 23.4-25.3. Weight no data.

MOULT The primary moult is serially descendant. No further data available.

GEOGRAPHICAL VARIATION Monotypic. Individual variation is evident in coloration: some birds are darker than others, some more heavily washed cinnamon, especially on the underparts. The amount and size of the spotting on the upperparts and wing-coverts are also variable.

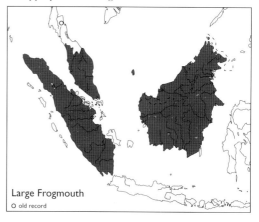

Large Frogmouth
○ old record

DISTRIBUTION AND MOVEMENTS A little known species confined to south-eastern Asia: Peninsular Thailand (Nakhon Si Thammarat), Malay Peninsula, northern Natuna Islands, Sumatra and Borneo. Sedentary.

STATUS Extremely rare in Thailand (perhaps only one record). Rarely recorded on the Malay Peninsula although still occurs in forest fragments around Kuala Lumpur. Local and very uncommon in Borneo and possibly threatened in Sumatra, where there are few records.

REFERENCES Mann (in prep.), Medway & Wells (1976), van Marle & Voous (1988), Smythies (1981), Stresemann (1937), Stresemann & Stresemann (1966).

---

6   DULIT FROGMOUTH
Batrachostomus harterti   Plate 2

Batrachostomus harterti Sharpe, 1892, *Ibis* p.323 (Mt Dulit, Borneo)

IDENTIFICATION Length 34-37cm. A large, darkish frogmouth, endemic to Borneo. Sexes similar. **At rest** Upperparts chestnut-brown, distinctly barred buffish on crown. Narrow buffish collar around hindneck. Wing-coverts chestnut-brown, boldly spotted buffish-white, spots bordered blackish. Scapulars tawny, barred brown and spotted blackish, black spots usually marked buffish-white on distal edge. Underparts chestnut-brown barred buffish, becoming pale brown boldly spotted greyish-buff or cinnamon-buff on belly and flanks, markings often T-shaped. **In flight** No information. Both sexes lack white markings on wings and tail. **Similar species** Large Frogmouth (5) is larger, paler and less chestnut in coloration; the crown is more spotted or vermiculated, rather than barred, the wing-coverts are more heavily spotted (spots often more 'tear-drop' shaped) and the underparts are paler and plainer.

VOICE Undescribed.

HABITAT Prefers submontane forests, occurring in both primary and secondary growths. 300–1,500m.

HABITS Nocturnal. No further information available.

FOOD No data available.

BREEDING No information available.

DESCRIPTION Adult male Forehead, crown and nape chestnut-brown, boldly barred pale buff. Distinct, narrow buffish collar around hindneck. Mantle and back chestnut-brown, speckled and faintly barred dark brown. Rump and uppertail-coverts chestnut-brown, broadly but often faintly barred dark brown. Lesser coverts chestnut-brown. Alula brown, barred pale tawny along outerweb, primary coverts brown, washed chestnut at tips. Median and greater coverts chestnut-brown, boldly spotted buffish-white bordered black at the centre of the feather-tips. Scapulars broad with pointed tips, tawny barred brown, with a blackish spot tipped buffish-white at the tip. Primaries brown, boldly spotted tawny along outerwebs; P4-P2 tipped buffish-white with a brown subterminal band, markings restricted to the centre of the feather-tips (perhaps on immature birds only). Secondaries and tertials brown, broadly barred tawny along outerwebs. Tail brownish-tawny broadly barred tawny, bars edged dark brown. Lores and ear-coverts chestnut-brown. Chin buff tinged chestnut. Throat and upper breast chestnut-brown, boldly barred buffish. Lower breast similar but buffish bars often T-shaped. Belly and flanks pale brown speckled brown, boldly spotted greyish-buff or cinnamon-buff, markings often T-shaped.

Undertail-coverts cinnamon-buff, lightly speckled and barred brown. Underwing-coverts brown barred buffish. **Adult female** Similar to the male but slightly darker and smaller, although perhaps longer-winged and -tailed (see below). Lacks the markings on the tips of P4-P2 and the underparts are more heavily speckled and vermiculated brown. **Immature** and **Juvenile** Not described. **Chick** Not known. **Bare parts** Iris dark brown; bill horn; legs and feet creamy horn.

MEASUREMENTS Wing (male, one) 216, (female) 229-244; tail (male, one) 150, (female) 165-169; bill (male, one) 30.2, (female, one) 29.6; tarsus (male, one) 21.1, (female) no data. Weight no data.

MOULT The primary moult is serially descendant. No further data available.

GEOGRAPHICAL VARIATION Monotypic.

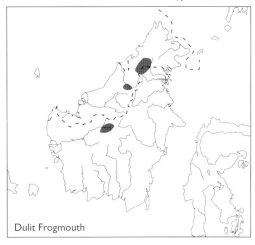

Dulit Frogmouth

DISTRIBUTION AND MOVEMENTS Endemic to the forests of central Borneo: Known only from Sarawak (Mt Dulit, Usun Apau Plateau and the Kelabit uplands) and Kalimantan Barat (Mt Liang Kubung). Sedentary.

STATUS No data available. Possibly not common, but under-recorded and little known. Only eight specimens apparently exist in museum collections.

REFERENCES Mann (in prep.), Smythies (1981), Stresemann (1937), Stresemann & Stresemann (1966).

---

7   PHILIPPINE FROGMOUTH
Batrachostomus septimus   Plate 3

Batrachostomus septimus Tweeddale, 1877, *Proc. Zool. Soc. London* p.542 (Pasananca, near Zamboanga, Mindanao)
Batrachostomus septimus microrhynchus Ogilvie-Grant, 1895, *Bull. Brit. Orn. Club* 4, p.41 (Mountains of Luzon = Mt Data, *ex Ibis*, 1899, p.384)
Batrachostomus septimus menagei Bourns and Worcester, 1894, *Occas. Pap. Minnesota Acad. Nat. Sci.* 1, p.11 (Philippine Islands; no exact locality)

IDENTIFICATION Length 24-26cm. A medium-sized brownish or rufescent frogmouth, endemic to the

Philippine Islands. Sexes similar, but females average darker and plainer than males. **At rest** Upperparts rufescent-brown tinged chestnut, barred tawny or buff on crown. Distinct buffish or buffish-white collar around hindneck. Wing-coverts rufescent-brown tinged chestnut, boldly spotted pale buff. Scapulars generally pale buff, speckled and vermiculated brown. Supercilium pale cinnamon-buff. Underparts rufescent-brown, tawny or buffish, speckled, spotted and barred pale buff and brown, with a broad pale buff band around the lower throat and another around the lower breast. **In flight** Both sexes lack white markings on wings and tail. **Similar species** None. There are no other frogmouths on the islands on which it occurs. It is replaced on Palawan by a race of Javan Frogmouth (13) which lacks the buffish bands around the lower throat and lower breast and the bold buffish spotting on the wing-coverts.

VOICE The song (perhaps call) of the male is a series of short, often crow-like *woah, waah, guaw* or *g-aw* notes. Also gives a short, even-pitched trill lasting c. 0.5 seconds. The call of the female is a short, loud 'mewing' cry that lasts c. 0.5 seconds and descends in pitch. No further information available.

HABITAT Prefers forests. No further information available. 0–2,500m.

HABITS Nocturnal. No published information available.

FOOD No data available.

BREEDING Breeding season May?–July? on Catanduanes; April?–July? on Samar; May?–July? on Leyte; April?–July? on Bohol and April?–June? on Mindanao. No data available from other islands.

Nests are small cups of vegetation, built on branches in trees. Clutch 1-2 ? Eggs 28.2 x 19.5mm. Incubating birds often sit crosswise on the nest branch. No further published information available.

DESCRIPTION *B. s. septimus* **Adult male** Forehead, crown and nape rufescent-brown tinged chestnut, barred tawny or buff and thinly barred brown. Distinct collar around hindneck buff or buffish-white, edged brown or blackish. Mantle and back rufescent-brown tinged chestnut, speckled and narrowly barred brown, some back feathers boldly spotted blackish with buff edges on feather-tips. Rump and uppertail-coverts dull rufescent-brown, thinly barred and vermiculated brown. Wing-coverts rufescent-brown tinged chestnut, speckled brown, boldly spotted pale buff on tips of outerwebs, each spot with a broad brown subterminal bar. Scapulars pale buff or tawny, speckled and vermiculated brown on innerwebs. Primaries and secondaries dull tawny on outerwebs, spotted pale buff and speckled brown, with innerwebs brown, mottled tawny on tips. Tertials tawny or rufescent-brown tinged chestnut and mottled brown. Tail rufescent-brown or tawny, speckled brown, barred pale tawny or tawny-buff, bars edged brown; central pair (R1) pale buff on outerwebs, boldly spotted pale buff on innerwebs; R2 boldly spotted pale buff along outerwebs. Supercilium pale cinnamon-buff barred brown. Lores and ear-coverts cinnamon-buff or rufescent-tawny. Chin and throat tawny-buff, barred or vermiculated brown. Broad band around lower throat pale buff, edged or barred brown. Breast rufescent-brown or tawny, speckled and barred brown and pale buff. Broad band around lower breast pale buff edged blackish-brown. Belly and flanks buff or tawny-buff, barred

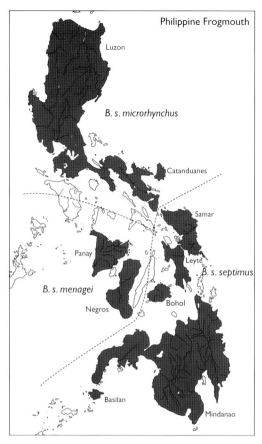

Philippine Frogmouth

Luzon

B. s. microrhynchus

Catanduanes

Samar

Panay

Leyte

B. s. septimus

B. s. menagei

Negros

Bohol

Basilan

Mindanao

and vermiculated brown. Undertail-coverts pale buff or cinnamon-buff. Underwing-coverts buff and tawny-buff, barred brown. **Adult female** Darker and plainer than the male. Has fewer and smaller buffish spots on the wing-coverts, the scapulars are usually duller, more tawny-buff, and the underparts are plainer, more tawny. **Immature** and **Juvenile** Not described. **Chick** Not described. **Bare parts** Iris yellowish or orange; bill brownish; legs and feet brownish.

MEASUREMENTS Wing (male) 153-167, (female) 145-165; tail (male) 104-126, (female) 103-115; bill (male) c. 30, (female) 25.6-26.5; tarsus (male) 19.2-21.8, (female) 17.0-20.8. Weight (male, one) 96.5g, (female, one) 81.0g.

MOULT No data available.

GEOGRAPHICAL VARIATION Three races are currently recognised.

B. s. septimus Described above. Little colour variation noted, although some males (perhaps Mindanao only) are paler and buffier, with bolder buffish markings on the crown.

B. s. microrhynchus Smaller than the nominate, with thinner, less distinct buffish bands around the hindneck, lower throat and lower breast and smaller spots on the wing-coverts. Some individuals are occasionally much darker than the nominate, almost blackish-brown in coloration (e.g. the type specimen of this race, a male). Wing (male) 128-133, (female) (three) 127-140; tail (male) 98-107, (female) (three) 100-104. Weight no data.

B. s. menagei Smaller and slightly darker than the nominate. Wing (male, one) 139, (female, one) 140, unsexed (one) 142; tail (male, one) 105, (female, one) 106. Weight of one (unsexed) 72.0g.

DISTRIBUTION AND MOVEMENTS A little known species endemic to the Philippine Islands, although absent from Palawan.

B. s. septimus Samar, Leyte, Bohol, Mindanao and Basilan. Sedentary.

B. s. microrhynchus Luzon and Catanduanes. Sedentary.

B. s. menagei Panay and Negros. Sedentary.

STATUS Little published data available but probably not common throughout its range, and possibly threatened by forest clearance.

REFERENCES Dickinson *et al.* (1991), Stresemann (1937).

---

8   GOULD'S FROGMOUTH
Batrachostomus stellatus   Plate 2

Podargus stellatus Gould, 1837, *Proc. Zool. Soc. London* p.43 (Java, error = Malacca)

IDENTIFICATION Length 23-26.5cm. A medium-sized Asian frogmouth. Sexes similar. **At rest** Upperparts tawny, chestnut or chestnut-brown. Narrow but distinct collar around hindneck white or buffish-white, barred or edged blackish-brown. Wing-coverts tawny, chestnut or chestnut-brown, boldly spotted whitish. Scapulars boldly marked with white or greyish-white oval-shaped spots. Supercilium buffish. Underparts tawny, boldly marked with buffish oval-shaped spots. **In flight** Both sexes lack white markings on wings and tail. **Similar species** Javan Frogmouth (13), race *affinis*, is smaller, the males greyer-brown and heavily spotted blackish, the female having darker underparts with bold whitish, oval-shaped spots edged blackish; both sexes lack bold whitish spots on the wing-coverts. Sunda Frogmouth (14) lacks bold whitish spots on the wing-coverts and usually has a white throat; males are greyer-brown and heavily spotted blackish, females have darker underparts with bold, whitish, oval-shaped spots edged blackish. Pale-headed Frogmouth (11) and Bornean Frogmouth (12) are slightly smaller, have longer facial bristles and ear-tufts, and are less densely or boldly spotted buffish on the underparts.

VOICE Highly vocal. Birds in Malaysia appear to have different vocalisations to those in Borneo.

In Borneo, the song (perhaps call) of the male is two short, whistled notes that rise in pitch and are connected by a wavering tremolo, *whaWWwee*, repeated at c. 7 second intervals. A variation is a loud whistle that rises in pitch in the middle but lacks the wavering quality, *whaAH-a*. In Malaysia, this species gives a double-noted whistle that rises in pitch on the second note, *woah-weeo*; occasionally, only gives the *weeo* note. Sings from branches in trees, c. 10-20m above ground. May be heard mainly at night.

In Malaysia, the female utters a variety of calls including a series of loud growls, a rapid series of high-pitched, yapping *wow* notes, 3-5 higher-pitched and faster *wek* notes and a descending whistled *weeeoh*.

A possible alarm call (presumably this species) is a series of 5-8 rising *whaAH* notes. When handled, utters a soft, kitten-like 'mew'.

HABITAT Prefers lowland and hill forests. Occurs in primary forest, rainforest and secondary forest. 0–500m.

HABITS Nocturnal. Often perches low down. Once recorded feeding by snapping at flying insects disturbed by other birds. No further information available.

FOOD Locusts, moths and beetles. No further data available.

BREEDING Breeding season June?–September? on the Malay Peninsula; late February?–July? in Borneo.

Nest-sites may be alongside footpaths in primary forest and as low as 1.3m above ground. Eggs elliptical and white, 28.0-30.5 x 20.0-21.7mm. A young bird was once seen sitting on the back of one of its parents, on the ground below their nest. No further information available.

DESCRIPTION Adult male Forehead, crown and nape rufescent-tawny. Narrow collar around hindneck white or buffish-white, barred or edged blackish-brown. Mantle and back rufescent-tawny. Rump and uppertail-coverts rufescent-tawny and either plain, or spotted pale buffish-tawny, or barred brown. Lesser coverts rufescent-tawny. Primary coverts brown. Alula brown, spotted rufescent-tawny along outerweb. Median and greater coverts rufescent-tawny, boldly spotted whitish on tips of outer-webs, spots bordered brown along upper edge. Scapulars rufescent-tawny, boldly marked with whitish or greyish-white oval-shaped spots which are bordered blackish-brown. Primaries brown, edged and spotted pale tawny or tawny-buff along outerwebs. Secondaries brown edged tawny and barred tawny-buff along outerwebs, bars edged blackish. Tertials rufescent-tawny, mottled brown and barred tawny-buff, bars edged blackish. Tail rufescent-tawny, broadly barred pale tawny, thinly edged and speckled brown on innerwebs of R5-R2 paler and plainer. Supercilium buffish. Lores and ear-coverts tawny-chestnut. Chin tawny or chestnut, often tinged buffish. Throat tawny, boldly spotted buffish and thinly barred brown. Breast tawny, boldly marked with pale buffish oval-shaped spots which are broadly bordered tawny. Belly and flanks similar to breast but buffish spots larger, with thinner tawny borders. Undertail-coverts buffish or buffish-white, plain but edged tawny or vermiculated brown. Underwing-coverts buffish barred blackish-brown, especially on marginal coverts. **Adult female** Similar to the male but may average darker and more reddish. **Immature** Similar to the adults but less boldly spotted on the scapulars and with plainer, paler (pale chestnut vermiculated brown) wing-coverts. **Juvenile** Similar to the immature but paler, especially on the underparts. **Chick** Not described. **Bare parts** Iris yellow (male) or brown (female); bill horn; legs and feet pinkish (male) or yellowish (female).

MEASUREMENTS Wing (male) 117-135, (female) 120-132; tail (male) 114-131, (female) 114-119; bill (male) 19.0-23.5, (female) 21.2-25.8; tarsus (male) 15.1-16.1, (female) 14.3-14.9. Weight unsexed (one) c. 48.5g.

MOULT The primary moult is serially descendant. No further data available.

GEOGRAPHICAL VARIATION Monotypic. There is some colour variation among adults of both sexes. Some individuals are more chestnut, others more chestnut-brown. Some authorities believe that birds from Borneo have whiter abdomens with more prominent rufous edges to the feathers, although this is not always evident on museum specimens.

127

Gould's Frogmouth

DISTRIBUTION AND MOVEMENTS South-east Asia in peninsular Thailand and Malaysia, Natuna Besar Island, Borneo and Sumatra (including Riau and Lingga Archipelagos). Sedentary.

STATUS Possibly not common anywhere within its range.

REFERENCES Croxall (1969), Mann (in prep.), van Marle & Voous (1988), Medway & Wells (1976), Smythies (1981), Stresemann (1937), Stresemann & Stresemann (1966).

---

9   CEYLON FROGMOUTH
Batrachostomus moniliger   Plate 3

Batrachostomus moniliger 'Layard', Blyth, 1849, *J. Asiatic Soc. Bengal* 18, pt. 2, p.806 (Ceylon). The date of publication is as above, not 1846 as given by some authors.

IDENTIFICATION Length 22.5-24.5cm. A medium-sized, greyish-brown frogmouth, confined to Sri Lanka and south-western India. Sexually dimorphic. **At rest** Upperparts greyish-brown or brownish, spotted blackish. Narrow greyish-white or buffish collar around hindneck. Wing-coverts greyish-brown or brownish, boldly spotted greyish-white or buffish. Scapulars whitish, speckled and vermiculated brown, boldly spotted blackish. Supercilium buffish. Row of white or pale buff spots around throat. Underparts greyish-brown or brownish, boldly spotted white or pale buff on belly and flanks. **In flight** Both sexes lack white markings on wings and tail. **Similar species** None within range.

VOICE The song is a rapid series of 10-15 soft, liquid *kooroo* or *coroo* notes. Occasionally sings in shorter bursts of 4-5 notes. Sings from branches in trees, 0.5-7m above ground. May be heard mainly at night but also sings at dusk and dawn. The call of the male is a plaintive whistle, *wheeow*. The call of the female is a slow screech that descends slightly in pitch towards the end, then rises sharply, *kaar-re-AH*. Adults also utter cat-like, rasping, hissing sounds. Chicks have a feeble chirping or chirruping call. No further information available.

HABITAT Prefers lowland and submontane forests. Occurs in dense, humid forest, thick, evergreen forest,

bamboo and 'eeta' forest with *Solanum* and *Strobilanthes*, thick bamboo forest and jungle and secondary forest with dense thickets and canebreaks. Avoids disturbed forests and plantations. 0–1,800m.

HABITS Crepuscular and nocturnal. Roosts on branches up to c. 5m above ground, perching across a branch with its body held at a slight angle. Roost-sites are usually in thickets, often bamboo. If danger approaches, the roosting bird assumes an alarm posture by slowly stretching up its neck and head, pointing its head and bill upwards. It then appears to remain perfectly still but will very slowly move its head to keep the threat in view. If the danger persists, it may perform a defence display by facing the intruder, gaping, then slowly closing its mouth before finally snapping shut its bill. If disturbed at the roost, it often looks from side to side, then bobs its head up and down 2-3 times, neck feathers ruffled and the tufts of feathers above its eyes raised. It may then fly off. If flushed from its roost, it only flies a short distance before re-alighting. Often roosts in pairs, the two birds huddled together but usually facing away from each other. Feeds by taking prey from the ground or from branches in trees; a pair were once noted capturing beetles flying about a tree.

FOOD Moths, beetles and Orthoptera (including Acrididae). No further data available.

BREEDING Breeding season January–April in S India; September?–April in Sri Lanka.
The nest is a small pad, c. 6cm in diameter, with a slight depression in which the egg is laid. The nest is made of dead leaves, pieces of bark and dry wood, lichen, other vegetation and down feathers from the adult birds. It is placed on a horizontal branch or in a fork of a small tree or sapling, c. 2-5m above ground, and is often shaded by clumps of foliage. Clutch 1. Egg elliptical and white, 24.4-31.1 x 16.3-22.0mm. The male incubates during the day, the female at night. The adult broods its chick in a relaxed posture, with its head hunched back onto its shoulders and facing forwards with its eyes open. If danger approaches, it slowly assumes an alarm posture by stretching its neck and head up, pointing its head and bill upwards, closing its eyes and then 'freezing'. If the danger approaches too closely, the brooding adult may perform a defence display by gaping and fluffing up its feathers. No further information available.

DESCRIPTION Adult male Forehead, crown and nape greyish-brown, vermiculated, barred and speckled greyish-white or buffish, boldly spotted blackish (spots with buffish upper edges). Narrow greyish-white or buffish collar around hindneck, often edged blackish. Mantle, back and rump greyish-brown, speckled greyish-white, buff and cinnamon, boldly spotted blackish. Uppertail-coverts similar to rest of upperparts but occasionally plainer and lacking the blackish spotting. Lesser coverts blackish-brown, speckled and mottled tawny, chestnut or cinnamon. Primary coverts brown, speckled and spotted buffish on outerwebs. Median and greater coverts greyish-brown, speckled brown and occasionally washed cinnamon, boldly spotted greyish-white, white or pale buff on tips of outerwebs. Scapulars whitish, speckled and vermiculated blackish-brown or brown, boldly spotted blackish at tips; spots edged or bordered tawny or cinnamon. Primaries brown, boldly spotted buffish along outerwebs and speckled buffish at tips. Secondaries brown, mottled whitish or greyish-buff on outerwebs. Tertials brown, densely mottled greyish-white or greyish-buff, spotted blackish on tips. Tail greyish-brown, mottled and thinly barred blackish and often spotted buff on tips. Supercilium buffish. Lores and ear-coverts buffish or pale cinnamon, barred blackish-brown. Chin buffish barred brown. Throat buffish or greyish-brown, speckled and spotted blackish-brown. Row of pale buff or whitish spots around lower throat; spots with brown subterminal bar. Breast greyish-brown, speckled and vermiculated brown, boldly spotted blackish-brown. Belly and flanks greyish-brown, speckled and vermiculated blackish-brown, boldly spotted pale buff or whitish. Undertail-coverts buff, lightly spotted or barred blackish-brown. Underwing-coverts buffish or greyish-buff, barred brown. **Adult female** Tawnier, browner or more chestnut than the male and often plainer, with smaller and fewer blackish spots on the upperparts. Often lacks a whitish collar around the hindneck, and has smaller whitish spots on the median and greater coverts, buffier scapulars and smaller and fewer whitish spots around the lower throat. **Immature** Similar to the adults but narrowly barred brown on the upperparts. **Juvenile** Paler than the adults and heavily barred or vermiculated brown. **Chick** At hatching, covered in white down. **Bare parts** Iris yellowish (perhaps male) or brownish (perhaps female); bill horn; legs and feet dusky-yellow or pinkish.

MEASUREMENTS Wing (male) 113-127, (female) 112-127; tail (male) 97-110, (female) 94-117; bill (male) 19.0-20.4, (female) 18.8-20.9; tarsus (male) 14.4-15.9, (female) 14.5-15.2. Weight (male, one) 46.5g, (female, one) 59.0g.

MOULT The primary moult is serially descendant. No further data available.

GEOGRAPHICAL VARIATION None, monotypic. There is some colour variation amongst adults of both sexes. Males are often tawnier than as described, especially on the upperparts, wing-coverts, throat and breast. Some individuals are more chestnut than others. Females are occasionally darker and browner.

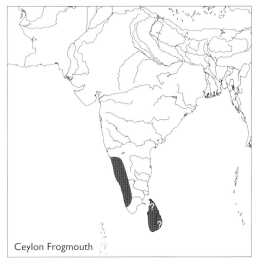

Ceylon Frogmouth

DISTRIBUTION AND MOVEMENTS Confined to southwestern India and Sri Lanka, where it is the only frogmouth present.

SW India (Western Ghats from c. 15°N in North Kanara

district, south to Trivandrum district, Kerala) and Sri Lanka (except in the north and south-east). Sedentary.

STATUS Not common but possibly under-recorded.

REFERENCES Ali & Ripley (1970), Kannan (1993), Legge (1880), Oates (1890), Phillips (1947), Stresemann (1937), Stresemann & Stresemann (1966), Sugathan (1981).

---

10   HODGSON'S FROGMOUTH
Batrachostomus hodgsoni   Plate 4

Otothrix hodgsoni G. R. Gray, 1859, *Proc. Zool. Soc. London* p.101, pl.CLII, Aves (Northern India = Darjeeling)
Batrachostomus hodgsoni indochinae Stresemann, 1937, *Mitt. Zool. Mus. Berlin* 22, p.320 (Dak-To, Annam)

IDENTIFICATION Length 24.5-27.5cm. A medium-sized Asian frogmouth. Sexually dimorphic. **At rest** Upperparts and wing-coverts greyish-brown tinged tawny or buff, heavily spotted blackish. Scapulars whitish, edged and spotted blackish. Narrow white or pale buff collar around hindneck. Supercilium buffish. Underparts greyish-brown tinged tawny or buff, boldly spotted creamy white or buffish and speckled blackish. Females are rufescent-tawny and plainer. **In flight** Both sexes lack white markings on wings and tail. **Similar species** Javan Frogmouth (13) is extremely similar but generally smaller, with shorter frontal bristles and ear-tufts and a deeper, heavier bill.

VOICE The song (perhaps call) is a series of soft, slightly trilled whistles that rise in pitch: *whaaeee, whaaow, wheeow* or *wheeow-a*. Up to 10 whistles may be given at a time, with a brief pause of 1-7 seconds between each. Also gives a chuckling *whoo* call. No further information available.

HABITAT Prefers submontane and montane forests but may also apparently sometimes be found in lowland forests. Occurs in dense, humid primary forest, mature secondary formations, and on wooded hills and steep slopes with a thick understorey. 300–1,800m.

HABITS Crepuscular and nocturnal. Often solitary. Roosts on branches in trees. Roost-sites are usually inside thick forest. If disturbed at its roost, it slowly assumes an alarm posture by stretching up its neck and head, pointing its head and bill upwards and 'freezing'. Forages in forest glades and clearings. Feeds by taking prey from the ground and from branches in trees; also hawks for insects in flight. No further information available.

FOOD Beetles and moths. No further data available.

BREEDING Breeding season April–July in NE India and possibly also Thailand. No data available from other regions.
    Both sexes help to build the nest, which is a flat construction c. 9cm in diameter, with a slight depression in which to lay the eggs. The nest is made with lichens and moss, overlaid with soft plant material. It is placed on a horizontal branch, up to c. 10m above the ground. Clutch 1-2. Eggs elliptical and white, 23.6-31.1 x 16.3-22.0mm. Incubation is usually by the male during the day and by the female (or perhaps both sexes) at night. No further information available.

DESCRIPTION *B. h. hodgsoni* **Adult male** Forehead, crown and nape greyish-brown, barred tawny and buff, heavily spotted blackish-brown. Collar around hindneck pale buff or whitish, barred brown. Mantle and back greyish-brown tinged tawny or tawny-buff, heavily spotted blackish. Rump and uppertail-coverts greyish-brown tinged tawny or tawny-buff, barred or vermiculated blackish. Primary coverts brown, boldly spotted buff along outerwebs. Rest of wing-coverts greyish-brown tinged tawny or tawny-buff, speckled brown and heavily spotted blackish. Scapulars creamy white or whitish, often on outerwebs only, edged and tipped blackish. Primaries brown, boldly spotted tawny or buff along outerwebs, mottled tawny or buff on tips of both webs. Secondaries brown, boldly spotted tawny or buff with brown speckling along outerwebs, mottled tawny or buff on tips. Tertials tawny-buff or buffish, mottled brown. Tail barred tawny and buff, bars speckled and edged brown. Supercilium buff. Lores and ear-coverts tawny barred brown. Chin and centre of throat buffish barred brown; sides of chin and throat tawny barred brown. Breast tawny, boldly spotted buff or creamy white, barred and speckled blackish. Belly, flanks and undertail-coverts buffish or creamy white, vermiculated and spotted blackish-brown. Underwing-coverts buffish barred brown. **Adult female** Generally rufescent-tawny on both upper- and underparts and plainer than the male. Has smallish white spots on the scapulars and the outerwebs of the primaries and secondaries are completely tawny. The throat and breast are distinctly marked with whitish spots narrowly bordered blackish. The tail is indistinctly barred with rows of blackish spots. **Immature** Perhaps similar to the adult female, but duller and barred dull blackish-brown on both the upperparts and underparts. **Juvenile** Upperparts cinnamon, heavily barred brown; underparts pale buffish, heavily barred brown. **Chick** At hatching, covered in rufous down. **Bare parts** Iris yellowish, buff, brown or grey; bill pinkish or yellowish-horn; legs and feet pinkish-flesh.

MEASUREMENTS Wing (male) 127-138, (female) 124-140; tail (male) 130-146, (female) 134-149; bill (male) 17.9-19.0, (female) 15.7-18.9; tarsus (male) 16.1-17.3, (female) 16.3-17.3. Weight (male, one) 50g, (female) no data, unsexed (one) 51g.

MOULT No data available.

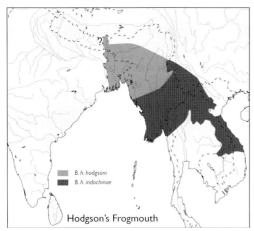

B. h. hodgsoni
B. h. indochinae

Hodgson's Frogmouth

GEOGRAPHICAL VARIATION Two races are currently recognised.

    B. h. hodgsoni Described above, with no colour

variation apparent.

    B. h. indochinae Averages smaller and shorter-tailed than the nominate. Females are more heavily spotted whitish on the underparts. Wing (male) 122-130, (female) 124-131; tail (male, one) 122, (female) 118-120. Weight no data.

DISTRIBUTION AND MOVEMENTS Confined to the forests of southern Asia.

    B. h. hodgsoni NE India (Sikkim east to Assam, south to Manipur), Bangladesh and N Burma. Possibly also occurs in E Nepal. Sedentary.

    B. h. indochinae S China (SW Yunnan), C Burma, NW Thailand, Laos and C Vietnam. Sedentary.

STATUS Little known and probably under-recorded throughout its range.

REFERENCES Ali & Ripley (1970), Oates (1890), Stresemann (1937).

---

11   PALE-HEADED FROGMOUTH
Batrachostomus poliolophus   Plate 3

Other name: Short-tailed Frogmouth

Batrachostomus poliolophus Hartert, 1892, *Notes Leyden Museum* 14, Apr., p.63 (Padang, Sumatra)

Forms a superspecies with Bornean Frogmouth, with which it was formerly considered conspecific.

IDENTIFICATION Length 20.5-22cm. A small, brownish frogmouth, endemic to Sumatra. Sexually dimorphic. **At rest** Upperparts of male rufescent-brown. Buffish-white collar around hindneck. Wing-coverts rufescent-brown, boldly spotted buffish-white on greater and median coverts. Scapulars very boldly spotted whitish. Underparts rufescent-brown boldly scalloped white on breast, generally buffish-white on belly and flanks, feathers edged brown or tawny. Female brighter, being rufescent-tawny all over, with fewer and smaller whitish spots on the wing-coverts, scapulars and underparts. Often has a narrower collar around the hindneck. **In flight** Both sexes lack white markings on wings and tail. **Similar species** Gould's Frogmouth (8) is slightly larger, more boldly and densely spotted buffish on the underparts, with shorter facial bristles and ear-tufts. Javan Frogmouth (13) is shorter-winged and has shorter facial bristles and ear-tufts: males are browner and distinctly spotted blackish, and both sexes are much less heavily spotted whitish on the underparts. Sunda Frogmouth (14) is larger: males are darker and heavily spotted blackish, and both sexes are less heavily spotted whitish on the underparts. Bornean Frogmouth (12), confined to Borneo, is less boldly spotted white on the underparts and has slightly more distinct markings on the tail; the male is browner.

VOICE The song (perhaps call) is a rather loud, undulating whistle that rises in pitch, followed by a series of 5-7 liquid *wa* notes, descending in pitch. No further information available.

HABITAT Prefers submontane forests, including primary forest and mixed pine forest. 600–1,400m.

HABITS Nocturnal. No further information available.

FOOD Insects. No further information available.

BREEDING Breeding season May?–August?

Nests in small trees, at the edges of forest clearings. The oval-shaped nest is placed in the fork of a branch, c. 5m above ground, and constructed with lichens, moss and down feathers. It is c. 7 x 5.5cm and c. 2.5cm deep, with a slight depression in which to lay the egg. Clutch 1. Egg 28.7 x 20.3mm. Incubation is by the male during the day. If danger approaches, the incubating bird slowly adopts an alarm posture by pointing its head and bill upwards and 'freezing', although it keeps its eyes open. No further information available.

DESCRIPTION Adult male Forehead, crown and nape rufescent-brown, finely barred and vermiculated brown. Collar on hindneck buffish-white edged dark brown, with a tawny subterminal band on the lower feathers. Mantle, back, rump and uppertail-coverts rufescent-brown, finely barred and vermiculated brown. Primary coverts dark brown. Lesser coverts rufescent-brown, finely barred, speckled and vermiculated brown. Median and greater coverts rufescent-brown speckled brown, boldly spotted buffish-white on tips (spots edged dark brown on the upper edge). Scapulars rufescent-brown speckled brown, often on upper half of innerwebs only, boldly spotted buffish-white on outerwebs, spots edged tawny and dark brown. Primaries brown on innerwebs, buff on outerwebs, tips speckled tawny. Secondaries brown, edged and speckled tawny on outerwebs. Tertials pale buffish-tawny speckled brown, tips with triangular buffish-white spots. Tail tawny, vermiculated brown; R5-R3 boldly tipped buffish-white with dark brown upper edges. Lores and ear-coverts rufescent-tawny. Chin and central throat buffish-white, sides of throat rufescent-tawny. Breast rufescent-brown vermiculated brown, boldly scalloped or spotted buffish-white. Belly, flanks and undertail-coverts buffish-white, many feathers edged tawny or dark brown. Underwing-coverts buffish-white. **Adult female** Rufescent-tawny all over, and plainer than male, with fewer and smaller white spots on the breast, wing-coverts and scapulars. The white feathers on the belly and flanks are edged rufescent-tawny. **Immature** and **Juvenile** Unknown. **Chick** Unknown. **Bare parts** Iris yellow; bill horn or brownish-horn; legs and feet flesh or pinkish.

MEASUREMENTS Wing (male, one) 135, (female, two) 133-136; tail (male, one) 93, (female, two) 94-98; bill (male, one) 20, (female, two) 18-20; tarsus (male, one) 17, (female, one) 17. Weight no data.

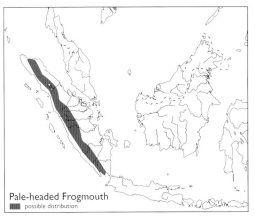

Pale-headed Frogmouth
■■■ possible distribution

MOULT One male (museum specimen) taken in mid-June appears to have the inner five primaries new, P6 nearly fully grown and the outer four primaries old, suggesting a descendant moult strategy. No further data available.

GEOGRAPHICAL VARIATION Monotypic.

DISTRIBUTION AND MOVEMENTS Endemic to Sumatra. Recorded from Aceh (Upper Mamas Valley), North Sumatra (Sibatuloteng, Simalungun and Berastagi), and West Sumatra (Mt Talamau in the Ophir district, Padang, Muara Sako and Sungailambat, Gunung Kerinci National Park). Sedentary.

STATUS Uncommon and little known.

REFERENCES Bartels (1938), van Marle & Voous (1988), Stresemann (1937).

---

12 BORNEAN FROGMOUTH
Batrachostomus mixtus   Plate 3

Other name: Sharpe's Frogmouth

Batrachostomus mixtus Sharpe, 1892, *Bull. Brit. Orn. Club* 1, Nov., p.4 (Mt Dulit, Borneo)

Forms a superspecies with Pale-headed Frogmouth, with which it was formerly considered conspecific.

IDENTIFICATION Length 20-22.5cm. A small, brownish frogmouth, endemic to Borneo. Sexually dimorphic. **At rest** Upperparts of male brown or light brown. Narrow white collar around the hindneck. Wing-coverts brown or light brown, boldly spotted whitish on greater coverts and some median coverts. Scapulars very boldly spotted whitish. Underparts light brown, boldly scalloped and spotted white. Female brighter, being rufescent-tawny all over, with fewer and smaller white spots on the wing-coverts, scapulars and underparts and with a narrower white collar around the hindneck. **In flight** Both sexes lack white markings on wings and tail. **Similar species** Gould's Frogmouth (8) is slightly larger, more boldly and densely spotted buffish on the underparts, with shorter facial bristles and ear-tufts. Javan Frogmouth (13) has shorter facial bristles and ear-tufts; males are distinctly spotted blackish, and are more boldly and densely spotted buffish on the underparts, while females are more boldly spotted whitish on the underparts. Sunda Frogmouth (14) is larger, with males darker and heavily spotted blackish, females more boldly spotted whitish on the underparts. Pale-headed Frogmouth (11) only occurs on Sumatra, has a slightly plainer tail, and are more boldly spotted whitish on the underparts: the male is more rufescent.

VOICE The song (perhaps call) is a whistled *weeow* or *weee-o*, repeated once every c. 3 seconds, also sometimes a whistled *weeow-w-w* that wavers towards the end of the note. Similar vocalisations also described include a series of short, whistled *tsiiu* notes, and a series of 3-7 disyllabic whistles, with each whistle being slightly longer than the preceeding one, i.e. *tsiutsiu, tsiiutsiiu, tsiiiutsiiiu*. Calls from perches. May be heard predominately at night. A series of high pitched *chiok, chiok, chiok* notes given in flight or whilst perched may possibly be an alarm call. No further information available.

HABITAT Prefers submontane and montane forests. 610–1,675m.

HABITS Nocturnal. No further information available.

FOOD Beetles and Orthoptera. No further data available.

BREEDING Breeding season March?–June?

The small, conical nest is constructed with small pieces of vegetation and has a saucer-shaped cup c. 7.5cm wide. The nest is built on a thin, horizontal branch, away from the trunk. The male incubates by day, sitting in an upright but hunched posture, with his eyes open. The female probably incubates at night. No further information available.

DESCRIPTION Adult male Forehead, crown and nape brown or light brown, finely speckled buff and pale cinnamon. Distinct, thin to very broad collar around hindneck white barred brown. Mantle, back, rump and uppertail-coverts brown or light brown, finely speckled dark brown, buff and pale cinnamon. Lesser coverts rufous or mahoganey-red, finely speckled buff and pale cinnamon. Rest of wing-coverts brown or light brown, finely speckled brown, buff and pale cinnamon, with the greater coverts and some median coverts boldly spotted whitish at the tips, the spots having thin, blackish-brown borders. Scapulars brown or light brown, with large whitish oval spots bordered blackish-brown. Primaries brown, P10-P5 smudged alternately tawny and buff along outerwebs, P4-P1 densely mottled tawny along outerwebs. Secondaries brown, mottled tawny along outerwebs. Tertials brown or light brown, finely speckled buff and pale cinnamon. Tail brown or light brown, tinged cinnamon-rufous and speckled brown; R5 boldly barred pale buff across both webs; R4-R2 boldly barred pale buff across innerwebs only; central pair (R1) broadly but indistinctly barred greyish-brown. Lores and ear-coverts pale tawny. Chin and throat pale buff, sides of chin and throat light brown or pale cinnamon finely speckled brown. Breast, belly, flanks and undertail-coverts light brown or pale cinnamon finely speckled brown and boldly scalloped buffish-white or pale buff, feathers thinly edged or tipped dark brown. Underwing-coverts dirty buffish-white barred brown. **Adult female** Rufescent-tawny all over, with a thinner, whitish collar around the hindneck, fewer and smaller white spots on the wing-coverts and scapulars, a less well-marked tail and much less whitish scalloping or spotting on the underparts. **Immature** Perhaps similar to the adults. **Juvenile** Not described. **Chick** Not described. **Bare parts** Iris yellow; bill brownish or brownish-horn; legs and feet flesh or brownish.

MEASUREMENTS Wing (male) 120-132, (female) 120-124; tail (male) 95-102, (female, one) 91; bill (male, one) 18.1, (female) 17.8-20.1; tarsus (male, one) 14.3, (female) 15.5-15.6. Weight no data.

MOULT No data available.

GEOGRAPHICAL VARIATION Monotypic.

DISTRIBUTION AND MOVEMENTS A little-known species, endemic to Borneo. Recorded from Sarawak (Mt Dulit, Mt Mulu, Merapok Hills in the Lewas District, Paku, Saribas River, River Bulungan, Arent, Koyan River and Kelabit Plateau), Sabah (Kinabalu National Park) and Kalimantan Timur (Badang on the Bahau River, Kayan Mentarang National Park, and the River Kayan region), and Kalimantan Selatan (Gunung Karokangan in the Muratus Mountains). Sedentary.

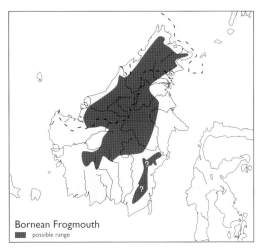

Bornean Frogmouth
▓ possible range

STATUS No data available, but probably not common.

REFERENCES Davison (1997), Mann (in prep.), Smythies (1981), Stresemann (1937).

13   JAVAN FROGMOUTH
Batrachostomus javensis   Plate 4

Other name: Horsfield's Frogmouth

Podargus Javensis Horsfield, 1821, *Trans. Linn. Soc. London* 13, pt. 1, p.141 (Java)
Batrachostomus javensis continentalis Stresemann, 1937, *Mitt. Zool. Mus. Berlin* 22, p.327 (Toungyeen, Tenasserim)
Batrachostomus javensis chaseni Stresemann, 1937, *Mitt. Zool. Mus. Berlin* 22, p.326 (Taguso, Palawan)
Batrachostomus javensis affinis Blyth, 1847, *J. Asiatic Soc. Bengal* 16, pt. 2, p.1180 (Malaya)

Formerly considered conspecific with Sunda Frogmouth but sympatric with it in Sumatra and Borneo.

IDENTIFICATION Length 20-23cm. A small to medium-sized brownish frogmouth, occurring throughout much of South-East Asia. Sexually dimorphic. **At rest** Upperparts and wing-coverts brown, speckled buff and white and distinctly spotted blackish. Scapulars boldly marked with whitish oval-shaped spots. Whitish collar around hindneck and distinct whitish supercilium. Underparts brown, speckled and spotted buff, cinnamon and white, becoming generally whitish with brown barring and brown and black spots on belly and flanks. Females are brighter, plainer and tawnier, with smaller whitish spots on the scapulars and less white on the underparts. **In flight** Flight undulating. Both sexes lack white markings on wings and tail. **Similar species** Sunda Frogmouth (14) is extremely similar but larger: males are less distinctly spotted blackish or brown on the underparts. Hodgson's Frogmouth (10) is also extremely similar but is generally larger, with longer frontal bristles and ear-tufts and a slighter bill. Pale-headed Frogmouth (11) is longer-winged with longer facial bristles and ear-tufts and heavier whitish spotting on the underparts; males are plainer and more rufescent. Bornean Frogmouth (12) has longer facial bristles and ear-tufts. Males are plainer and less heavily spotted buffish on the underparts, females are less boldly spotted whitish on the underparts. Philippine Frogmouth (7) has buffish bands around the lower throat and lower breast and has bold buffish spotting on the wing-coverts. See also Gould's Frogmouth (8).

VOICE The call of the male is a series of plaintive whistles (see below). Also gives a series of *KWAHa* or *e-ah* notes or of more drawn-out *kwaaha* notes. Calls from perches above ground. May be heard at dusk, dawn and throughout the night. Another call given is a loud *whah*. The call of the female is a descending series of almost laugh-like *gra* notes, *grra-ga-ga*. Pairs together utter soft trills. This species may also give a double-noted, crow-like *kaarrr-kaarrr*. If alarmed, gives a *trüt, trüt, trüt* call.

Calls of male Javan Frogmouths depend on subspecies. *B. j. javensis*: a series of long, hoarse whistles, each note starting flat and then rising in pitch at the end; *B. j. continentalis*: a series of long, mournful and often warbled whistles, each note starting flat, then descending and rising in pitch; *B. j. chaseni*: a series of long, drawn-out whistles, each note starting flat and then descending in pitch at the end, also a series of mournful whistles similar to those given by *continentalis*; *B. j. affinis*: a series of short, often warbled, whistles, each note descending then rising in pitch.

HABITAT Prefers lowland and hill forests, with thick understorey, but may also be found at higher altitudes (see below). Occurs in both evergreen and deciduous rainforests, and also inhabits secondary growth. 0–800m, throughout much of range, 0-1700m in W and C Java, and up to 2,150m in E Java. *B. j. affinis* occurs to 1600m.

HABITS Crepuscular and nocturnal. Roosts on branches in trees, often quite low down. Pairs occasionally roost together, perching crosswise on branches. If danger approaches, a roosting bird slowly assumes an alarm posture by stretching up its neck and head, pointing its head and bill upwards and 'freezing'. During the night, birds often fly up and perch in the tops of tall trees. Possibly feeds by taking prey from leaves, branches and the ground, or by flycatching. No further information available.

FOOD Moths, butterflies (including Pieridae), beetles (including Carabidae, Cerambycidae and Chrysomelidae), Orthoptera (including Tettigoniidae and Gryllidae), earwigs (including Blattidae), caterpillars, cockroaches, termites, ants, cicadas and small snails. No further data available.

BREEDING Breeding season March?–August in Thailand and on the Malaysian Peninsula, January–April in Borneo, June?–August? on Palawan and February to mid-June in Java. No data available from other regions.

The small, cup-shaped nest measures 7-8cm in diameter and about 1cm in depth, and is constructed with moss, down feathers and small pieces of bark. It is usually built on a thin, horizontal branch up to 45mm in diameter, and may be as low as c. 1m above ground. Clutch 1-2. Eggs oval and white, 25.0-31.9 x 16.0-21.2mm. The eggs of the race *B. j. affinis* are smaller, 23.2-27.7 x 16.3-19.2mm. The adult often incubates with its body along the branch supporting the nest. No further information available.

DESCRIPTION *B. j. javensis* **Adult male** Forehead, crown and nape brown, speckled and spotted buff, white and blackish. Collar around hindneck white, occasionally spotted blackish. Mantle, back, rump and uppertail-coverts brown, speckled and spotted buff, white and blackish.

Lesser coverts brown, speckled or barred blackish, primary coverts brown, occasionally spotted tawny along outerwebs. Rest of wing-coverts brown, mottled and barred buff, white and dark brown, distinctly spotted blackish. Scapulars brown, speckled whitish on innerwebs, boldly marked with large whitish oval-shaped spots on tips of outerwebs. Primaries brown tipped with buffish or tawny speckling, boldly spotted buff or pale tawny along outerwebs. Secondaries brown, tipped and barred with buffish speckling. Tertials brown, mottled buff, white and blackish. Tail brown mottled dark brown, broadly barred pale buffish-brown or greyish-brown, bars mottled and edged dark brown. Broad whitish supercilium. Lores and ear-coverts brown speckled buff. Chin buff, speckled or barred brown. Throat brownish-white barred brown. Breast brown, faintly speckled and barred brown, boldly spotted white. Belly and flanks white or buffish-white, feathers narrowly edged brown and distinctly spotted brown or blackish at tips. Undertail-coverts buffish or whitish, barred or spotted brown or blackish. Underwing-coverts buffish or whitish, barred brown. **Adult female** Brighter, paler and tawnier than the male. Upperparts and wing-coverts tawny or rufescent-tawny. Scapulars with fewer whitish oval-shaped spots. Underparts generally tawny or rufescent-tawny, with some bold whitish spotting. **Immature** and **Juvenile** Similar to the adults but paler and plainer. Upperparts pale rufous, faintly barred and speckled brown. Underparts pale rufous tinged cinnamon, becoming buffish on belly and flanks. **Chick** Not described. **Bare parts** Iris yellow; bill brownish; legs and feet brownish.

MEASUREMENTS Wing (male) 125-127, (female) 121-129; tail (male) 107-122, (female) 103-110; bill (male) 19.0-23.0, (female) 16.9-21.0; tarsus (male) 15-17, (female) 14-17. Weight no data.

MOULT The primary moult is serially descendant. No further data available.

GEOGRAPHICAL VARIATION Four races are currently recognised. However, all races require further study to determine their true taxonomic status, and it is quite possible that more than one species may be involved.

B. j. javensis Described above. Both sexes show variation in ground colour: males are often tinged tawny or rufous, females are often rufescent-brown or tawny-brown.

B. j. continentalis (Indochinese Frogmouth) Length 20-22.5cm. Smaller, paler and less boldly marked than the nominate and often with a much less distinct collar around the hindneck. Wing (male) 120-123, (female) 117-122; tail (male) 116-118, (female) no data. Weight (male, one) 50.0g, (female) no data.

B. j. chaseni (Palawan Frogmouth) Length 22-23cm. Similar to the nominate but smaller and less boldly marked. Wing (male) 115-124, (female, one) 125; tail (male) 110-115, (female, one) 117. Weight no data.

B. j. affinis (Blyth's Frogmouth) Length 21.5-23cm. Similar to the nominate but smaller and often less boldly marked. Wing (male) 105-118, (female) 109-118; tail (male) 95-111, (female) 90-107. Weight no data.

DISTRIBUTION AND MOVEMENTS Widely distributed throughout South-East Asia.

B. j. javensis Java. Sedentary.

B. j. continentalis C (possibly) and S Burma (south to Tenasserim), NW and S Thailand (south to Nakhon Si Thammarat on the peninsula), S Laos and C Vietnam (Annam). Sedentary.

B. j. chaseni Palawan and the Calamian Group (Culion Island). Sedentary,

B. j. affinis Extreme S Thailand (Narathiwat on the peninsula), Malay Peninsula (south to Rompin River, Pahang and Malacca), Sumatra (including the Riau Archipelago) and Borneo (including Banggi Island in the north). Sedentary.

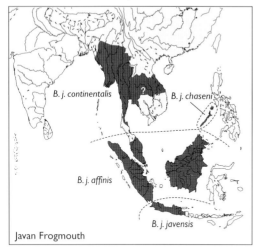

Javan Frogmouth

STATUS Widely distributed, but poorly known and probably under-recorded in many parts of its range.

REFERENCES Bartels (1938), Coomans de Ruiter (1931), Dickinson *et al.* (1991), Hellebrekers & Hoogerwerf (1967), Mann (in prep.), van Marle & Voous (1988), Marshall (1978), Medway & Wells (1976), Smythies (1981), Stresemann (1937), Stresemann & Stresemann (1966), Thewlis *et al.* (1995).

14   SUNDA FROGMOUTH
Batrachostomus cornutus   Plate 4

Other names: Long-tailed Frogmouth, Horned Frogmouth

Podargus cornutus "Horsfield" Temminck, 1822, *Pl. Col.* livr. 27, pl.159 (Benkulen, Sumatra)
Batrachostomus cornutus longicaudatus Hoogerwerf, 1962, *Ardea* 50, p.204 (Pulau Sepandjang, Kangean Archipelago)

Formerly considered conspecific with Javan Frogmouth but sympatric with it in Sumatra and Borneo.

IDENTIFICATION Length 25-28cm. A medium-sized brownish frogmouth, confined to Borneo, Sumatra and several islands in the Javan Sea. Sexually dimorphic. **At rest** Upperparts and wing-coverts brown, speckled and spotted buff, white and blackish. Scapulars boldly marked with whitish oval-shaped spots. Whitish collar around the hindneck and broad whitish supercilium. Underparts brown, speckled and spotted buff, white and cinnamon, becoming generally whitish, streaked, spotted and barred brown, on belly and flanks. Females are brighter, tawnier and plainer, with smaller whitish spots on the scapulars. **In flight** No information. Both sexes lack white markings on wings and tail. **Similar species** Javan Frogmouth (13) is extremely similar but smaller: males are more distinctly

spotted blackish or brown below. Pale-headed Frogmouth (11) is smaller and more heavily spotted whitish below, and males are paler, plainer and more rufescent. Bornean Frogmouth (12) is also smaller, males paler and plainer, females less heavily spotted whitish below. See also Gould's Frogmouth (8).

VOICE The song (perhaps call) is a series of crow-like, croaking *krraaw* or *gwaa* notes. No further information available.

HABITAT Prefers the edges of lowland forests. Occurs in rainforest, riparian forest, secondary growth and, occasionally, mangroves and gardens near towns and villages. In Sumatra, also occurs in low bushes along rivers and near the seashore and in tobacco and rubber plantations. 0–1,000m.

HABITS Crepuscular (possibly) and nocturnal. Roosts on low branches. Roost-sites are often in thickets. If danger approaches too closely, a roosting bird may perform a defence display by spreading its wings and tail and gaping at the intruder. Birds may also perform this display when handled. No further information available.

FOOD No data available.

BREEDING Breeding season May?–July? in Sumatra, April?–June? on Belitung and January?–April? in Borneo.
    Prefers to nest in secondary growth at the edge of primary forest but in Brunei it has been found to nest in suburban gardens. The nest is a small, flimsy structure, c. 6-7 x 5-6cm, with a shallow depression c. 1cm deep in which to lay the egg. The nest is composed of down, hair?, moss and small pieces of bark and is built on a horizontal branch, often close to the trunk, up to c. 1.5m above ground. Rotten branches with peeling bark are often chosen as nest-sites. In suburban gardens, exotic trees, e.g. *Mimosa*, may be used. Clutch 1. Egg elliptical and white, 27.3-31.9 x 18.8-21.2mm.
    If danger approaches, the incubating or brooding adult slowly assumes an alarm posture by pointing its head and bill upwards, closing its eyes and 'freezing'. It has been speculated that in greater danger the brooding adult may carry its offspring away by holding the chick between its legs, although it is not clear whether, if this does happen, it is done accidentally. No further information available.

DESCRIPTION *B. c. cornutus* Adult male Forehead, crown and nape brown, speckled and spotted buffish, white and blackish. Collar around hindneck buffish-white or white, speckled or barred brown. Mantle, back, rump and uppertail-coverts brown, speckled and barred pale buff, white and blackish. Lesser coverts brown, finely speckled pale buff and pale tawny, primary coverts brown, occasionally spotted tawny along outerwebs. Rest of wing-coverts brown, mottled and spotted buffish-white, greyish-white and blackish. Scapulars brown, speckled buffish-white or greyish-white on innerwebs, boldly marked with large buffish- or greyish-white oval-shaped spots on tips of outerwebs. Primaries brown tipped with buffish speckling, boldly spotted pale tawny along outerwebs. Secondaries brown narrowly tipped pale buff, barred with pale buff speckling along the outerwebs. Tertials brown, mottled cinnamon-buff, white and blackish. Tail brown mottled greyish-brown or pale buff, broadly barred pale buff or greyish-buff, bars mottled brown and edged dark brown. Broad supercilium buffish or whitish, speckled brown.

Lores and ear-coverts brown speckled buff. Chin buff, speckled or barred brown. Throat buffish-white or whitish, barred brown. Breast brown, speckled and spotted cinnamon, buff, white and blackish. Belly and flanks buffish-white or whitish, feathers streaked, spotted and narrowly edged blackish-brown. Undertail-coverts buffish barred brown. Underwing-coverts buffish-white or greyish-white, barred brown. **Adult female** Brighter, paler and tawnier than the male. Upperparts and wing-coverts tawny or rufescent-tawny, plain or speckled brown. Scapulars less boldly marked, with smaller whitish oval-shaped spots. Underparts with fewer bold whitish spots. **Immature** Similar to the adults but paler, buffier and plainer. The upperparts are finely vermiculated brown, the underparts are indistinctly spotted whitish. **Juvenile** Presumably similar to the immature. **Chick** Not described. **Bare parts** Iris yellow; bill dark horn; legs and feet pale brown.

MEASUREMENTS Wing (male) 130-139, (female) 129-143; tail (male) 118-142, (female) 120-131; bill (male) 20.8-23.2, (female) 20.1-22.1; tarsus (male) 15.2-16.5, (female) 16.4-17.0. Weight no data.

MOULT No published data available.

GEOGRAPHICAL VARIATION Two races are currently recognised.

　　B. c. cornutus Described above. Both sexes may be extremely variable in colour. Males often have the ground colour of the upperparts, wing-coverts and breast tinged rufous or tawny, others are blackish-brown with whiter markings. Females are often more rufescent-brown or tawny-brown, whilst others are darker and approach males in overall coloration.

　　B. c. longicaudatus Has a less contrasting plumage than the nominate race, less white on the forehead, a less extensive whitish collar around the hindneck and is, on average, longer-tailed and narrower-billed. Wing (male) 133-140, (female) no data; tail (male) 131-145, (female) no data. Weight (male, one) 60.0g, (female) no data.

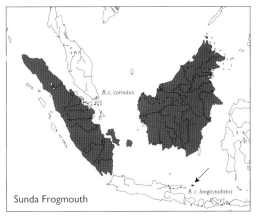

Sunda Frogmouth

DISTRIBUTION AND MOVEMENTS A little-known species, restricted to Borneo, Sumatra and, despite its apparent absence from Java, the Kangean Islands off the north-east coast of Java.

　　B. c. cornutus Sumatra, Bangka Island, Belitung (Billiton) Island and Borneo, including Banggi Island in the north. Sedentary.

　　B. c. longicaudatus Kangean Islands. Sedentary.

STATUS Possibly the commonest of the smaller frogmouths in Borneo. No data available from other regions.

REFERENCES Hoogerwerf (1962), Mann (1991, in prep), van Marle & Voous (1988), Smythies (1981), Stresemann (1937).

POTOOS NYCTIBIIDAE

NYCTIBIUS

Nyctibius Vieillot, 1816, Analyse, p. 38. Type by monotypy, Grand Engoulevent de Cayenne, Buffon, = *Caprimulgus grandis* Gmelin 1789.

Seven Neotropical species. Potoos have large bills that are hooked at the tip, partly forward-facing eyes, long, stiff wings and tail and a powder-down patch on either side of the rump. They also have short tarsi and strong, clawed feet, with the middle toe not pectinated. A rather unique feature of the potoos is the presence of two small slits in their upper eyelids, which enables them to observe their surroundings with their eyes shut. This adaptation is particularly important at the roost site or nest, when threatened or disturbed birds automatically 'freeze' to blend in with their surroundings. Arboreal. Potoos do not build nests but lay their single egg directly onto a branch, snag or stump. They hunt in flight or by flycatching from a perch.

15 GREAT POTOO
Nyctibius grandis   Plate 5

Other name: Grand Potoo

Caprimulgus grandis Gmelin, 1789, *Syst. Nat.* 1, pt. 2, p.1029 (Cayenne)

IDENTIFICATION Length 45-54cm. A very large, pale, greyish-white potoo, the largest of its family at least in terms of body size. Sexes similar. **At rest** Upperparts and wing-coverts greyish-white, speckled and mottled black, brown, tawny and buff. No collar around hindneck. No obvious scapular pattern, supercilium or submoustachial stripe. Throat buffish. Underparts greyish-white, barred and speckled buff, brown and blackish-brown, becoming buff or whitish, barred brown on belly and flanks. At night, generally shows a reddish-orange eyeshine in artificial light. **In flight** Flies with slow, deep wingbeats. Both sexes lack white markings on wings and tail; the underwing appears spotted and the tail is rather squarish. **Similar species** Grey Potoo (18) and Northern Potoo (17) are smaller and generally darker. Long-tailed Potoo (16) often appears as large as Great Potoo but is darker, browner and longer-tailed.

VOICE The song is a strong, guttural *wah-h-h-oo* or *wah-h-h, oo-oo-oo*. Sings from perches up to c. 50m apart throughout its territory. May be heard mainly during the night. The call is a long, harsh, deep *kwak, kaw* or *graw-ar* note, repeated once every 10-20 seconds for up to 10 minutes at a time. Also gives a barking *ahrrr* or *bgrr* note, followed by a hoarse *baahoo* or a guttural *wah-h-oo-oo*. This call is repeated at short intervals and may be an alarm. Other calls include an eerie *whoap* or *w-whoap*, a vibrating *irrr* or *rirrr* and an owl-like *oo-rroo*. If disturbed, males may utter a *grook* sound. Adults often give an *oorrr* call when alighting. Whilst perched, juveniles utter short, deep *mbuo* or *wow* notes. Chicks may utter a soft call during threat/defence displays but this has yet to be fully documented.

HABITAT Prefers lowland forest and woodland, where it tends to inhabit clearings, edges and borders. Occurs in evergreen or deciduous forests, tropical rainforest, gallery forest and open woodland. Also frequents second growth, savannas, plantations, gardens, open fields and coastal sand-ridges. Generally 0-500m but up to 1,050m, e.g. in central Bolivia.

HABITS Crepuscular and nocturnal. Roosts on branches in trees, up to 40m above ground, usually in an upright position, facing forward, with eyes closed and feathers erect. Sometimes adopts a more horizontal position. Occasionally stretches its wings, opens its eyes and looks around or scratches its head by bringing one of its feet up over the wing; half-opens its bill and pants when too hot in full sun. If danger approaches a roosting bird, it assumes an alarm position by slowly raising and pointing up its neck and head, depressing its head feathers. Roost-sites may be used for up to six months at a time.

At night, a calling bird throws back its head so that the bill points upwards (it opens with each call). Forages from perches, usually returning to the same perch after each foray. Hunting perches range from the tops of trees to c. 1-2m above ground; feeding flights often cover long distances. No further information available.

FOOD Beetles (including Cerambycidae, Hydrophilidae, Passalidae and *Lamellicornia*). No further data available.

BREEDING Breeding season April?–June? in S Mexico; April–August in C Venezuela; February–April? in Guyana; February?–December? in Surinam (breeding female late February, juvenile mid-June, almost fledged young early October, fledgling early November and egg late November); March–April? in Colombia; July?–December in Brazil and July?–August? in E Bolivia. No further data available.

No nest is constructed; the egg is laid in a slight depression on a branch, up to c. 12m above ground and often well away from the tree-trunk. Clutch 1. Egg elliptical, white, spotted brown and lilac-grey, markings concentrated around the blunt end, 52.1-60.0 x 38.3-44.0mm. Both sexes incubate, although only one parent attends the nest at any one time. No published data available on the incubation period.

The adult broods its young by sitting at its back, both birds facing the same way. At c. 14 days of age, the chick occasionally perches in front of and facing its parent, its bill partially concealed in the adult's breast feathers. At c. 29 days of age, chicks may be left unattended, although they rarely stray more than 1m from the nest-site. If danger approaches, the chick may perform a threat/defence display by gaping and calling (see Voice). Fledging occurs at c. 55 days. No further information available.

DESCRIPTION Adult male Forehead, crown and nape greyish-white, densely speckled greyish-brown, buff and cinnamon, streaked blackish-brown. No collar around hindneck. Mantle and back greyish-white, densely mottled brown, black, white, tawny and buff. Rump and uppertail-coverts greyish-white, barred brown and greyish-brown. Alula and primary coverts brown. Rest of wing-coverts and scapulars greyish-white, mottled brown, black, white, buff and tawny. Primaries brown, boldly spotted greyish-white along outerwebs, barred greyish-white along innerwebs. Secondaries brown, indistinctly barred greyish-white and buff. Tertials greyish-white, mottled and vermiculated brown. Tail brown, mottled and barred greyish-white. Lores buff, speckled or barred brown; ear-coverts buff streaked brown. No submoustachial stripe. Chin and throat buff, barred and vermiculated brown. Breast greyish-white, barred and densely speckled brown, buff and blackish-brown. Belly, flanks and undertail-coverts pale buff or creamy white, barred and vermiculated brown. Underwing-coverts brown, barred greyish-white or pale buff. **Adult female** Similar to the male. **Immature** Similar to the adults but paler. **Juvenile** Generally white or greyish-white, barred brown and often tinged buffish. Crown speckled brown. **Chick** At hatching, covered in white down. **Bare parts** Iris brown, dark chestnut or dark blue?; bill brown or horn, tipped blackish; legs and feet yellowish-tan or brownish.

MEASUREMENTS Wing (male) 342-391, (female) 347-402; tail (male) 219-259, (female) 227-282; bill (male) 43.3-46.6, (female, one) 46.3; tarsus (male) 16.4-21.5, (female) 16.5-21.0. Weight (male) 450-624g, (female) 504-640g.

MOULT The primary moult is serially descendant. No further data available.

GEOGRAPHICAL VARIATION Monotypic. Colour variation is evident throughout the range, with some birds being paler, whiter and often tinged cinnamon, some being quite buffish and others browner and darker.

Great Potoo

DISTRIBUTION AND MOVEMENTS Widely distributed throughout Central and South America. S Mexico (Chiapas), E Guatemala (possibly Hon-duras), Nicaragua, Costa Rica, Panama (Bocas del Toro, Canal Zone, E Panamá, San Blas and Darién), Colombia (Magdalena, Cesar/Norte de Santander, Chocó, S Córdoba, E Caldas, W Meta, SE Nariño, W Putumayo and SE Amazonas), Venezuela (NW Zulia, Táchira, Trujillo, W Apure, Aragua, Monagas, Delta Amacuro, NW Bolívar and C Amazonas), Guyana, Surinam, French Guiana, Brazil (Amazonas east to Bahia, south to São Paulo), E Ecuador, E Peru and N and C Bolivia (Pando, Beni, La Paz, Cochabamba and Santa Cruz). Sedentary.

STATUS Rare and endangered or threatened in much of Central America, generally rare to uncommon and poorly known throughout South American range.

REFERENCES Haverschmidt (1948), Haverschmidt & Mees (1994), Hilty & Brown (1986), Howell & Webb (1995), Land (1970), Meyer de Schauensee & Phelps (1978), Perry (1979), Rangel-Salazar *et al.* (1991), Ridgely & Gwynne (1989), Slud (1979), Vanderwerf (1988), Wetmore (1968).

16   LONG-TAILED POTOO
Nyctibius aethereus   Plate 6

Caprimulgus aethereus Wied, 1820, *Reise Bras.* 1, p.236, note (Rio Mucuri [Macuré], Bahia)
Nyctibius aethereus chocoensis Chapman, 1921, *Amer. Mus. Novit.* 18, p.5 (Novitá, 400 feet, Rio San Juan, Chocó, Colombia)
Nyctibius aethereus longicaudatus (Spix, 1825), *Av. Bras.* 2, p.1, pl.1 (Rio Japurá, Brazil)

IDENTIFICATION Length 42-56cm. A very large, long-tailed, brownish potoo. Sexes similar. **At rest** Often appears dark-crowned. Upperparts and wing-coverts brownish, mottled and spotted buff and brown and with blackish-brown spots and streaks. No collar around hindneck. Distinct buffish panel across shoulders, but no obvious scapular pattern. Buffish supercilium, feathers often protruding above the eye. Buff submoustachial stripe broadens along the sides of the throat. Underparts brownish, streaked and speckled buff and blackish-brown. **In flight** Both sexes lack white markings on the wings and also lack white on the tail, which is long and graduated. **Similar species** Great Potoo (15) is paler, greyer and shorter-tailed. Grey Potoo (18) brown phase, is smaller and shorter-tailed.

VOICE The song is a soft, undulating *waa-OO-uh*, repeated once every c. 7 seconds. Sings from branches within the forest canopy. May be heard mainly at night, especially when there is plenty of moonlight. No further information available.

HABITAT Prefers the interiors of lowland forests. Occurs in humid forest and evergreen rainforest. 0-500m.

HABITS Nocturnal. Usually roosts on dead, vertical or horizontal branches in open canopy trees, up to c. 20m or more above ground. Also often sits on perches close to the ground, i.e. stakes or tree-stumps sometimes out in the open, and is also occasionally flushed from the ground during the day. Roosting birds usually sit with their tails pressed close to the perch on which they are sitting. If danger approaches a roosting bird, it slowly assumes an alarm posture by stretching up its neck and head and pointing its head and bill upwards, 'freezing' in this position until the danger has passed. No further information available.

FOOD No data available.

BREEDING Breeding season is late August–November in Paraguay. No data available from other countries.
  No nest is constructed; the egg is laid in a slight depression on top of a vertical tree-stump, in a snag protruding from a tree-trunk or at the bend of a sloping branch. Clutch 1. Egg 38.2 x 26.0mm.
  The adult broods its offspring by sitting behind it, the chick facing outwards from beneath the adult's belly feathers. No further information available.

DESCRIPTION *N. a. aethereus* **Adult male** Forehead, crown and nape tawny-brown, speckled and spotted buff, boldly streaked or spotted blackish-brown. No collar around hindneck. Mantle, back and rump tawny-brown, mottled brown and buff, streaked blackish-brown. Uppertail-coverts tawny or tawny-brown, boldly mottled or vermiculated brown. Alula and primary coverts brown, faintly barred tawny. Upper and outer rows of lesser coverts blackish-brown, rest of lesser coverts buff, pale buff or whitish, forming distinct pale panel across shoulders. Rest of wing-coverts brown, densely mottled pale buff, buff and tawny. Scapulars tawny-brown, mottled buff, tawny and brown, streaked blackish-brown. Primaries and secondaries brown, broadly barred pale tawny. Tertials tawny-brown, mottled brown, tawny and buff. Strongly gradated tail brown, broadly barred tawny-buff, bars streaked or vermiculated brown; central pair (R1) with pointed tips. Lores and ear-coverts tawny speckled brown. Bold buffish submoustachial stripe, becoming broader along sides of throat. Chin and throat greyish-buff, speckled brown. Breast, upper belly and flanks brown or greyish-brown, speckled buff, streaked blackish-brown and boldly spotted buff and blackish-brown. Lower belly and undertail-coverts buff, streaked and vermiculated brown. Underwing-coverts brown barred buff. **Adult female** Similar to the male. **Immature** and **Juvenile** Similar to the adults but paler and often tinged pale cinnamon? **Chick** At hatching, covered in white down. **Bare parts** Iris yellowish, greenish-chestnut? or bluish-grey?; bill blackish; legs and feet brownish.

MEASUREMENTS Wing (male, one) 338, (female, one) 345, unsexed 325-342; tail (male, one) 328, (female, one) 310, unsexed 281-315; bill (male, one) 32.0, (female, one) 35.5; tarsus (male, one) 18.7, (female, one) 19.2. Weight no data.

MOULT The primaries are possibly moulted descendantly. No further data available.

GEOGRAPHICAL VARIATION Three races are currently recognised. The nominate is called Large-tailed Potoo by some authorities and considered to be a separate species from *N. a. longicaudatus*, as both occur in eastern Pará, Brazil, where they may breed sympatrically.

  N. a. aethereus Described above. Colour variation is uncommon, although some are greyer on the breast and others have buffier or whiter panels across the lesser coverts. Paler birds may be immatures.
  N. a. chocoensis Similar to *longicaudatus* but upperparts darker, more chestnut-brown, with stronger blackish streaking. Wing (male, one) 305, (female, one) 305; tail (male, one) 271, (female, one) 265. Weight no data. Probably more closely related to *N. a. longicaudatus* than to *N. a. aethereus*.
  N. a. longicaudatus Length 42-49cm. Smaller and often tawnier-brown than the nominate race, especially on the breast. Wing (male) no data, (female) 283-303, unsexed 305-312; tail (male) no data, (female) 245-283, unsexed 269-285. Weight (male) no data, (female, one) 300g.

DISTRIBUTION AND MOVEMENTS A widely distributed South American species, about which very little appears to be known.

  N. a. aethereus N and SE Brazil (Mexiana Island and possibly E Pará, Bahia, Minas Gerais, Rio de Janeiro, São Paulo and Paraná), NE Argentina (NE Misiones)

and S Paraguay (Canendiyú, Cordillera and Caaguazú). Presumably sedentary.
  N. a. chocoensis W Colombia (S Chocó, Valle, Cauca and C Nariño). Presumably sedentary.
  N. a. longicaudatus SE Colombia (Vaupés), E Venezuela (NE Bolívar), Guyana (known only from two museum specimens taken at Bartica Grove?), W and N Brazil (Amazonas east to Pará), E Ecuador, N and E Peru (Amazonas and Madre de Dios) and NE Bolivia (NE Santa Cruz). Presumably sedentary.

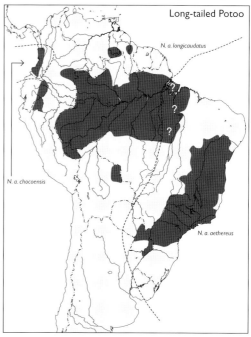

Long-tailed Potoo

N. a. longicaudatus

N. a. chocoensis

N. a. aethereus

STATUS Rare throughout its range. No further information available.

REFERENCES Hilty & Brown (1986), Sibley & Monroe (1990), Straneck & Johnson (1990).

17 NORTHERN POTOO
Nyctibius jamaicensis   Plate 5

Other names: Common Potoo, Antillean Potoo

Caprimulgus jamaicensis Gmelin, 1789, *Syst. Nat.* 1, pt. 2, p.1029, No. 6 (Jamaica)
Nyctibius jamaicensis lambi Davis, 1959, *Condor* 61, p.300 (La Juela, Colima, Mexico)
Nyctibius jamaicensis mexicanus Nelson, 1900, *Auk* 17, p.260 (Metlaltoyuca, Pueblo, Mexico)
Nyctibius jamaicensis abbotti Richmond, 1917, *Smiths. Misc. Coll.* 68, No. 7, p.1 (Port-à-Piment, Haiti)

Probably forms a superspecies with Grey Potoo, with which it was formerly considered conspecific.

IDENTIFICATION Length 36-45cm. A large, greyish-brown or brownish potoo. Sexes similar, although females are often greyer than males. **At rest** Upperparts greyish-brown, streaked blackish-brown. No collar around hindneck. Wing-coverts greyish-brown, mottled greyish-white, buff and tawny. No obvious scapular pattern. Underparts greyish-brown, streaked blackish-brown, spotted blackish-brown on centre of throat and upper breast and usually with a row of large blackish spots across the upper breast (sometimes restricted to the centre only). At night, generally shows a reddish-orange or orange eyeshine in artificial light. **In flight** Flies with strong, deep wingbeats. Both sexes lack white markings on wings and tail. **Similar species** Grey Potoo (18) is extremely similar but averages slightly smaller, is more finely streaked blackish, often has more blackish spotting on the centre of the throat and upper breast, often shows a more distinct row of blackish spots across the upper breast, and is probably most easily separated by voice; Occurs further south than the Northern Potoo, their ranges possibly not overlapping. Great Potoo (15) is larger and generally paler.

VOICE The song is a series of 3–6 deep, guttural *kwah* notes, the first being more drawn-out than the rest, i.e. *kwaah, kwah, kwah, kwah*. A variation of the song often sounds like *kwaaah, baw, baw, baw*. Has a barking alarm call, rather like a similar call given by the Great Potoo. No further information available.

HABITAT Prefers lowland forests and woodlands, where it inhabits openings, clearings and edges. Occurs in gallery forest, tropical evergreen forest and swamp forest. Also frequents open and semi-open country with scattered trees and hedgerows, savannas, shrubby fields and pastures. 0–1,500m.

HABITS Nocturnal. Roosts on branches, usually high up in trees. When active, frequently perches on branches, snags, posts and stumps. Inquisitive, often hovering near intruders in its territory. Hawks for food from low perches such as fence-posts and cornstalks, returning to the same perch after each foray. Also forages in the forest canopy, or in and around animal corrals. Sometimes feeds on small birds, which are possibly disturbed from their roosts during the night. No further information available.

FOOD Moths, beetles (including Passalidae, Cerambycidae and Geotrupidae), locustid eggs and occasionally small birds (including White-collared Seedeaters *Sporophila torqueola*).

BREEDING Breeding season April–June in S Mexico. No data available from other countries.

Territorial. No nest is constructed; the egg is laid in a slight depression or hollow, c. 80mm in diameter, on top of a broken snag, up to c. 25m above ground. The nest-site is often partly shaded. Clutch 1. Egg elliptical and white, blotched and streaked brown and black around the blunt end, 40.4 x 30.1mm. Unfledged young are occasionally found on the ground. No further information available.

DESCRIPTION *N. j. jamaicensis* **Adult male** Forehead, crown and nape greyish-brown, broadly streaked blackish-brown. No collar around hindneck. Mantle and back greyish-brown, broadly streaked blackish-brown. Rump greyish-brown speckled brown, streaked and spotted blackish-brown. Uppertail-coverts brown barred greyish-brown. Primary coverts and alula brown barred greyish-white or -brown. Upper and lower lesser coverts blackish-brown, middle lesser coverts and rest of wing-coverts greyish-brown, often tinged buff or tawny, mottled greyish-white, buff and tawny, broadly streaked blackish. Scapulars greyish-brown mottled whitish, streaked and spotted

blackish-brown. Primaries brown, boldly spotted greyish-brown along outerwebs, faintly mottled or barred greyish-brown along innerwebs. Secondaries brown barred greyish-brown. Tertials greyish-brown mottled brown, spotted and boldly streaked blackish-brown. Tail brown, broadly barred greyish-brown or -white. Lores and ear-coverts greyish-buff streaked dark brown. Chin and throat pale greyish-brown, thinly streaked blackish-brown. Breast and flanks greyish-brown speckled brown, boldly streaked and spotted blackish-brown. Belly and undertail-coverts buffish, speckled and vermiculated brown, streaked dark brown. Underwing-coverts dark brown, barred pale buff or greyish-white. **Adult female** Similar to the male but often greyer and less brownish. **Immature** Similar to the adults but paler and whiter. **Juvenile** Similar to the immature but whiter and spotted blackish-brown along the scapulars. **Chick** At hatching, covered in white down. **Bare parts** Iris yellowish; bill black; legs and feet greyish.

MEASUREMENTS Wing (male, one) 301, (female) no data, unsexed 269–289; tail (male, one) 204, (female) no data, unsexed 205–206; bill (male, one) 35.5, (female) no data; tarsus (male, one) 16.1, (female) no data. Weight no data.

MOULT No published data available.

GEOGRAPHICAL VARIATION Four races are currently recognised.

N. j. jamaicensis Described above. Some birds are browner than the typical greyish-brown form, others are much paler, especially on the underparts, and are more thinly streaked blackish-brown.

N. j. lambi The largest race. Similar to *mexicanus* but longer-winged and -tailed and has a longer, wider bill. Wing (male) 315–321, (female) no data; tail (male) 222–231, (female) no data. Weight no data.

N. j. mexicanus Larger and browner than the nominate. The lesser coverts are especially browner and the pale spots along the outerwebs of the primaries are duller grey. Wing (male) 292–310, (female, one) 304, unsexed (one) 308; tail (male) 205–215, (female, one) 224. Weight (male) 210.2–274.0g, (female, one) 251.0g.

N. j. abbotti (Abbott's Potoo, Hispaniolan Potoo). Similar to the nominate but less heavily streaked blackish-brown. Wing (male, one) 297, (female, one) 295; tail (male, one) 218, (female, one) 212. Weight (male, one) 282g, (female) no data.

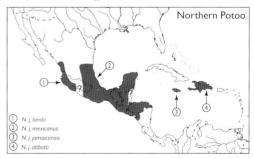

Northern Potoo

① *N. j. lambi*
② *N. j. mexicanus*
③ *N. j. jamaicensis*
④ *N. j. abbotti*

DISTRIBUTION AND MOVEMENTS Restricted to the northern and central parts of Central America and the islands of Jamaica and Hispaniola in the Greater Antilles.

N. j. jamaicensis Jamaica. Presumably sedentary.

N. j. lambi WC Mexico (S Sinaloa south to at least Colima). Presumably sedentary.

N. j. mexicanus E and S Mexico (S San Luis Potosi and

S Tamaulipas south to Chiapas and east to the Yucatán Peninsula, including Cozumel Island), Guatemala, El Salvador, Honduras, Ruatan Island and NW Costa Rica. Presumably sedentary.

N. j. abbotti Hispaniola (Dominican Republic, Haiti and Gonave Island). Presumably sedentary.

STATUS Rare to very uncommon in southern Mexico, rare on the Pacific coast of Guatemala and El Salvador and not uncommon on Gonave Island. No data available from other countries.

REFERENCES Davis (1978), Howell & Webb (1995), Land (1970), Stuart-Rowley (1984), Thurber & Serrano (1987).

---

18   GREY POTOO
Nyctibius griseus   Plate 5

Other names: Common Potoo, Lesser Potoo

Caprimulgus griseus Gmelin, 1789, *Syst. Nat.* 1, pt. 2, p.1029, No. 5 (Cayenne)
Nyctibius griseus costaricensis Ridgway, 1912, *Proc. Biol. Soc. Wash.* 25, p.91 (Sarchí, Alajuela, Costa Rica)
Nyctibius griseus cornutus (Vieillot, 1817), *Nouv. Dict. Hist. Nat.* 10, p.245 (Paraguay)

Probably forms a superspecies with Northern Potoo, with which it was formerly considered conspecific.

IDENTIFICATION Length 31-41cm. A large potoo with two distinct colour phases, a greyish-brown morph (described below) and a browner, more rufous morph. Sexes similar, although females are often greyer than males. **At rest** Upperparts greyish-brown, streaked blackish-brown. No collar around hindneck. Wing-coverts greyish-brown, mottled greyish-white, buff and tawny. No obvious scapular pattern. Underparts greyish-brown streaked blackish-brown, boldly spotted blackish-brown on centre of throat and upper breast and usually with a row of large blackish spots across the upper breast. At night, generally shows a reddish-orange or orange eyeshine in artificial light. **In flight** Flies with regular, heavy wingbeats. Both sexes lack white markings on wings and tail and the underwing appears spotted. **Similar species** Northern Potoo (17) is extremely similar (see that species for differences); occurs further north than Grey Potoo, their ranges possibly not overlapping. Great Potoo (15) is larger and generally paler. Long-tailed Potoo (16) is similar to brown-phase birds but is larger and longer-tailed.

VOICE The song is a descending series of 5-7 melancholy notes which often begins rather harshly, i.e. *poh-o, oh, oh, oh, oh* or *pi-oh, oh, oh, oh*. Sings from perches. May be heard mainly at dusk, dawn and throughout the night, especially when there is plenty of moonlight. Tends to sing less during the breeding season, although at dusk brooding males may give a subdued version of the song when they awake, usually 1-4 notes only.

Has a *rak* call note, which may possibly be given in flight. Chicks utter a hoarse buzzing sound when begging for food. Calls (apparently undescribed) have been heard from an adult during distraction displays. The adults give soft, melodious calls (apparently undescribed) when searching for their recently fledged offspring. No further information available.

HABITAT Prefers lowland forests, forest edges and borders, woodland and open or semi-open woods and forests. Also occurs in cerrado, shrubby woodland, woodlots, plantations, second growth, mangrove swamps and open fields. 0–1,900m.

HABITS Nocturnal and partially crepuscular. Roosts on branches and snags in trees, up to c. 15m above ground. Occasionally roosts lower down and out in the open, on tree-stumps and fence-posts. At the roost-site, usually sits in an upright position with head and bill pointing forwards and eyes closed. If danger approaches, it slowly raises its head until its bill is pointing upwards. In this posture, it watches the intruder through the slits in its upper eyelids and it occasionally turns its head slowly or moves its body, to keep the danger in view. Roost-sites are usually used for some time.

When active, frequently alights on exposed perches, such as snags or the tops of dead trees. Occasionally perches across branches. Also sits on stumps and fence-posts 0.5-2m high. Forages in short flycatching flights from a perch, often hawking around open ground and clearings, and sometimes gliding down from high up in trees. Probably also takes prey from tree-trunks, branches, foliage and low herbage, especially when feeding young. No further information available.

FOOD Beetles (including Elateridae, Scarabaeidae, Curculionidae, Dermestidae and Passalidae), beetle larvae, moths, fireflies and Orthoptera (including Tettigoniidae). Pieces of rotten wood are also ingested by young birds, perhaps accidentally.

BREEDING Breeding season ?–July–? (dry season) in Costa Rica; November–December in Panama; January–May? in Colombia; May–August (wet season) in C Venezuela; April–August in Trinidad; ?–August–? in Ecuador; April–? in Surinam and November–December in Brazil. No further data available.

No data on territory size, although pairs may nest as close as 500m. No nest is constructed; the egg is laid in a shallow depression or cavity up to c. 15cm in diameter, on top of a stump, a broken vertical branch or dead snag, or at a bend in a branch, up to c. 18m above ground. If the cavity or depression is small enough, the egg may sit more or less upright. Nest-sites may be in full sunlight or in partial shade. Clutch 1. Egg elliptical or subelliptical, white, streaked and spotted brown, lilac and grey, 35.9-41.5 x 25.0-32.0mm.

Incubation is by both parents but is often (perhaps usually) by the male during the day and by the female at night. The incubating adult sits upright with its feathers puffed up, its head and bill pointing forwards and its eyes partially open. If potential danger approaches, the adult assumes an alarm posture by slowly stretching its neck, raising its head until its bill is pointing upwards, almost closing its eyes and compressing its feathers. These actions take between 10-23 seconds and might be triggered by mammals walking or foraging nearby or by birds of prey flying overhead. The adult moves its head extremely slowly to keep the threat in view. If the danger persists and approaches the nest too closely, the adult performs a defence display, during which it fluffs out its feathers, spreads its wings and tail, opens its eyes, gapes and makes sudden bill-snapping movements towards the intruder. If the danger subsides, the adult relaxes and assumes its normal incubating posture. This may take up to c. 15

minutes during the day, or only 2-3 minutes at night. At dusk, the incubating bird (perhaps male) awakes, and often looks around and yawns. It then stretches its wings out and above its back, spreads its tail, preens and calls (see Voice). It departs from the nest by dropping away from the egg and often alights nearby to stretch and preen again before flying off. The egg is often left unattended at dusk and dawn for periods of up to 95 minutes, presumably whilst the female is hunting. Absences from the egg are slightly longer at dusk than at dawn. At the changeover, the incoming adult flies straight onto the egg and sits in an upright position. The incubating bird does not turn the egg and often faces towards the tree-trunk. In sunlight, the incubating bird sometimes adopts a more horizontal posture, with its wings half-spread and its tail fanned, appearing to sunbathe, after which it usually preens. In showers of rain, the incubating bird becomes more huddled and fluffs out its feathers. The incubation period is c. 30-33 days.

The chick is brooded by the male during the day and by both adults at night, the changeover occurring quite frequently, each time the chick is fed. The adult broods its chick by sitting at its back, with both adult and chick facing in the same direction. During rainstorms, the adult leans forward to shield its offspring from the rain. If danger approaches, both adult and chick adopt the upright alarm posture; after it has passed, the chick relaxes much sooner than its parent. The adult may also very slowly move its position to conceal its offspring, such movements taking up to three minutes. The chick is fed by regurgitation, turning its head sideways as the adult bends forward. During the first night after hatching, a series of feeds during a single visit to the nest may last five minutes, but they get shorter as the chick gets older, with single feeds per visit lasting 2-4 seconds up to 10 days of age and 1-2 seconds after that. During the day, older chicks are not brooded by the adult but sit beside or in front of their parent at the nest-site. From c. 17 days of age the chick may be left on its own for brief periods, and is not brooded after c. 25 days, at which point it leaves the nest-site and moves to and perches in other nearby branches. In hot weather, a chick pants and gular-flutters to keep cool. If danger approaches an unattended chick, it immediately adopts the upright alarm posture, and will duly perform a threat/defence display by facing the intruder and gaping. Both parents may take part in a distraction display to lure away a potential threat at the nest-site: one adult calls from a perch near the nest and the other flies off and gives a different call (undescribed). Both adults then alternately fly off in the same direction, land on exposed perches and call (undescribed). This series of short, leapfrogging flights may last for up to c. 300m from the nest-site. At c. 45 days of age, the chick may peck at food around it. It fledges at 47-51 days but is often still fed by the adults at perches near the nest-site.

DESCRIPTION *N. g. griseus* **Adult male** Forehead, crown and nape greyish-brown, broadly streaked blackish-brown. No collar around hindneck. Mantle and back greyish-brown, streaked blackish-brown. Rump greyish-brown speckled brown, streaked and spotted blackish-brown. Uppertail-coverts brown barred greyish-brown. Primary coverts and alula brown barred greyish-white or greyish-brown. Upper and lower lesser coverts blackish-brown, middle lesser coverts and rest of wing-coverts greyish-brown, often tinged buffish or tawny, mottled greyish-

white, buff and tawny and streaked blackish-brown. Scapulars greyish-brown mottled whitish, streaked and spotted blackish-brown. Primaries brown, boldly spotted greyish-brown along outerwebs, faintly mottled or barred greyish-brown along innerwebs. Secondaries brown barred greyish-brown. Tertials greyish-brown mottled brown, streaked and spotted blackish-brown. Tail brown, broadly barred greyish-brown or greyish-white. Lores and ear-coverts greyish-buff streaked dark brown. Chin and throat pale greyish-brown, thinly streaked brown. Breast and flanks greyish-brown speckled brown, thinly streaked and boldly spotted blackish-brown. Belly and undertail-coverts buffish, often tinged cinnamon or tawny, speckled and vermiculated brown and thinly streaked dark brown. Underwing-coverts dark brown barred pale buff or greyish-white. **Adult female** Similar to the male but often greyer and less brownish. **Immature** Similar to the adults but paler and whiter. **Juvenile** Much whiter than the immature and boldly spotted blackish-brown along the scapulars. **Chick** At hatching, covered in white down, tinged pinkish-buff on the upperparts and thinly streaked blackish. **Bare parts** Iris yellow; bill blackish; legs and feet greyish, tan or yellowish-brown.

MEASUREMENTS Wing (male) 245-282, (female) 247-282, unsexed (one) 244; tail (male) 174-198, (female) 178-196; bill (male) 24.2-29.8, (female) 25.5-27.6; tarsus (male) 12.0-14.8, (female) 13.0-15.4. Weight (male) 146-167g, (female) 145-213g, unsexed (one) 132g.

MOULT The primary moult is serially descendant. No further data available.

GEOGRAPHICAL VARIATION Three races are currently recognised.

N. g. griseus There are two distinct colour phases, the greyish morph (described above) and the brownish morph (used to describe birds with a browner or more rufous-brown ground colour).

N. g. costaricensis Larger and often paler than the nominate. Wing (male, one) 285, (female, one) 290; tail (male, one) 205, (female, one) 202. Weight (male) 242-249g, (female, one) 293g.

N. g. cornutus (Paraguayan Potoo) Often darker on the upperparts than the nominate, with the underparts more uniform and the undertail-coverts more densely mottled. The pale markings on the primaries are often indistinct. Wing (male) 263-287, (female, two) 270-276; tail (male) 177-207, (female, one) 190. Weight (male) 178-208g, (female, one) 187g. The validity of this race is questionable.

DISTRIBUTION AND MOVEMENTS Widely distributed in southern Central America and throughout the northern and central parts of South America.

N. g. griseus Panama, Colombia, Venezuela, Trinidad and Tobago, Guyana, Surinam, French Guiana, N Brazil (south to the Amazon, south-east to N Maranhão), Ecuador and possibly N Peru. Presumably sedentary.

N. g. costaricensis E Nicaragua, Costa Rica (except the north-west) and extreme W Panama. Presumably sedentary.

N. g. cornutus SE Peru (Madre de Dios), Brazil (south of the Amazon), N and E Bolivia (La Paz, Pando, Beni, Santa Cruz and Tarija), Paraguay, N Argentina (south to La Rioja, Santiago del Estero, N Santa Fe and Entre Ríos) and N Uruguay. Presumably sedentary.

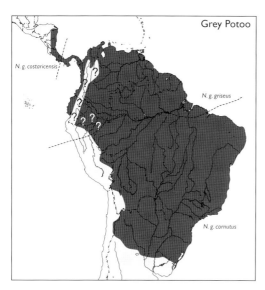

Grey Potoo

N. g. costaricensis

N. g. griseus

N. g. cornutus

STATUS Although distribution is fairly extensive, generally uncommon to locally common throughout its range, although possibly under-recorded in many regions.

REFERENCES Belton (1984), Foster & Johnson (1974), Haverschmidt (1958), Haverschmidt and Mees (1994), Helme (1996), Hilty & Brown (1986), Skutch (1970, 1983), Slud (1964), Stresemann & Stresemann (1966), Tate (1994).

---

19   ANDEAN POTOO
Nyctibius maculosus   Plate 6

Nyctibius maculosus Ridgway, 1912, *Proc. Biol. Soc. Wash.* 25, p.92 (Ambato, Ecuador; the type locality is more probably the region near Baños in central Ecuador, *fide* Chapman, 1926, *Bull. Amer. Mus. Nat. Hist.* 55, p.273)

Possibly forms a superspecies with White-winged Potoo, with which it was formerly considered conspecific, and not with Grey Potoo and Northern Potoo.

IDENTIFICATION Length 34-38cm. A large, brownish potoo, endemic to the Andes of South America. Sexually dimorphic, although not greatly so. **At rest** Upperparts brown, streaked white, buff, tawny and blackish-brown. No collar around hindneck. Large white (male) or buffish-white (female) wing-panel. Throat whitish, underparts brown spotted black and buff, becoming buff barred brown and spotted blackish-brown on belly and flanks. **In flight** Both sexes lack white markings on wings and tail. **Similar species** None within range. White-winged Potoo (20) is much smaller and has a larger white wing-panel.

VOICE The song is a loud *raa-âa* or *aah-aa*, repeated once every 8-10 seconds, for up to 2-3 minutes at a time. Sings from perches throughout its territory. Song-posts may be c. 50-75m apart and spread over distances of up to 700m. The call (perhaps of the female) consists of three short notes that descend slightly in pitch, e.g. *aah aah aah*. No further information available.

HABITAT Occurs in humid, montane cloud forests. 1,800–2,800m.

HABITS Nocturnal. Roosts on top of vertical tree-stumps and branches. Roost-sites may be used for up to several weeks at a time. No further information available.

FOOD Beetles and moths. No further data available.

BREEDING No data on breeding season.

Prior to mating, the female calls (see Voice) and alights on one of the male's song-posts. The male then alights, and copulation may then take place. No further information available.

DESCRIPTION Adult male Forehead, crown and nape brown streaked white and buff, broadly streaked blackish. No collar around hindneck. Mantle and back brown, barred and spotted pale tawny and buff, streaked blackish-brown. Rump and uppertail-coverts brown, sparsely barred or spotted buff. Primary coverts brown. Outer greater coverts brown, mottled greyish-white; inner greater coverts often white. Lesser coverts brown or blackish-brown. Median coverts white or buff, streaked and tipped blackish-brown. Scapulars white, buff and brown, mottled brown and streaked blackish-brown. Primaries brown, boldly spotted greyish along outerwebs. Secondaries brown mottled pale buff, especially on edges of outerwebs. Tertials brown, mottled greyish-brown, greyish-white, buff and pale tawny. Tail brown, faintly barred brownish-buff. Lores and ear-coverts brown or blackish-brown, streaked buff and tawny. Chin and throat white or greyish-white, lower feathers washed cinnamon. Breast brown, feathers tipped blackish-brown with a broad buff or pale tawny subterminal band. Belly and flanks buffish, barred and vermiculated brown, boldly spotted blackish-brown. Lower belly and undertail-coverts pale buff, cinnamon-buff or whitish, streaked and spotted blackish-brown. Underwing-

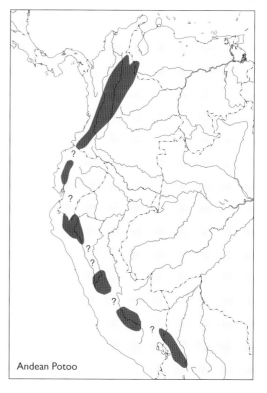

Andean Potoo

coverts brown, marginal coverts spotted greyish-white or barred cinnamon-buff. **Adult female** Similar to the male but averages slightly buffier or tawnier, especially on the upperparts and breast, and with the white wing-panel heavily tinged buff. **Immature** and **Juvenile** Not described. **Chick** Not described. **Bare parts** Iris yellow; bill blackish; legs and feet brownish or pinkish.

MEASUREMENTS Wing (male) 272-280, (female) 276-277, unsexed (one) 266; tail (male) 180-198, (female) 192-197, unsexed (one) 199; bill (male) 20.0-29.2, (female, one) 25.2; tarsus (male) no data, (female, one) 25.1. Weight (male, one) 195g, (female, one) 200g.

MOULT No data available.

GEOGRAPHICAL VARIATION Monotypic.

DISTRIBUTION AND MOVEMENTS Endemic to the Andes of north-western and west-central South America, from W Venezuela (E Táchira), W Colombia (eastern Andes from Norte de Santander south to SE Nariño) through C Ecuador (Pichincha, Tungurahua and W Pastaza) W to SE Peru (Piura, Cajamarca, Pasco and Cuzco) and W Bolivia (La Paz). Presumably sedentary.

STATUS Possibly not uncommon locally in many parts of its range, although considered rare in western Colombia.

REFERENCES Fjeldså & Krabbe (1990), Hilty & Brown (1986), Krabbe (1992), Mariaux & Braun (1996), Schulenberg *et al.* (1984).

---

20 WHITE-WINGED POTOO
Nyctibius leucopterus   Plate 6

Caprimulgus leucopterus Wied, 1821, *Reise Bras.* 2, p.227, note (Forests in the vicinity of Conquista, Bahia)

Possibly forms a superspecies with Andean Potoo, with which it was formerly considered conspecific.

IDENTIFICATION Length c. 26-28cm. One of the smallest potoos. Sexes similar. **At rest** Upperparts greyish-brown streaked blackish-brown. Lower lesser coverts, median coverts and greater coverts whitish, forming broad white wing-panel, although this may often be obscured by scapulars. No obvious scapular pattern. Indistinct greyish-white or pale buffish collar around the hindneck. Pale buffish or greyish-white throat. Underparts greyish-brown, streaked and spotted blackish-brown. **In flight** No information. **Similar species** None within range. The Andean Potoo (19) is an Andean endemic, occurring at much higher altitudes. It is larger, with a smaller white wing-panel and less-defined markings on the underparts.

VOICE The song is a plaintive whistle *weuuuuuu*, gradually descending in pitch. Sings from perches in the canopy, up to 40m above ground. May be heard predominantly during the night, especially when there is plenty of moonlight. The contact call, given from a perch or in flight, is a short, high-pitched *bweep* that may be repeated several times in quick succession. No further information available.

HABITAT Prefers undisturbed forests. Occurs in primary forest and humid forest. In south-western Guyana, it is found near streams in tall, *Mora*-dominated forest, and in central Guyana it inhabits the edges of rivers in seasonally flooded mixed *Mora* forest. 0-900m.

HABITS Nocturnal. Roosts on top of stumps, up to 20m above ground. At night, frequently perches upright on snags, stumps and exposed branches within the canopy. No further information available.

FOOD Moths, bugs and beetles (including Cerambycidae and Curculionidae). No further data available.

BREEDING No information available.

DESCRIPTION Adult male Not examined, but similar to the female, with a larger, whiter wing-patch. **Adult female** Forehead, crown and nape greyish-brown, central feathers broadly streaked blackish-brown. Indistinct collar around the hindneck greyish-white or pale buffish, speckled and barred brown. Mantle, back, rump and uppertail-coverts brown or greyish-brown, thinly barred pale buff and cinnamon, broadly streaked blackish-brown. Upper lesser coverts brown or greyish-brown, lower lesser coverts buffish-white or white, tipped brown. Median and greater coverts buffish-white or white, speckled brown at tips. Primary coverts brown. Scapulars brown or greyish-brown, thinly barred pale buff and cinnamon, streaked blackish-brown. Primaries brown, P9-P6 spotted pale brownish-buff or greyish-white along outerwebs, P5-P1 indistinctly barred and spotted cinnamon, pale buff and greyish-white. Secondaries brown, indistinctly barred and spotted cinnamon, pale buff and greyish-white. Tertials brown, densely mottled pale buff. Tail brown, faintly but broadly barred greyish-brown or brownish-buff, occasionally narrowly tipped (c. 2mm) buffish. Lores dark brown; ear-coverts brown, feathers narrowly edged and tipped buff. Chin and throat greyish-white tinged buffish, streaked and barred brown. Breast greyish-brown thinly barred buffish-brown, feathers broadly tipped blackish-brown on lower breast. Belly and flanks greyish-brown, barred, spotted and streaked blackish-brown. Undertail-coverts greyish-white or pale buff, barred and spotted pale brown. Underwing-coverts blackish-brown spotted pale buff. **Immature** and **Juvenile** Not known. **Chick** Not known. **Bare parts** Iris yellow; bill black; legs and feet brown.

MEASUREMENTS Wing (male, four) 182-186, (female, three) 182-207, unsexed (one) 202; tail (male, four) 114-118, (female, three) 114-140, unsexed (one) 132; bill (male, three) 15.3-16.5, (female, three) 15.3-21.8, unsexed (one) c. 22; tarsus both sexes (five) 9.6-10.0. Weight (male, four) 78.5-82.5g, (female, two) 85g. Note: most of the biometrics are taken from specimens collected from the Iwokrama Reserve in central Guyana and near Manaus in Amazonian Brazil (see Geographical Variation).

MOULT No data available.

GEOGRAPHICAL VARIATION Monotypic. Specimens taken from central Guyana and Amazonian Brazil are smaller than two other specimens (one of which is from Bahia in eastern Brazil), and are therefore worthy of further study.

DISTRIBUTION AND MOVEMENTS A little-known South American species, recorded only from four or five localities. C and SW Guyana (Iwokrama Reserve and Maipaima Creek, western Kanuku Mountains) and N and E Brazil (Jaú National Park, west of the Rio Negro, and near Manaus, both in Amazonas, and near Vitória da Conquista in S Bahia). Presumably sedentary.

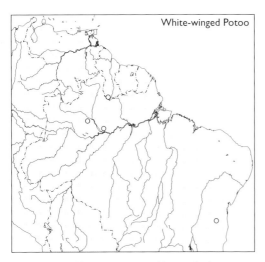

White-winged Potoo

STATUS Possibly common near Manaus in Amazonas, Brazil, and relatively common in the Iwokrama Reserve, central Guyana. No data available from other localities.

REFERENCES Cohn-Haft (1993), Parker *et al.* (1993), Schulenburg *et al.* (1984).

---

21   RUFOUS POTOO
Nyctibius bracteatus   Plate 6

Nyctibius bracteatus Gould, 1846, *Proc. Zool. Soc. London* p.1 (Bogotá, Colombia)

IDENTIFICATION Length 21.5-24.5cm. The smallest and most brightly coloured potoo. Sexes similar. **At rest** Upperparts rufescent-tawny, barred and spotted blackish, especially on head. No collar around hindneck. Wing-coverts rufescent-tawny, speckled dark brown. Scapulars rufescent-tawny, boldly spotted whitish. Underparts rufescent-tawny, boldly spotted whitish. **In flight** Both sexes lack white markings on wings and tail. **Similar species** None.

VOICE The song is a descending, occasionally quavering *boobooboobooboo*. Sings from perches such as horizontal branches c. 7m above ground. May be heard mainly at night. No further information available.

HABITAT Prefers forest interiors, e.g. of evergreen rainforests. c. 500m. No further information available.

HABITS Nocturnal. Roost-sites may be in palm thickets in the forest understorey. No further information available.

FOOD No data available.

BREEDING No data on breeding season.
   No nest is constructed; the egg is laid in a slight depression in the top of a vertical tree-stump, in a snag on a tree-trunk, or at the bend of a sloping branch. Clutch 1. The adult broods its offspring by sitting at its back, the chick facing forwards from beneath the adult's belly feathers. No further information available.

DESCRIPTION Adult male Forehead, crown and nape rufescent-tawny, barred and spotted blackish-brown. No

collar around hindneck. Mantle and back rufescent-tawny, indistinctly barred or vermiculated dark brown. Rump and uppertail-coverts rufescent-tawny or tawny, indistinctly vermiculated dark brown. Alula and primary coverts brownish. Rest of wing-coverts rufescent-tawny, speckled and vermiculated dark brown. Scapulars rufescent-tawny speckled brown, boldly spotted whitish towards tips of outerwebs, spots bordered blackish-brown and often rather square-shaped. Primaries brown, P10-P5 buffish on outerwebs, P4-P1 rufescent-tawny on outerwebs. Secondaries brown, edged rufescent-tawny along outerwebs. Tertials rufescent-tawny speckled brown, broadly tipped whitish with a dark brown subterminal band. Tail rufescent-tawny, broadly barred dark brown, R5 often with a small buffish-white spot on tip of outerweb. Lores and ear-coverts rufescent-tawny, speckled or barred brown. Chin and throat rufescent-tawny, thinly barred brown. Breast rufescent-tawny, barred and vermiculated brown, boldly spotted whitish, spots edged or bordered blackish-brown. Belly, flanks and undertail-coverts tawny or buff, boldly spotted whitish. Underwing-coverts brown, lightly barred tawny. **Adult female** Similar to the male. **Immature** and **Juvenile** Similar to the adults but more heavily spotted blackish-brown on the upperparts and with paler, buffier scapulars and wing-coverts? **Chick** Not described. **Bare parts** Iris yellowish; bill blackish; legs and feet brownish. **Measurements** (both sexes) wing 159-168; tail 121-131; bill 18.4-19.3; tarsus no data. Weight no data.

MOULT The primary moult is serially descendant. No further information available.

GEOGRAPHICAL VARIATION Monotypic.

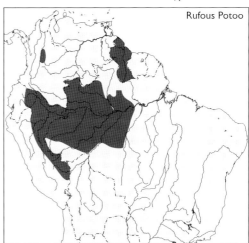

Rufous Potoo

DISTRIBUTION AND MOVEMENTS A little-known species, restricted to the northern parts of South America in WC Colombia (Cundinamarca), E Ecuador (Napo and Pastaza), E Peru, NW Brazil (Amazonas) and Guyana. Presumably sedentary.

STATUS Rare and local throughout range. No further information available.

REFERENCES Hilty & Brown (1986), Sick (1993).

144

OWLET-NIGHTJARS AEGOTHELIDAE

AEGOTHELES

Aegotheles Vigors and Horsfield, 1827, Trans. Linn. Soc. London, 15, pt. 1, p. 194. Type by monotypy, *Caprimulgus novaehollandiae* Latham 1790 = *Caprimulgus cristatus* (Shaw 1790).

Eight Australasian species, with most occurring in New Guinea. Owlet-nightjars are small to medium-sized birds with forward-facing eyes, broad, flat bills surrounded by long facial bristles, rounded tails, long tarsi and feet that have long, curved and sharply pointed claws, the middle toe not being pectinated. Arboreal. Owlet-nightjars generally breed and roost in holes and hollows. Small clutches of white, unmarked eggs are laid on simple linings of vegetation and other materials. They forage by hawking for food in flight, by pouncing onto prey from a perch, by flycatching from a low perch or by chasing after food on the ground.

22   MOLUCCAN OWLET-NIGHTJAR
Aegotheles crinifrons   Plate 7

Other name: Long-whiskered Owlet-nightjar

Batrachostomus crinifrons "Temminck" Bonaparte, 1850, *Consp. Av.* p.57 (No locality = Halmahera)

An allospecies of Large Owlet-nightjar.

IDENTIFICATION Length 26.5-31cm. A large, brownish or rufescent owlet-nightjar, endemic to the Moluccas. Sexes may be similar, in which case there is a rufous phase, or else rufous birds are female and/or immature (see Moult, Geographical Variation). **At rest** Upperparts (male) brown, finely barred greyish-brown. Buffish lateral crown-stripes. No collar around hindneck. Wing-coverts brown finely barred greyish-brown, spotted pale buff on median and greater coverts. No obvious scapular pattern. Underparts buffish-brown speckled and spotted dark brown on breast, becoming buff spotted brown on belly and flanks. 'Rufous-phase' birds (see above) are paler and plainer, being rufescent-tawny on the upperparts and breast. **In flight** Often flies with weak, fluttering wingbeats. Both sexes lack white markings on wings and tail. **Similar species** None within range, but there are two other large species of owlet-nightjar: Large Owlet-nightjar (23), found in New Guinea, is either brownish or rufescent on the upperparts while the underparts are boldly spotted whitish (see that species); New Caledonian Owlet-nightjar (25), known by a single museum specimen from New Caledonia, is brown barred greyish-white all over.

VOICE The song (perhaps call) is a series of 3-5 laugh-like *kaah* notes, evenly pitched or descending slightly as they trail off. May be heard throughout the night. Also utters a high-pitched, shrill *ke-aah*. If alarmed, calls include screams and moans. No further information available.

HABITAT Prefers forests and well-wooded areas. Occurs in primary, mature secondary and lightly logged forest and forest edges. Also inhabits coconut plantations and cultivated areas. 0–1,250m on Halmahera, 0–1,800m on Bacan.

HABITS Nocturnal. Occurs singly, or in small groups (perhaps family parties) of 2-5 birds. At night, 2-3 birds may alight near each other and call loudly (see Voice). Feeds by flycatching from branches in trees, often returning to the same perch. Also hovers near vegetation and takes prey from leaves. No further information available.

FOOD Insects. No further data available.

BREEDING No information available.

DESCRIPTION Adult male (or older or brown-phase bird) Forehead, crown and nape brown, finely barred with greyish-brown speckling. Buffish lateral crown-stripes. No collar around hindneck. Mantle, back, rump, uppertail-coverts and wing-coverts brown, finely barred with greyish-brown speckling; median and greater coverts spotted pale buff on feather-tips. Scapulars brown, finely barred with greyish-brown speckling. Outer 5-6 primaries brown, boldly and regularly spotted or barred buff along outerwebs; inner 4-5 primaries and all secondaries brown, thinly barred with buff or greyish-brown speckling along outerwebs. Tertials brown, finely barred with greyish-brown speckling. Tail brown, barred with pale buff and tawny speckling. Lores and ear-coverts rufescent-brown speckled brown. Chin and throat buffish, thinly streaked brown. Sides of throat and all of breast buffish-brown, speckled and spotted dark brown. Belly, flanks and undertail-coverts buff, spotted and occasionally speckled brown. Underwing-coverts brownish-buff. **Adult female** Similar to the male (unless females are the paler, plainer, more rufescent birds: see Geographical Variation). **Immature** and **Juvenile** Not described, but possibly similar to the rufescent (perhaps adult female) birds. **Chick** Unknown. **Bare parts** Iris brown; bill brownish; legs and feet brownish-straw.

MEASUREMENTS Wing (male) (three) 163-172, (female) 156-162; tail (male) (three) 130-148, (female) 127-150; bill (male) (three) 21.1-22.3, (female) 19.3-20.6; tarsus (male) (three) 23.1-27.1, (female) 21.0-24.3. Weight no data.

MOULT Few data available, although one bird (museum specimen) taken in early June was in full moult: on both wings, all primaries new, the outer two secondaries (S1 and S2) new, S3 growing and the remaining inner secondaries all old. The tail moult appeared to be centrifugal, with R1 and R2 new, R3 growing and R4 and R5 old. Many body feathers and wing-coverts had also been replaced. In addition, it was noted that the old, unmoulted feathers were rufous and the new, moulted feathers were brown (see Identification and Geographical Variation).

GEOGRAPHICAL VARIATION Monotypic. There may be two colour phases, brown (see Description) and rufous (unless these are females or immatures). Rufous-phase birds are paler and plainer than brownish birds. Upperparts rufescent-tawny, spotted buffish-white on median and greater wing-coverts. Breast rufescent-tawny, spotted buffish-white. Belly and flanks buffish-white, lightly spotted brown or unmarked.

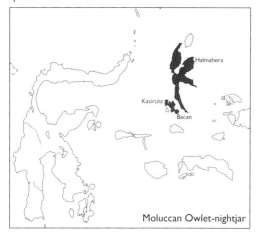

Moluccan Owlet-nightjar

DISTRIBUTION AND MOVEMENTS A little-known species endemic to the northern Moluccas, recorded only from Halmahera, Bacan and Kasiruta. Sedentary.

STATUS Common on Halmahera. No data available from Bacan or Kasiruta.

REFERENCES Coates & Bishop (1997), White & Bruce (1986).

23   LARGE OWLET-NIGHTJAR
Aegotheles insignis   Plate 7

Other names: Feline Owlet-nightjar, Rufous Owlet-nightjar

Aegotheles insignis Salvadori, 1875, *Ann. Mus. Civ. Genova* 7, p.916 (Hatam, Arfak, New Guinea)
Aegotheles insignis tatei Rand, 1941, *Amer. Mus. Novit.* 1102, p.10 (near Palmer junction, Fly River, New Guinea)

An allospecies of Moluccan Owlet-nightjar.

IDENTIFICATION Length 25-30cm. A large, brownish or rufescent owlet-nightjar, endemic to New Guinea. Brown and rufous phases. Sexes similar. **At rest** Upperparts and wing-coverts rufescent-brown or -tawny, lightly spotted or speckled white or buff. Scapulars boldly spotted white or buff, spots broadly bordered blackish-brown. Bold whitish or buffish lateral crown-stripes. No collar around hindneck. Underparts rufescent-brown or -tawny but chin and throat whitish or buff and centre of breast, flanks and lower belly boldly spotted white. **In flight** Both sexes lack white markings on wings and tail. **Similar species** None in New Guinea, but there are two other large species of owlet-nightjar (see under Moluccan Owlet-nightjar, 22).

VOICE The song (perhaps call) is an ascending series of 4-5, rather loud *owrr* notes, each note slightly trilled at the end. Other calls include single squeaky *kee-h* notes and a rapid series of up to 11 higher-pitched *kee* notes which increase in speed. No further information available.

HABITAT Prefers montane forests. Occurs in primary forest and areas of second growth, forest edges, open forest

and woodland and riverine formations bordering grasslands. 1,200–2,700m. The distinct south-eastern race *tatei* occurs at 80m in the lowlands.

HABITS Crepuscular (perhaps) and nocturnal. Solitary. Roosts in holes in trees, in tangles of vines or in clumps of dead leaves, up to 20m above ground. At tree-hole roost-sites, entrance holes may be 9-10cm in diameter. No further information available.

FOOD Beetles and other large insects. No further data available.

BREEDING Breeding season May?–November? (female in breeding condition in May, fledgling collected in November). Nest-sites probably in hollows in trees. No further information available.

DESCRIPTION *A. i. insignis* **Adult male** (brown phase) Forehead, crown and nape brown or rufescent-brown, lightly spotted or speckled white or buff. Bold lateral crown-stripes formed by large whitish or buffish spots, edged blackish-brown. No collar around hindneck. Mantle and back brown or rufescent-brown, lightly spotted or speckled white or buff. Rump and uppertail-coverts brown or rufescent-brown, lightly speckled, spotted or barred buffish or whitish. Primary coverts dark brown, speckled buffish at tips. Rest of wing-coverts brown or rufescent-brown, speckled buffish, with whitish 'tear-drop' shaped spots at centre of feather-tips. Scapulars brown or rufescent-brown, boldly spotted buffish or whitish, spots broadly bordered blackish-brown. Primaries brown, spotted buff along outerwebs. Secondaries brown, speckled and barred pale tawny along outerwebs. Tertials brown or rufescent-brown, speckled and barred buff or white. Tail rufescent-brown, distinctly barred dark brown, R1 boldly spotted pale buff along outerwebs. Lores blackish-brown, ear-coverts brown or rufescent-brown, speckled blackish-brown. Chin and central throat whitish or buffish, broadly edged blackish-brown. Sides of throat brown, cinnamon-brown or rufescent-brown, barred blackish-brown. Centre of breast whitish or buffish, broadly edged blackish-brown. Sides of breast and centre of belly brown or rufescent-brown, spotted and speckled buffish. Sides of belly and flanks buffish or whitish, feathers broadly edged or tipped blackish-brown. Undertail-coverts buffish, rufescent-brown or cinnamon-brown, spotted greyish-white, speckled and occasionally barred brown. Underwing-coverts brown or rufescent-brown, unmarked or barred or spotted white or buff. **Adult female** Similar to the male. **Immature** and **Juvenile** Similar to the adults, although some have more uniform upperparts. **Chick** Not described. **Bare parts** Iris brown; bill brownish or horn; legs and feet pinkish or flesh. **Measurements** Wing (male) 152-176, (female) 160-180; tail (male) 117-134, (female) 126-141; bill (male) 17.9-23.0, (female) c. 16.0-20.7; tarsus (male) 18.0-24.3, (female) 18.0-25.2. Weight (male) 67-85g, (female) 74-82g.

MOULT Few data available. Primary moult appears to be serially descendant, i.e. one museum specimen taken in April was renewing P5 and P8 on both wings. A second specimen taken in late March was in active body moult.

GEOGRAPHICAL VARIATION Two races are currently recognised.

  A. i. insignis Described above. Individual variation is quite common, with many birds having a bright, rufescent-tawny plumage. Birds of this colour type

146

often have bolder, whiter spots on the scapulars and wing-coverts, less spotting on the crown, mantle and back, plainer primaries, secondaries and tertials and plainer, less distinctly barred tails (the outer tail feathers, R5, often being edged whitish on the outerwebs).

A. i. tatei Smaller than the nominate, with smaller white spots along the lateral crown-stripes, smaller white spots on the underparts and brighter, more rufous-brown wings. The tail feathers are thinly barred pale buff, not brown as in the nominate. Wing (male) no data, (female) 138-146; tail (male) no data, (female) 117-137. Weight no data.

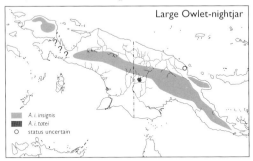

DISTRIBUTION AND MOVEMENTS An endemic species to New Guinea, where it is widely distributed throughout the mountain ranges.

A. i. insignis Irian Jaya (mountains in the Vogelkop and from the Weyland Mountains presumably eastwards) and Papua New Guinea (central highlands east to the Huon Peninsula and south-east to the Owen Stanley Range). Presumably sedentary.

A. i. tatei SW Papua New Guinea (a lowland race known only from the type locality, five miles below the Palmer Junction, Fly River). Presumably sedentary.

STATUS Little known and secretive but possibly fairly common throughout its range.

REFERENCES Beehler *et al.* (1986), Coates (1985), Gilliard & LeCroy (1961), Rand & Gilliard (1967).

---

24   AUSTRALIAN OWLET-NIGHTJAR
Aegotheles cristatus   Plate 7

Other name: Crested Owlet-nightjar

Caprimulgus cristatus Shaw in J. White, 1790, *J. Voy. New South Wales* p.241 and pl. (New South Wales)
Aegotheles cristatus tasmanicus Mathews, 1918, *Bds. Austr.* 7, p.65 (Prospect, near Launceston, Tasmania)

Formerly considered conspecific with Barred Owlet-nightjar.

IDENTIFICATION Length 19-25cm. A small to medium-sized Australasian owlet-nightjar, variable in colour, birds ranging from grey to rufous (these extremes treated as phases). Sexes similar. At rest Upperparts and wing-coverts greyish, speckled greyish-white. Distinct greyish-white lateral crown-stripes, greyish-white band around rear of crown and greyish-white collar around hindneck. No obvious scapular pattern. Underparts pale buffish-white,

narrowly barred or vermiculated brown. In flight Flight often buoyant with fluttering wingbeats, but when foraging wingbeats become faster and more regular. Both sexes lack white markings on wings and tail. Similar species None in Australia. In southern Papua New Guinea, Barred Owlet-nightjar (26) is slightly smaller and darker and less coarsely barred on the upperparts and breast, has brownish lores and ear-coverts and duller, buffish or greyish-white flanks and belly. Wallace's Owlet-nightjar (27) is slightly smaller and darker, usually lacks lateral crown-stripes, lacks a collar around the hindneck and has the wing-coverts speckled and spotted whitish.

VOICE The song (perhaps call) is a short, mellow *kair* note, repeated once every c. 5 seconds for long periods, or a high-pitched, churring *chirr-chirr* that is either evenly pitched or slightly undulating. Sings from perches. May be heard mainly at dusk and dawn and throughout the night. Occasionally sings or calls from its roost during the day, especially on overcast, rainy days, giving a loud, abrupt *chirk chirk chirk*. In Papua New Guinea, utters 2-10 (usually 2-3) short shriek-like notes, generally during the latter part of the night (00h00-04h00). If disturbed, occasionally gives a rather loud, strident *kurrr, ka-ah*. When alarmed, utters several short, harsh rattling notes. During threat/defence displays, adults hiss at the potential danger. They make trilling sounds when feeding their young and the chicks utter low trills when begging for food. When the young are ready to fledge, the adults call them from the nest with single soft, yelping *yuk* notes.

HABITAT Prefers forests and woodland, but avoids mangroves and treeless plains or deserts. Occurs in eucalyptus forests and woodland, acacia woodland, open eucalyptus forest with acacia understorey, Sclerophyllos forest, open forest, riparian woodland, heathland, scrubland and mallee. Also inhabits farmland with trees, suburban gardens, towns, and occasionally rainforests. In southern Papua New Guinea, occurs in savanna woodland. 0–1,000m.

HABITS Crepuscular and nocturnal. Roosts in hollows and crevices in trees, tree-stumps, banks, breakaways and cliffs. Also roosts in hollow fence posts, roof cavities, termite mounds and abandoned babbler nests, and occasionally roosts in nest boxes, pipes, chimneys, beneath logs, or amongst long grass or rocks. Roost-sites may be shallow or up to 2m deep and the entrances are usually 2-8m above ground. Territories may contain up to six roost-sites, which may be used for several years. Paired males and females roost close to one another but never together. An owlet-nightjar may dispossess other birds, e.g. White-throated Treecreepers *Climacteris leucophaea*, nesting in one of its roost-sites. At the roost-site, birds appear to roost in a crouched but generally alert posture. They occasionally scratch and preen themselves and sometimes call (see Voice). Roosting birds occasionally sun themselves at the entrance to the roost-site. If flushed from its roost, a bird flies 10-30m in a direct, undulating flight and either dives sharply into another roost-site or alights briefly on a low, open perch, sitting crosswise and upright and occasionally bobs its head up and down, looks around, and raises the feathers on the sides of its neck. Out in the open, they are occasionally mobbed by birds, e.g. honeyeaters *Meliphaga* sp., or preyed upon by Grey Butcherbird *Cracticus torquatus*.

Often drinks just after dusk and just before dawn,

usually from still water. To drink, it flies down and alights at the edge of a shallow pool, dam or billabong. Forages in open spaces beneath and amongst trees, 1-5m above ground, hawking for insects in direct flight over distances of up to 30m. Hunts from the ground or a low perch, twisting, turning and skimming after prey before alighting on a different perch. Also feeds from a perch by swooping onto prey on the ground or in boles of trees, often without landing. Often sits on roads and tracks at night, from where it may flycatch, making short sallies after insects, and can run and chase after prey along the ground. Frequently hunts insects attracted to artificial light.

FOOD Moths and moth caterpillars, beetles (including Carabidae, Staphylinidae, Scarabaeidae, Elateridae, Cleridae, Chrysomelidae, Curculionidae, Tenebrionidae, Coccinellidae and Cerambycidae), Orthoptera (including Tettigoniidae, Gryllidae and Acrididae), ants and ant pupae, centipedes and millipedes, spiders, bugs, cockroaches (including Blattidae) and earwigs. Occasionally ingests small stones, although these may be taken accidentally.

BREEDING Breeding season throughout Australia generally August–December but may breed in any month, especially after the rains in dry and arid regions. No data available from southern Papua New Guinea.

Permanently territorial and appears to mate for life. Territories may possibly cover up to c. 100ha. A simple nest is often constructed inside a hollow, by lining the base with fresh eucalyptus or acacia leaves, dry gum leaves and dry grass. Both sexes participate in lining the nest. Some nests may be left unlined. Nest-sites are usually in vertical, horizontal or sloping hollows in trees or tree-stumps, 0.5-5m above ground, occasionally higher. Typical nest hollows are 0.3-3.5m deep with entrance holes of 7-25cm diameter. Also nests in hollows and crevices in buildings, fallen logs or fence-posts, in burrows or tunnels in riverbanks and in nest-boxes. Also known to have nested in hollows previously used by *Climacteris* species, in the old nest of a Sugar Glider *Petaurus breviceps*, in the radiator of a disused tractor, in a waterpipe beside a dam and in a dead tree surrounded by deep water. Nest-sites may be re-used within the same breeding season (see below) or from one year to another. If a breeding bird is killed and its nest fails, the nest-site may be re-used within the same breeding season (possibly by the remaining adult with a new mate).

Clutch 2-5, usually 3-4. Larger clutches are more often laid in more arid regions. Eggs elliptical and white, occasionally lightly marked pale brown, 25.9-32.0 x 20.8-24.7mm. Incubation is possibly by both sexes, although usually by the female and commences when the first egg is laid. If the first clutch is lost, a replacement may be laid within c. 18 days, in a new nest-site. If approaching danger is noticed by an incubating bird, it usually flushes off the nest. The eggs hatch asynchronously and the incubation period is 25-27 days.

The semi-altricial, nidicolous chicks are usually brooded by the female, the male roosting in a hollow nearby. If disturbed at the nest, the brooding adult may fly off or perform a defence display by puffing up its plumage, gaping and hissing (see Voice). The chicks are brooded continually for the first four days, only by day at 4-11 days of age, and not at all thereafter, the adults roosting close by. The chicks are fed by both parents, the feeding visits tending to be quite brief. Up to c. 7 days of age, the chicks are generally fed once every half-hour

during the first half of the night. The frequency of feeding visits increases as the chicks get older, and from c. 7 days of age they are fed every 10-15 minutes throughout the night. Very little, if any, nest sanitation is carried out by the adults. The chicks fledge after 21-32 days, usually 21-29 days, and generally leave the nest in the middle of the night; if disturbed, theay may leave during the day. After fledging, a chick may roost by itself within 300m of the nest-site, using different roost-sites on different days.

Single- or perhaps double-brooded. In arid regions, second and even third clutches may be laid during prolonged wet periods or when there are several separate wet spells in a year. Second broods are occasionally invaded by feral bees, which build their hives inside the nest-site.

DESCRIPTION *A. c. cristatus* **Adult male** (grey phase) Forehead, crown and nape greyish, speckled dark grey. Bold lateral crown-stripes, band around rear of crown and distinct collar (c. 5 mm wide) around hindneck greyish-white speckled grey or brown. Mantle, back, rump and uppertail-coverts greyish, speckled and narrowly barred greyish-white. Wing-coverts and scapulars greyish, speckled and finely barred greyish-white. Primaries brown, P10-P8 barred buff along outerwebs, rest of primaries faintly speckled and mottled buff. Secondaries brown, faintly speckled and mottled buff. Tertials greyish, speckled and faintly barred greyish-white. Tail brown, broadly but indistinctly barred with greyish-white or pale buff speckling. Orbital ring pale grey, lores pale grey speckled whitish, ear-coverts greyish-white tinged rufous. Chin, throat and breast pale buffish-white, narrowly barred brown or light brown. Belly and flanks buffish-white or yellowish-white, barred or vermiculated brown. Undertail-coverts white, plain or narrowly barred brown. Underwing-coverts whitish, speckled or barred brown. **Adult female** Similar to the male. **Immature** and **Juvenile** Similar to the adults but with a less distinct head pattern, although pale buff orbital ring more prominent. **Chick** At hatching, covered in dense long white down. After 7-10 days, the white down is replaced by a greyer down, which is then fairly quickly replaced by the juvenile plumage. **Bare parts** Iris brown; bill blackish-brown, becoming flesh-bone at the base of the lower mandible; legs and feet flesh or greyish-pink.

MEASUREMENTS Wing (male) 117-143, (female) 118-149; tail (male) 99-127, (female) 94-130; bill (male) 11.4-17.1, (female) 11.3-17.3; tarsus (male) 20.0-26.0, (female) 20.5-26.5. Weight (male) 35-60g, (female) 21-65g.

MOULT Adults undertake a complete post-breeding moult. The primaries are moulted descendantly, the sequence of secondary moult is undocumented.The tail appears to be replaced quickly, with all feathers moulting almost simultaneously. Juveniles have a partial post-breeding moult, during which they replace some head and body feathers, and possibly some wing-coverts. They do not moult again until after the following breeding season, when they undergo a complete moult similar to that of the adults.

GEOGRAPHICAL VARIATION Two races are currently recognised, but *tasmanicus* may prove to be merely an end point in a cline.

A. c. cristatus As well as the grey phase described above, there is also a rufous phase, although coloration is extremely variable and many birds show characteristics between the two, i.e. in the amount and degree of rufous on parts of the plumage. Variation in size is clinal, the largest birds occurring in southern Papua New Guinea, with birds gradually becoming slightly smaller southwards across Australia. Northern populations are paler, more often tinged rufous and have more distinct head markings and tail barring. Birds become darker southwards, with less distinct head makings and tail barring. The amount and frequency of rufous in the plumage also decreases southwards.

A. c. tasmanicus Darker and sootier than the nominate and smaller on average. Wing (male) 114-127, (female) 118-130; tail (male) 91-109, (female) 95-111. Weight (male) 37-44g, (female) 31-60g.

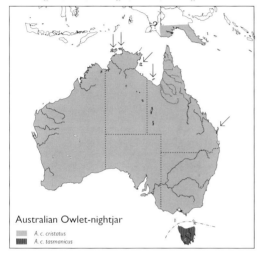

Australian Owlet-nightjar

■ *A. c. cristatus*
▓ *A. c. tasmanicus*

DISTRIBUTION AND MOVEMENTS Widespread over all of Australia, including its larger islands, and reaching southern Papua New Guinea, where there is a small population.

    A. c. cristatus S and SE Papua New Guinea, and Australia, including Melville Island, Bathurst Island, Groote Eylandt, Mornington Island, Fraser Island and Kangaroo Island. Sedentary.

    A. c. tasmanicus Tasmania. Also, presumably this race, Flinders Island. Sedentary.

STATUS Not uncommon locally in southern Papua New Guinea, common over much of Australia, especially in inland areas, and uncommon in Tasmania.

REFERENCES Barker & Vestjens (1989), Beehler *et al.* (1986), Brigham & Geiser (in press), Brigham *et al.* (1997), Coates (1985), Higgins (in press), Mayr & Rand (1937), Rand & Gilliard (1967), Schodde & Mason (1981, 1997), Webb (1989).

25   NEW CALEDONIAN OWLET-NIGHTJAR
Aegotheles savesi   Plate 7

Aegotheles savesi Layard and Layard, 1881, *Ibis* p.132, pl.5 (Tongue, near Nouméa, New Caledonia)

IDENTIFICATION Length 29cm. A large brownish owlet-nightjar, endemic to New Caledonia. Known only from a single specimen, a male. **At rest** Upperparts and wing-coverts brown, thinly barred greyish-white. No lateral crown-stripes, no collar around the hindneck and no obvious scapular pattern. Lacks a white throat-patch. Underparts brown, densely barred greyish-white. **In flight** Long-tailed. Lacks white markings on wings and tail, which are brown thinly barred greyish-white. **Similar species** None within range. There are two other large species of owlet-nightjar, Moluccan (22) and Large (23), which see for differences.

VOICE Unknown.

HABITAT No information.

HABITS No information.

FOOD Small beetles. No further information.

BREEDING No information.

DESCRIPTION Adult male Forehead, crown and nape brown thinly barred greyish-white. No collar around the hindneck. Mantle, back, rump, uppertail-coverts, wing-coverts and scapulars brown, thinly barred greyish-white. Primaries and secondaries brown, narrowly barred greyish-white along outerwebs. Tertials brown, thinly barred greyish-white across both webs. Tail brown, R5-R2 thinly barred greyish-white along outerwebs, central pair (R1) thinly barred greyish-white across both webs. Lores and ear-coverts darkish brown, thinly barred greyish-white. Chin and throat brown, narrowly barred greyish-white. Breast, belly, flanks and undertail-coverts brown, densely barred greyish-white. Underwing-coverts brown barred greyish-white. **Adult female** Unknown. **Immature** and **Juvenile** Unknown. **Chick** Unknown. **Bare parts** Iris sienna-yellow; bill blackish; legs and feet brownish.

MEASUREMENTS (One male only) Wing 163; tail 160; bill 18.2; tarsus 33.2. Weight no data.

MOULT No information.

GEOGRAPHICAL VARIATION Monotypic.

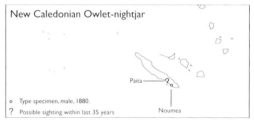

New Caledonian Owlet-nightjar

○ Type specimen, male, 1880.
? Possible sighting within last 35 years

Paita

Noumea

DISTRIBUTION AND MOVEMENTS New Caledonia. The only known specimen flew into a bedroom in Tongue, near Nouméa, on 11 April 1880. There has been a recent, possible sighting in the Paita region (see Status).

STATUS Unknown. In recent times (early 1960s?), a local hunter claims to have shot a roosting bird near Paita, although no further details are available.

REFERENCES Hannecart & Letocart (1983), Layard & Layard (1881), Olson *et al.* (1987).

Aegotheles bennettii Salvadori and D'Albertis, 1875, *Ann. Mus. Civ. Genova* 7, p.816 (south-eastern New Guinea)
Aegotheles bennettii affinis Salvadori, 1875, *Ann. Mus. Civ. Genova* 7, p.917 (Arfak Mountains, New Guinea)
Aegotheles bennettii wiedenfeldi Laubmann, 1914, *Orn. Monatsb.* 22, p.7 (Sattelberg, New Guinea)
Aegotheles bennettii terborghi Diamond, 1967, *Amer. Mus. Novit.* 2284, p.5 (Karimui, eastern Highlands District, New Guinea)
Aegotheles bennettii plumiferus Ramsay, 1883, *Proc. Linn. Soc. New South Wales* 8, p.21 (south-east New Guinea, error = Fergusson Island)

Formerly considered conspecific with Australian Owlet-nightjar.

IDENTIFICATION Length 20-24.5cm. A small to medium-sized greyish-brown owlet-nightjar, endemic to New Guinea and the D'Entrecasteaux Archipelago. Sexes similar. **At rest** Upperparts and wing-coverts brownish or blackish, finely barred and vermiculated greyish-white. Has broad, buffish lateral crown-stripes and a distinct buffish or whitish collar around the hindneck. No obvious scapular pattern. Underparts buffish to greyish-white, spotted, speckled and vermiculated brown. **In flight** Both sexes lack white markings on wings and tail. **Similar species** Wallace's Owlet-nightjar (27) is darker on the upperparts and breast, has some bold whitish spotting on the wing-coverts, lacks (or has indistinct) lateral crown-stripes, usually has no collar around the hindneck and has a buffish throat that contrasts with the darker breast and sides of throat; generally occurs at higher altitudes. Grey-phase Australian Owlet-nightjar (24) is slightly larger and paler, has rufous lores and ear-coverts, coarser barring on the upperparts, coarser but less extensive barring on the breast and paler, whiter flanks and belly.

VOICE The song (perhaps call) is a descending, hollow churr or deep trill. No further information available.

HABITAT Prefers rainforest and monsoon forest. Occurs in lowland and hill forests. 0–1,100m.

HABITS Crepuscular (perhaps) and nocturnal. Roosts in hollows in trees, often perching at or near the entrance. Roost holes may be used for periods of several months. Also roosts on branches in trees. No further information available.

FOOD No data available.

BREEDING Breeding season not documented, although a recently fledged juvenile was noted in early October. Nest-sites are probably in hollows in trees. Eggs are elliptical and white, 28.4-32.2 x 21.5-24.8mm. No further information available.

DESCRIPTION *A. b. bennettii* **Adult male** Forehead, crown and nape dark brown or blackish, with buffish-brown, speckled greyish-white, lateral crown-stripes. Distinct collar around hindneck greyish-white or buffish, speckled brown. Mantle, back, rump, uppertail-coverts, wing-coverts and scapulars brown or dusky, greyish-brown, finely barred or vermiculated greyish-white. Primaries brown, faintly spotted buff along outerwebs. Secondaries brown, faintly barred buff along outerwebs. Tertials brown or dusky, greyish-brown, finely vermiculated or barred greyish-white.

Tail brown, regularly but faintly barred greyish-white. Lores brownish, ear-coverts brown barred greyish-white or speckled buffish. Chin and throat pale buff or greyish-white, speckled and spotted brown. Breast, upper belly and flanks buffish or greyish-white, speckled and vermiculated brown, lower belly buffish-white and usually plainer. Undertail-coverts buffish-white vermiculated brown. Underwing-coverts greyish-white speckled brown. **Adult female** Similar to the male. **Immature** and **Juvenile** Not described. **Chick** Not described. **Bare parts** Iris brown; bill dark grey or blackish; legs and feet pale flesh.

MEASUREMENTS Wing (male) 114-128, (female) 116-130; tail (male) 98-120, (female) 106-125; bill (male) 14.9-16.0, (female) 14.3-15.2; tarsus (male, one) 20.5, (female, one) 20.6. Weight (male, one) 45.0g, (female) no data.

MOULT Very few data available. Wing moult noted on museum specimens taken in February and April. The primaries are moulted descendantly.

GEOGRAPHICAL VARIATION Five races are currently recognised. The race *affinis* is considered by some authorities to be a race of Australian Owlet-nightjar.

A. b. bennettii Described above. There appears to be little variation in colour, although some individuals are tinged rufous on the head and breast, a few heavily so.
A. b. affinis Larger, browner and longer-winged than the nominate, with more heavily barred upperparts. Wing (male) 129-136, (female, two) 138-139; tail (male) 110-115, (female, one) 126. Weight (male) 41.5-53.0g, (female, one) 60.0g.
A. b. wiedenfeldi Slightly larger, darker and longer-winged than the nominate. Wing (male, one) 135, (female) 133-138; tail (male, one) 114, (female) 120-130. Weight no data.
A. b. terborghi The largest and darkest race. The upperparts are blackish, distinctly barred whitish. Wing (male, one) 154, (female) no data; tail (male, one) 142, (female) no data. Weight no data.
A. b. plumiferus Differs from the nominate in its browner upperparts and less heavily barred under-parts, from *terborghi* in its smaller size, browner, less distinctly barred upperparts, buffier underparts and less heavily barred breast. Wing (male, one) 114, (female) 116-125; tail (male, one) 107, (female) 103-109. Weight no data.

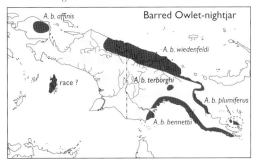

DISTRIBUTION AND MOVEMENTS A generally lowland species, endemic to New Guinea, the Aru Islands (race unclear) and the D'Entrecasteaux Archipelago.
A. b. bennettii SE New Guinea (southern coastal lowlands west to Koembe River and Eramboe). Presumably sedentary.
A. b. affinis NW Irian Jaya (Arfak Mountains, Vogel-

kop). Presumably sedentary.

A. b. wiedenfeldi N Irian Jaya (Idenburg River eastwards) and N Papua New Guinea (Sepik River east to Holncote Bay, Northern Province). Presumably sedentary.

A. b. terborghi C Papua New Guinea (known only from the type locality in the Karimui Basin, Chimbu Province). Presumably sedentary.

A. b. plumiferus The D'Entrecasteaux Archipelago (Fergusson and Goodenough Islands). Presumably sedentary.

STATUS Under-recorded but possibly not uncommon throughout its range.

REFERENCES Beehler *et al.* (1986), Coates (1985), Diamond (1967, 1972), Mayr (1937), Mayr & Rand (1937), Mees (1982), Rand & Gilliard (1967).

---

27   WALLACE'S OWLET-NIGHTJAR
Aegotheles wallacii   Plate 8

Aegotheles wallacii G. R. Gray, 1859, *Proc. Zool. Soc. London* p.154 (Dorey [now Manokwari], New Guinea)
Aegotheles wallacii gigas Rothschild, 1931, *Novit. Zool.* 36, p.268 (Mount Derimapa, Gebruders Range, New Guinea)
Aegotheles wallacii manni Diamond, 1969, *Amer. Mus. Novit.* 2362, p.12 (Mount Menawa, Bewani Mountains, Sepik, New Guinea)

IDENTIFICATION Length 20-23cm. A small to medium-sized greyish-brown owlet-nightjar, endemic to New Guinea and the Aru Islands. Sexes similar. **At rest** Upperparts dark brown or blackish-brown, finely speckled and vermiculated greyish-white or buffish-white. Lacks or has only indistinct lateral crown-stripes; no collar on the hindneck. Wing-coverts dark brown, speckled greyish-white and spotted buffish-white. No obvious scapular pattern. Throat buffish, breast dark brown, rest of under-parts buffish-white or greyish-white, boldly spotted or vermiculated brown. **In flight** Both sexes lack white markings on wings and tail. **Similar species** Barred Owlet-nightjar (26) is usually paler and greyer, has buffish lateral crown-stripes, a whitish collar around the hindneck and paler underparts (lightly spotted and finely barred or vermiculated brown), and lacks bold, whitish spotting on the wing-coverts. Generally occurs at lower altitudes. Grey-phase Australian Owlet-nightjar (24) is slightly larger and paler, has buffish lateral crown-stripes and a whitish collar around the hindneck, and lacks white spots on the wing-coverts.

VOICE The song (perhaps call) is a series of two-note whistles, the first rising in pitch, the second descending and often trilled. Occasionally, gives the first note only. No further information available.

HABITAT Prefers hill and lower montane forests. It may also occur in gardens. 0–1,500m.

HABITS Crepuscular and nocturnal. No further information available.

FOOD Beetles. No further data available.

BREEDING Breeding season April?–June? on the Aru Islands (young juvenile in May). No further data available.
The nest is constructed with leaves and feathers. Nest-sites are probably in holes and hollows in trees. Clutch 1.

Egg cream with greyish markings. No further information available.

DESCRIPTION *A. w. wallacii* **Adult male** Forehead, crown and nape dark brown or blackish, finely vermiculated buffish-white. No collar around hindneck. Mantle, back, rump and uppertail-coverts brown, finely vermiculated buffish-white. Wing-coverts brown, finely vermiculated buffish-white, spotted buff or whitish on median and greater coverts. Scapulars brown, finely vermiculated buffish-white. Primaries brown, speckled buffish-white along outerwebs. Secondaries brown, spotted and barred buffish-white along outerwebs. Tertials brown, finely vermiculated buffish-white. Tail brown, regularly barred with greyish-white speckling. Lores and ear-coverts brown, speckled greyish-white. Centre of chin and throat buffish or buffish-white, sides of chin and throat brown, finely vermiculated buffish-white. Breast buffish-white barred brown, sides of breast brown, finely vermiculated buffish-white. Belly, flanks and undertail-coverts greyish-white, thickly vermiculated or barred brown. Underwing-coverts greyish-white, barred or vermiculated brown. **Adult female** Similar to the male but central crown feathers broadly tipped buff, throat and breast darker buff, primaries plainer brown and tail almost plain, with fewer bars. **Immature** and **Juvenile** Similar to the adult female, perhaps more heavily spotted on the crown. **Chick** Not described. **Bare parts** Iris brown; bill horn (upper mandible darker than the lower mandible); legs and feet brownish.

MEASUREMENTS Wing (male) 115-122, (female) 113-127; tail (male) 95-109, (female) 94-110; bill (male) c. 13.0, (female) 14.3-16.0; tarsus (male, one) 19.5, (female, one) 19.3. Weight (male, one) 48.5g, (female, one) 46.5g.

MOULT No data available.

GEOGRAPHICAL VARIATION Three races are currently recognised.

A. w. wallacii Described above.

A. w. gigas Larger than the nominate. Some authorities have indicated that males have browner, more rufous crowns, greyer backs and larger buffish-white spots on the wing-coverts and tertials, with underparts buffish-white, streaked rufous and spotted black, undertail-coverts whitish, streaked and barred dark grey, while females have a black central crown-stripe and the underparts are more heavily barred. This race occasionally shows traces of a collar around the hindneck. Wing (male) 128-133, (female) 127-139; tail (male) 104-117, (female) 102-117. Weight no data.

A. w. manni Intermediate in size between the nominate and *gigas*. Has darker, blacker upperparts than the other two races and paler, whiter underparts, with thinner, less barring on the undertail-coverts than *gigas*. The primaries have whitish spots along the outerwebs. Occasionally shows traces of a whitish collar around the hindneck. Wing (male) 125-126, (female, one) c. 130; tail (male) 101-107, (female, one) 105. Weight (male, one) 50.5g, (female, one) 52g.

DISTRIBUTION AND MOVEMENTS A lowland species, endemic to New Guinea and the Aru Islands.

A. w. wallacii Irian Jaya (recorded from Tamrau Mountains, Arfak Mountains, Wataikwa River and Eilanden River), Aru Islands and Papua New Guinea (recorded from the Tabubil region, Fly River and Karimui). Presumably sedentary.

A. w. gigas WC Irian Jaya (recorded from the

Gebruders Range and Mt Kunupi in the Weyland Mountains). Presumably sedentary.

A. w. manni N Papua New Guinea (known only from the North Coastal Range, where it has been recorded from Mt Menawa in the Bewani Mountains and Mt Turu in the Prince Alexander Mountains). Presumably sedentary.

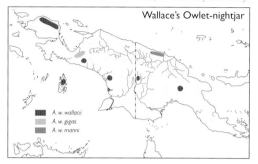

STATUS Local and rare throughout New Guinea.

REFERENCES Beehler *et al.* (1986), Coates (1985), Diamond (1969, 1972), Rand & Gilliard (1967).

28 MOUNTAIN OWLET-NIGHTJAR
Aegotheles albertisi   Plate 8

Aegotheles albertisi Sclater, 1873 (March 1874), *Proc. Zool. Soc. London* p.696 (Atam, Arfak Mountains, New Guinea)
Aegotheles albertisi wondiwoi Mayr and Rand, 1936, *Mitt. Zool. Mus. Berlin* 21, p.242 (Wondiwoi, Wandammen Mountains, New Guinea)
Aegotheles albertisi salvadorii Hartert, 1892, *Cat. Bds. Brit. Mus.* 16, p.649 (Astrolabe Mountains, New Guinea)

Forms a superspecies with Archbold's Owlet-nightjar, with which it was formerly considered conspecific but is sympatric in the Wissel Lakes region, Irian Jaya.

IDENTIFICATION Length 18-22cm. A small, darkish, spotted owlet-nightjar, endemic to New Guinea. Sexes similar. **At rest** Upperparts and wing-coverts brown or rufous-brown, spotted greyish-white. Buffish lateral crown-stripes and prominent tawny patch behind the eyes. Narrow greyish-white or pale buff collar around the hind-neck, sides of neck and throat finely speckled and barred brown. No obvious scapular pattern. Underparts pale buff or whitish, streaked, spotted and blotched brown, markings often forming a bold V-shaped pattern down the breast and belly. **In flight** Both sexes lack white markings on wings and tail. **Similar species** Archbold's Owlet-nightjar (29) is often more boldly spotted whitish on the crown, upperparts and wing-coverts and can appear more coarsely patterned. Sides of neck and throat mottled brown.

VOICE The song (perhaps call) is a series of rather squeaky *kee-kee* notes. Also described is a series of 2-4 slightly hoarse whistles, *whor whor whor* or *who who who*, even in pitch or slightly downslurred. No further information available.

HABITAT Prefers montane forests and forest edges. Also occurs in alpine tree-fern savannas and gardens. 770–3,700m.

HABITS Crepuscular (perhaps) and nocturnal. Roosts in hollows such as the hollow ends of tree-ferns and in tangles of shrubs and bamboo in the lower parts of forests. Roost-

sites may be used for several months. Often perches at the entrance of a roost hollow during the day. If flushed from its roost, flies a short distance and alights on a low perch, where it sits upright with its eyes open. Forages in forests, either beneath the canopy or in clearings. No further information available.

FOOD Insects. No further data available.

BREEDING Breeding season April?–November? (nestlings found in April/May, juvenile collected in mid-June, nest found in August and aggressive display by a female at a nest-site noted in early November).

The eggs are laid in holes, hollows and shallow cavities, usually in trees. Nest-sites have been recorded in a dead tree-stump at the edge of a forest and in a shallow tree-cavity c. 2 m above ground. Clutch 1. Egg white. No further information available.

DESCRIPTION *A. a. albertisi* **Adult male** Forehead, crown and nape brown, lightly spotted buffish-white; lateral crown-stripes buffish, lightly spotted and barred brown. Narrow collar around hindneck greyish-white or pale buff, barred brown. Mantle and back rufous-brown barred brown, lower back, rump and uppertail-coverts rufous-brown spotted pale buff and barred brown. Lesser coverts rufous or brown, barred and spotted brown. Rest of wing-coverts brown, spotted and broadly tipped greyish-white. Scapulars rufous-brown spotted pale buff, spots edged brown. Primaries brown, P10-P5 boldly spotted buff along outerwebs, P4-P1 spotted tawny along outerwebs. Secondaries brown, spotted tawny along outerwebs. Tertials brown, barred and tipped buffish. Tail brown, R5 regularly barred tawny-buff along both webs, R4 barred pale tawny along both webs, R3-R1 barred tawny. Lores brown spotted pale tawny-buff, ear-coverts tawny. Chin buff, throat pale buff, spotted and streaked brown. Breast, upper belly and flanks pale buff tinged tawny, streaked and spotted brown, with irregularly shaped brown markings on feather-centres. Lower belly and undertail-coverts pale, dirty buff, lightly barred brown. Underwing-coverts pale, dirty buff barred brown. **Adult female** Similar to the male. **Immature** and **Juvenile** Similar to the adults but often rather rufous on the upperparts. **Chick** Not described. **Bare parts** Iris brown; bill dark brown or blackish; legs and feet flesh.

MEASUREMENTS Wing (male) 113-123, (female, one) 124; tail (male, one) 97, (female, one) 106; bill (male) 11.5-13.3, (female, one) 14.7; tarsus (male) 18.6-21.1, (female, one) 19.8. Weight (male) 25.0-33.5g, (female) no data, unsexed (one) 39.0g.

MOULT Moult noted on museum specimens taken in July and September. No further data available.

GEOGRAPHICAL VARIATION Three races are currently recognised.

A. a. albertisi Described above.

A. a. wondiwoi Length 22cm. Similar to the nominate, but larger. Known only from the type specimen?, a female. Wing (female, one) 135 (137?); tail (female, one) 107. Weight no data.

A. a. salvadorii Duller than the nominate, with fewer and finer markings on the upperparts and less well-defined spotting along the outerwebs of the primaries and secondaries. The size and amount of white spotting on the scapulars and wing-coverts varies (large and numerous to small and few or even almost absent). Variable in overall coloration, ranging from very dark, almost blackish, to brown, pale greyish-brown and extremely rufous (possibly immatures). Wing (male) 112-127, (female) 117-129; tail (male) 93-107, (female) 97-113. Weight (male) 36.0-39.0g, (female, one) 37.0g.

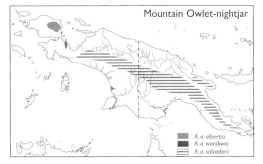
Mountain Owlet-nightjar

A. a. albertisi
A. a. wondiwoi
A. a. salvadorii

DISTRIBUTION AND MOVEMENTS A montane forest species, endemic to New Guinea.
  A. a. albertisi NW Irian Jaya (Arfak Mountains, Vogelkop). Presumably sedentary.
  A. a. wondiwoi W Irian Jaya (known only from the type locality on Mt Wondiwoi in the Wandammen Mountains). Presumably sedentary.
  A. a. salvadorii C Irian Jaya (Weyland Mountains east to Star Mountains) and C and SE Papua New Guinea (Central Highlands east to the Huon Peninsula and south-east to the Owen Stanley Range). Presumably sedentary.

STATUS A secretive species that is probably fairly common to common in many parts of its range.

REFERENCES Beehler *et al.* (1986), Coates (1985), Diamond (1972), Mayr & Rand (1936, 1937), Rand & Gilliard (1967).

29 ARCHBOLD'S OWLET-NIGHTJAR
Aegotheles archboldi   Plate 8

Other name: Eastern Mountain Owlet-nightjar

Aegotheles archboldi Rand, 1941, *Amer. Mus. Novit.* 1102, p.10 (near Lake Habbema, Netherlands New Guinea)

Forms a superspecies with Mountain Owlet-nightjar, with which it was formerly considered conspecific but is sympatric in the Wissel Lakes region, Irian Jaya.

IDENTIFICATION Length 18-20cm. A small, dark, heavily spotted owlet-nightjar, endemic to New Guinea, apparently in rufous and grey phases. Sexes similar. **At rest** Upperparts and wing-coverts dark brown tinged rufous, boldly spotted whitish. Pale buffish lateral crown-stripes. Thin but distinct whitish collar around the hindneck; sides of neck and throat mottled brown. No obvious scapular pattern. Underparts pale buff tinged tawny, boldly blotched and spotted dark brown. **In flight** Both sexes lack white markings on wings and tail. **Similar species** Mountain Owlet-nightjar (28) is often less boldly spotted whitish on the crown, upperparts and wing-coverts and can therefore appear slightly plainer; sides of neck and throat finely speckled and barred brown.

VOICE Unknown.

HABITAT Prefers montane forests. Occurs in moss forest up to the timberline and may also be found in subalpine thickets. 1,460-3,600m.

HABITS No information available.

FOOD No data available.

BREEDING No information available.

DESCRIPTION Adult male Forehead, crown and nape brown, boldly spotted rufous, pale tawny and white, lateral crown-stripes boldly spotted pale buff. Narrow greyish-white collar around hindneck. Mantle, back, rump and uppertail-coverts brown, boldly spotted rufous, pale tawny and white, the white spots often edged blackish-brown. Wing-coverts brown, barred and spotted rufous or pale tawny, spotted and boldly spotted greyish-white or whitish. Scapulars brown, boldly spotted rufous, pale tawny and white. Primaries brown, P10-P5 spotted pale buff along outerwebs, P4-P1 spotted tawny along outerwebs. Secondaries brown, spotted tawny along outerwebs. Tertials brown barred tawny. Tail brown, R5 spotted greyish-white along outerweb, barred tawny along innerweb, R4 barred greyish-white or tawny along outerweb, barred tawny along innerweb, R3-R1 barred tawny along both webs. Lores and ear-coverts dark brown spotted pale tawny. Chin and central throat buff, sides of throat brown. Breast, upper belly and flanks pale buff tinged tawny, irregularly blotched and spotted dark brown. Lower belly and undertail-coverts pale greyish-buff, smudged brown. Underwing-coverts greyish-buff, spotted and barred brown. **Adult female** Similar to the male. **Immature** and **Juvenile** Not described. **Chick** Not known. **Bare parts** Iris pale brown; bill dark brown; legs and feet pinkish-flesh or brownish.

MEASUREMENTS Wing (male) 111-126, (female) 109-127; tail (male) 90-101, (female) 90-102; bill (male) 10.1-13.9, (female) 11.5-13.2; tarsus (male) 19.6-22.5, (female) 19.3-21.2. Weight (male) 29.0-30.0g, (female) 29.0-35.0 g.

MOULT No data available.

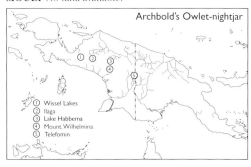
Archbold's Owlet-nightjar

1 Wissel Lakes
2 Ilaga
3 Lake Habbema
4 Mount Wilhelmina
5 Telefomin

GEOGRAPHICAL VARIATION Monotypic. Some birds are more heavily tinged rufous on the upperparts, wing-coverts and breast, and may appear fractionally paler than browner birds.

DISTRIBUTION AND MOVEMENTS A montane forest species, endemic to central New Guinea: C Irian Jaya (Weyland Mountains, Snow Mountains and Star Mountains) and WC Papua New Guinea (Victor Emanuel Mountains). From these localities, recorded only from Wissel Lakes, Ilaga, Mt Wilhelmina, Lake Habbema and near Telefomin. Possibly also occurs in the Central Highlands (Mt Giluwe). Presumably sedentary.

STATUS Little known but possibly common locally.

REFERENCES Beehler *et al.* (1986), Coates (1985), Gilliard & LeCroy (1961), Rand & Gilliard (1967).

NIGHTJARS CAPRIMULGIDAE

SUBFAMILY CHORDEILINAE

LUROCALIS

Lurocalis Cassin, 1851, Proc. Acad. Nat. Sci. Phil., 5, p. 189. Type by subsequent designation, *Caprimulgus nattereri* Temminck 1822 (G.R.Gray, 1855, Cat. Gen. Subgen. Bds., p. 12).

Two Neotropical species. *Lurocalis* nighthawks are long-winged, short-tailed and have short tarsi that are feathered at the front. They lack rictal bristles around the gape and white markings on the wings. All tail feathers are narrowly tipped whitish. Partially (or wholly?) arboreal and known to breed and roost in trees. They do not build nests and may lay their single egg in depressions in horizontal branches. Aerial feeders.

30   SEMI-COLLARED NIGHTHAWK
Lurocalis semitorquatus   Plate 9

Other name: Short-tailed Nighthawk

Caprimulgus semitorquatus Gmelin, 1789, *Syst. Nat.* 1, pt. 2, p.1031 (Cayenne)
Lurocalis semitorquatus stonei Huber, 1923, *Auk* 40, p.300 (Ten miles above the mouth of the Rio Banbana, Nicaragua)
Lurocalis semitorquatus noctivagus Griswold, 1936, *Proc. New England Zoöl. Club* 15, p.101 (Salamanca Hydrographic Station, Rio Pequení, Panama)
Lurocalis semitorquatus schaeferi Phelps and Phelps, Jr., 1952, *Proc. Biol. Soc. Wash.* 65, p.40 (Rancho Grande, Estado Aragua, Venezuela)
Lurocalis semitorquatus nattereri (Temminck, 1822), *Pl. Col.*, livr. 18, pl.107 (Brazil, Ypanema, São Paulo, fixed as type locality by Hellmayr, 1910)

Forms a superspecies with Rufous-bellied Nighthawk, with which it was formerly considered conspecific.

IDENTIFICATION Length 19-29cm. A generally medium-sized to large, dark and stocky Neotropical nighthawk. Sexes similar. **At rest** Wing-tips project well beyond the tip of the tail. Upperparts dark brown, speckled and spotted rufous and buff. No collar around the hindneck. Wing-coverts dark brown, speckled and spotted rufous, tawny and buff. No obvious scapular pattern. White throat-patch. Underparts dark brown, speckled greyish-white and pale buff, becoming tawny-buff barred brown on lower belly and flanks. **In flight** Long-winged and short-tailed, flight bat-like. Both sexes lack white markings on wings and tail. **Similar species** Rufous-bellied Nighthawk (31) is extremely similar, but the underparts are generally un-barred and it is restricted to higher altitudes along the Andes.

VOICE The main, perhaps territorial call is a wader-like whistle, *tsc-it, too-it,* or occasionally a shorter *toic*. The call is repeated several times in succession, with a slight pause between each set of notes, and is given mainly in flight, or sometimes whilst perched or on the ground. May be heard predominantly at dusk and dawn. Also gives rapid *kee kee kee* or *kit kit kit* notes in flight. From the nest, an incubating female may give a short *waow* in response to a calling male (perhaps race *nattereri* only).

HABITAT Prefers forested, wooded or partly wooded lowlands. Occurs in rainforest, humid lowland forests, forested foothills, forest edges, second growth, semi-open woodland, plantations, the edges of marshes and water-

courses, scrubland and open countryside. 0–1,800m, occasionally higher, to 2,550m.

HABITS Crepuscular; possibly also nocturnal and partially diurnal. Roosts lengthways along thick branches. Roost-sites are often in the canopy of tall trees.

When feeding, occurs in pairs or small flocks, and flight is fast and erratic, with bursts of rapid, shallow wingbeats and frequent glides with wings held slightly above the body. Forages in and above the tree canopy, and over open ground, clearings, roads, rivers and cities, e.g. Rio de Janeiro. No further information available.

FOOD Moths, beetles and bugs.

BREEDING Breeding season late January to early April in Panama; May?–June? in Venezuela; October–December in Brazil and late November–January in Argentina. No data available from other countries.

No nest is constructed, the egg being laid in a slight depression in the horizontal branch of a tree. The nest may be up to 5m away from the trunk, and 6-18m above ground. Nest-sites may be in trees alongside forest trails, near woodland clearings or beside roads. Clutch 1. Egg elliptical, whitish, speckled brown and grey, the markings denser around the middle and at one end, or light blue streaked chestnut (perhaps race *nattereri* only), 31.2-37.0 x 22.0-25.0mm. A record of this species incubating a small egg, 23.5 x 16.0mm, laid on the ground in savanna, Trinidad, requires further examination.The incubation period is c. 22 days. Both adults feed the young, and the fledging period is c. 24 days. No further information available.

DESCRIPTION *L. s. semitorquatus* **Adult male** Forehead, crown and nape dark brown, spotted and speckled rufous and buff. No collar around the hindneck. Mantle, back, rump and uppertail-coverts dark brown, speckled, spotted and ocellated rufous and buff. Lesser coverts dark brown, spotted and ocellated greyish-white and cinnamon, primary coverts dark brown, barred deep cinnamon-rufous (40), rest of wing-coverts dark brown, spotted and ocellated cinnamon, rufous, tawny, buff and greyish-white. Scapulars greyish-white mottled brown. Primaries brown, boldly ocellated tawny along outerwebs, barred greyish-brown along innerwebs. Inner primaries narrowly tipped buffish or greyish-white. Secondaries brown spotted pale buff or tawny, barred and narrowly tipped greyish-white. Tertials brownish-white mottled brown. Tail brown, barred tawny or greyish-brown, R5, R4 and R1 narrowly tipped brownish-buff, R3 and R2 narrowly tipped whitish. Lores and ear-coverts dark brown spotted rufous. Chin and sides of throat dark brown barred white, throat white. Breast dark brown, speckled and spotted greyish-white and pale buff, lower breast pale buff barred brown. Belly and flanks tawny-buff barred brown, undertail-coverts pale tawny-buff barred brown. Underwing-coverts tawny-buff barred brown. **Adult female** Similar to the male. **Immature** and **Juvenile** Similar to the adults, but the upperparts and wing-coverts are sprinkled with brownish-white feathers, boldly spotted tawny with blackish-brown tips; the scapulars and tertials are brownish-white or frosty white, vermiculated brown and boldly spotted blackish-brown and tawny, the primaries broadly tipped brownish-white mottled brown, and all the tail feathers narrowly tipped greyish-brown mottled brown. **Chick** At hatching, covered in greyish down. **Bare parts** Iris dark brown; bill blackish; legs and feet brownish or greyish-flesh.

MEASUREMENTS Wing (male) 189-227, (female) 181-215; tail (male) 75-94, (female) 71-80; bill (male) 11.5-13.3, (female) 11.2-13.7; tarsus (male) 13.8-15.2, (female) 13.8-15.9. Weight (male) no data, female (one) 79g.

MOULT No data available.

GEOGRAPHICAL VARIATION Five races are currently recognised, of which *nattereri* is regarded as a separate species by some authorities.

L. s. semitorquatus Described above. Birds from Trinidad appear to be rather small, with wing (male, three) 163-181, (female, three) 175-177; tail (male, three) 71-75, (female, three) 71-80.

L. s. stonei (Red-vented Nighthawk) Possibly smaller than the nominate, with upperparts more brightly spotted cinnamon-rufous, spotting on breast smaller and darker brown, and underparts more densely barred brown. Wing (male, one) 188, (female, one) 203; tail (male, one) 83, (female, one) 85. Weight no data.

L. s. noctivagus Darker than the nominate, with upperparts more heavily spotted tawny and cinnamon, breast darker, more heavily spotted cinnamon. Wing (male) 177-192, (female) 172-174; tail (male) 71-83, (female) 73-74. Weight (male) no data, (female, one) 81g. The validity of this race is questionable and it may prove to be synonymous with *stonei*.

L. s. schaeferi Similar to the nominate, but throat and breast blacker, less brownish, with paler buffish speckling. Wing (male) 175-210, (female) 183-198; tail (male) 75 -98, (female) 73-88. Weight no data.

L. s. nattereri (Chestnut-banded Nighthawk) Similar to the nominate, but underparts darker and more densely barred brown. Wing (male) 201-208, (female) 196-225; tail (male) 81-89, (female) 82-103. Weight (male) 82-89g, (female) no data.

DISTRIBUTION AND MOVEMENTS A widely distributed but little-known lowland species, found along both coasts of southern Central America, and throughout much of lowland South America.

L. s. semitorquatus NE Colombia (Magdalena, southeast to SE Guainía); W, C and S Venezuela (SE Zulia, Aragua, NE Portuguesa, S Amazonas and SE Bolívar); Trinidad and Tobago (presumably this race), Guyana, Surinam, French Guiana and extreme NW Brazil (Rio Negro region, N Amazonas) Presumably sedentary.

L. s. stonei SE Mexico (E Chiapas), NE Guatemala, N Honduras and NE Nicaragua. Presumably sedentary.

L. s. noctivagus Costa Rica (Heredia and Puntarenas), Panama (Bocas del Toro, Veraguas, Cébaco Island, Los Santos and Darién), coastal W Colombia? (also, this race SE Nariño?) and NW Ecuador (west of the

Andes). Presumably sedentary.

L. s. schaeferi N Venezuela (E Aragua). Known only from the region of the type locality. Presumably sedentary.

L. s. nattereri C Ecuador (east of the Andes), N and E Peru (east of the Andes), Brazil (south of the Amazon, from Amazonas east to Alagoas, south to Rio Grande do Sul), N and E Bolivia (Pando, Beni, Cochabamba and Santa Cruz), Paraguay and N Argentina (Salta and Misiones). Partially? migratory. In the south of its range, e.g. S Brazil (Minas Gerais? and Rio Grande do Sul), present only from October? to early March? Winters as far north as Venezuela.

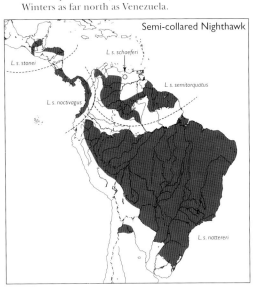

STATUS Locally uncommon to common in Central America, where possibly expanding range northwards, uncommon to locally common in much of South American range.

REFERENCES Bustamante & Simon (1996), ffrench & O'Neill (1991), Haverschmidt & Mees (1994), Hilty & Brown (1986), Howell & Webb (1995), Meyer de Schauensee & Phelps (1978), Phelps & Phelps (1952), Ridgely & Gwynne (1989), Seutin & Letzer (1995), Sick (1985), Stiles & Skutch (1989), Straneck *et al.* (1987), Wetmore (1968).

31 RUFOUS-BELLIED NIGHTHAWK
Lurocalis rufiventris   Plate 9

Lurocalis rufiventris Taczanowski, 1884, *Orn. Pérou* 1, p.209 (Tambillo, Peru)

Forms a superspecies with Semi-collared Nighthawk, with which it was formerly considered conspecific.

IDENTIFICATION Length 25-25.5cm. A medium-sized, dark and stocky Neotropical nighthawk. Sexes similar. **At rest** Wing-tips project well beyond the tip of the tail. Upperparts dark brown, speckled and spotted rufous and buff. No collar around the hindneck. Wing-coverts dark brown, speckled and spotted rufous, tawny and buff. No obvious scapular pattern. White throat-patch. Underparts dark brown spotted pale tawny and greyish-white, becoming tawny-buff on belly and flanks. **In flight** Long-winged and short-tailed; flight bat-like. Both sexes lack white markings on the wing and tail. **Similar species** Semi-collared Nighthawk (30) is extremely similar, but has barred underparts and occurs at lower altitudes throughout much of South America.

VOICE The main, perhaps territorial call is a series of even-pitched or slightly descending *kwa kwa kwa kwa* notes given in flight, often high above ground. May be heard predominantly at dusk and dawn. Also gives *kwo kwo kwo* calls in flight.

HABITAT Prefers montane woods, rainforest, cloud-forest and forest edges. Also occurs in second growth. 1,650–3,000m.

HABITS Probably much the same as Semi-collared Nighthawk (see that species). Occurs singly or in pairs.

FOOD Insects. No further data available.

BREEDING Breeding season late March–? in Colombia. The breeding habits of this species are not documented. No further information available.

DESCRIPTION Adult male Forehead, crown and nape dark brown, spotted and speckled rufous and buff. No collar around the hindneck. Mantle, back, rump and uppertail-coverts dark brown, speckled, spotted and ocellated rufous and buff. Primary coverts dark brown, barred deep cinnamon-rufous; rest of wing-coverts dark brown, variegated rufous, tawny, buff and greyish-white. Scapulars greyish-white mottled brown. Primaries brown, boldly ocellated tawny along the outerwebs, barred greyish-brown along the innerwebs; inner primaries narrowly tipped buffish or greyish-white. Secondaries brown spotted tawny, barred and narrowly tipped greyish-white. Tertials brownish-white mottled brown. Tail brown, barred tawny or greyish-brown, R5, R4 and R1 narrowly tipped brownish-buff, R3 and R2 narrowly tipped whitish. Lores and ear-coverts dark brown spotted rufous. Chin and sides of throat dark brown barred white, throat white. Breast dark brown, faintly spotted and barred pale tawny, lower breast barred greyish-white. Belly and flanks tawny-buff. Undertail-coverts tawny-buff, broadly barred brown. Underwing-coverts tawny-buff barred brown. **Adult female** Similar to the male. **Immature** and **Juvenile** Similar to the adults, but the upperparts and wing-coverts are sprinkled with brownish-white feathers, boldly spotted tawny with blackish-brown tips. The scapulars and tertials are

brownish-white or frosty white, vermiculated brown and boldly spotted blackish-brown and tawny. The primaries are broadly tipped brownish-white mottled brown, and all tail feathers are narrowly tipped greyish-brown mottled brown. **Chick** Unknown. **Bare parts** Iris dark brown; bill blackish; legs and feet brownish.

MEASUREMENTS Wing (male) 208-219, (female) 205-210; tail (male) 83-85, (female) 80-84; bill (male) 13.2-15.5, (female) 13.2-15.5; tarsus (male) 14.0-16.2, (female) 14.0-16.2. Weight no data.

MOULT No data available.

GEOGRAPHICAL VARIATION Monotypic.

DISTRIBUTION AND MOVEMENTS A highland forest species occurring along the Andes of Western South America, from W Venezuela (Mérida, Táchira and W Barinas?) and W Colombia (E and C Andes, south to Cauca and W Putumayo, possibly also this species in SE Nariño), south along the Andes of C Ecuador, W Peru and S Peru to W Bolivia. Sedentary, and perhaps partially nomadic. Specimens have been taken in Brazil (no data).

Rufous-bellied Nighthawk

STATUS Widely distributed in suitable habitat along the Andes, but little known.

REFERENCES Fjeldså & Krabbe (1990), Parker *et al.* (1991).

CHORDEILES

Chordeiles Swainson, 1831 (1832), in Swainson and Richardson's Fauna Bor. - Am., 2, p. 496. Type by original designation, *Caprimulgus virginianus* Gmelin 1789 = *Caprimulgus minor* J.R.Forster 1771.

Six small or medium-sized species in the Americas. *Chordeiles* nighthawks are generally long-winged, have slightly forked tails and lack rictal bristles around the gape. Three species are migratory, two highly so. All species show some degree of sexual dimorphism, usually evident in the white markings on the throat, wings and tail. At least four species are partially diurnal. They do not build nests and generally lay their eggs on the ground, although one species has also taken to using the roofs of buildings. All species roost on perches or on the ground. Aerial feeders.

One species, the recently described Bahian Nighthawk *Chordeiles vielliardi*, may well prove to be closely related to Band-tailed Nighthawk *Nyctiprogne leucopyga*, and therefore belong in the genus *Nyctiprogne* Bonaparte 1857.

32 LEAST NIGHTHAWK
Chordeiles pusillus **Plate 10**

Chordeiles pusillus Gould, 1861, *Proc. Zool. Soc. London* p.182 (supposed to be from Bahia, Brazil; the type is a Bahia trade skin. Restricted to Rio Thesouras, Goiás, Brazil, by Dickerman, 1988, *Bull. Brit. Orn. Club* 108, p.123)
Chordeiles pusillus septentrionalis (Hellmayr, 1908), *Novit. Zool.* 15, p.78 (Maipures, Rio Orinoco, Venezuela [=Colombia], *fide* Greenway 1978, *Bull. Amer. Mus. Nat. Hist.* 161, p.145)
Chordeiles pusillus esmeraldae Zimmer and Phelps, 1947, *Amer. Mus. Novit.* 133, p.8 (Esmeralda, Territorio Amazonas, Venezuela)
Chordeiles pusillus xerophilus Dickerman, 1988, *Bull. Brit. Orn. Club* 108, p.123 (Santa Luiza, State of Paraíba, Brazil)
Chordeiles pusillus novaesi Dickerman, 1988, *Bull. Brit. Orn. Club* 108, p.124 (Flores, State of Maranhão, Brazil)
Chordeiles pusillus saturatus Pinto and Camargo, 1957, *Pap. Avuls. Dep. Zool.* 8, p.51 (southern Pará, east of the Tapajos River)

Sympatric with Bahian Nighthawk in north-eastern Brazil.

IDENTIFICATION Length 15-19cm. A small, heavily mottled Neotropical nighthawk, quite variable in colour. Sexually dimorphic, although not greatly so. **At rest** Upperparts generally brownish, spotted greyish-white, buff and pale tawny. No collar on hindneck. Wing-coverts brownish, heavily spotted buff and pale buff. No obvious scapular pattern. Small white patch on lower throat or small white spot on either side of lower throat. Underparts brown spotted and barred buffish, becoming white barred brown on belly and flanks. **In flight** Flight is buoyant and erratic, with fast wingbeats. Has longish, slender wings and pointed wing-tips. Slightly fork-tailed. The male has a well-defined white band towards the wing-tip across the four outer primaries, a white trailing edge to the inner wing, and white tips to the innerwebs of all but the central pair of tail feathers. The female has a thinner white band across the four outer primaries, a duller, buffier trailing edge to the inner wing and lacks white tips to some or all of the tail feathers. **Similar species** Bahian Nighthawk (33) is extremely similar in both size and structure but lacks white on the throat, wings and tail. Lesser Nighthawk (35) is much larger, longer-winged and lacks a white trailing edge to the inner wing. Band-tailed Nighthawk (38) is browner on the upperparts, with a contrasting scapular pattern (blackish-brown, broadly edged buff on the outerwebs), no distinct white throat-patch, the white being restricted to a small spot on either side of the lower throat; lacks white markings on the wings, but has a white band across the middle of the three outer tail feathers (innerweb only on outermost). Pygmy Nightjar (75) is generally greyer overall, with a larger white throat-patch, darker underparts, more rounded wings and squarer (not forked) tail; the male has a white spot on the four outer primaries, white tips to the two outer tail feathers (innerweb only on outermost) and no white trailing edge to the inner wing, while the female has smaller white spots on the four outer primaries and no white on the tail. Two other small species, Little Nightjar (70) and Spot-tailed Nightjar (69), are more variegated, with a broad rufous, tawny or buff collar on the hindneck; for a fuller description, see those species.

VOICE The song is a rapid series of 5-10 resonant notes *k-k-k-k-k-kurree*, the last note rising in pitch at the end.

Occasionally, the last note is prolonged and churred. The flight call is a short, sharp *whit* or *bit*, often repeated in quick succession, e.g. *whit whit whit whit*.

HABITAT Prefers open savannas and grasslands with scattered trees and scrub. Also occurs along forest edges, especially where there are clearings or pockets of savanna and scrubland. In Bolivia it has also been recorded in dry, seasonally flooded grasslands and on rocky hillsides. On migration, it may be abundant in pastureland. Generally a lowland species, 0–1,000m.

HABITS Crepuscular. Roosts on the ground, although the only data available for roost-sites is from Bolivia, where birds have been found on sparsely vegetated gravelly slopes. Usually occurs singly or in pairs, although large flocks may occur during migration. Forages over open country, occasionally with Lesser Nighthawks. No further information available.

FOOD No data available.

BREEDING Breeding season January–? in Colombia, ?–October–? in southern Venezuela, north-western Brazil and north-eastern Argentina. No data available for other localities.
    Nest-sites may be beneath vegetation in open woodland. Eggs are elliptical, creamy white or pale cream, faintly blotched and spotted brown and purplish-grey or speckled brownish-rufous, 22.7-25.0 x 17.2-19.0mm. No further information available.

DESCRIPTION *C. p. pusillus* **Adult male** Forehead brown spotted tawny, crown and nape brown spotted greyish-white and pale tawny. No collar on hindneck. Mantle, back, rump and uppertail-coverts brown spotted greyish-white, tawny, buff and pale buff. Wing-coverts brown, heavily spotted buff and pale buff. Scapulars brown, spotted greyish-white, buff and tawny. Primaries brown; white spot, almost midway along feather, on P10-P7; vestigial white mark on P6; P3-P1 broadly tipped buffish-white. Secondaries brown, broadly tipped buffish-white. Tertials brown, mottled greyish-white and spotted buff and pale tawny on feather-tips. Tail brown, faintly and indistinctly barred brownish-white; R4-R2 tipped white, often on innerwebs only; central pair (R1) brown indistinctly barred greyish-brown. Lores and ear-coverts brown spotted pale buff. Chin and upper throat brown spotted pale buff. Small white patch on lower throat or smaller white patch on either side of lower throat. Breast brown heavily spotted buff and pale buff, becoming brown barred dirty buff on lower breast. Belly and flanks whitish barred brown. Undertail-coverts whitish, lightly barred brown. Underwing-coverts greyish-white tinged cinnamon, barred brown. **Adult female** Similar to the male. The spots on the four outer primaries are smaller and the tips to the secondaries and inner primaries are duller and buffier. Generally lacks white tips to some or all of the tail feathers. **Immature** Similar to the adults. **Juvenile** Not known. **Chick** At hatching, covered in rufous-buff down. **Bare parts** Iris dark brown; bill blackish; legs and feet brownish.

MEASUREMENTS Wing (male) 130-141, (female) 132-139; tail (male) 72-79, (female) 75-79; bill (male) 10-15, (female) 10-14; tarsus (male) c. 8.5-13.5, (female) c. 8.5-13.5. Weight no data.

MOULT No data available.

GEOGRAPHICAL VARIATION Six races are currently recognised.

157

C. p. pusillus Described above. Birds from coastal Bahia, Brazil, appear to be smaller, and may be worthy of further study. Wing (two unsexed) 127, tail (two unsexed) 71-72.

C. p. septentrionalis Similar to the nominate but smaller and more finely barred on the underparts than other races, with lightly vermiculated or unmarked undertail-coverts. Has smaller black markings on the upperparts than *esmeraldae*, especially on the crown. It is slightly duller than *saturatus*, darker than *xerophilus* and less rufous than *novaesi*. Wing (male) 120-128, (female) 121-126; tail (male) 61-68, (female) 65-69. Weight no data.

C. p. esmeraldae Smaller than the nominate and supposedly larger than *septentrionalis*, but possibly only longer-tailed. It is heavily barred blackish on the lower belly and undertail-coverts. It has paler edges to the upperpart feathers than *saturatus*. Wing (male) 120-132, (female) 122-131; tail (male) 68-78, (female) 70-75. Weight no data.

C. p. xerophilus The palest race, with rather tawny upperparts, less distinct barring on the underparts and unmarked undertail-coverts. Wing (unsexed) 129-132; tail (unsexed) c. 72. Weight no data. Birds from Ceará, north-east Brazil, appear to be paler, greyer and smaller than *septentrionalis* but not as pale or buff as *xerophilus*, and may be worthy of further study. Wing (unsexed) 118-121.

C. p. novaesi Darker than both the nominate and *septentrionalis* but paler than *saturatus*. The upperparts are sooty-grey, richly marked chestnut and brick red. The undertail-coverts are indistinctly barred brown or unmarked. Wing (male) 126-133, (female) 126-130; tail (male) 67-73, (female) 67-73. Weight no data.

C. p. saturatus The darkest race and smaller than the nominate. The upperparts are dark sooty-grey, with cinnamon markings. The underparts are heavily barred, the undertail-coverts are unmarked or very faintly vermiculated brown. Wing (male) 130-145, (female) 130-139; tail (male) 68-80, (female) 76-82. Weight no data.

DISTRIBUTION AND MOVEMENTS Occurs discontinuously across northern and north-eastern South America.

C. p. pusillus E Brazil (Goiás, Bahia and perhaps this race in Minas Gerais). Presumably sedentary.

C. p. septentrionalis NE Colombia (NE Vichada and perhaps this race in NC Meta), C and E Venezuela (E Apure and SE Guárico east through Bolívar and Anzoátegui to Delta Amacuro), Guyana and W Surinam. Migratory?

C. p. esmeraldae E Colombia (Guainía and Vaupés), S Venezuela (Amazonas and S Bolívar) and extreme NW Brazil (N Amazonas and NW Roraima). Migratory? moving east through northern Brazil to Amapá and N Pará, including the island of Marajó.

C. p. xerophilus NE Brazil (Paraíba and perhaps this race in Bahia). Presumably sedentary.

C. p. novaesi NE Brazil (Maranhão and Piauí). Presumably sedentary.

C. p. saturatus WC Brazil (S Pará and Mato Grosso) and perhaps this race in NE Bolivia (NE Santa Cruz). Presumably sedentary.

There are also records (race unknown) from N Brazil (Ceará), W Brazil (Acre) and SE Brazil (São Paulo), and a recent breeding record from NE Argentina (Misiones).

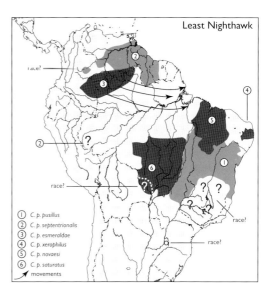

STATUS Fairly common to locally abundant throughout much of its range.

REFERENCES Dickerman (1988), Hilty & Brown (1986), Mazar Barnett & Pearman (in press), Meyer de Schauensee & Phelps (1978).

33   BAHIAN NIGHTHAWK
Chordeiles vielliardi   Plate 10

Chordeiles vielliardi Lencioni-Neto, 1994, *Alauda* 62, p.241 (Manga, Bahia, Brazil)

Sympatric with Least Nighthawk in north-east Brazil.

IDENTIFICATION Length 17.5cm. A small, brownish Neotropical nighthawk. **At rest** Upperparts dark chestnut spotted chestnut-brown, broadly streaked blackish-brown on crown. Wing-coverts dark chestnut, barred dark brown. Scapulars blackish-brown edged chestnut-brown. Lacks white on the throat. Underparts dark chestnut-brown, spotted and barred buff, becoming white barred dark chestnut on belly and flanks. **In flight** Round-winged and longish-tailed. Flies with shallow, fluttering wingbeats, interspersed with frequent glides. Lack white markings on wings and tail. **Similar species** Least Nighthawk (32) has a small white throat-patch and a white band across the four outer primaries: males also have a white trailing edge to the inner wing and white tips on the innerwebs of all but the central pair of tail feathers, while females have a buffish trailing edge to the inner wing and lack white tips to some or all of the tail feathers. Band-tailed Nighthawk (38) is slightly larger, with a small white patch on either side of the throat and a prominent white band, almost midway along feather, across the three outer tail feathers.

VOICE Song unknown. Utters weak *weet-weet* or *wick-wick* notes in flight or whilst perched. No further information available.

HABITAT Prefers dry, wooded areas (caatinga) along river banks, with dunes and rocky outcrops. 200–500m.

158

HABITS Crepuscular and presumably nocturnal. Roosts on the ground or on low branches. Roost-sites are usually on, or close to, river banks. If flushed from its roost, calls (see Voice), flies a short distance, then re-alights on the ground or on bushes. When nervous, perched birds 'bob' their heads up and down and call (see Voice). At dusk, birds leave their roost, fly up to 50m above ground and head out over rivers. Occurs in loose flocks of up to c. 20 birds. No further information available.

FOOD Insects. No further data available.

BREEDING No information available.

DESCRIPTION Adult male (from Lencioni-Neto, specimen not examined by me). Forehead, crown and nape dark chestnut or warm reddish-brown, spotted chestnut-brown or buff and streaked blackish. Mantle, back, rump, uppertail-coverts and wing-coverts dark chestnut or warm reddish-brown, spotted chestnut-brown or buff, wing-coverts also transversely striped dark brown. Scapulars blackish, bordered bright chestnut-brown. Primaries chestnut, spotted buff, secondaries chestnut, with darker spots and feather-shafts. Tertials not described. Tail dark, finely barred whitish at feather-bases; R1, R2 and outerwebs of R5 spotted chestnut. Lores and ear-coverts chestnut-brown, spotted buff. Chin and throat dark chestnut-brown, spotted buff. Breast dark chestnut-brown, barred buff. Belly, flanks and undertail-coverts whitish barred dark chestnut. Underwing-coverts not described. **Adult female** Unknown. **Immature male** (from Lencioni-Neto, specimen not examined by me) Tawnier on the upperparts than the adult, with blackish-chestnut spots on the head and dark streaking on the back and rump. Scapulars variably spotted dark chestnut-brown. Primaries chestnut-brown, tipped buff and spotted buff along outerwebs. Secondaries chestnut-brown, streaked and edged buff distally. Tail dark but R1 buff, barred chestnut. Chin, throat and breast whitish, with fine, dark streaking, belly dirty white, with broader dark streaking. **Juvenile** Unknown. **Chick** Unknown. **Bare parts** Iris yellowish-brown in adult, chestnut-brown in immature; bill undescribed; tarsus yellowish-brown in adult, chestnut-brown in immature.

MEASUREMENTS Wing (male, two) 122-135, (female) unknown; tail (male, two) 78-93, (female) unknown; bill (male) no data, (female) unknown; tarsus (male) no data, (female) unknown. Weight no data.

MOULT No data available.

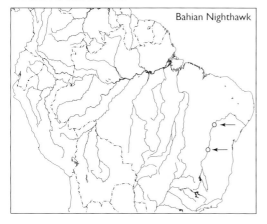

Bahian Nighthawk

GEOGRAPHICAL VARIATION Monotypic.

DISTRIBUTION AND MOVEMENTS North-eastern South America. Known only from the caatinga in E Brazil (near Manga, on the left bank of the Rio São Francisco, Bahia, and c. 10km south of Januaria, also on the Rio São Francisco, Minas Gerais). Presumably sedentary.

STATUS Only recently described to science, and only recorded from two sites along the Rio São Francisco in eastern Brazil, where it is possibly not uncommon.

REFERENCES Lencioni-Neto (1994).

---

34   SAND-COLOURED NIGHTHAWK
Chordeiles rupestris   Plate 9

Caprimulgus rupestris Spix, 1825, *Av. Bras.* 2, p.2, pl.2 (Rocky islands in the Rio Negro, Brazil)
Chordeiles rupestris xyostictus Oberholser, 1914, *Bull. U.S. Natn. Mus.* 86, p.23 (in key), p.116 (Bogotá, Colombia)

IDENTIFICATION Length 19-24cm. A small to medium-sized pale Neotropical nighthawk. Sexes similar. **At rest** Small-headed. Upperparts pale greyish-brown, mottled and streaked brown and cinnamon. No collar on hind-neck. Wing-coverts pale greyish-brown, cinnamon and whitish, boldly spotted with blackish star-shaped markings. No obvious scapular pattern. White throat-patch. Under-parts greyish-white tinged cinnamon, barred and spotted brown, becoming white tinged buff on belly and flanks. **In flight** Wings long and pointed wings and tail deeply tailed. Flies with deep wingbeats reminiscent of a tern or wader. Flight is less erratic than that of other nighthawks. Both sexes have a large white patch across the rear of the wings; the trailing edge and wing-tips are brownish. All but the central pair of tail feathers are white, broadly tipped brown. **Similar species** None.

VOICE The song (perhaps call) is a trilled *rrrrr-wo-wo-wo*. Sings in flight or whilst perched. The call is a series of tern-like *ow-ow-ow* notes.

HABITAT Prefers rivers and marshes in rainforest, open forest and secondary growth, occurring on rocky islands, sandy beaches and sandbars. Also frequents open spaces near or along large rivers, such as airstrips and village streets. 0–500m.

HABITS Diurnal and crepuscular. Roosts on the ground, usually on sandbars. Roost-sites are amongst branches, piles of driftwood or scrubby thickets. During floods when sandbars, beaches and islands are covered in water, birds perch on branches of trees overhanging rivers, often in flocks of hundreds. On the ground, walks and waddles like a gull. Forages in loose flocks of up to 50 birds or more, low over sandbars and beaches or higher up over rivers. Also feeds over open spaces near rivers such as airstrips, and around riverside village lights. No further information available.

FOOD Termites. No further data available.

BREEDING Breeding season January and July–late September? in Colombia; May–August in Peru and June–September in Brazil. No information available from other countries. Courtship display takes place on the ground. The male stretches his neck up vertically, inflates his throat, fans his tail and walks towards the female, swaying from side to side. He then sits suddenly and stretches horizontally, touching the ground with his inflated throat. His tail remains fanned. During courtship, the wings are also raised to show off the underwing pattern.

No nest is constructed; the eggs are laid on sand. Nest-sites are usually on sandbars or beaches along rivers during low water periods in the dry season. Often nests in loose colonies of up to 200 pairs close to (mixed) colonies of other beach-nesting species, i.e. Black Skimmer *Rynchops niger*, Large-billed Tern *Phaetusa simplex* and Yellow-billed Tern *Sterna superciliaris*. Breeding success is often higher when nesting close to these other species, as terns and skimmers aggressively defend their nests by mobbing any potential danger that approaches too closely, although the nighthawks themselves are also mobbed if they stray within range. Clutch 1-2. Eggs elliptical, sandy-buff tinged bluish? densely blotched and scrawled brown, 24.1-28.6 x 19.0-20.8mm. The eggs are laid at c. 24-hour intervals. Replacement clutches may be laid if the first is lost through predation or flooding. Eggs and chicks may be taken by predators such as Black Caracara *Daptrius ater*, Great Black Hawk *Buteogallus urubitinga*, Roadside Hawk *Buteo magnirostris*, Bat Falcon *Falco rufigularis*, snakes, iguanas and tyras, and a few may even be taken by neighbouring Black Skimmers. Eggs are also taken by humans. If flushed from the nest, the adult may perform an injury-feigning distraction display, but at colonies disturbed birds may only fly about the nesting area without displaying to the potential danger. The incubation period is c. 21 days. No further information available.

DESCRIPTION *C. r. rupestris* **Adult male** Forehead, crown and nape pale greyish-brown tinged cinnamon, heavily spotted blackish-brown. Sides of crown above eyes whiter or buffier. No collar on hindneck. Mantle, back, rump and uppertail-coverts pale greyish-brown, streaked, barred and star-spotted brown. Wing-coverts and scapulars pale greyish-brown washed white and true cinnamon, star-spotted blackish-brown. Outer primaries, P10-P7, brown; P6-P1 largely white, tipped brown. Secondaries largely white, tipped brown. Tertials pale greyish-brown tinged cinnamon, barred and streaked brown, tipped white. Tail largely white; R5-R2 generally white broadly (c. 20mm) tipped brown, outerweb of R5 also brown; central pair (R1) pale greyish-brown thinly barred brown, c. 22mm shorter than outer pair. Lores and ear-coverts true cinnamon. Chin and throat white or buffish-white. Breast greyish-white tinged cinnamon, barred and spotted brown. Upper belly white with gorget of brown spots. Rest of belly and flanks white, often tinged buffish. Undertail-covers white. Underwing-coverts white. **Adult female** Similar to the male. **Immature** and **Juvenile** Similar to adults but perhaps paler. The white wing-patch extends to the inner-web of P7. **Chick** Not described. **Bare parts** Iris dark brown; bill greyish-black; legs and feet greyish-brown.

MEASUREMENTS Wing (male) 167-176, (female) 160-175; tail (male) 93-96, (female) 83-95; bill (male) 9.3-11.5, (female) 9.3-11.5; tarsus (male) c. 15, (female) c. 15. Weight no data.

MOULT No data available.

GEOGRAPHICAL VARIATION Two races are currently recognised.
    C. r. rupestris Described above.
    C. r. xyostictus Sandier than the nominate, the upper-

part ground colour being pale tawny with smaller blackish-brown markings, the breast more heavily spotted brown. Wing (male, one) 172, (female, one) 165; tail (male, one) 100, (female, one) 92. Weight no data.

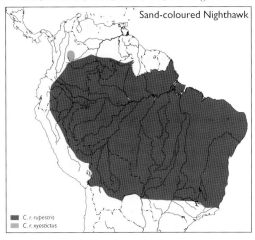

Sand-coloured Nighthawk

■ *C. r. rupestris*
■ *C. r. xyostictus*

DISTRIBUTION AND MOVEMENTS Occurs in suitable habitat throughout the northern half of South America.
    C. r. rupestris E Ecuador, E Peru, N and C Bolivia (Pando, Beni, La Paz, Cochabamba and Santa Cruz), SE Colombia (Amazonas north to Meta and Guainía) and S Venezuela (S and C Amazonas) east through N and C Brazil (Pernambuco and Bahia south to Mato Grosso). Sedentary or partially migratory, with some birds undertaking local movements in parts of its range.
    C. r. xyostictus Known only from C Colombia (Cundin-amarca) ? Presumably sedentary.

STATUS Locally common in suitable habitat throughout range.

REFERENCES Groom (1992), Hilty & Brown (1986), Meyer de Schauensee & Phelps (1978), Sick (1950, 1993).

---

35   LESSER NIGHTHAWK
Chordeiles acutipennis   Plate 11

Other name: Trilling Nighthawk

Caprimulgus acutipennis Hermann, 1783, *Tab. Affin. Anim.* p.230 (Cayenne).
Chordeiles acutipennis texensis Lawrence, 1856, *Ann. Lyc. Nat. Hist. N.Y.* 6, p.167 (Texas; restricted to Ringgold Barracks, near Rio Grande City, by Oberholser, 1914, p.104)
Chordeiles acutipennis micromeris Oberholser, 1914, *Bull. U.S. Nat. Mus.* 86, p.24 (in key), p.100 (Xbac, Yucatán)
Chordeiles acutipennis littoralis Brodkorb, 1940, *Auk* 57, p.543 (Arriaga, Chiapas)
Chordeiles acutipennis crissalis Miller, 1959, *Proc. Biol. Soc. Wash.* 72, p.155 (near Villavieja, Huila, Colombia)
Chordeiles acutipennis aequatorialis Chapman, 1923, *Amer. Mus. Novit.* 67, p.1 (Duran, Prov. of Guayas, Ecuador)
Chordeiles acutipennis exilis (Lesson, 1839), *Rev. Zool.* p.44 (Chile, error = Callao, Peru)

IDENTIFICATION Length 19-23cm. A medium-sized,

brownish or greyish-brown Neotropical nighthawk. Sexually dimorphic. **At rest** Small-headed; wing-tips reach the tip of the tail. Crown generally blackish-brown, rest of upperparts brownish, speckled greyish-white and boldly spotted blackish-brown. Often has a very indistinct buffish or greyish-white collar around the hindneck. Wing-coverts brownish, speckled greyish-white and -brown, speckled and spotted buff. Often shows white on the lower marginal coverts. Scapulars blackish-brown, broadly bordered buff on the outerwebs. Throat-patch large and white in the male, buffish in the female. Underparts brownish, speckled and spotted greyish-white, cinnamon, tawny and buff, becoming buff barred brown on the belly and flanks. **In flight** Wings fairly pointed (second outermost primary, P9, the longest). Fork-tailed. The male has a white band towards the wing-tip across the four outer primaries, and a narrow, white subterminal band across all but the central pair of tail feathers. The female has a buffish or buffish-white band across the four outer primaries and lacks white on the tail. On both sexes, the band across the outer primaries becomes narrower towards the trailing edge of the wing. Above the band, the inner primaries are spotted buffish. **Similar species** Common Nighthawk (36) is slightly larger with marginally more pointed wings (outermost primary, P10, the longest), both sexes having a white band, almost midway along the outer wing, across the five outer primaries, becoming broader towards the trailing edge of the wing, above which the inner primaries appear blackish and unmarked; the male has a white subterminal band across all but the central pair of tail feathers (lacking in the female). See also Antillean Nighthawk (37). Least Nighthawk (32) is much smaller, shorter-winged and has a white trailing edge to the inner wing.

VOICE The song is a resonant, generally even-pitched, toad-like trill or slow churr that occasionally ends with a deep *tchrrr* or a guttural *wahugh*. Sings for three minutes or more at a time, with a pause of 1-3 seconds between each set of notes. Sings in flight, from a low perch or from the ground. May be heard predominantly at dusk and dawn.

During courtship flights, possibly both sexes utter several different types of call, all of which can be quite variable. Two or more birds together may make winnowing or bleating sounds, or give slow, melodious trills. Drawn-out, nasal *whaa, whoo, w-a-ng* or *twang* notes are also given. When pursuing a female, the male may utter several *chuck, cluck* or *tuc* notes, followed by a dove-like call, e.g. *tuc tuc tuc-a-tuc tuc c-r-rooo.* Males often trill when chasing intruding males from their territory. When nervous, roosting birds (perhaps males only) give a *thunk-unk* call.

During defence displays at the nest, females repeatedly utter low *whunk* notes, or make guttural hissing sounds (which they also use during distraction displays). If flushed from the chicks during the night, the male also utters several *whunk* notes and the chicks may give a high-pitched, wheezy *chee-ee-ee-ee* call. Adults call the chicks to them with soft *chunk* notes and the chicks may answer with a weak *chee-uk* as they move towards their parents. If distressed, chicks utter low, plaintive *whee-ur* or *chee-urr* calls. Adults, possibly of this species, may very rarely give a loud, ringing, whistled *whee-eep-poor-will.*

HABITAT Prefers open country, inhabiting deserts and semi-desert, scrubland, savannas and farmland. Also occurs in humid woodland, riverine woodland, gardens, sandy flats, fields, mangroves, salt lagoons and on ocean beaches.

May also be found in and around towns. 0–1,200m, occasionally to 2,500m.

HABITS Crepuscular, nocturnal and partly diurnal. Roosts on the ground or lengthways along branches. Roost-sites may be in thickets, mangroves or trees. Ground roost-sites are usually close to bushes or other vegetation. Roost-sites are often used regularly over periods of time. Several birds may often roost close to one another (see also Breeding). If approached whilst on the ground, roosting birds become nervous, 'bob' their heads up and down and call (see Voice).

Often sits on roads and tracks at night. Occasionally dust-bathes. If disturbed or active during the day, may be mobbed or chased by other birds, such as grackles *Quiscalus*, Cliff Swallows *Petrochelidon spilodera* or kingbirds *Tyrannus*. Occurs singly or in pairs or loose flocks of up to 100 birds or more. Migrates at night and during the day, often at high altitudes. On migration, flies with leisurely wingbeats, and frequent glides on wings held in a V above its back. Often migrates in loose flocks, and large numbers may stream through a given area.

Drinks in flight by gliding with its wings held in a V above its back and dipping its bill into the surface of still water, or by hovering above the water's surface. Also alights beside waterholes, to drink from the water's edge. When hunting, flies rapidly with strong wingbeats. Flight is extremely buoyant, with long sweeps or glides and sudden twists and turns. Forages low over savannas, fields, airstrips and roads, or over plazas in towns. Also feeds by making short sallies from the ground, or hunts insects attracted to water or artificial lights. Occasionally hunts during the day, especially when the weather is dull and cloudy.

FOOD Crickets, beetles (including Elateriade, Curculionidae, Dyliscidae, Hydrophilidae, Chrysomelidae, Nitidulidae, Pentatomidae, Staphylinidae, Scarabaeidae and Carabidae), winged ants (Formicidae), moths, mayflies, termites (including Hodotermitidae), dragonflies, flies, mosquitoes (including Culicidae) and bugs (including Belostomatidae, Gerridae, Veliidae, Cercopidae, Cicadellidae, Cicadidae, Delphacidae, Fulgoridae and Membracidae).

BREEDING Breeding season April–August in SW USA; May–July/August in Mexico; late April?–July? in El Salvador; March?–July in Costa Rica; February–May in Trinidad and Tobago; June–July in N Colombia; January–February in S Colombia and February–March in Ecuador. Breeding periods are possibly longer than as stated for some countries. No data available from other regions.

Territorial. Males chase away other males in flight, during which they call (see Voice) and display their puffed-up white throat-patches. During courtship flights low over the ground, the male pursues the female with wings held stiffly downwards, calls (see Voice) and makes short dives towards her, his white throat-patch always extremely conspicuous. Both sexes often alight on the ground for short periods.

No nest is constructed; the eggs are laid on sand (including beaches), gravel, bare ground, rock or leaf-litter. Also recorded, once, on a small piece of tin. Nest-sites are often near or beneath bushes, or close to vegetation. Also nests on flat surfaces of boulders and on flat roofs of adobe houses. Occasionally nests semi-colonially, with nests as close as c. 25m. In Central America, beach-nesting pairs may lay their eggs close to breeding colonies of other birds, i.e. Wilson's Plovers *Charadrius wilsonia* or

Least Terns *Sterna antillarum*. Clutch 1-2. Eggs elliptical or elliptical-ovate, glossy, pale grey to pale creamy white, speckled vinaceous-buff, spotted and marked grey, lilac and brown; occasionally they are unmarked; 23.1-30.0 x 18.0-21.9mm. Eggs are laid on consecutive days. Incubation is mainly by the female during the day, with the male often roosting within the territory. Communal roosts of up to 20 birds may also occur in breeding areas, and these may be composed of local breeding males, non-breeding males and perhaps non-breeding females (see also Habits). In hot weather, the female may keep cool by either gular fluttering, fluffing up her plumage, or positioning herself to face away from the sun, or she may move the eggs into shade, moving them back again in cooler temperatures. If danger approaches, the incubating female adopts a flattened posture and sits tightly, with her eyes almost completely closed. If flushed from the eggs, she may perform a distraction display (see below), and/or perform a defence display by spreading her tail, raising her wings and making a guttural hissing sound (see Voice). The incubation period is generally 18-19 days, the eggs hatching asynchronously.

The semi-precocial young are mainly brooded by the female, at least during the day. Males often roost close by. Males may brood the chicks for short periods during the night, usually after he has fed them (see below). The chicks appear to be fed mainly by the male, although females do occasionally feed them also. The male flies around the nest-site calling (see Voice), alights near the nest and waddles over to the chicks. The chicks may raise their wings, call softly (see Voice) and open their bills. The male places his bill into a chick's bill, both birds jerk their heads back and forth and the chick is fed by regurgitation. During each visit to the nest, the chicks are fed more than once. Afterwards the male may call softly (see Voice) and fly off, or stay and brood if the chicks crawl beneath him. If the chicks are separated, he may brood one chick for a short while before moving it back towards the other. Whilst the male is brooding the chicks, the female may fly above him and both sexes call to one another (see Voice). After brooding the chicks for up to five minutes or more, the male flies off. The female often alights nearby whilst the male is at the nest, but usually does not feed the chicks. After the male has flown off, the female may call the chicks to her (see Voice), or the chicks call (see Voice) and the female approaches them. Adults move their offspring by flying or walking a short distance away and calling (see Voice). The chicks follow, are brooded briefly and the adult often then repeats the manoeuvre. At c. 2-3 days of age, chicks can walk or run short distances with their wings held above their backs and can be moved up to c. 30m in two days.

If flushed from the chicks, the adult may perform a distraction display by fluttering along the ground for up to 15m. Alternatively, the female may fly off with her tail drooped, alight up to 10m away with her wings and tail spread, sway from side to side then fly off again, flapping her wings along the ground. If the danger follows, she repeats her display. Adults may also fly around an intruder at the nest-site, calling (see Voice). Occasionally, the female sits tightly and then performs a defence display by gaping and flapping her wings at an intruder, or backs off the chicks and calls with her bill closed (see Voice). If danger approaches the chicks whilst they are unattended, they usually 'freeze' in a crouched position. Older chicks may perform a defence display by gaping and spreading

their wings, before running off. At c. 21 days of age chicks can fly short distances of up to 13–30m, and can fly strongly at c. 23 days.

Possibly double-brooded in some regions.

DESCRIPTION *C. a. acutipennis* **Adult male** Forehead, crown and nape blackish-brown spotted pale tawny, cinnamon or greyish-white; sides of crown densely spotted greyish-white or greyish-buff. Hindneck spotted buffish or greyish-white, which may show as a very indistinct collar. Mantle and back brown speckled greyish-white, boldly spotted blackish-brown. Rump and uppertail-coverts brown, barred and speckled greyish-white. Wing-coverts brown, speckled buff, greyish-white and -brown, boldly spotted buff and pale buff. Scapulars blackish-brown, spotted buff or tawny on tips of innerwebs, and broadly bordered buff on outerwebs. Primaries dark brown; broad white band, almost midway along feather, across P10-P7; vestigial white mark or band on P6; P6 (innerweb only)-P1 irregularly patterned with buff markings. Secondaries dark brown with paler tips, barred buff along edges of innerwebs. Tertials brown, mottled greyish-white tinged buffish. Tail dark brown; narrow (c. 5mm) white sub-terminal band, c. 15mm from feather-tips, across R5 (innerweb only)-R2; R5-R2 barred buffish or pale buff, above white band; central pair (R1) barred with greyish-brown mottling. Lores and ear-coverts dark brown spotted tawny-buff. Chin and sides of throat dark brown, spotted buff or tawny-buff. Large white triangular throat-patch, the lower feathers of which are faintly tipped blackish with a buffish subterminal band. Lower throat and upper breast brown, spotted tawny- or cinnamon-buff. Breast brown, speckled and spotted greyish-white. Upper belly greyish-buff barred brown, lower belly, flanks, undertail-coverts and underwing-coverts buff barred brown. **Adult female** Similar to the male but perhaps slightly paler and browner; the throat-patch is buffish-white or buffish, the band across P10-P6 is buffish-white or buff, the secondaries and inner primaries are regularly spotted and barred tawny, and there is no white subterminal band across R5-R2. **Immature** and **Juvenile** Similar to the adults, but often greyer or buffier. The primaries and secondaries are tipped greyish-white or tawny. **Chick** At hatching, covered in buffish down, mottled brown on the upperparts. **Bare parts** Iris dark brown; bill blackish; legs and feet greyish or brownish.

MEASUREMENTS Wing (male) 167-188, (female) 166-175; tail (male) 90-106, (female) 86-94; bill (male) 9.2-9.9, (female) 9.3-9.9; tarsus (male) c. 17, (female) c. 16. Weight (male) 34.0-52.0g, (female) 40.2-55.0g.

MOULT Adults usually undertake a complete post-breeding moult, which begins whilst the birds are still on the breeding grounds, although some may retain a few inner flight feathers (often S2-S6) until the following moult cycle. The primaries are moulted descendantly and the secondaries are moulted ascendantly. The tail moult is centrifugal. Immatures undergo a partial post-breeding moult, during which body feathers, wing-coverts and some inner primaries are replaced.

GEOGRAPHICAL VARIATION Seven races are currently recognised.

C. a. acutipennis Described above. Birds from SE Brazil average larger than elsewhere. Males from the Amazonian region have broader white bands across the four outer primaries than males from Cayenne. Birds from the humid Pacific slope of Colombia (perhaps this race) are often darker and ruddier.

C. a. texensis Paler than the nominate and the largest race overall. The male has a broader white band across the four outer primaries and a broader white subterminal band across the four outer tail feathers. The juveniles are paler grey than other races, and have more cinnamon on the upperparts. Intergrades (in size at least) with *littoralis* across C Mexico. Wing (male) 165-191, (female) 162-180; tail (male) 94-118, (female) 92-112. Weight (male) 37.0-61.4g, (female) 34.1-64.1g.

C. a. micromeris Similar to *texensis* but smaller. Juveniles are darker than juvenile *texensis*, with coarser markings, and greyer than juvenile *littoralis*. Wing (male) 159-175, (female) 151-171; tail (male) 91-103, (female) 90-103. Weight (male, one) 49g, (female) no data.

C. a. littoralis Darker and smaller than *texensis*, darker and more richly ochraceous than *micromeris*. Juveniles are darker grey, with a generally browner cast, than juvenile *texensis* and *micromeris*. Intergrades with *texensis* across C Mexico (see above). Wing (male) 165-180; tail (male) 91-101; (female) no data. Weight no data.

C. a. crissalis Similar to the nominate but with paler, less heavily barred underparts. Darker than *aequatorialis*. Wing and tail measurements no data. Weight (male, one) 40.1g, (female) no data.

C. a. aequatorialis Greyer and paler than the nominate, with paler ochraceous markings. Juveniles are like juvenile *exilis* but buffish, not grey. Wing (male, one) 157, (female) 155-162; tail (male, one) 96, (female) 84-90. Weight, no data.

C. a. exilis Paler and plainer than the nominate, with streakier upperparts and more widely spaced barring on the undertail-coverts. The male's white band across the four outer primaries and the four outer tail feathers is broader, with whitish (not buffish) barring above the subterminal tail band. Juveniles are pale grey, plainer than those of other C and S American populations. Wing (male) 160-167, (female) 157-163; tail (male) c. 90, (female) c. 90. Weight (male, one) 40.3g, (female, one) 35g.

Breeding ranges
1. *C. a. acutipennis*
2. *C. a. texensis*
3. *C. a. micromeris*
4. *C. a. littoralis*
5. *C. a. crissalis*
6. *C. a. aequatorialis*
7. *C. a. exilis*
○ vagrants

Lesser Nighthawk

DISTRIBUTION AND MOVEMENTS Widely distributed over much of South America, range extending northwards through Central America to the south-western states of USA.

C. a. acutipennis Colombia, Venezuela (including Margarita Island, Cayos Sal and Aruba), Trinidad and Tobago, Guyana, Surinam, French Guiana, Brazil (south to Mato Grosso and São Paulo, although absent from much of Amazonia), E Ecuador, Peru, N Bolivia (Beni) and Paraguay. Presumably sedentary.

C. a. texensis SW USA (C and S California, east to Texas, and sporadically to Oklahoma and S Louisiana), N Mexico (including Baja California) and C Mexico. Intergrades with *C. a. littoralis* across C Mexico (Sinola to Vera Cruz?). Migratory, arriving on North American breeding grounds early March - mid-May and departing early August - late October. Winters in extreme S Baja Califorma, and from C and S Mexico, south to Panama (October-April) and W Colombia (December-April). Very rarely, also occurs in winter in S California, S Arizona, Texas, Louisiana and Florida.

C. a. micromeris N Yucatán Peninsula, Mexico (Yucatán, Quintana Roo and Cozumel Island). Migratory, moving south through the mainland, and across the Gulf of Honduras? Winters in Costa Rica and W Panama (east to the Canal zone?).

C. a. littoralis S Mexico (Colima to Chiapas) south through Guatemala, presumably Belize, El Salvador, Honduras and Nicaragua to Costa Rica, and possibly Panama. No migratory data available.

C. a. crissalis SW Colombia (Huila = tropical zone of the upper Magdalena valley). Presumably sedentary.

C. a. aequatorialis W Colombia, W Ecuador (tropical zone) and NW Peru? Presumably sedentary.

C. a. exilis W Peru (tropical zone south to Arequipa) and rarely to extreme N Chile (N Tarapacá). Presumably sedentary.

Vagrants (race undetermined) have also occurred in Ontario (Point Pelee), Alabama (Dauphin Island), Trinidad (Colorado) and Bermuda.

STATUS Uncommon to locally abundant throughout its range. In North America, figures for 1966-1991 suggest numbers are generally increasing, especially in the west, where the population may be rising by up to 8% annually. Local declines may occur in some regions, possibly as a result of habitat loss, disturbance, or the use of insecticides. Increasing road traffic is also a potential threat, especially to immature birds. Few data available on predators, but in Mexico, adults are known to be taken by Aplomado Falcons *Falco femoralis*.

REFERENCES Belton (1984), Bent (1940), Dickerman (1981,1982,1985), Eisenmann (1962), ffrench & O'Neill (1991), Haverschmidt & Mees (1994), Hilty & Brown (1986), Howell & Webb (1995), Komar & Rodríguez (1997), Latta & Baltz (1997), Meyer de Schauensee & Phelps (1978), Pickwell & Smith (1938), Ridgely & Gwynne (1989), Slud (1964), de Urioste (1994), Wetmore (1968), Woods (1924).

36   COMMON NIGHTHAWK
Chordeiles minor   Plate 11

Other name: Booming Nighthawk

Caprimulgus minor J. R. Forster, 1771, *Cat. Anim. N. Amer.* p.13 (South Carolina)

Chordeiles minor sennetti Coues, 1888, *Auk* 5, p.37 (Pembina Mountains, North Dakota)

Chordeiles minor hesperis Grinnell, 1905, *Condor* 7, p.170 (Bear Lake, San Bernardino Mountains, California)

Chordeiles minor henryi Cassin, 1855, *Illustr. Bds. Cal. Texas,* etc. 1, p.239 (Fort Webster, New Mexico)

Chordeiles minor howelli Oberholser, 1914, *Bull. U.S. Natn. Mus.* 86, p.25 (in key), p.57 (Lipscomb, Texas)

Chordeiles minor chapmani Coues, 1888, *Auk* 5, p.37 (Gainesville, Florida)

Chordeiles minor neotropicalis Selander and Alvarez del Toro, 1955, *Condor* 57, 3, p.144 (Rancho Meyapac, near Ocozocoautla, Chiapas, Mexico)

Chordeiles minor aserriensis Cherrie, 1896, *Auk* 13, p.136 (Valley of Aserri River, San José, Costa Rica)

Chordeiles minor panamensis Eisenmann, 1962, *Amer. Mus. Novit.* 2094, p.4 (Cerro Campana, Panama Province, Panama)

Forms a superspecies with Antillean Nighthawk, with which it was formerly considered conspecific.

IDENTIFICATION Length 22-25cm. A medium-sized, greyish-brown Nearctic nighthawk which also breeds throughout Central America. Winters in South America. Sexually dimorphic. **At rest** Small-headed. Wing-tips usually extend well beyond the tip of the tail. Crown darkish brown spotted buff or tawny. Upperparts brown or blackish-brown, spotted and speckled greyish-white, buff and cinnamon. No collar around the hindneck, although the nape is spotted buff, occasionally heavily so. Lesser coverts darkish brown, lightly spotted greyish-white, cinnamon or pale buff, often giving a dark-shouldered appearance. Rest of wing-coverts brown, speckled and spotted greyish-white, white or pale buff. Often shows white on the lower marginal coverts. No obvious pattern on the scapulars, which are brown spotted buff. Greyish-white supercilium. Throat-patch large and white in male, buffish in female. Underparts brown barred greyish-white, becoming greyish-white tinged buff and barred brown on the belly and flanks. **In flight** Wings pointed (outermost primary, P10, usually the longest), flight often fast and erratic. Fork-tailed. The male has a broad white band, almost midway along the outer wing, across the five outer primaries, and a broad white subterminal band across all but the central pair of tail feathers. The female has a thinner, less distinct white band across the outer primaries and lacks white on the tail. On both sexes, the white band across the outer primaries becomes broader towards the trailing edge of the wing. Above the white band, the inner primaries appear blackish and unmarked. **Similar species** Antillean Nighthawk (37) is extremely similar, but averages slightly smaller and shorter-winged, with the wing-tips occasionally falling short of the tip of the tail at rest; the two are best told apart on calls (see Voice, both species). Lesser Nighthawk (35) is slightly smaller, marginally rounder-winged in flight, with the white band (in male, buffish in female) nearer the wing-tips and narrowing towards the trailing edge (above which the inner primaries

are spotted buffish); usually forages lower than Common Nighthawk, often with shallower, fluttery wingbeats.

VOICE The typical territorial or courtship call of the male is a nasal *peent*, usually given in flight 15-40m above ground, occasionally up to c. 250 m, although it may also sometimes be given from a perch or from the ground. Calls at all times of the year, but may be heard chiefly at dusk and dawn, during the day and occasionally at night. Also gives this *peent* call during 'booming' courtship display flights, although the 'booms' themselves are not vocalisations (see Breeding). During 'throat-puffing' displays prior to copulation, males often make guttural croaking sounds.

In aerial pursuit of another bird (sex unclear), the male utters a rapid series of *kit-kit-kit-kit* or *yap-yap-yap-yap* notes. In response to potential danger within its territory or near its nest-site, the male repeatedly gives *cho-ic* or *che-wip* alarm calls. Both sexes give a similar call when flushed. After alighting near a female or near to its mate on the nest, the male often gives guttural, croaking *awk awk awk* notes or nasal, growling sounds. The female often replies with guttural *kra-a* notes.

On the nest, the female utters a guttural hissing sound whenever the male flies overhead giving the *peent* call. If approached, e.g. by humans, whilst incubating or brooding, she often utters a throaty chuckle or grunt, and may call louder to attract the male down to the nest (see Breeding). When walking back onto the nest she often utters *chuck* notes, and calls the chicks to her with low, nasal *kurr* or *kra* notes or guttural *chuck* calls. During distraction or threat/defence displays at the nest she makes a guttural hissing. Both sexes utter a similar sound when handled.

When active, chicks make faint peeping sounds. If responding to the *peent* call of the male or the hissing of the female, the chicks give longer, more drawn-out peeps. During threat/defence display, they make a hissing sound similar to that given by the adults.

HABITAT Prefers generally arid conditions, in open or semi-open country. Occurs in savanna, open grasslands, grassland with scattered trees, fields, pastures and open marshland, plains, airstrips, golf courses, barren hillsides and gravelly ridges. Also occurs in open coniferous forest, thick spruce forest, forest or woodland edges, open logged woodland, burnt land, rocky brushland sand-dunes, beaches and desert scrub flats. It is also found around human settlements, including towns and cities, and along the edges of roads and railway tracks. In southern Florida it may also breed on coral flats with scattered vegetation, and in Central America it also occurs in more humid regions. 0–2,600m.

HABITS Crepuscular and occasionally diurnal. Roosts during the day and at night. Roosts on the ground, on gravel roofs or lengthways on (rarely across) horizontal branches. Males sometimes roost together. Roost-sites may be changed, on average, every 3.6 days. In some towns and cities prefers natural roost-sites to gravel roofs, but will rest on tile roofs. If flushed during the day, often alights on lamp posts, fence-posts or overhead wires.

During abnormally cold weather, may become torpid for short periods.

When active, may be hunted by birds of prey, such as accipiters and Peregrines *Falco peregrinus*; in towns and cities enemies include dogs and cats. May also be mobbed by smaller birds, such as Tree Swallows *Tachycineta bicolor,* House Sparrows *Passer domesticus* or American Robins

Turdus migratorius, and males may be chased away during the breeding season by male Antillean Nighthawks holding territory. In areas with a poor food supply, may be chased by Lesser Nighthawks.

Like all nightjars this species is extremely agile in flight, especially when feeding (see below). Can interrupt normal flight by suddenly fanning its tail, causing it briefly to hang in the air in-between wingbeats. May use this technique to bathe in wind-driven rain: birds leave the roost in slow flight, hang in the air by facing into the wind, and ruffle their feathers whilst bathing, holding their position with occasional short series of rapid wingbeats, otherwise circling round to bathe again.

Drinks in flight by dipping bill into water, either whilst skimming low over the surface or whilst fluttering above the water with wings held in a high V. Forages over open ground or water in a fast, erratic flight, interspersed with short glides, with wings held in a V. Feeds from late afternoon into the dusk and from dawn into early morning, tending to forage longer at dusk, (up to 45 minutes) than at dawn (up to 25 minutes). If dusk feeding is prevented by bad weather, birds may feed later in the day, occasionally in company with other species, e.g. Violet-green Swallows *Tachycineta thalassina*. Forages relatively high in sky, up to c. 175m above ground, often coming lower later in feeding bout. May forage in large flocks of as many as 200–300 birds. Also feeds in a slow, flapping flight, interspersed with short glides, on insects attracted to lights and campfires. At these food sources, foraging birds are often chased by bats. Birds may forage up to 12km from their roost-site. After feeding, occasionally regurgitates pellets of indigestible matter.

Migrates in loose flocks of up to 20-40 birds, often in waves along favoured routes, e.g. c. 2,500 birds through one site in 25 minutes. In the autumn, flocks of up to c. 1,000 birds are not uncommon.

FOOD Moths, bugs, wasps, flies, mosquitoes, mayflies, caddisflies, gnats, flying ants, plant lice, grasshoppers, locusts, crickets and beetles (including Geotrupidae, Cerambycidae, Scarabaeidae, Curculionidae, Lampyridae and Scolytidae?). Small pieces of wood, vegetation and gravel are occasionally ingested, suggesting food may also be taken from branches or from the ground.

BREEDING Breeding season May–July in Canada; late April–August in N USA; late March–August in S USA and mid-May–August in Central America.

Territorial, territory sizes ranging from 4.14 to 33.6ha, although sometimes breeds in loose flocks where there is a shortage of suitable nesting sites (see below); on Key Largo, Florida, occasionally nests in a loose colony with the sympatric Antillean Nighthawk. Males will chase off other males and those of other co-occurring nightjars, e.g. Antillean Nighthawks or Chuck-wills-widows (55). Males also defend their territories against humans, vehicles and raccoons *Procyon lotor* by diving at them. Males occasionally pursue or display to females of other species, e.g. Antillean Nighthawks or Chuck-wills- widows.

During the courtship display, the male circles the proposed nesting site, calling (see Voice), and occasionally hovers or soars high above the ground. He also performs a 'booming' display by diving steeply 5–60m towards the ground with his wings held in a (bowed?) V above his back. At the bottom of the dive, the wings are suddenly and sharply bent downwards, and a 'booming' sound is produced, possibly by the vibration of the primaries. The male then sharply rises 3-5m by using his wings and tail, and resumes flying. 'Booms' are sometimes preceded by shorter, quieter vibrating sounds. The male also dives and booms at intruding males. Following the aerial display, the male may alight, stand close to the female and display in a rocking motion by waggling his spread tail from side to side. He also puffs out his throat, displaying the white patch, calls (see Voice) and sometimes takes flight and circles the female, calling (see Voice). She may fly a short distance with the male following, and when they both alight he repeats his display. Copulation may then take place. Occasionally, on flat terrain, the male may pursue his mate along the ground by running after her for up to 2m. Aerial displays and booming flights continue throughout the breeding season. Should the female die within the breeding area, the male may continue to display above her.

No nest is constructed; the eggs are laid on the ground, on leaf-litter, pine needles, gravel (including rooftops), brick rubble, burnt land, sand, rock or occasionally coarse moss, lichens or other vegetation. Nest-sites are chosen by the female and may be in open, barren country, in rocky areas, on rocky outcrops, in sparsely vegetated or burnt out areas in forests and woods, on gravel beaches or coral flats, in fields, vineyards or gardens, on stumps or fence rails up to 2.5m above ground, in-between rails on railway tracks still in use and on gravel roofs up to 15m above ground, in towns and cities. Gravel roofs have been used as nest-sites since at least 1869. Also known to use old American Robin nests. Females may return to the same breeding areas for up to nine years running, using the same nest-site for up to five consecutive years. Usually nests singly, although where there is a shortage of suitable nest-sites, up to 16 pairs may breed semi-colonially, e.g. in southern Florida. Clutch 1-2 (usually 2), very rarely 3. Eggs elliptical and extremely variable in colour, ranging from dull white, greyish-white or pale creamy white to creamy olive-buff or olive-grey, speckled and streaked grey, black, brown, olive and lilac, 24.6-34.0 x 19.0-23.8mm. Smaller, rounder eggs are occasionally laid. The eggs are laid on consecutive days and incubation begins when the clutch is complete. Incubation is usually by the female, whilst the male usually roosts close by. The nest is occasionally left unattended for periods of up to 20 minutes, although the male sometimes stands close by. If an egg becomes separated from the clutch, the female rolls it back to the nest by using her breast or flanks. Once the egg is close enough to the nest, she returns to the clutch and tucks the separated egg beneath her. By pushing or pulling the eggs beneath her with her bill, they may be moved away from the original nest-site, and during the incubation period eggs may be moved distances of up to 1.5m. Some incubating females prefer to face the sun at certain times of the day, especially sunrise and sunset; others prefer to face away from the sun. During hot weather, incubating females often gular-flutter to keep cool, some also ruffling up their head and back feathers. If left unattended during hot weather, eggs laid on gravel roofs may become embedded in tar melting beneath the gravel. If danger approaches an unattended nest, the male may fly over and circle the intruder, wing-clapping and calling (see Voice). Incubating females sit tightly, and if danger approaches they may perform a defence display by raising their wings and hissing (see Voice), or fly off with slow, flapping wingbeats (see below). The incubation period is generally 17-20 days.

The chicks are semi-precocial, and are brooded by the female. She removes the egg shells in her bill and drops them in flight, up to 100m away from the nest-site. The brooding female usually sits with her back to the sun or strong winds, offering the chicks maximum shade and protection. In very hot sunlight, she may move the chicks into shade by calling them to her (see Voice). If flushed from the chicks, she may perform an injury-feigning distraction display by fluttering along the ground and calling (see Voice), or flying off in a laboured manner, with her tail held vertically downwards. Alternatively, she may face the danger, fluff up her feathers and back away from the chicks. She then raises and quivers her wings and spreads her tail, whilst gaping and uttering a guttural hissing sound (see Voice). Distraction displays tend to be more intense shortly after the eggs have hatched. Before returning to the nest, the female often 'bobs' her head, looks around and then flies either over the nest-site several times or to a nearby perch (at urban rooftop nests, perches may include walls or television aerials); she then alights near the nest-site and walks to the nest, calling (see Voice).

Both adults feed the chicks by regurgitation. They usually thrust their beaks into the open gapes of the chicks, but sometimes the young put their beaks into the open mouths of the adults. Chicks may occasionally pick food items from the open gapes of the adults. Sometimes, if the female is at the nest-site with the chicks, she may call loudly to the male until he lands and feeds them (see Voice).

The chicks may perform a threat/defence display when danger approaches, by standing up, gaping, uttering a guttural hissing (see Voice) and even lunging at the intruder. If the danger persists they may then run off with their wings held above their backs. The female generally broods the chicks until they are about 20 days old. She may then roost up to 12m away from them. The young can make short flights at c. 18 days of age and catch their own food at c. 25 days of age.

Occasionally double-brooded. If a second clutch is laid, the male continues to feed the first brood whilst the female incubates the second clutch.

DESCRIPTION *C. m. minor* **Adult male** Forehead and crown blackish-brown spotted greyish-white, tawny or buff, sides and rear of crown greyish-white. Nape blackish-brown spotted buff, sometimes showing as an indistinct hindneck collar. Mantle, back, rump and uppertail-coverts blackish-brown, spotted and speckled greyish-white, cinnamon and buff. Lesser coverts blackish-brown, lightly spotted greyish-white, cinnamon and pale buff; marginal wing-coverts closest to alula, white. Rest of wing-coverts blackish-brown speckled greyish-white or whitish. Scapulars blackish-brown fringed with buff spotting. Primaries blackish-brown; broad white patch, c. 25mm, almost midway along feather, on innerweb of P10 and across both webs of P9-P6; P1-P3 spotted greyish-white on innerwebs, and very narrowly tipped greyish-white. Secondaries blackish-brown very narrowly tipped greyish-white, with greyish-white bars along edges of innerwebs. Tertials blackish-brown, densely mottled greyish-white. Tail dark brown; white subterminal band, c. 8mm wide and c. 15mm from feather-tips, across both webs of R5-R2; R5-R2 with indistinct greyish-white bars or pale buff mottling above white band; central pair (R1) indistinctly barred with greyish-brown or cinnamon mottling. Greyish-white supercilium. Lores buff lightly spotted brown; ear-coverts

and chin dark brown spotted buff. Large triangular white patch on throat. Lower throat dark brown spotted buff. Breast blackish-brown, barred and spotted greyish-white. Belly and flanks greyish-white tinged buffish and barred brown. Undertail-coverts white or buffish-white, barred brown. Underwing-coverts greyish-white barred brown. **Adult female** Similar to the male but with a buffish or buffish-white throat-patch, buffier underparts, a thinner, less well-defined white band across P10-P6 and no white subterminal band on the tail. **Immature** Similar to the adults but more heavily barred on the underparts, with a paler throat-patch, barred or spotted brown, and no white subterminal band on the tail; all primaries and secondaries are narrowly tipped white. **Juvenile** Similar to the immature but paler, with less heavily barred underparts and occasionally buffier upperparts. The primaries are often narrowly tipped buffish. **Chick** At hatching, covered in grey and buffish down, with blackish-brown blotches. **Bare parts** Iris dark brown; bill blackish; legs and feet brownish.

MEASUREMENTS Wing (male) 184-208, (female) 187-203; tail (male) 103-118, (female) 105-118; bill (male) 9.7-12.1, (female) 10.2-11.9; tarsus (male) 16.7-18.2, (female) 14.8-17.4. Weight (male) 46-107g, (female) 49-101.2g. Higher values possibly relate to gravid females or migration weights; the average appears to be c. 80g.

MOULT Published data appear to be rather scarce. Adults undergo a complete post-breeding moult, beginning on the breeding grounds with the body feathers, wing-coverts and scapulars. The moult is completed on the wintering grounds by January/February, although some may complete later, in the spring, March/April. Immatures undergo either a partial or complete post-breeding moult, beginning on the breeding grounds with the body feathers. The moult may be completed on the wintering grounds, as with the adults, although some birds may retain a few old primaries, secondaries and upperwing-coverts.

GEOGRAPHICAL VARIATION Nine races are currently recognised, although intermediates occur in areas of intergradation (see Distribution and Movements).

C. m. minor Described above.

C. m. sennetti Paler than the nominate, with upperparts more silvery-grey. Differs from *hesperis* in the paler ground colour of its upperparts, which are densely covered in finer markings. The underparts are greyer, with paler and narrower brown bars. Wing (male) 186-223, (female) 175-201; tail (male) 101-114, (female) 102-115. Weight, no data.

C. m. hesperis Similar to the nominate, but upperparts less blackish, with whiter markings. The underparts are sparsely, more narrowly barred brown. The white markings on the throat, rectrices (male only) and outer primaries are noticeably larger than in the nominate. This race is darker than both *sennetti* and *henryi*. Wing (male) 188-208, tail (male) 100-120; (female) no data. Weight (male) 58.2-87.0g, (female) 61.2-91.2g.

C. m. henryi Similar to *hesperis* but browner, with coarser, more rufescent markings on the upperparts. The underparts are usually suffused buff or pale tawny, with narrower, paler barring. The white band across P10-P6 is often thinner and less distinct than on other races. This race shows a north–south cline in colour, southern birds being the darkest. Wing (male) 188-

209, (female) 188-209; tail (male) 103-115, (female) 103-115. Weight (male) 57.8-68.8g, (female) 63.0-76.0g.

C. m. howelli Paler and browner than the nominate, with buffier or more ochraceous markings on the upperparts. The underparts are less heavily barred. More rufescent than *sennetti*; slightly browner than *henryi* with denser, finer markings on the upperparts, paler, more finely barred underparts and a broader white patch across P10-P6. Wing (male) 185-211, (female) 185-203; tail (male) 104-121, (female) 104-122. Weight, no data.

C. m. chapmani Similar to the nominate, but smaller. Upperparts fractionally paler, less blackish, with slightly more whitish and buff spotting. The belly and undertail-coverts average whiter. Wing (male) 178-196, (female) 172-184; tail (male) 98-110, (female) 99-108. Weight (male) no data, (female, one) 71.2g.

C. m. neotropicalis Darker than *henryi*, with fewer but coarser and buffier markings on the upperparts. The underparts are pale buff, not tawny. The white patch across P10-P6 and the male's white subterminal tail-band are thinner. Wing (male) 188-199, (female) 178-187; tail (male) 103-112, (female) 95-96. Weight, no data.

C. m. aserriensis Smaller and paler than the nominate, with less barring on the underparts. Wing (male) 183-193, (female) 179-184; tail (male) 95-106, (female) 101-103. Weight (male, one) 57g, (female) no data.

C. m. panamensis Similar to *chapmani*, but markings on the upperparts tawnier, more rufous, the white patch across P10-P6 thinner and the underparts more tawny-buff. Wing (male) 181-189, (female) 172-184; tail (male) 96-99, (female) 93-99. Weight, no data.

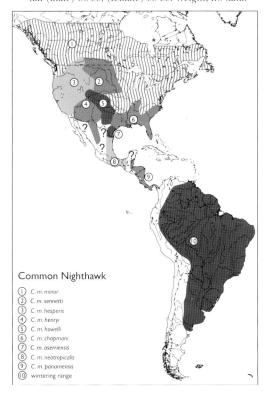

Common Nighthawk

① *C. m. minor*
② *C. m. sennetti*
③ *C. m. hesperis*
④ *C. m. henryi*
⑤ *C. m. howelli*
⑥ *C. m. chapmani*
⑦ *C. m. aserriensis*
⑧ *C. m. neotropicalis*
⑨ *C. m. panamensis*
⑩ wintering range

DISTRIBUTION AND MOVEMENTS A highly migratory species, breeding throughout North and Central America, and wintering in South America as far south as northern? Patagonia.

C. m. minor Canada (S Yukon and British Columbia, including Vancouver Island, east through Alberta, Saskatchewan and Manitoba to Ontario, S Quebec and S Newfoundland) and N and NE USA (NC and W Washington to extreme NW Oregon and Minnesota south to NW Arkansas, east to the east coast). Birds in Washington and NW Oregon are of an atypical form. Intergrades with *hesperis* in SE British Columbia, S Alberta, SE Washington and C Oregon; with *sennetti* in C Saskatchewan and SW Manitoba, and possibly with *chapmani* in the south-east of its range. Migratory. Leaves the breeding grounds from late July to early October (mainly mid-August to early September), most populations moving south through Central America, although some eastern populations use the transoceanic routes. Regular and sometimes very common autumn migrant on Bermuda. Winters in South America, east of the Andes, as far south as northern Argentina (Córdoba and Buenos Aires). In the spring, birds return to their breeding grounds from late April to late May (mainly mid- to late May). Occurs casually on Queen Charlotte Islands (British Columbia) and in N Yukon, Alaska, Melville Island, coastal Labrador, Newfoundland and Greenland. Vagrants, presumably this race, have occurred in the autumn in Western Europe: Great Britain (mid-September to late October), Iceland, the Faeroes and at sea near the Azores.

C. m. sennetti CS Canada (S Saskatchewan and extreme SW Manitoba) and NC USA (North and South Dakota, NW Iowa, N Nebraska, E Montana east of the Rocky Mountains, E Wyoming and extreme NW Colorado east of the Front Range). Intergrades with the nominate in C Saskatchewan and SW Manitoba, with *hesperis* in S Saskatchewan, C Montana and C Wyoming, and with *howelli* in NE Colorado. Migratory. Moves south through Colorado, Texas, Oklahoma and the eastern? side of Central America. The winter quarters are probably in South America. The periods of migration are probably similar to those of the nominate race. Migrating birds are occasionally recorded as far east as Ohio and Florida.

C. m. hesperis SW Canada (SE British Columbia and S Alberta) and W USA (SE Washington, E and S Oregon, Idaho, W and C Montana, W Wyoming, extreme N Colorado west of the Front Range, C and W Utah, Nevada and California, Cascade–Sierra Nevada region and San Bernardino Mountains). Intergrades with the nominate in S British Columbia, S Alberta, SE Washington and C Oregon, with *sennetti* in S Saskatchewan, C Montana and C Wyoming, with *howelli* in SC Wyoming and NW Colorado, with *henryi* and *howelli* in E Utah and W Colorado, and with *henryi* in SE Utah. Migratory. Moves south through SW USA and Central America. The winter quarters are probably in South America. The migration periods are probably similar to those of the nominate. Migrating birds are occasionally recorded east of the normal routes, in Louisiana, Mexico (Sonora and Campeche) and Nicaragua.

C. m. henryi SW USA (SE Utah, SW Colorado, Arizona, New Mexico and extreme W Texas) and CN Mexico (south to S Durango). Intergrades with *hesperis* in SE Utah and SW Colorado and with *howelli* in SW Colorado. Migratory. Moves south-east through Central America and the Gulf of Mexico? The winter quarters are probably in South America. The migration periods are similar to those of the nominate.

C. m. howelli WC and SC USA (SC Wyoming, NE Utah, E and C Colorado, W Kansas, W and C Oklahoma and NC Texas). Intergrades with *henryi* in SW Colorado, with *hesperis* and *henryi* in NC Wyoming and extreme N Colorado, and with *sennetti* in NE Colorado. Migratory. Moves south through the central southern states, Mexico (Campeche) and Nicaragua; The winter quarters are probably in South America. The periods of migration are similar to those of the other races.

C. m. chapmani SE USA (E Texas and SE Arkansas, north along the Mississippi Valley to S Indiana, east to the east coast, from North Carolina to Florida). Probably intergrades with the nominate in the north and with *howelli* in the west. Migratory. Moves south-east?, wintering from C Brazil (Mato Grosso) to N Argentina (Santiago del Estero to Entre Ríos). The migration times are similar to those of the other races.

C. m. neotropicalis E and S Mexico (Tamaulipas south to C Guerrero, south-east to Chiapas). Migratory. Leaves breeding grounds in August and September? The winter quarters are probably in South America. In the spring, the first returning birds may begin arriving in January, although the normal arrival period is March–May.

C. m. aserriensis SC USA (SE Texas) and extreme NE Mexico (N Tamaulipas)? Migratory. Moves south-east through Central America. The winter quarters are probably in South America. The migration periods are similar to the other north American races.

C. m. panamensis S Central America. Locally distributed from Belize? and E Honduras? through Nicaragua to NW Costa Rica (Guanacaste) and Panama (W Chiriquí to E Panama). Migratory. The winter quarters are probably in South America. Migrates at similar times to the other races.

There is one record of a vagrant, race undetermined, on Tristan da Cunha in late November.

STATUS Widespread and generally common throughout much of its breeding range; widespread in Central America, especially on passage; widely distributed on South American wintering grounds, generally east of the Andes.

REFERENCES Aldridge & Brigham (1991), Bent (1940), Bjorklund & Bjorklund (1983), Brigham & Fenton (1991), Brigham *et al.* (1995), Dexter (1961), Eisenmann (1962), Gramza (1967), Hilty & Brown (1986), Howell & Webb (1995), McGowan & Woolfenden (1986), Meyer de Schauensee & Phelps (1978), Miller (1925), Oberholser (1914), Poulin *et al.* (1996), Ridgely & Gwynne (1989), Rust (1947), Selander (1954), Shields & Bildstein (1979), Stevenson *et al.* (1983), Stiles & Skutch (1989), Sutherland (1963), Tomkins (1942), Weller (1958), Wetmore (1968).

37   ANTILLEAN NIGHTHAWK
Chordeiles gundlachii   Plate 11

Chordeiles gundlachii Lawrence, 1856, *Ann. Lyc. Nat. Hist. N.Y.* 6, p.165 (Cuba)
Chordeiles gundlachii vicinus Riley, 1903, *Auk* 20, p.432 (Long Island, Bahama Islands)

Forms a superspecies with Common Nighthawk, with which it was formerly considered conspecific.

IDENTIFICATION Length 20-21cm. A medium-sized, greyish-brown Caribbean nighthawk, not readily separable from Common Nighthawk except by voice. Sexually dimorphic. **At rest** Small-headed. Wing-tips occasionally do not reach the tip of the tail. Crown darkish brown, spotted pale buff. Upperparts brown or blackish-brown, densely spotted greyish-white, buff and cinnamon. No collar around the hindneck, the nape being brown spotted pale buff and greyish-white. Lesser coverts dark brown, lightly spotted greyish-white, pale buff or cinnamon, often giving a dark-shouldered appearance. Rest of wing-coverts brown, speckled and spotted greyish-white and cinnamon. Often shows white on the lower marginal coverts. No obvious pattern on the scapulars, which are brown, speckled and spotted greyish-white and cinnamon, occasionally edged buff on the outerwebs. Greyish-white supercilium. Throat-patch large and white in the male, buffish or buffish-white in the female. Underparts brown barred greyish-white, becoming buffish barred brown on the belly and flanks. **In flight** Wings pointed, flight often fast and erratic. Fork-tailed. The male has a broadish white band, almost midway along the outer wing, across the five outer primaries, and a broadish white subterminal band across all but the central pair of tail feathers. The female has a less distinct white band across the five outer primaries and lacks white on the tail. Above the white patch, on both sexes, the inner primaries appear blackish and unmarked. **Similar species** Common Nighthawk (36) is extremely similar, but averages slightly larger and longer-winged, so that at rest the wing-tips usually extend well beyond the tip of the tail; vocalisations are the only reliable way of telling the two species apart (see Voice, both species). Lesser Nighthawk (35) is separated by same characters used for separation from Common Nighthawk (see Identification under either species).

VOICE The typical courtship or territorial call of the male is a distinctive *chitty-chit* or *killadick*, usually given in flight. The call is often repeated several times, with a slight pause between each set of notes. Also utters a more nasal *penk-dick*. No further information available.

HABITAT Prefers generally arid, open or semi-open country, including recently cleared areas. In Puerto Rico, also occurs in limestone forests. No further information available.

HABITS Crepuscular, nocturnal? and partially diurnal. Often occurs in large flocks on cloudy, rainy days. Roosts on the ground, or lengthways along horizontal branches. Forages high over shorelines, fields, pastures and towns, or hunts above forest canopies. Flight is fast and erratic, and it often dives steeply after insects. Feeding birds occur singly, in pairs or in small flocks of up to 30 birds. No further information available.

FOOD Moths and beetles. No further information available.

BREEDING Breeding season mid-April–mid-August in Florida, USA; late May–July in the Bahamas; late April–mid-July in Cuba and the Isle of Pines; early May–July in Jamaica; late April–July in Hispaniola and May–early August in Puerto Rico.

Territorial, although on Key Largo, Florida, occasionally nests in a loose colony with the sympatric Common Nighthawk. Males will chase off other males and also male Common Nighthawks where the two species breed together. Females are occasionally pursued by male Common Nighthawks. During courtship flight the male performs a 'booming' or 'whirring' display by diving steeply towards the ground. The booms are weaker, higher-pitched and less resonant than those produced by male Common Nighthawks.

No nest is constructed; the eggs are laid on earth, gravel or sand. Nest-sites may be in open patches of ground, amongst pebbles or small stones, in cavities of rough coral rock or occasionally in the middle of dirt tracks. Clutch 1-2. Eggs pale greyish to greenish-white, blotched and scrawled dark grey and plumbeous, 27.5-30.2 x 20.3-22.0mm. Smaller, rounder eggs are occasionally laid, once 23.4 x 12.5mm. Incubation is by the female and the incubation period is c. 19 days.

The chicks are semi-precocial, and often move away from the nest-site to the cover of nearby vegetation. No further information available.

DESCRIPTION *C. g. gundlachii* **Adult male** Forehead and crown blackish-brown spotted pale buff or greyish-white; sides and rear of crown spotted greyish-white. Nape blackish-brown, spotted pale buff and greyish-white, which may show as an indistinct collar around the hindneck on some individuals. Mantle, back, rump and uppertail-coverts blackish-brown, densely spotted greyish-white, buff or cinnamon. Marginal wing-coverts closest to alula, white. Lesser coverts blackish-brown, lightly spotted greyish-white, pale buff or cinnamon. Rest of wing-coverts blackish-brown, spotted and speckled greyish-white and cinnamon, tipped greyish-white. Scapulars blackish-brown speckled greyish-white and cinnamon, occasionally edged buff on the outerwebs. Primaries dark brown; broad (c. 15mm) white patch almost midway along feather on innerweb of P10 and across both webs of P9-P6; P5-P1 faintly spotted greyish-white on innerwebs; P3-P1 narrowly tipped greyish-white. Secondaries blackish-brown very narrowly tipped greyish-white, with greyish-white bands along the edges of the innerwebs. Tertials dark brown, densely mottled greyish-white and buff. Tail dark brown; white subterminal band, c. 8mm wide and c. 15mm away from feather-tips, across both webs of R5-R2; R5-R2 indistinctly barred with pale buff mottling above white band; central pair (R1) indistinctly barred with greyish-brown or cinnamon mottling. Greyish-white supercilium. Lores buffish, ear-coverts dark brown, spotted buff or tawny. Chin dark brown spotted buff. Large triangular white patch on throat. Lower throat dark brown spotted buff. Breast dark brown, barred and spotted greyish-white. Belly, flanks and undertail-coverts buff tinged greyish-white, barred brown. Underwing-coverts buff or pale buff, barred brown. **Adult female** Similar to the male but with a buffish or buffish-white throat-patch, buffier underparts, a thinner, less well-defined white patch across P10-P6 and no white sub-terminal band on the tail. **Immature** Similar to the adult

but more heavily barred on the underparts, with a paler throat-patch, barred or spotted brown, and no white subterminal band on the tail; all primaries and secondaries are narrowly tipped white. **Juvenile** Similar to the immature but paler; the primaries are often narrowly tipped buffish. **Chick** At hatching covered in cinnamon-brown, greyish-brown or creamy buff down, with greyish-black markings. **Bare parts** Iris dark brown; bill blackish; legs and feet brownish.

MEASUREMENTS Wing (male) 165-180, (female) 166-170; tail (male) 89-97, (female) 88-93; bill (male) c. 11, (female) c. 10; tarsus (male) c. 16, (female) c. 16. Weight, no data available.

MOULT No data available.

GEOGRAPHICAL VARIATION Two races are often recognised. The validity of *vicinus* is questionable.

C. g. gundlachii There appear to be two colour types, the greyish phase described above, and a tawnier, more ochraceous phase.

C. g. vicinus Supposedly smaller than the nominate and with no tawny phase. Wing (male) 169-176, (female) no data; tail (male) 93-100, (female) no data. Weight no data.

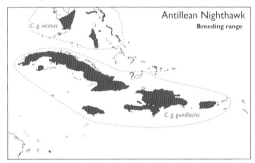

DISTRIBUTION AND MOVEMENTS A breeding summer visitor to much of the Caribbean.

C. g. gundlachii Cuba including the Isle of Pines, Cayman Islands, Jamaica, Hispaniola, Puerto Rico and the Virgin Islands. Migratory, leaving the breeding grounds by August?–September. The winter quarters are unknown, but probably in South America. Begins arriving back on the breeding grounds by April.

C. g. vicinus SE USA (S Florida and the Florida Keys) and the Bahamas. Migratory, leaving the breeding grounds by August?–September. The winter quarters are unknown, but probably in South America. Begins arriving back on the breeding grounds by late April. This species (race unclear) has recently been reported from Texas and North and South Carolina.

STATUS Generally quite common throughout much of its breeding range.

REFERENCES Eisenmann (1962), Kepler & Kepler (1973), Oberholser (1914), Poulin *et al.* (1996), Stevenson *et al.* (1983).

Nyctiprogne Bonaparte, 1857, Riv. Contemp. Turin 9, p. 215. Type by monotypy, *Caprimulgus leucopygus* Spix 1825.

One small and surprisingly little-known Neotropical species. It has a small bill with rather concealed nostrils, lacks rictal bristles around the gape and lacks white markings on the wings. Gregarious and may be partially diurnal. It does not build a nest and lays its eggs on the ground. It generally roosts on perches. Aerial feeder.

The recently described Bahian Nighthawk *Chordeiles vielliardi*, may prove to be closely related to the Band-tailed Nighthawk *Nyctiprogne leucopyga*, and therefore also belong in this genus.

38 BAND-TAILED NIGHTHAWK
Nyctiprogne leucopyga   Plate 10

Caprimulgus leucopygus Spix, 1825, *Av. Brazil* 2, p.3, pl 3, f. 2 (Wooded shores of the Amazon)
Nyctiprogne leucopyga pallida Phelps and Phelps Jr., 1952, *Proc. Biol. Soc. Wash.* 65, p.42 (San Fernando de Apure, Estado Apure, Venezuela)
Nyctiprogne leucopyga exigua Friedmann, 1945, *Proc. Biol. Soc. Wash.* 58, p.117 (Upper Orinoco, opposite Corocoro Island, Venezuela)
Nyctiprogne leucopyga latifascia Friedmann, 1945, *Proc. Biol. Soc. Wash.* 58, p.118 (Raudal, Quirabuena, Brazo Casiquiare, Venezuela)
Nyctiprogne leucopyga majuscula Pinto and Camargo, 1952, *Pap. Avuls. Dep. Zool.*, 10, No. 11, p.216 (Dumba, valley of the Rio das Mortes, Mato Grosso)

IDENTIFICATION Length 16-20cm. A small, brown, variegated Neotropical nighthawk. Sexes similar. **At rest** Upperparts brown, speckled pale brown, greyish-brown and cinnamon. No collar around the hindneck. Wing-coverts brown, speckled and spotted pale brown, greyish-brown and cinnamon. Scapulars blackish-brown, broadly edged buff on outerwebs. Has a small white patch on either side of the lower throat. Underparts brown, speckled cinnamon and barred buff, becoming greyish-white barred brown on belly and flanks. **In flight** Has long, pointed wings and a forked tail. Flight is often erratic, with fluttering wingbeats. Both sexes lack white markings on the wings, which are brown lightly spotted tawny, but have a prominent white band, almost midway across the three outer tail feathers (innerweb only on outermost). **Similar species** Least Nighthawk (32) is variable in colour, with a more spotted appearance, no obvious scapular pattern and often a white throat-patch; the male has a white band across the four outer primaries, a white trailing edge to the inner wing and white tips to all but the central pair of tail feathers, while the female has a thinner white band across the four outer primaries, a buffier trailing edge to the inner wing and no white tips to some or all of the tail feathers. Bahian Nighthawk (33) is slightly smaller and lacks white on the throat and tail.

VOICE The song is a treble-noted *gole-kwoik kwak* with a slight pause between the second and third notes. The call is a low, guttural *qurk*. No further information available.

HABITAT Prefers forests and savannas, usually close to water. Occurs in rainforest, gallery forest, forest edges, clearings and savannas, along the banks of large rivers and near marshes, ponds, streams and rivers. 0–500m.

HABITS Crepuscular and nocturnal? Also partly diurnal, although perhaps only rarely so. Roosts on horizontal branches, usually perching crossways. Up to 10 birds may roost together in a huddle, all facing in the same direction. Roost-sites are usually in dense thickets, and are often alongside rivers or ponds.

Flies or flutters with stiff wings and shallow wingbeats. Also glides short distances with wings held in a V above its back. When hunting, flight is fast and erratic, with frequent twists and turns, and sudden fluttery rises into the air. Occasionally occurs in flocks of up to 60+ birds. Forages 1-12m above ground, over marshland, shrubby vegetation beside rivers, along riverbanks and above water. No further information available.

FOOD Beetles (including Carabidae, Curculionidae, Elateridae, Hydrophilidae, Pentatomidae, Staphylinidae and Platypodidae), bugs and ants. No further data available.

BREEDING Breeding season January–March? in Venezuela and Guyana? No data available from other countries.

Eggs whitish, speckled pale and dark grey, 26.6-27.7 x 19.8-20.3mm. No further information available.

DESCRIPTION *N. l. leucopyga* **Adult male** Forehead, crown and nape brown, speckled pale brown and cinnamon. No collar around the hindneck. Mantle, back, rump and uppertail-coverts brown, speckled pale brown, greyish-brown and cinnamon. Wing-coverts brown, speckled and spotted pale brown, greyish-brown and cinnamon. Scapulars blackish-brown, broadly edged buff or pale buff on outerwebs. Primaries brown, spotted cinnamon or tawny along edges of outerwebs. Secondaries brown, spotted cinnamon or tawny on outerwebs, be-coming barred cinnamon or tawny on both webs of inner secondaries. Tertials brown, mottled pale brown, greyish-brown and cinnamon. Tail brown; broad white band c.10mm wide, almost midway along feather, across innerweb of R5 and both webs of R4 and R3; Above the white band, R5-R3 spotted cinnamon along the edges of the outerwebs, faintly barred whitish on the innerwebs; R2 and R1 faintly and indistinctly barred greyish-brown, tinged tawny and cinnamon; R1 c. 5mm shorter than R5. Lores and ear-coverts tawny or rufous, barred brown. Chin and throat brown barred buff. Small white patch either side of lower throat. Breast brown speckled cinnamon, becoming brown barred buff on lower breast. Belly and flanks greyish-white barred brown, occasionally tinged buffish. Undertail-coverts whitish barred brown. Under-wing-coverts greyish-white barred brown, marginal wing-coverts buff or tawny-buff, barred brown. **Adult female** Similar to the male. **Immature** and **Juvenile** Similar to the adults but slightly paler and plainer. The primaries (except P10 and P9) and secondaries are broadly tipped cinnamon-tawny; the tertials and lower scapulars are pale greyish-brown, boldly spotted dark brown on feather-tips. The white band across R5-R3 is narrower, and all tail feathers are tipped with cinnamon-tawny and greyish speckling, or narrowly tipped whitish. **Chick** Not known. **Bare parts** Iris dark brown; bill blackish; legs and feet blackish.

MEASUREMENTS Wing (male) 129-139, (female) 137-141; tail (male) 82-97, (female) 95-97; bill (male) 9.0-9.7, (female) 9.0-9.7; tarsus (male) 11.8-12.4, (female) 11.8-12.4. Weight (male) 23-24g, (female) 23-26g.

MOULT Few data available. The primaries are moulted descendantly; the tail moult is centrifugal. One immature from Paraguay (museum specimen) moulting into adult plumage late September.

GEOGRAPHICAL VARIATION Five races are currently recognised.

N. l. leucopyga Described above. Intermediates between this race and *pallida* occur (see Distribution and Movements).

N. l. pallida Paler and smaller than the nominate. Supposedly differs from *exigua* by paler upperparts, with lighter, more extensive buffish markings and less extensive blackish markings. Wing (male) 125-136, (female) 123-127; tail (male) 84-86, (female) 82-87. Weight no data. Intermediates between this race and *leucopyga* or *exigua* occur (see Distribution and Movements).

N. l. exigua Smaller and perhaps darker than the nominate, with larger blackish markings on the upperparts. The cinnamon or tawny spots on the outerwebs of the wing and tail feathers are smaller and fewer. Wing (male) 131-136, (female) 128-135; tail (male) 83-84, (female) 83-84. Weight no data. Intermediates between this race and *pallida* occur (see Distribution and Movements).

N. l. latifascia Darker than *exigua*. Lacks cinnamon or tawny markings on the outerwebs of the wing and tail feathers, and has the white band across R5-R3 further away from the feather tips. Wing (male) 133-137, (female) 135-137; tail (male) 87-96, (female) 83-93. Weight no data.

N. l. majuscula Larger than other races. Paler than *exigua*, with whiter underparts. Wing (male) 147-150, (female) 146-154; tail (male) 100-105, (female) 101-104. Weight no data.

DISTRIBUTION AND MOVEMENTS A widely distributed but little-known species, occurring throughout much of tropical South America.

N. l. leucopyga E Venezuela (Monagas to Bolívar), Guyana, Surinam, French Guiana and N Brazil (south to C Pará?). Presumably sedentary. Intergrades with *pallida* from Barrancas to Ciudad Bolívar.

N. l. pallida C and W Venezuela (SE Monagas east through N Bolívar and N Apure) and NE Colombia? Its range follows the lower Orinoco River from Barrancas to Caicara, and the Apure River up to San Fernando de Apure and Guasdualito. It also occurs on the lower Paragua River. Presumably sedentary.

Intergrades with *leucopyga* in the east of its range, from Ciudad Bolívar to Barrancas, and *exigua* in the south, from San Fernando de Atabapo and Maipures.

N. l. exigua S Venezuela (Amazonas) and E Colombia? (Arauca? south to Amazonas). Its Venezuelan range follows the upper stretches of the Orinoco River, from

opposite Corocoro Island south to the northern part of the Brazo Casiquiare (at the mouth of the Río Pacila). Presumably sedentary.

Intergrades with *pallida* in the north of its range, from San Fernando de Atabapo and Maipures.

N. l. latifascia Extreme S Venezuela (SE Amazonas, where it occurs between San Carlos on the uppermost reaches of the Río Negro and Raudal Quirabuena on the Brazo Casiquiare) and NW Brazil? (N Amazonas; see below). Presumably sedentary.

N. l. majuscula C Brazil (E Amazonas? east to Piauí, south to SW Mato Grosso) and N and E Bolivia (Pando, Beni and Santa Cruz). Presumably sedentary.

The population in NW Brazil may be worthy of further study, as some birds (museum specimens) from the Barcelos region on the Rio Negro, northern Amazonas, resemble the nominate race while others resemble *latifascia*.

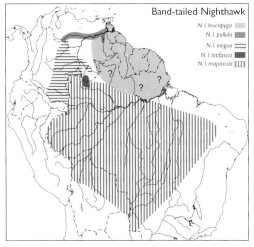

Band-tailed Nighthawk

N. l. leucopyga
N. l. pallida
N. l. exigua
N. l. latifascia
N. l. majuscula

STATUS Generally not uncommon throughout its range.

REFERENCES Hilty & Brown (1986), Meyer de Schauensee & Phelps (1978), Parker *et al.* (1991), de Urioste (1994).

Podager Wagler, 1832, Isis von Oken, col. 227. Type by original designation and monotypy, *Caprimulgus diurnus* Wied 1830 = *Caprimulgus nacunda* Vieillot 1817.

One large, Neotropical species which shows sexual dimorphism. It is long-winged and lacks rictal bristles around the gape. It is often gregarious, partially diurnal and partially migratory. It roosts and breeds on the ground. No nest is constructed. Aerial feeder.

39 NACUNDA NIGHTHAWK
Podager nacunda   Plate 9

Caprimulgus nacunda Vieillot, 1817, *Nouv. Dict. Hist. Nat.* 10, p.240 (Paraguay)
Podager nacunda minor Cory, 1915, *Field Mus. Nat. Hist. Publ. Orn. Ser.* 1, p.300 (Boa Vista, Rio Branco, Brazil)

IDENTIFICATION Length 23-32cm. A stocky, medium-sized to large Neotropical nighthawk. Sexually dimorphic. **At rest** Upperparts and wing-coverts brown speckled greyish-white and greyish-brown, heavily spotted blackish. No obvious scapular pattern and no collar on hindneck. Large white patch on throat may show only as a white band. Underparts brown spotted buff, becoming white on belly and flanks, unmarked (male) or barred brown (female). **In flight** Long-winged and square- or slightly fork-tailed. Flight is loose, bounding and direct, with deliberate wingbeats, and often holds its wings in a V above its back. The male has a white band, towards the wing-tip, across the outer five or six primaries and broad white tips to all but the central pair of tail feathers. The female has a smaller white band across the outer primaries and lacks white markings on the tail. Both have a brown trailing edge to the wing, inside the white band, and darkish wing-tips. The pattern of the underparts is striking, the dark head and breast contrasting with the white belly, flanks and underwing-coverts. **Similar species** None.

VOICE The song is a low, dove-like *prrrrr-doo*, repeated several times in succession. Sings from the ground and occasionally from tall trees. The call is a series of short *whup* notes, given in flight? and also when flushed or alighting. The alarm call is a musical *cherk-cherk*.

HABITAT Prefers savannas and grasslands. Also occurs in marshland, at the edges of rainforest and gallery forest, along rivers and seashores and in xerophytic country. 0–1,000m.

HABITS Crepuscular, nocturnal and often diurnal. Roosts, or rests, on rocky outcrops in grassland, on open ground, or on sandbars and saltflats, often close to pieces of wood or dry cow dung. Often roosts in loose flocks of up to 40 birds or more. If flushed, birds call (see Voice) and fly around over open countryside before alighting. After landing, birds stand upright with neck and legs out-stretched, often call (see Voice), and make nervous, jerky movements, before gradually relaxing, often calling again (see Voice) as they do so. Often stands, rather than sits, on roads at night, occurring singly or in pairs, occasionally in large flocks comprising hundreds of birds. Drinks from streams by swooping over the surface, hovering and dipping beak into the water. Forages high over marshes, reservoirs, open country, airports and cities, along rivers and around lights in urban and suburban habitats. Also

feeds on insects disturbed by grassland fires. No further information available.

FOOD Froghoppers, beetles (including Cerambycidae, Elateridae, Curculionidae, Lampiridae, Carabidae, Hydrophilidae, Chrysomelidae, Scarabaeidae, Scolytidae, Staphylinidae and Dytiscidae), bugs (including Belostomatidae, Gerridae, Pentatomidae, Miridae, Naucoridae, Reduviidae, Cercopidae, Cicadidae, Delphacidae and Membracidae), winged ants, dragonflies, damselflies, Orthoptera (including Acrididae, Gryllotalpidae, Gryllidae, Tetrigidae, Tettigoniidae and Blattodea), moths (including Noctuidae), earwigs and flies.

BREEDING Breeding season April? in Trinidad; January–June? in Colombia; mid-September–November in Brazil, November in Uruguay and Bolivia, and October–November in Paraguay. No nest is constructed; the eggs are laid on leaf-litter on the ground. Nest-sites are usually on rocky outcrops in grasslands or on rocky ground beside marshes. Clutch 1-2. Eggs elliptical, cream or pinkish-cream, blotched and scrawled rich brown, especially around the blunt end, occasionally with underlying spots of lavender-grey, 33.5-37.3 x 23.5-27.7mm. No further information available.

DESCRIPTION *P. n. nacunda* **Adult male** Forehead, crown and nape brown speckled buff, pale buff and greyish-white, heavily spotted blackish-brown, feathers tipped buff. Either no hindcollar or with a very thin, indistinct, buff collar around hindneck. Mantle, back, rump and uppertail-coverts brown speckled greyish-brown and buff, spotted blackish-brown. Wing-coverts and scapulars brown densely speckled dark brown, buff, greyish-buff and cinnamon, heavily spotted blackish-brown. Primaries brown; large white spot, almost midway along feather, on P10-P6, occasionally on P5, and vestigial white mark on P5-P3; inner five primaries mottled cinnamon, buff or greyish-white. Secondaries brown mottled greyish-white, cinnamon and buff. Tertials brown densely speckled buff, greyish-buff and cinnamon, barred blackish-brown. Tail brown broadly barred greyish-buff mottled brown; R5-R3 broadly (c. 35mm) tipped white; R2 tipped with less white, edged brownish-buff; central pair (R1) greyish-brown mottled brown, thinly barred blackish-brown. Lores and ear-coverts brown barred buff. Buff submoustachial stripe. Chin buff barred brown. Large triangular white patch on throat, the lower feathers of which are tipped buff. Breast brown barred, speckled and spotted greyish-buff and -white. Upper belly white, often thinly barred or vermiculated brown. Belly and flanks generally white. Undertail-coverts white, occasionally barred brown. Underwing-coverts white or buffish-white, barred brown. **Adult female** Similar to the male, perhaps slightly smaller. Belly, flanks and undertail-coverts white, thinly barred brown. The white spots on the outer primaries are smaller, speckled brown on the outerwebs. Generally lacks white on the tail, although some females have R5 and R4 tipped (c. 14mm) brownish-white speckled brown. **Immature** and **Juvenile** Apparently similar to adult female. **Chick** Not described. **Bare parts** Iris light brown; bill brownish with dark tip or blackish; legs and feet greyish-brown.

MEASUREMENTS Wing (male) 250-263, (female) 230-238; tail (male) 109-123, (female) 112-116; bill (male) 14.8-16.4, (female) 13.5-14.9; tarsus (male) 25.1-26.6, (female) 22.9-25.4. Weight (male, one) 188g, (female) 161-170g.

MOULT No data available.

GEOGRAPHICAL VARIATION Two races are currently recognised.

    P. n. nacunda Described above.

    P. n. minor Smaller, shorter-winged and paler than the nominate, with much smaller black markings on the crown and scapulars. Wing (male) 223-225, (female) 204-234; tail (male) 110-114, (female) 91-110. Weight (male, one) 142.4g, (female) 124-162g.

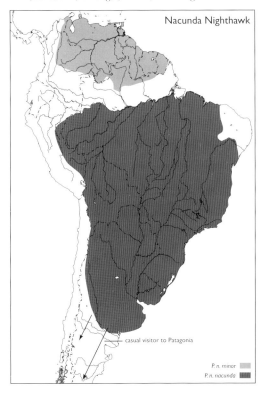

Nacunda Nighthawk

casual visitor to Patagonia

P. n. minor
P. n. nacunda

DISTRIBUTION AND MOVEMENTS Widely distributed over much of South America, but migrations of both subspecies poorly understood.

    P. n. nacunda E Peru, Brazil (south of the Amazon, from Amazonas east to Piauí and Bahia, south to Rio Grande do Sul), Bolivia, Paraguay, Uruguay and N and C Argentina (south to Mendoza, La Pamba and Buenos Aires, and recently recorded in Santa Cruz). Presumably sedentary in parts of its range, migratory in others, e.g. summer visitor to S Brazil (Rio Grande do Sul, mid-August to mid-May) and Uruguay (September–April). Casual visitor to Patagonia.

    P. n. minor N and C Colombia (La Guajira and Magdalena, south to Huila and Meta?), Venezuela, Trinidad, Tobago, Guyana, Surinam and N Brazil (Roraima and N Pará). Migratory? In Colombia, flocks noted from September to late November in the Santa Marta region, and from July to late October in Meta.

STATUS Fairly common locally, in many parts of its range.

REFERENCES Belton (1984), Beltzer *et al.* (1988), ffrench & O'Neill (1991), Haverschmidt & Mees (1994), Hilty & Brown (1986), Meyer de Schauensee & Phelps (1978), de Urioste (1994).

NIGHTJARS CAPRIMULGIDAE
SUBFAMILY CAPRIMULGINAE
EUROSTOPODUS

Eurostopodus Gould, April, 1838, Syn. Bds. Austr., pt. 4, app., p. 1. Type by subsequent designation, *Caprimulgus guttatus* Vigors and Horsfield 1827 (Gray 1840, List Gen. Bds., p.7). Also described as a new genus in Proc. Zool. Soc. London, 1837 (1838), p. 142.

Seven large species, ranging from India, through South-East Asia, to New Guinea and Australia. *Eurostopodus* nightjars lack pronounced rictal bristles around the gape, lack white markings on the outer tail feathers and have thickly feathered tarsi and strong feet. Most species also lack white markings on the wings. Two species have dense clumps of elongated feathers on each side of the hindcrown that form 'ear-tufts'. Breeds and generally roosts on the ground. No nest is constructed and clutches consist of one egg. Aerial feeders.

This genus has been the subject of some discussion in recent times. In 1975, Condon treated it as being synonymous with the genus *Caprimulgus*, when referring to the two species that occur in Australia. Sibley, Ahlquist and Monroe (1988) considered that all species within this genus differed sufficiently from all other genera within the Caprimulgidae, to warrant placing them in a new family, the Eurostopodidae, a view supported by Mariaux and Braun (1996). Apart from the DNA–DNA hybridisation evidence, reasons for this proposed treatment are that all species within this group tend to be larger and darker than other nightjars, lack the long rictal bristles around the gape and have long, erectile feathers behind the ear-coverts. The presence of erectile feathers or 'ear-tufts', together with long, pointed wings, has also been used to separate some species into the genus *Lyncornis*, although only two species, *E. macrotis* and *E. temminckii*, appear to have these 'ear-tufts'; if *Lyncornis* should prove to be a valid genus, it might apply to these two species only.

40   SPOTTED NIGHTJAR
Eurostopodus argus   Plate 36

Eurostopodus argus Hartert, 1892, *Cat. Bds. Brit. Mus.* 16, p.607 (in key), p.608 (Australia, Aru Islands and probably New Ireland)

IDENTIFICATION Length 27-35cm. A large, heavily spotted Australian nightjar. Sexes similar. **At rest** Upperparts greyish-brown speckled greyish-white; central crown broadly streaked blackish-brown edged tawny or buff. Broad buffish collar around the hindneck. Wing-coverts greyish-brown speckled greyish-white, boldly spotted buff or pale buff. Prominent buffish line along the scapulars. Buff submoustachial stripe. Large white throat-patch. Underparts greyish-brown spotted buff, becoming buff barred brown on belly and flanks. **In flight** Both sexes have a large white spot, towards the wing-tip, on the four outer primaries (innerweb only on the outer-most), and lack white on the tail. **Similar species** White-throated Nightjar (41) is slightly larger and darker, with variegated, not spotted, upperparts. Both sexes lack prominent white spots on the wings and white on the tail.

VOICE The song is a rapid series of 7-8 ascending *whaw* notes, followed by 8-14 bubbling *gobble* notes. Sings from the ground at several sites within the breeding territory, standing with body horizontal, bill closed and white throat-patch puffed out; also occasionally in flight? throughout the territory. Sings 5-6 times at each site before moving to another. May be heard predominantly at dusk and dawn, occasionally throughout the night. Sings rarely during the day, possibly following disturbance at the roost-site. Females are also thought to sing occasionally.

If danger approaches, gives a deep churr followed by the *whaw* notes. If flushed, makes grunting, gurgling or popping sounds. When alarmed, gives several short, deep barks. During threat/defence displays, utters a guttural hissing. The adults call to their young with low grunts. The chicks utter soft cheeps, a trilled *treeew* and continuous *beep beep beep* notes.

HABITAT Prefers open woodland, savanna and grassland. Occurs in forests and woods, acacia scrub with little undergrowth, spinifex and tussock grassland, savanna woodland and mangroves. Often prefers sandy or stony ground with plenty of leaf-litter. In northern Australia, also occurs on low gravelly hills and ranges in rolling woodland and scrubland. On the Aru Islands in winter, inhabits the edges of rainforest, savannas and grasslands.

HABITS Crepuscular and nocturnal. Roosts on leaf-litter or on stony ground. Roost-sites are usually partly shaded, but are exposed to full sunlight for short periods during the day. Roosting birds often keep their backs to the sun, and keep cool by gular-fluttering. If flushed from its roost, flaps and glides away in a low zigzagging flight, flying up to 50m before suddenly re-alighting on the ground. Very rarely, a flushed bird will alight on a fallen log, and perched lengthways. If danger persists, flies off out of sight. Occasionally, up to 15 birds may roost semi-colonially, and these may be family parties, or groups on migration.

Often sits on roads and tracks at night. Frequently walks and runs along the ground, and rarely perches in trees. Usually occurs singly, although prior to and during migrations often forms loose flocks of 10-15 birds.

Drinks in flight by scooping up water whilst skimming or darting low over pools or waterholes. Forages with sudden twists, turns and dives amongst trees and shrubs. Usually hunts low down, within 20-30m of the ground. Also feeds in sustained flights with jerky, double wingbeats and frequent glides on raised wings. May forage over areas of c. 1km. Also catches insects by fluttering and hovering around flowering bushes, artificial lights, and campfires. Occasionally feeds on the ground, or makes short sallies from roads and tracks. No further information available.

FOOD Mantids, Orthoptera (including Tettigoniidae, Gryllotalpidae, Gryllidae and Acrididae), bugs (including Pentatomidae), lacewings, beetles (including Carabidae, Silphidae, Scarabaeidae, Elateridae, Bostrychidae, Chrysomelidae and Curculionidae), moths (including Sphingidae) and winged ants.

BREEDING Breeding season August–February (mainly September?–November?). Tends not to breed if preceding winter is too dry.

Territorial, territory sizes averaging 1-2 ha. No nest is constructed; the eggs are laid on leaf-litter or on bare soil. Nest-sites may be beneath trees or amongst stones, often near hilltops or on ridges. Territories may be occupied for several years in succession, with nest-sites within a few metres of a previous year's nest. Clutch 1. Egg elliptical, glossy, pale yellowish-green, yellowish-olive or olive-green, lightly spotted and blotched purplish-brown, 31.6-37.0 x 22.7-26.2mm. Southern populations tend to lay larger eggs than northern birds. Both sexes probably incubate, with the female possibly incubating during the day. The male roosts up to 50m away from the nest-site and probably relieves the female at dusk. During warm weather, the incubating bird may move off the egg, and sit beside it for short periods. If danger approaches, the incubating adult adopts a flattened posture and closes its eyes, or performs a defence display (see below); if flushed from the egg, it may fly off and alight on the ground, up to c. 6m away, with its head lowered and its tail raised. It may also perform a distraction display by jumping and fluttering about on the ground, or move away in a series of short runs, adopting a squatting posture each time it pauses. The incubation period may be as long as 29-33 days.

The chick is semi-precocial and able to walk soon after hatching. It responds to the calls of the adults (see Voice), moving up to 12m during the first night, and up to 50m during the next 5-7 nights. If disturbed at the nest-site, an adult may later coax its offspring to move up to 2m away, by using one of its wings. Both parents take turns in brooding their young. If flushed from the chick, the brooding adult may perform a distraction display (see above), or a defence display, spreading out its wings and tail, puffing out and quivering its white throat-patch, gaping and uttering a guttural hissing (see Voice). It may even fly at the intruder. After the chick is c. 7 days old, the adult tends to brood it less frequently, preferring to roost next to it, with the other parent roosting close by. The juvenile can flutter short distances when 18-20 days old, and is almost independent after c. 30 days.

Usually single-brooded, occasionally double-brooded, and rarely triple?-brooded. If conditions are favourable, the female may lay a second egg when the first chick is c. 22 days old. A replacement clutch may be laid if one is lost, and females may lay up to five eggs during a single breeding season.

DESCRIPTION Adult male Forehead, crown and nape greyish-brown speckled greyish-white, central feathers broadly streaked blackish-brown with broad buff, tawny or rufous edges. Buff or tawny-buff collar around hind-neck. Mantle, back, rump and uppertail-coverts greyish-brown streaked blackish-brown and speckled greyish-white. Wing-coverts greyish-brown speckled greyish-white, boldly spotted buff or pale buff. Scapulars blackish-brown, edged and tipped buff, rufous or cinnamon. Primaries

brown; large white spot, almost midway along feather, on innerweb of P10 and across both webs of P9-P7 (often edged buffish on P7); P10-P7 boldly spotted buff above the white spot; P6-P1 regularly spotted buffish, the spots being paler on the innerwebs. Secondaries brown regularly spotted buff, the spots also being paler on the innerwebs. Tertials greyish-brown speckled pale buff, boldly spotted buff on tips of outerwebs. Tail brown; R5-R3 regularly barred with buff or tawny spotting and very narrowly (c. 3mm) tipped pale buff; R2 darker with greyish barring; central pair (R1) greyish-brown, mottled and barred brown. Lores and ear-coverts brown spotted buff, orbital ring buff. Chin and throat dark brown, spotted and barred buff. Buff submoustachial stripe. Large white patch on lower throat. Breast greyish-brown, spotted or scalloped buff. Belly and flanks buff barred brown, lower belly and undertail-coverts plainer buff. Underwing-coverts buff with some brown barring. **Adult female** Similar to the male but slightly smaller and paler. The white spots on the four outer primaries may also be slightly smaller. **Immature** Paler than the adults, with smaller white spots on the four outer primaries. The outer three primaries are tipped pinkish-buff. **Juvenile** Redder, more rufous, than the immature with cinnamon or rufous spotting on the upperparts, many feathers having blackish-brown centres. The outer three primaries are tipped pinkish-buff. **Chick** At hatching, covered in thick reddish-brown or chestnut down. **Bare parts** Iris dark brown; bill dark brown; legs and feet brownish.

MEASUREMENTS Wing (male) 205-239, (female) 201-235; tail (male) 134-165, (female) 134-168; bill (male) 15-24.5, (female) 15.3-25.0; tarsus (male) 17.0-25.6, (female) 17.3-29.0. Weight (male) 81.0-132.0g, (female) 74.0-123.3g.

MOULT Adults probably undertake a complete post-breeding moult, which may begin on the breeding grounds. Young birds appear to have a partial post-juvenile moult, during which they often replace all or most head and body feathers, most wing-coverts, up to 8 primaries, some tertials, and the central pair of tail feathers. Several months later, they may undergo a partial pre-breeding moult, during which they again replace head and body feathers, wing-coverts, and possibly some flight feathers, and this is then followed by a complete post-breeding moult, similar to that of the adults. The primaries are moulted descendantly, the secondary moult is serially ascendant, commencing at S1 and S11. The tail moult is generally centrifugal, following the sequence R1, R2, R3, R5, R4, or R1, R3, R5, R2, R4. Very rarely, the tail may be moulted centripetally.

GEOGRAPHICAL VARIATION Possibly monotypic. Within Australia, variation appears to be clinal, birds becoming larger and darker southwards.

Birds occurring on Babar and Roma Islands in the Banda Sea may be separable as *E. a. insulanus* Deignan, 1950, although this awaits the discovery of a breeding population as confirmation.

DISTRIBUTION AND MOVEMENTS Occurs locally throughout much of Australia, including Groote Eylandt Island, but is generally absent from eastern and south-eastern coastal areas, from C Queensland south to SE South Australia. It does not occur in Tasmania.

Sedentary and locally nomadic in the north, migratory and partially sedentary in the south. Southern populations leave the breeding grounds March?–May, and move north through C Australia (mainly May–June) to winter throughout N Australia during May–September? Overshooting and wintering birds also occur on islands in the Banda Sea, e.g. Roma (July), Babar Island (August–September) and the Aru Islands (April–September), and vagrants reach Irian Jaya. Returning birds pass through C Australia during August–October.

Northern populations appear to move to well-drained, sparsely grassed hills and ridges during the wet season (November–March), returning to the lower-lying plains during the dry season. Records of this species from New Ireland in the Bismarck Sea are doubtful, and require confirmation.

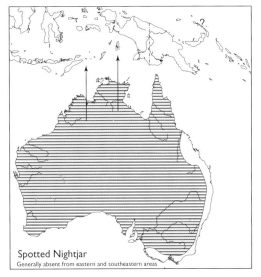

Spotted Nightjar
Generally absent from eastern and southeastern areas

STATUS Widespread but local throughout its range. In some regions, numbers may suffer as a result of habitat loss to agriculture. Road traffic, and domestic or feral cats, are also problems in some areas.

REFERENCES Barker & Vestjens (1989), Higgins (in press), Schodde & Mason (1981, 1997).

---

41   WHITE-THROATED NIGHTJAR
Eurostopodus mystacalis   Plate 36

Caprimulgus mystacalis Temminck, 1826, *Pl. Col.* Oiseaux 4, pl.410 (New Holland = New South Wales)
Eurostopodus mystacalis nigripennis Ramsay, 1881, *Proc. Linn. Soc. New South Wales* 6, p.843 (One of the Solomon Islands)
Eurostopodus mystacalis exul Mayr, 1941, *Amer. Mus. Novit.* 1152, p.6 (Tao, New Caledonia)

IDENTIFICATION Length 30-37cm. A large, dark, variegated Australasian nightjar. Sexes similar. **At rest** Upperparts greyish-brown broadly streaked blackish-brown. Buff or tawny-buff collar around hindneck often indistinct. Wing-coverts greyish-brown, speckled greyish-white and spotted buff. Scapulars greyish-white or greyish-brown, broadly bordered blackish-brown on outerwebs. Has a large white patch on either side of the throat. Underparts brown spotted and barred rufous, also spotted greyish-

white, becoming greyish-white barred brown on upper belly. Rest of underparts buff or tawny-buff barred brown. **In flight** Has long pointed wings and a strong, buoyant flight, with frequent glides followed by double wingbeats. Both sexes have brown wings, which are regularly spotted and barred buff, although the distal spot on the outer four primaries is white. Both sexes lack white markings on the tail. **Similar species** Spotted Nightjar (40) is slightly smaller and paler, with heavily spotted upperparts and a large white spot on the four outer primaries. Large-tailed Nightjar (87) is smaller, the male with a large white spot on the four outer primaries and broad white tips to the two outer tail feathers, the female with buff spots on the four outer primaries and smaller buffish-white or buff tips to the two outer tail feathers.

VOICE The song is an ascending series of rapid, bubbling notes, lasting for 3-6 seconds, e.g. *wow-wow-wow-wow-ho-ho-ho-ho-o-o-o*. Sings from often rather high branches, or in flight. Whilst singing, the white throat-patch is puffed out and extremely visible. May be heard predominantly at dusk and dawn, occasionally throughout the night. Like other nightjars, tends to sing less once breeding has commenced. The female may also occasionally give this call. During courtship, both sexes give low croaks and *tock* notes. When approaching its nest, the adult utters low cooing sounds, and gives a similar call when agitated. Adults call chicks to them with low husky notes. Chicks utter harsh *khaah* notes, but give cheeping sounds when begging for food. During distraction display, the adult barks, tocks or utters a throaty hiss.

On the Solomon Islands, the song of the race *nigripennis* is a rising series of c. 20 staccato notes, delivered at a rate of about five per second, reminiscent of an axe striking wood.

HABITAT In Australia, prefers eucalypt forest, dry, sclerophyll forest, woodlands and dry, sparsely forested ridges with a discontinuous understorey. In the north, also occurs along the edges of rainforests and the landward side of mangroves. In New Guinea (presumably the wintering grounds) occurs along forest edges, in savanna, scrubland, open grassland, gardens, secondary growth and lagoon marshland near forests. On the Solomon Islands, usually occurs on or near beaches and on offshore islets. 0–?1,650m.

HABITS Crepuscular and nocturnal. Roosts on the ground amongst leaf-litter and rocks. Roost-sites are often on low ironstone or quartzite ridges in open forest. Outside the breeding season, roosts in forest thickets, but the use of tree hollows is questionable. If then flushed, it re-alights on the ground 20-100m away, or lengthways on a fallen log or horizontal branch in a tree. At night, often perches lengthways or across branches and often sits on roads and tracks. Frequently hovers (see Breeding). Usually hunts above forests, woodlands or trees, up to c. 50m above ground. Also forages amongst trees and along forest edges, gullies and streams, or flycatches from a perch or from the ground. Flight is extremely buoyant with double wingbeats and long glides with wings raised. Its feeding range can be up to 100ha or more. Often feeds on insects attracted to lights and camp fires. In New Guinea, it has been noted hawking above villages, and in Australia it may hunt in suburban areas. On migration, it often occurs and feeds in loose flocks of up to 20 or more. No further information available.

FOOD Moths (including Agaristidae and Noctuidae), beetles (including Scarabaeidae, Melolonthinae, Rutelinae, Elateridae, Cerambycidae and Curculionidae), flying ants, bugs (including Cicadidae), insect cocoons, Orthoptera (including Tettigoniidae, Gryllidae, Gryllotalpidae, Pyrgomorphidae and Acrididae) and mantids.

BREEDING Breeding season September–February but mainly October–December in Australia, perhaps later in the south; October–November on the Solomon Islands and August?–September? on New Caledonia.

Probable courtship behaviour involves the male chasing the female in flight, he then lands on the ground or on a fallen log, spreads out his wings, waves them up and down, and calls (see Voice). The male also dives in flight, making a loud rushing sound with his wings. A pair will also flutter together and jump about on the ground, bill-snapping and calling (see Voice). Breeding territories are usually 1ha or less.

No nest is constructed; the egg is laid on bare ground or on leaf-litter. Nest-sites are usually in clearings, beneath trees, near burnt logs or amongst rocks and stones. Favourite sites are on the sides and tops of stony ridges. Clutch 1. Egg elliptical, yellowish, buff or dark cream, spotted and blotched brown and black with underlying lavender marks, 35.4-42.0 x 26.2-29.6mm. On the Solomon Islands, eggs of the race *nigripennis* are generally smaller, whitish or pinkish, and more heavily spotted, 33.3-37.8 x 25.0-26.3mm. Incubation is usually by the female during the day, the male roosting close by. The adult may move its egg a short distance, by raking it up to 0.5m along the ground with its bill. When approaching its nest, the adult often hovers before landing, then shuffles onto the egg. It will also hover close to an intruder near the nest, continuously calling (see Voice) and making clacking sounds, sometimes also swooping at the intruder, bill-snapping. If flushed from the egg, the adult flies off for up to 40m and alights, sometimes on a branch up to 6m above ground, or performs a distraction display by flapping about on the ground or a low branch with wings drooped, bill-snapping and calling (see Voice); another display involves crouching open-winged, puffing out throat, gaping and calling (see Voice). Generally single-brooded (but see below). The incubation period is generally 22-28 days.

When approaching the nest, the adult lands a short distance away and cautiously walks to the chick. The semi-precocial, nidifugous young are able to move almost 10m daily during the first ten days and then over 20m daily until fledging. Daily movements result in a zigzag pattern away from nest-site. During the day, the chick is brooded by one adult, whilst the other generally roosts 5-30m away. If flushed from a chick, the adult often flies 20-30m before alighting on the ground, on a fallen log or on a low branch. The adult occasionally performs a distraction display by raising, flapping and drooping its wings for up to two minutes before flying off. At night, the chick is fed by both parents. The adult bends over the chick and gapes, and the chick reaches up and picks out balls of insects. From about 11 days of age, the adult ceases to brood the young, but tends to roost nearby. From then on the chick can run away from danger, running with its wings held above its back; at about 27 days old it also gapes and bill-snaps when threatened. Foxes, dogs and cats are potential predators.

Some pairs often breed in the same spot year after year, nest-sites being within a few metres of each other. Pairs may not breed in some years if the preceding winter is extremely dry. In ideal conditions in northern Australia, some pairs may rear 2-3 young successfully during the spring and summer.

DESCRIPTION *E. m. mystacalis* **Adult male** Forehead, crown and nape greyish-brown speckled brown; central feathers broadly streaked blackish-brown. Buff or tawny-buff collar around hindneck may be indistinct on some individuals. Mantle, back, rump and uppertail-coverts brown speckled greyish-white, streaked blackish-brown. Wing-coverts brown speckled greyish-white. Primary coverts, median coverts and outer lesser coverts also spotted buff, especially on outerwebs. Scapulars generally greyish-white or -brown speckled and mottled brown on innerwebs, and blackish-brown on outerwebs, with buff or pale tawny ocellation at tips. Primaries brown, regularly spotted buff or buffish-white along outerwebs, barred buff along innerwebs, all markings restricted to inner two-thirds of feathers on P10-P8 (P7); distal spot(s) on P10-P7 largest, being buffish-white on edge of innerweb of P10, white or buffish-white on edges of both webs of P9, white on edges of both webs of P8 and buffish-white on edge of outerweb of P7. Secondaries brown regularly spotted buff along outerwebs, barred buff along innerwebs. Tertials brown densely mottled greyish-white or -brown. Tail brown; R5-R3 broadly barred tawny on innerwebs, faintly and thinly barred pale tawny on outerwebs; R2 barred greyish on outerwebs, tawny on innerwebs; central pair (R1) greyish-brown mottled and barred brown. Lores and ear-coverts dark brown speckled rufous. Chin and throat brown spotted buff or tawny. Large white patch on either side of lower throat. Upper breast brown spotted and thinly barred rufous, lower breast brown speckled and spotted greyish-white. Upper belly greyish-white barred brown, lower belly and flanks tawny-buff barred brown. Undertail-coverts buff barred brown. Underwing-coverts tawny-buff barred brown. **Adult female** Similar to the male. **Immature** and **Juvenile** Paler, more vinaceous than adults. Crown spotted blackish-brown rather than streaked, and wings entirely spotted buff with pale tips to the primaries and secondaries. **Chick** At hatching, covered in chestnut or reddish-brown down. **Bare parts** Iris dark brown; bill blackish; legs and feet blackish-brown.

MEASUREMENTS Wing (male) 234-262, (female) 243-268; tail (male) 148-170, (female) 147-168; bill (male) 15.2-24.8, (female) 16.8-24.2; tarsus (male) 17.7-22.0, (female) 18.1-22.7. Weight (male) 98-145g, (female) 140-180g.

MOULT Adults undertake a complete post-breeding moult. The primaries are moulted descendantly, the secondary moult is serially ascendant, commencing at S1 and S10 or S11. The tail moult is centrifugal. Adults also have a partial pre-breeding moult, during which they replace some head and neck feathers, and some scapulars. Juveniles undergo a partial post-juvenile moult, during which many head and body feathers, the tertials and some wing-coverts are renewed. Immature birds have two moults, a partial pre-breeding moult, in which some head feathers and some retained wing- and tail-coverts are replaced, and a complete post-breeding moult, similar to that of the adults.

GEOGRAPHICAL VARIATION Three races are currently recognised, but *nigripennis* and *exul* may each represent distinct species.

E. m. mystacalis Described above. Variation appears

to be slight, with a clinal decrease in size northwards.
E. m. nigripennis Length 26-28.5cm. Smaller and slightly paler than the nominate race, with a generally tawnier, more distinct collar around the hindneck. The extent and structure of the distal white markings on the four outer primaries differ. P10 and P9 are brown, usually unmarked. P8 has a very small white mark on the edges of both webs. P7 has a white band across the outerweb and the innerweb, the bands not meeting evenly at the feather shaft. Females have slightly less white on P7 or buff markings on P8 and P7. Wing (male) 218-230, (female) 207-223; tail (male) 138-150, (female) 134-158. Weight no data.
E. m. exul Known only from a single female specimen. Length 26cm. An extremely distinct subspecies. Upperparts greyish-white streaked blackish-brown, very boldly spotted blackish-brown on crown. Wing-coverts greyish-brown speckled brown, broadly spotted whitish-buff. Lesser coverts and primary coverts barred cinnamon. Scapulars greyish-brown on innerwebs, greyish-white on outerwebs, broadly streaked blackish-brown in centre. No collar on hindneck. Lores and ear-coverts pale tawny speckled blackish-brown. Breast brown, frosted greyish-white and -brown. Primaries brown, spotted and indistinctly barred pale buffish-brown at tips. P10 unmarked, P9 with small white bar smudged tawny, almost midway along feather, on outerweb, P8 with small white bar on outerweb, P7 with broad white band edged tawny across outerweb, and vestigial white mark on innerweb. Wing 182; tail 138. Weight 77g.

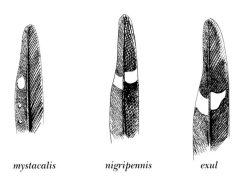

mystacalis   ***nigripennis***   ***exul***

4th primary markings of White-throated Nightjar races.

DISTRIBUTION AND MOVEMENTS Endemic to the Australasian region.
  E. m. mystacalis Coastal and Great Dividing Range of E Australia, from the Cape York Peninsula of NE Queensland, south through E Queensland and E New South Wales to E and CS Victoria. Sedentary and partially migratory in the north of its range, migratory in the south. In E Victoria, present November–March. Southern populations winter in N Australia and New Guinea. In NE Queensland it is resident north of Townsville, but further north on the Atherton Tableland large numbers occasionally arrive, stay a few months and then depart. In New Guinea, winters late March–September from the south-east, west to the Fly river and north to Astrolabe Bay. Has occurred as an apparent vagrant as far north as the Idenburg

River in N Irian Jaya. Occurs as a passage migrant through the Torres Strait, but only recorded September–October?
  E. m. nigripennis N and C Solomon Islands, on Bougainville, Shortland, Gizo, Guadalcanal, Santa Isabel, Rendova, Kulambangra and Rubiana. Sedentary.
  E. m. exul The only known specimen was taken from Tao, on coastal flats near Mount Panié, NW New Caledonia, on 1 August 1939. Presumably sedentary.

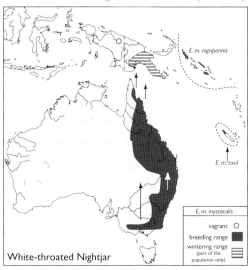

White-throated Nightjar

STATUS Fairly common in eastern Australia. No data from the Solomon Islands and not recorded since 1939 on New Caledonia.

REFERENCES Barker & Vestjens (1989), Beruldsen (1980), Blakers *et al.* (1984), Coates (1985), Conule (1987), Diamond (1972), Elliot (1935), Higgins (in press), Hollands (1991), Marchant (1987), Mayr (1941), Schodde & Mason (1981, 1997).

42   HEINRICH'S NIGHTJAR
Eurostopodus diabolicus   Plate 35

Other names: Satanic Nightjar, Devilish Nightjar

Eurostopodus diabolicus Stresemann, 1931, *Orn. Monatsb.* 39, p.103 (Kumarsot, base of Kalabat Volcano, Celebes)

IDENTIFICATION Length 26cm. A medium-sized to large, dark, Indonesian nightjar, endemic to Sulawesi. Until recently, known only from a single female specimen. **At rest** Upperparts greyish-brown, speckled and spotted brown, buff and pale tawny; crown broadly streaked blackish. No collar on hindneck. Wing-coverts brown, spotted and ocellated cinnamon-tawny. Scapulars blackish, ocellated cinnamon on tips. Band around throat white edged rust-brown (apparently male), or buffish (female). Underparts brown barred and spotted cinnamon and pale buff, becoming pale buff barred brown on belly and flanks. **In flight** Has rounded wing-tips and a short, square tail. Shows a small whitish spot on the innerweb of the third outermost primary and on the outerweb of the fourth outermost primary. Tail very narrowly tipped buffish.

Similar species Great Eared-nightjar (46) is larger and longer-winged, with a paler crown and wing-coverts contrasting with the rest of the upperparts, a broad, buffish collar around the hindneck, a small white patch on either side of the lower throat and paler, buffier underparts. Sulawesi Nightjar (90) is greyer-brown and more variegated, with a white throat-patch (rather than a broad band around the throat) and distinct white spots on the outer primaries and tail feathers.

VOICE Unknown. Songs and calls attributed to this species include a double-noted *plip-plop* call (sounding like dripping water), and a short, bubbling trill that rises in pitch in the middle, then slows and trails off. Flight calls given by unidentified birds include weak screams that rise then descend in pitch, and loud, disyllabic *whirrips* or *quirrips*. Agitated birds may give soft, growling churrs. No further information available.

HABITAT Prefers primary forest. Occurs in clearings and openings, or along forest edges, in lowland forest, hill forest or lightly logged montane forest. 250–1,735m.

HABITS Crepuscular and nocturnal. Possibly roosts on the ground; roost-sites may be in thickets. Sits on the ground at night. Hunts along forest edges, often along roads, from ground level up to the forest canopy c. 35m up. When foraging, frequently glides with its wings held level to the body. No further information available.

FOOD Insects. No further data available.

BREEDING The type specimen had enlarged ovaries when it was taken in early March, suggesting a readiness for breeding. No further information available.

DESCRIPTION Adult male Undescribed. **Adult female** Forehead, crown and nape greyish-white speckled brown, streaked dark brown; central feathers broadly streaked blackish-brown. No collar on hindneck. Mantle, back, rump and uppertail-coverts brown, speckled and spotted pale buff, brownish-buff and pale tawny. Lesser coverts blackish-brown barred cinnamon. Rest of wing-coverts brown, distinctly spotted cinnamon-buff or -tawny with brown centres. Some coverts are tipped buffish-white or buff. Scapulars blackish-brown, spotted cinnamon with brown centres on tips. Primaries brown; thin buffish-white bar almost midway along feather, on innerweb of P8; broader buffish-white bar on outerweb of P7; P6-P1 sparsely and faintly speckled cinnamon. Secondaries brown, sparsely and faintly speckled cinnamon. Tertials brown spotted cinnamon-buff or -tawny, with brown centres. Tail brown, very narrowly (c. 1-2mm) tipped buffish; R5-R2 indistinctly barred tawny; central pair (R1) broadly barred with greyish-brown mottling. Lores and ear-coverts rufous speckled brown. Chin blackish-brown. Throat buff, becoming tawny on the sides of the head. Breast dark brown, barred cinnamon on upper breast, spotted pale buff with brown centres on lower breast. Belly and flanks buffish-white and pale buff, barred brown. Undertail-coverts buff, broadly barred brown. Underwing-coverts cinnamon-buff barred blackish-brown. **Immature** and **Juvenile** Unknown. **Chick** Unknown. **Bare parts** Iris dark brown; bill black; legs and feet dark brown.

MEASUREMENTS (one female) Wing 202; tail 140; bill 18.5; tarsus 19.1. Weight no data.

MOULT No data available.

GEOGRAPHICAL VARIATION Monotypic.

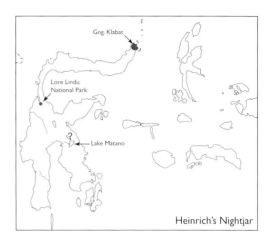

Heinrich's Nightjar

DISTRIBUTION AND MOVEMENTS A little-known species, endemic to Sulawesi. The type specimen was taken from Kumarsot, at the base of the Kalabat Volcano (= Gng. Klabat), Minahassa, in NE Sulawesi on 5 March 1931. The species is now known to occur in Lore Lindu National Park, NC Sulawesi, where it has been recorded in forest on the eastern flanks of Gng. Nokilalaki and on the western slopes of Gng. Rorekatimbu, just outside the eastern boundary of the park. Presumably sedentary.

STATUS Until recently this species had not been located with certainty except at the type locality. In addition to unidentified calls heard at night at Lake Matano (see Voice), a nightjar probably this species was seen at dawn on 30 July 1993, perched on a small branch beside a road through Lore Lindu National Park, at an altitude of c. 1,700m. The species was rediscovered in May 1996, when birds were seen on four occasions at two different sites within the same park.

REFERENCES Bishop & Diamond (1997), Coates & Bishop (1997), Holmes & Wood (1980), King (1994), Stresemann (1931).

---

43 PAPUAN NIGHTJAR
Eurostopodus papuensis   Plate 35

Caprimulgus papuensis Schlegel, 1866, *Nederl. Tijdschr. Dierk.* 3, p.340 (Salawati and the opposite coast of New Guinea)

IDENTIFICATION Length 25-27cm. A medium to large, dark, variegated, lowland forest nightjar, endemic to New Guinea. Sexes similar. **At rest** Upperparts brown speckled and barred greyish-brown, cinnamon and rufous, broadly streaked blackish-brown on crown. No collar on hindneck. Wing-coverts brown speckled and tipped tawny and buff. Scapulars cinnamon-buff speckled greyish-brown, boldly spotted blackish-brown. Large white throat-patch. Underparts cinnamon-rufous barred brown, becoming buff barred brown on belly and flanks. **In flight** Has pointed wings and slightly rounded tail. Buoyant flight. Lacks white or other obvious markings on the wings and tail. **Similar species** Archbold's Nightjar (44) is slightly larger and paler, appears more spotted, less variegated, and is restricted to the high mountains of New Guinea.

VOICE The song is a rapid series of *coo-coo-coo-coo-coo-coo* notes, lasting up to seven seconds or more. Also has a low throaty chattering.

HABITAT Prefers lowland rainforest, occurring in clearings and glades. Typically inhabits open forests, where fallen trees leave openings in the canopy and secondary growth gives good ground cover. 0–400m.

HABITS Crepuscular and nocturnal. Roosts on the ground in forests. When flushed from roost, often flies up to a perch. Occurs singly or in pairs. Hawks for insects from the ground, hunts prey over clearings and native gardens within forests or forages over the forest canopy. No further information available.

FOOD Moths and other insects. No further data available.

BREEDING Breeding season June?–August. No nest is constructed; the egg is laid on bare ground or on leaf-litter. Nest-sites are usually in small clearings amongst forest undergrowth. Clutch 1. Egg elliptical, pinkish-brown heavily blotched dark and pale brown, with underlying grey patches, 32 x 25mm. Incubation appears to be by the female during the day, the male taking over at dusk. No further information available.

DESCRIPTION Adult male Forehead, crown and nape greyish-brown speckled brown, broadly streaked blackish-brown. No collar on hindneck. Mantle, back, rump and uppertail-coverts brown, speckled and barred cinnamon and rufous, streaked dark brown. Wing-coverts brown, speckled and tipped tawny and buff. Primary coverts brown, unmarked. Scapulars cinnamon-buff speckled greyish-brown, boldly spotted blackish-brown. Primaries brown; one or two very small buff spots, almost midway along the feather, on the edge of the outerwebs of P9-P7; P6-P1 spotted or vermiculated tawny along the outer edges of both webs. Secondaries brown, spotted or vermiculated tawny along the outer edges of both webs. Tertials brown, mottled greyish-brown and buff. Tail brown barred tawny or pale tawny; central pair (R1) with broad bars or chevrons of greyish-brown mottling, tinged tawny. Lores and ear-coverts rufous, thinly barred brown. Chin rufous barred brown. Throat white, the lower feathers tipped blackish-brown with a buff subterminal band. Breast cinnamon-rufous barred brown. Belly and flanks distinctly scalloped buff, barred brown. Undertail-coverts dark brown barred brownish-buff. Underwing-coverts dark brown barred buffish-brown. **Adult female** Similar to the male. **Immature** and **Juvenile** Similar to the adults, although paler, more rufous on the wing-coverts and tertials. The crown is spotted black. **Chick** Not known. **Bare parts** Iris dark brown; bill black; legs and feet blackish.

MEASUREMENTS Wing (male) 189-207, (female) 190-202; tail (male) 131-153, (female) 130-142; bill (male) 14.3-17.2, (female) 13.1-15.0; tarsus (male, one) 18.2, (female) 15.7-17.1. Weight (male), no data, (female) 80-81g.

MOULT No data available.

GEOGRAPHICAL VARIATION Monotypic.

DISTRIBUTION AND MOVEMENTS Endemic to New Guinea. It has been recorded from Salawati Island, Sorong, Yeflio, Arfak, Andai, Muinka river, Setakwa river, Keku? Madana, Astrolabe Bay, Idenberg river, Fly river, Veimauri area, Lakekamu-Kunamaipa Basin, Selch Kabobo? and Sainkeduck? Sedentary.

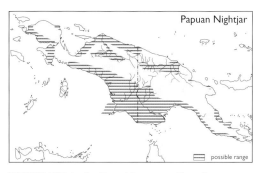

STATUS Widely distributed but generally rather scarce.

REFERENCES Beehler *et al.* (1986), Coates (1985), Mayr (1937), Rand & Gilliard (1967).

---

44   ARCHBOLD'S NIGHTJAR
Eurostopodus archboldi   Plate 35

Lyncornis archboldi Mayr and Rand, 1935, *Amer. Mus. Novit.* 814, p.4 (west slope of Mount Tafa, New Guinea)

IDENTIFICATION Length 26-30cm. A large, dark, rather spotted montane forest nightjar, endemic to New Guinea. Sexes similar. **At rest** Upperparts brown spotted buff and greyish-white, crown often greyish-brown broadly streaked blackish-brown. Indistinct collar around hindneck light greyish-brown admixed with dark brown. Wing-coverts brown spotted cinnamon, buff and tawny. Scapulars greyish-brown basally (not always visible) and blackish-brown distally, with cinnamon or buff spots on tips. Underparts brown, spotted buff or whitish, becoming buffish barred brown on belly and flanks. Tail fairly stiff with a 'tented' structure. **In flight** Often shows blunt-ended, fingered wing-tips. Flight is undulating, with alternate flaps and glides. Both sexes have brown un-marked wings. The male has extremely narrow greyish-white tips to the tail feathers; the female has buffier tips, but this feature cannot always be visible in the field. **Similar species** Papuan Nightjar (43) is slightly smaller and darker, appears more variegated, less spotted, and occurs at much lower altitudes.

VOICE The song possibly consists of 2-3 short, slightly trilled *tchrrt* notes, although this requires confirmation. Apparently heard predominantly at dusk. Near the nest-site, the adults give soft, liquid, trilled *whur-whur-whur* notes, which may be for contact. If flushed from the nest, the adult (perhaps female) utters a harsh explosive alarm call (not transliterated). Whilst hovering above an intruder at the nest-site, the adult (perhaps female) repeatedly utters a throaty hissing.

HABITAT Occurs only in montane forests with clearings and open areas of heath. 1,800?–3,225m.

HABITS Crepuscular? and nocturnal. Roosts on the ground, on low, moss-covered branches and logs or on branches in trees. Two or three birds occasionally roost together, sitting side-by-side across small branches. Roost-sites are usually in small forest clearings. Occurs singly, in pairs or small groups (perhaps family parties). When feeding, flies with rapid fluttering wingbeats, interspersed with long glides. Forages over grassy plains close to forest, or in and above forest clearings. Whilst hunting, frequently alights on perches, e.g. in dead trees. Also forages in short sallies from branches, fallen logs and the sides of high embankments, often returning to the same perch. No further information available.

FOOD Moths, beetles, bugs and cicadas. No further data available.

BREEDING Breeding season is from October to early December throughout its range.

No nest is constructed; the egg is laid on leaf-litter. Nest-sites may be on the ground, amongst stones and heather, or on banks or narrow ridges 1.3-1.5m above ground level. Clutch 1. Egg white and unmarked.

If flushed from the nest, the adult either calls (see Voice) and flies a short distance, alighting on the ground, on a low branch or on a small sapling, or performs a fluttering distraction display. If danger persists at the nest-site, the adult may fly back and hover near the intruder. No further information available.

DESCRIPTION Adult male Forehead, crown and nape dark brown spotted whitish and pale buff. Sides of crown pale greyish-brown. Indistinct collar around hindneck light greyish-brown admixed with dark brown. Mantle and back dark brown spotted buff, becoming slightly paler on rump and uppertail-coverts. Wing-coverts dark brown, spotted cinnamon, buff and tawny, spotting denser on lesser coverts. Scapulars greyish-brown basally (usually hidden) and blackish-brown distally, with cinnamon, buff or tawny spots on the tips. Primaries brown. Secondaries brown, spotted greyish-brown along edge of outerwebs, faintly barred tawny along edge of innerwebs. Tertials dark brown mottled greyish-brown, spotted cinnamon and tawny. Tail brown; R5 and R4 faintly barred tawny along edges of both webs, with small, pale buff spot on tips of both webs; R3 and R2 barred pale greyish-white on outerwebs, barred tawny on innerwebs and very narrowly tipped greyish-white; central pair (R1) broadly but indistinctly barred greyish-white, and very narrowly tipped greyish-white. Lores and ear-coverts dark brown, lightly speckled rufous and buff. Chin and throat dark brown, indistinctly barred buff. Fairly large white patch on either side of lower throat. Breast dark brown, feathers tipped whitish or buff, separated by dark feather-shaft. Belly and flanks dark brown, heavily spotted buff, buffish-white and cinnamon. Undertail-coverts buff barred brown. Underwing-coverts dark brown. **Adult female** Similar to the male, perhaps more densely spotted cinnamon and tawny on the upperparts and breast. Tail feathers very narrowly tipped buffish. **Immature** Not known. **Juvenile** Generally white, with blackish spots on the upperparts. **Chick** Not described. **Bare parts** Iris dark brown; bill blackish; legs and feet brownish or dark grey.

MEASUREMENTS Wing (male) 196-215, (female) 206-219; tail (male) 134-157, (female) 137-153; bill (male) 14.6-16.1, (female) 13.5-15.1; tarsus (male) c. 17, (female) 15.3-16.0. Weight (male, one) 74g, (female) no data, unsexed (one) c. 80g.

MOULT No data available.

GEOGRAPHICAL VARIATION Monotypic. No colour variation noted.

DISTRIBUTION AND MOVEMENTS Endemic to New Guinea, where it is patchily distributed in montane forests.

In Irian Jaya, it has been recorded from Mt Indon in the Arfak Mountains and Habbema Lake and the Bele range in the Snow Mountains. In Papua New Guinea, it has been recorded from Finimterr Plateau in the Hindenburg Range, the Mt Giluwe region, the Tari and Mt Hagen region, Mt Tafa, the Huon Peninsula, the Morobe district, Mt Albert Edward and the Wharton Range. Presumably sedentary.

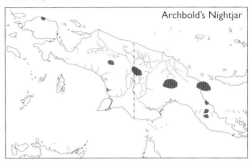

STATUS No information, but probably not common.

REFERENCES Beehler *et al.* (1986), Coates (1985), Gibbs (1996), Mayr & Rand (1935), Rand & Gilliard (1967), Tano (1996).

45   MALAYSIAN EARED-NIGHTJAR
Eurostopodus temminckii   Plate 34

Lyncornis temminckii Gould, 1838, *Icones Av.* pt. 2, pl.[16] and text (Borneo)

IDENTIFICATION Length 25-28cm. A large brown Asian nightjar. Sexes similar. **At rest** May show 'ear-tufts' at rear of crown. Upperparts brown speckled buff, pale buff and cinnamon, crown boldly spotted blackish-brown. Thin buff collar on hindneck, usually distinct. Wing-coverts brown, speckled buff, pale buff, buffish-white, tawny and cinnamon. Scapulars brown speckled buff and tawny, boldly spotted blackish-brown. White patch on lower throat or white spot on either side of lower throat. Underparts buffish, indistinctly barred brown. **In flight** Both sexes lack white markings on the wings and tail. **Similar species** Great Eared-nightjar (46) is larger, generally paler and longer-winged, with a slower, less erratic flight. Bonaparte's Nightjar (104) is smaller and has no collar around the hindneck; on the two outer tail feathers the male has white tips, the female very narrow whitish tips.

VOICE The song (perhaps call) is a treble-noted *tut wee-ow*, with a slight pause after the rather abrupt first note; the second and third notes are whistled, the third often trilled and descending slightly in pitch as it trails off. Sings several (5-7) times in succession, with only a short pause between each set of notes. Sings in flight. May be heard predominantly at dusk and dawn.

HABITAT A lowland/hill species. Prefers forest edges, open country, open scrub forest and riparian woodland. In Sumatra, it occurs in primary and secondary forest, and in areas of second growth. In Borneo, it occurs in dipterocarp forest, alluvial forest, scrubland, grassland, grassy swampland and coastal vegetation. 0–1,065m.

181

HABITS Crepuscular and nocturnal? Roosts on the ground, usually inside woods and forests. At dusk, often flies rather high in the air with wings held vertically in a V and calls (see Voice), then descends and flits low after food, often soaring up after insects. Often settles on posts, trees or dead branches. In trees, perches crossways on thin branches 1.5-5m up. Forages over open country, ricefields and other cultivation, forest clearings, lakes and ponds, rivers and estuaries. During the night, birds may perch high up in trees and rest. No further information available.

FOOD Beetles and moths. No further data available.

BREEDING Breeding seasons not fully documented, but may cover January–July on the Malay Peninsula, March–April on Belitung, October–November in Sumatra, and February–? in Borneo.

No nest is constructed, the eggs are laid on leaf-litter on the ground. Nest sites may be situated beneath trees or bushes. Clutch 1-2. Eggs elliptical, white, spotted, speckled and scrawled grey and brown, 34.4-34.5 x 25.5-27.8mm. No further information available.

DESCRIPTION Adult male Forehead, crown and nape greyish-brown speckled cinnamon-brown, central feathers boldly spotted blackish-brown. Erectile crown feathers behind the eye may show as 'ear-tufts'. Distinct, thin buff collar around hindneck, occasionally bordered blackish-brown. On some birds, collar may be indistinct or almost absent. Mantle, back, rump and uppertail-coverts dark brown, speckled buff, pale buff and cinnamon. Wing-coverts brown, speckled buff, pale buff, buffish-white, tawny and cinnamon. Scapulars brown speckled buff and tawny, boldly spotted blackish-brown on tips of outerwebs. Primaries and secondaries brown, spotted and thinly barred pale tawny. Tertials brown mottled buffish. Tail brown, indistinctly speckled and thinly barred buff or pale tawny. Lores and ear-coverts chestnut barred dark brown. Chin and throat dark brown barred cinnamon or chestnut. On lower throat either a small white spot on either side or occasionally a line across the whole. Breast brown thinly barred cinnamon and buff, with broad buff or sometimes whitish tips. Belly, flanks and undertail-coverts buffish-white, buff or occasionally whitish, indistinctly barred brown. Underwing-coverts buff barred brown. **Adult female** Similar to the male but often more rufescent. **Immature** and **Juvenile** Similar to the adults but upperparts rather cinnamon or tawny, less heavily speckled, with less buff on the underparts. **Chick** At hatching, covered in yellowish down, which is darker on the crown and nape. **Bare parts** Iris dark brown; bill pale horn with blackish tip; legs and feet dark brown.

MEASUREMENTS Wing (male) 197-213, (female) 198-218; tail (male) 121-132, (female) 111-139; bill (male) 11.2-14.8, (female) 11.2-14.8; tarsus (male) 15.2-19.2, (female) 15.2-19.2. Weight no data.

MOULT No data available.

GEOGRAPHICAL VARIATION Monotypic.

DISTRIBUTION AND MOVEMENTS Confined to the Thailand/Malaysian Peninsula, Sumatra and Borneo. Occurs from the extreme south-eastern parts of the Thailand Peninsula, south through the Malay Peninsula to Singapore, on Pienang Island, throughout Borneo and Sumatra including Nias, Bangka and Belitung (Billiton). Sedentary.

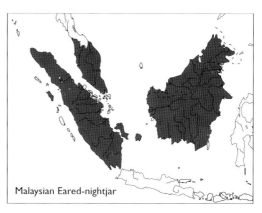

Malaysian Eared-nightjar

STATUS Locally common throughout most of its range, but uncommon in southern Thailand.

REFERENCES MacKinnon & Phillipps (1993), Madoc (1936), Mann (in prep.), van Marle & Voous (1988), Medway & Wells (1976).

46   GREAT EARED-NIGHTJAR
Eurostopodus macrotis   Plate 34

Caprimulgus macrotis Vigors, 1830-1831, *Proc. Comm. Zool. Soc. London* p.97 (Manila)
Eurostopodus macrotis cerviniceps (Gould, 1838), *Icones Av.* pt. 2, pl.[14] and text (Trang, Peninsular Siam, by designation of Robinson and Kloss, 1923. *J. Nat. Hist. Soc. Siam* 5, p.140)
Eurostopodus macrotis bourdilloni (Hume, 1875), *Stray Feathers* 3, p.302 (Kalland, Khauni, Travancore)
Eurostopodus macrotis jacobsoni (Junge, 1936), *Temminckia* 1, p.39, pl.2 (Sinabang, Simalur Island)
Eurostopodus macrotis macropterus (Bonaparte, 1850), *Consp. Av.* 1, p.62 (Celebes)

IDENTIFICATION Length 31-40cm. A widely distributed and very large brown Asian nightjar. Sexes similar. **At rest** May show 'ear-tufts' at rear of crown. Upperparts brown, speckled and spotted buff, cinnamon and greyish-white, crown boldly spotted blackish-brown. Broad tawny-buff or buff collar around hindneck. Wing-coverts brown, speckled and spotted tawny, buff and cinnamon. Scapulars brown, boldly spotted blackish-brown. Large white spot, occasionally tinged buff, on either side of lower throat. Underparts buffish, indistinctly barred brown. **In flight** Flies with leisurely, deliberate wingbeats. Both sexes lack white markings on the wings and tail. **Similar species** Malaysian Eared-nightjar (45) is smaller, darker, shorter-winged and has a faster, more erratic flight. Heinrich's Nightjar (42) is smaller, darker, shorter-winged and has a distinct white or buff band around the throat.

VOICE The song is a treble-noted *put wee-oo* or *put pee-ou-w*, with a slight pause after the abrupt, fairly soft first note. The second and third notes are whistled, the third descending slightly in pitch as it trails off. Sings in flight or from perches such as tree-stumps. When singing from a perch, the head jerks forward with each call. May be heard predominantly at dusk and dawn, and sporadically throughout moonlit nights. The song of the race *cerviniceps* in Thailand differs slightly by dipping in pitch in the middle of the whistle, and may be rendered *put weeow-ooo* or *put peeow-eeooo*.

HABITAT Prefers forests. Occurs in secondary forest, along forest edges, near rivers in primary forest, in second growth and scrubland, in clearings and wooded grasslands. Also inhabits more open country. 0–1,000m (to 1,750m on Sulawesi).

HABITS Crepuscular and nocturnal. Roosts on the ground or on fallen logs. Roost-sites are usually amongst shrubby undergrowth. In Tenasserim, Burma, it is said to roost in caves. At dusk, circles high above tree-tops in leisurely flight, descending after dusk to glide low over clearings on stiff wings, reminiscent of a harrier. Sometimes roosts or occurs in loose flocks of 6-10 birds. Forages over clearings, neighbouring grasslands and near habitation. During the night, birds may alight high up in trees and rest. No further information available.

FOOD Moths, beetles, bugs (including Cicadidae) and termites. No further data available.

BREEDING Breeding season January–May (mainly February–March) in S India and January–May on the Malay Peninsula. No data from other countries. No nest is constructed; the egg is laid on leaf-litter or bare ground. Nest-sites are often under thick bushes or bamboo clumps. Nests in lightly wooded country or in bamboo jungle. Clutch 1. Eggs elliptical, creamy white or deep salmon-pink, marbled and blotched pale grey and reddish, especially around the blunt end, (36.1) 37.8-44.1 x (25.6) 27.5-31.5mm. The same nest-sites may be used year after year. No further information available.

DESCRIPTION *E. m. macrotis* **Adult male** Forehead, crown and nape greyish-brown or rufous, speckled buff and greyish-white; central crown boldly spotted blackish-brown. Erectile post-ocular crown feathers may show as 'ear-tufts'. Broad buff or tawny-buff collar around hindneck. Mantle, back, rump and uppertail-coverts brown or dark brown, spotted and speckled buff, pale buff and cinnamon. Wing-coverts brown, speckled and spotted tawny, buff and cinnamon. Scapulars brown or buffish-brown speckled brown, boldly spotted blackish-brown. Primaries and secondaries brown, spotted and thinly barred pale tawny. Tertials brown mottled buffish. Tail brown or dark brown, speckled buff, broadly barred buff with brown speckling. Lores and ear-coverts chestnut barred dark brown. Chin and throat dark brown, thinly barred rufous, chestnut or buff. Lower throat brown barred buff, with large white spot (occasionally tinged buff) on either side. Upper breast brown, narrowly barred chestnut or buff. Lower breast, belly and flanks buff and buffish-white, indistinctly barred brown. Undertail-coverts buff barred brown. Underwing-coverts buff barred brown. **Adult female** Similar to the male. **Immature** and **Juvenile** Not described. **Chick** Not described. **Bare parts** Iris dark brown; bill brownish; legs and feet fleshy-brown.

MEASUREMENTS Wing (male) 253-281, (female, one) 271; tail (male) 157-180, (female, one) 175; bill (male) c. 13.5, (female) c. 13.5; tarsus (male) c. 19, (female) c. 18.5. Weight no data.

MOULT Few published data available. Possibly undertakes a post-breeding moult.

GEOGRAPHICAL VARIATION Five races are currently

recognised, although each form is extremely variable in colour.

E. m. macrotis Described above.

E. m. cerviniceps (Burmese Great Eared-nightjar) As large as the nominate but longer-winged and -tailed, with paler, buffier-brown upperparts, paler, more buffish collar around the hindneck and darker, less buff underparts. Wing (male) 292-317, (female) 292-317; tail (male) 207-225, (female) 207-225. Weight no data.

E. m. bourdilloni (Bourdillon's Great Eared-nightjar) Very similar to *cerviniceps* but shorter-winged and fractionally shorter-tailed. Some may be a little darker, with greyer, less buffish, wing-coverts. Wing (male) 274-287, (female) 274-287; tail (male) 182-204, (female) 182-203. Weight no data.

E. m. jacobsoni The darkest race and one of the smallest. The upperparts are generally dark chestnut, the underparts blackish. Wing (male) 254-264, (female) 241-272; tail (male) 153-178, (female) 156-187. Weight no data.

E. m. macropterus Similar to *jacobsoni*, but not as dark. The upperparts are dark brown, not chestnut, the underparts dark buff. Wing (male) 244-272, (female) 232-262; tail (male) 140-175, (female) 154-176. Weight no data.

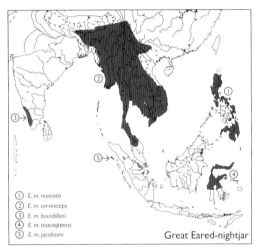

① *E. m. macrotis*
② *E. m. cerviniceps*
③ *E. m. bourdilloni*
④ *E. m. macropterus*
⑤ *E. m. jacobsoni*

Great Eared-nightjar

DISTRIBUTION AND MOVEMENTS Occurs throughout the Oriental faunal zone and on Sulawesi.

E. m. macrotis Restricted to the Philippines and found on Luzon, Mindoro, Catanduanes, Marinduque, Samar, Leyte, Bohol, Dinagat, Siargao, Biliran, Mindanao and Basilan. Not recorded Panay? and Negros? Sedentary.

E. m. cerviniceps NE India (Assam, Nagaland, Manipur, Tripura and Mizoram), NE and C Bangladesh (Chittagong Hills, Modhupur Forest and Samanbagh Tea Estate), S China (Yunnan), Burma, Laos, Thailand (including Phuket Island), S Vietnam, Cambodia and N Malaya (Kedah and Kelantan). Sedentary, but local migrant to parts of NE India, e.g. arrives NE Cachar in August and is then common until September, disappearing after the rains.

E. m. bourdilloni SW India (Kerala). Sedentary.

E. m. jacobsoni Known only from Simeulue Island off western Sumatra. Sedentary.

E. m. macropterus N and C Sulawesi (Fondano,

Pagoeat, Manado, Boné, Hadelido, Minahassa, Iamula and Dantan), Banggai Islands (Peleng and Labobo), Talaud Island, Sangihe and the Sula Islands (Taliabu and Mangole). Sedentary.

STATUS Fairly common throughout the Philippines, locally common in Sulawesi, moderately common on the Banggai Islands and the Sula Islands, locally common on Simeulue and local but not uncommon in southern India. Common? throughout much of the remainder of its range but rare in Bangladesh.

REFERENCES Ali & Ripley (1970), Coates & Bishop (1997), Dickinson *et al.* (1991), Medway & Wells (1976).

NYCTIDROMUS

Nyctidromus Gould, 1838, Icones Av., pt. 2, pl. [12] and text. Type by monotypy, *Nyctidromus derbyanus* Gould 1838.

One Neotropical species. A characteristic of the sole member of this genus is its long, bare tarsi, which are an adaptation to its rather terrestrial habits. Shows sexual dimorphism. Partially migratory, with a small population reaching southern Texas, U.S.A. Breeds and generally roosts on the ground. No nest is constructed. Aerial feeder.

47 PAURAQUE
Nyctidromus albicollis   Plate 12

Caprimulgus albicollis Gmelin, 1789, *Syst. Nat.* 1, pt. 2, p.1030 (Cayenne)
Nyctidromus albicollis merrilli Sennett, 1888, *Auk* 5, p.44 (Nueces River, Nueces County, Texas)
Nyctidromus albicollis insularis Nelson, 1898, *Proc. Biol. Soc. Wash.* 12, p.9 (María Madre Island, Tres Marías Islands, Mexico)
Nyctidromus albicollis yucatanensis Nelson, 1901, *Proc. Biol. Soc. Wash.* 14, p.171 (Tunkas, Yucatán)
Nyctidromus albicollis intercedens Griscom, 1929, *Amer. Mus. Novit.* 379, p.8 (Tela, Honduras)
Nyctidromus albicollis gilvus Bangs, 1902, *Proc. New England Zool. Club* 3, p.82 (Santa Marta, Colombia)
Nyctidromus albicollis derbyanus Gould, 1838, *Icones Av.* pt. 2, pl.[12] and text (South America; Ipanema, São Paulo suggested as type locality by Pinto, 1935, *Rev. Mus. Paulista* 19, p.133)

IDENTIFICATION Length 22-28cm. A medium-sized, variegated and long-tailed Neotropical nightjar with two distinct colour phases, greyish-brown and reddish-brown or tawny. Sexually dimorphic. **At rest** The wing-tips reach only half-way along the tail. Upperparts greyish-brown tinged rufous, mottled brown and speckled greyish-white; central crown broadly streaked blackish-brown. No collar around the hindneck. Lesser coverts chestnut speckled brown, rest of wing-coverts greyish-brown boldly spotted buff. Scapulars have buff, tawny or chestnut innerwebs, blackish-brown centres, and outerwebs edged buff or tawny. Sides of head distinctive, with buffish eye-ring and submoustachial stripe contrasting with rufous or chestnut lores and ear-coverts. Has a white throat-patch, or sometimes just a small white spot either side of the lower throat. Underparts greyish-brown tinged rufous, speckled and vermiculated brown, becoming buff barred brown on belly and flanks. **In flight** Broad, rather rounded wings and long tail. The male has a broad white band, near the wing-tip, across the five outer primaries, and the three outer tail feathers are largely white. The female has a thinner white band (washed buff or tawny on the outerwebs), across the three or four outermost primaries, and narrow white tips to the second and third outermost tail feathers. **Similar species** None.

VOICE The song is an extremely variable, short whistle, *wheeeow wheeoo-who*, or *whew whew whew whe-e-e-w* with the final note prolonged. The song is often preceded by soft *ko*, *put* or *puk* notes, e.g. *ko-ko-ko-kowhe-e-e-w* or *puk-puk-whow*. In Venezuela, the song may also be given as *kowup-kowup-kowup-kewhowww*, with the final note rising slightly in pitch. Sings from the ground or from perches such as fence-posts and rocks. May be heard predominantly at dusk and dawn, and throughout moonlit nights.

The female's call is a rapid series of *whip* notes, given from the ground or in flight. When nervous, perched birds of both sexes may utter low clucks. If flushed, often gives a single *whup*.

During the courtship display, the male utters soft *whip* calls whilst flitting around a female. During changeovers at the nest, the adults utter low, harsh notes. To call the chicks to it, the adult makes low croaking or clucking sounds, the chicks responding with peeping calls. During distraction displays or when being handled, the adults make guttural hissing, rattling or grunting sounds. Juveniles give strange *whoo* calls when escaping from danger at the nest-site.

HABITAT Prefers forested or wooded country. Inhabits forest edges and clearings, open woodland, riparian woodland, second growth and plantations. Also occurs in scrubland, open thicketed country, cultivated land, semi-arid regions, xerophytic areas, llanos, swampy areas and mangroves. 0–2,300 m, occasionally to 3,000m?

HABITS Crepuscular and nocturnal. Roosts on leaf-litter on the ground, or occasionally on a low branch up to 0.3m above ground. Roost-sites may be near the base of a bush, amongst fallen branches, in or amongst dense thickets or copses at the edges of woods, or in coffee or banana plantations. If danger approaches, a roosting bird initially adopts a flattened posture (see Breeding). If flushed from its roost, it flies off in a zigzagging flight and drops suddenly to the ground up to c. 20m away, turning as it re-alights to face the intruder, or alights on a low perch, up to 1.3m above ground. If danger persists, it 'bobs' nervously, and occasionally runs quickly away, with body crouched low to the ground. Also when flushed, sometimes flies to a low branch, and perches lengthways or across it.

Often sits on roads and tracks at night, and perches on branches, rocks and fence-posts. Occurs singly or in pairs. Drinks in flight from still water, including cattle 'tanks', by flying low over the surface and dipping its bill into the water. Hunts for food in short sallies from the ground, or by flycatching from low perches such as branches, tree-stumps, fence-posts, logs or the tops of bushes. Also forages over open areas such as clearings, lawns, pastures, fields, roads and railways, often fluttering close to the ground after insects. No further information available.

FOOD Beetles (including Scarabaeidae, Elateridae, Curculionidae, Cerambycidae, Passalidae, Carabidae, Lampyridae, Hydrophilidae, Chrysomelidae, Tenebrionidae and Staphylinidae), moths (including Sphingidae), butterflies, bugs (including Belostomatidae, Pieidae, Reduviidae and Cicadidae), bees, wasps, antlions, ants and Orthoptera (including Acrididae, Gryllidae, Mantidae and Trydactylidae).

BREEDING Breeding season March–July in Texas, USA; late March–late June in Mexico; February–May in Nicaragua and Costa Rica; late February–June in Panama; January–May, occasionally to August? in Colombia; March–June in Ecuador and Venezuela; February–July in Trinidad; March–October in Surinam (although eggs found in every month except February); ?–late August in French Guiana; September?–January? in SE Brazil and October–November in Paraguay. No data available from other regions, but thought to be July–January in southern latitudes.

The courtship display often commences with both sexes on the ground. The male flies up, flits around the female, calls (see Voice) and lands nearby, where he 'bobs' up and down. The female remains quiet and occasionally also 'bobs'. No nest is constructed; the eggs are laid on leaf-litter, bare ground, stony ground or pebbly sand. Nest-sites may be at the base of a bush or a small tree, in small openings and clearings in thickets or low vegetation, in clearings or along roadsides in forests, amongst scattered vegetation in open or semi-open country, in pastures and fields, along the edges of cultivated land, and amongst stones and boulders on dry beds of rivers and streams. Clutch 1-2. Eggs elliptical, elliptical-ovate or ovate, slightly glossy, pale salmon-pink tinged ochraceous, or pinkish-buff, blotched and spotted brown, buff and lilac, markings concentrated around the blunt end. Occasionally the eggs are almost unmarked, 27.2-35.1 x 19.4-24.6mm. The eggs are often laid in the late afternoon, and up to two days apart. Incubation is often by the male during the day and by the female during the night, although changeovers may take place every 2-3 hours (perhaps at night only).

During rain showers, the incubating adult may bathe by sitting upright with eyes open and head drawn back. An incubating male may leave the eggs after a heavy shower and alight a short distance away, preen and loaf for up to c. 2.5 hours, but always facing the eggs. In full sun, an incubating male may sit upright and gular-flutter to keep cool. Occasionally, he rapidly opens and closes his bill, producing a low, clicking sound. This bill-clicking may be repeated in short bouts for up to an hour. An incubating adult occasionally gapes or 'yawns' widely. Incubating males tend to face away from the sun.

If danger approaches, an incubating bird initially adopts a flattened posture by stretching out its body and lowering its head to the ground. Its eyes are closed almost shut, but it always keeps the danger in view, occasionally turning its head slowly to do so. If flushed from the eggs, the adult flies a short distance before re-alighting on the ground, where it nervously 'bobs' its head up and down and calls (see Voice). The adult occasionally performs a distraction display or circles the intruder (see below). If the eggs are accidentally dislodged from the nest the adult often moves them back again. Unattended eggs are occasionally trampled by cattle. Clutches laid on beds of rivers and streams may be washed away by rising water. Ground fires are also a threat. The incubation period is generally 19-20 days.

The semi-precocial young can move short distances from the nest-site within the first day after hatching. The eggshells may be removed from the nest by the adult shortly after the young have hatched. The chicks may be brooded by both parents. Newly hatched chicks may occasionally fall victim to fire-ants. If danger approaches, a brooding adult initially adopts a flattened posture (see above). If flushed from the young, the adult performs an injury-feigning distraction display by fluttering along the ground and uttering a guttural hissing (see Voice). If the danger persists, the adult flits a short distance, re-alights and repeats the display. If the flushed bird is a male, he may also fly in circles around the intruder.

The chicks usually move from one spot to another in response to the calls of the adult (see Voice). Adults often move their chicks into the cover of nearby vegetation during heavy rain. The chicks are fed from dusk onwards; the first food is often brought by the female. The chicks beg for food by standing upright and stretching their necks upwards to touch bills with the adult. The adult puts its bill into the open gape of the chick and regurgitates food. Juveniles that have not yet fledged flee danger by hopping away with their wings held above their backs and calling (see Voice).

DESCRIPTION *N. a. albicollis* **Adult male** Forehead, crown and nape greyish-brown tinged rufous, and speckled greyish-white; central crown broadly streaked blackish-brown. No collar around the hindneck. Mantle, back, rump and uppertail-coverts greyish-brown tinged rufous, barred and mottled brown. Lesser coverts chestnut, speckled dark brown. Primary coverts brown. Rest of wing-coverts greyish-brown or brownish, speckled and vermiculated buff and pale tawny, boldly spotted pale buff and buff. Scapulars variable, the innerwebs generally buffish-brown, tawny-brown or chestnut, speckled brown, the outerwebs blackish-brown, edged and tipped buff. Primaries brown; broad white band, angled across P10-P6, runs from almost midway between mid-wing and wing-tip on P10 to almost the feather-tip on P6; inner primaries and secondaries brown indistinctly and faintly barred pale tawny. Tertials greyish-brown washed buff or pale tawny, and mottled brown. Tail brown, R5-R3 with variable amounts of white; R5 has white from the feather-shaft diagonally across the innerweb almost to the tip; R4 is white on the upper half of the outerweb and entirely white on the innerweb, R3 generally entirely white, R2 broadly barred pale tawny, central pair (R1) greyish-brown tinged rufous, barred and mottled brown. Lores and ear-coverts rufous or chestnut, speckled brown. Buff eye-ring and buffish submoustachial stripe. Chin and throat greyish-brown, barred pale tawny or buff. Sides of neck buff barred blackish-brown. Small white spot either side of lower throat, or white patch across whole of lower throat, the lower feathers of which are tipped blackish-brown with a buff subterminal band. Breast greyish-brown tinged rufous, speckled and vermiculated brown. Belly, flanks, undertail-and underwing-coverts buff barred brown. **Adult female** Similar to the male, but with a thinner white band across P10-P8, occasionally to P7, edged buff and washed tawny or buff on the outerwebs. R4 and occasionally R3 are narrowly tipped white, c. 15mm, on the innerwebs. **Immature** and **Juvenile** Similar to the adults, but males have a thinner white band across the outer primaries, females a tawny band. **Chick** At hatching, covered in brown and pinkish-buff down. **Bare parts** Iris dark brown; bill blackish; legs and feet greyish.

MEASUREMENTS Wing (male) 144-157, (female) 140-160; tail (male) 132-157, (female, one) 149; bill (male) 13.1-15.1, (female) 13.1-15.1; tarsus (male) 22.8-28.3, (female) 18.7-24.0. Weight (male) 44-66g, (female) 43-60g.

MOULT Little published data available, but probably undertakes a complete post-breeding moult.

GEOGRAPHICAL VARIATION Seven races are currently recognised.

N. a. albicollis Described above. Colour variation is evident, with some birds being more rufous than others.

N. a. merrilli Larger and greyer than the nominate. Some males have no white on the outermost (R5) tail feathers. Wing (male) 180-184, (female, one) 176; tail (male) 165-172, (female, one) 155. Weight (male, one) 86.5g, (female) no data.

N. a. insularis Duller and greyer-brown than *yucatanensis*, with darker underparts and longer wings and tail. Wing (male) 170-171, (female) 170-173; tail (male) c. 162, (female) 157-163. Weight no data.

N. a. yucatanensis Larger and greyer than the nominate, with paler underparts. Slightly smaller and darker grey than *merrilli*, with smaller buffish spots on the wing-coverts. Wing (male) 160-175, (female) 160-172; tail (male) 141-171, (female) 141-158. Weight (male) 61-84g, (female) 57-65 (90 ?)g.

N. a. intercedens Similar to the nominate but has paler underparts. Smaller and darker than *yucatanensis*. Wing (male) 150-158, (female) 150-158; tail (male) 131-152, (female) 127-143. Weight (male) 56.0-72.7g, (female) 53.0-62.2g. The validity of this race is questionable, and it has been considered synonymous with the nominate by some authorities.

N. a. gilvus Paler and greyer than the nominate, and one of the smallest and palest races overall. Wing (male) 143-154, (female) 138-155; tail (male) 130-152, (female) 120-136. Weight no data.

N. a. derbyanus Larger than the nominate and fairly greyish. The male generally has white along the edge of the innerweb of the outermost tail feather (R5), with the second and third outermost tail feathers (R4 and R3) entirely white. Wing (male) 155-181, (female) 154-181; tail (male) 146-174, (female) 134 -165. Weight (male) 73-80g, (female) 60-70g.

DISTRIBUTION AND MOVEMENTS A widespread Neotropical species, ranging from northern Argentina to southern USA.

N. a. albicollis E and S Venezuela, Trinidad, Guyana, Surinam, French Guiana, N and NE Brazil (south to Bahia and Espírito Santo), E and S Colombia?, Ecuador? and NW and E Peru. Sedentary.

N. a. merrilli S USA (S Texas) and NE Mexico (Tamaulipas and E Nuevo León). Partially migratory, northern birds moving south? after breeding to E? Mexico (Veracruz and Puebla).

N. a. insularis Tres Marías Islands, W Mexico. Sedentary.

N. a. yucatanensis W Mexico (Sinaloa southwards) and E Mexico (S Tamaulipas southwards, including the Yucatán Peninsula and Cozumel Island), south to Belize and C Guatemala. Sedentary.

N. a. intercedens S Guatemala, Honduras, El Salvador, Nicaragua, Costa Rica and W Panama (W Bocas del Toro and W Chiriquí). Sedentary.

N. a. gilvus Panama (including islands of Gobernadora and Cébaco, and the Pearl Islands), N Colombia (Córdoba and Magdalena?) and Venezuela? (north of S Amazonas). Sedentary.

N. a. derbyanus C and S Brazil (Mato Grosso, Goiás and W Minas Gerais southwards), N and E Bolivia, Paraguay and NE Argentina (Misiones and Entre Rios). Presumably sedentary.

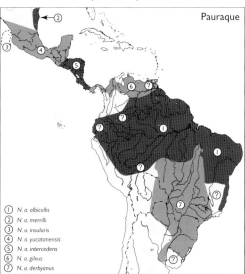

Pauraque

① N. a. albicollis
② N. a. merrilli
③ N. a. insularis
④ N. a. yucatanensis
⑤ N. a. intercedens
⑥ N. a. gilvus
⑦ N. a. derbyanus

STATUS Fairly common to abundant throughout much of its range.

REFERENCES Aragones (in press), Bent (1940), ffrench & O'Neill (1991), Haverschmidt & Mees (1994), Hilty & Brown (1986), Howell & Webb (1995), Meyer de Schauensee & Phelps (1978), Ridgely & Gwynne (1989), Skutch (1972), Slud (1964), de Urioste (1994), Wetmore (1968).

PHALAENOPTILUS

Phalaenoptilus Ridgway, 1880, Proc. U.S. Nat. Mus., 3, p. 5. Type by original designation, *Caprimulgus nuttallii* Audubon 1844.

One small, Nearctic species. Exhibits only mild sexual dimorphism. Partially migratory. Roosts on the ground or on low perches. Breeds on the ground. No nest is constructed and the eggs are whitish and generally unmarked. Aerial feeder.

48   COMMON POORWILL
Phalaenoptilus nuttallii   **Plate 12**

Caprimulgus nuttallii Audubon, 1844, *Bds. Amer.* octavo ed. 7, p.350, pl.495 (upper Missouri = between Fort Pierre and mouth of the Cheyenne River, South Dakota)
Phalaenoptilus nuttallii californicus Ridgway, 1887, *Man. North Amer. Bds.* p.588, note (Nicasio and Calaveras County, California)
Phalaenoptilus nuttallii hueyi Dickey, 1928, *Condor* 30, p.152 (Bard, Imperial County, California)
Phalaenoptilus nuttallii dickeyi Grinnell, 1928, *Condor* 30, p.153 (San Ignacio, lat. 27°N, Lower California)
Phalaenoptilus nuttallii adustus van Rossem, 1941, *Condor* 43, p.247 (Bates Well, Pima County, Arizona)

IDENTIFICATION Length 18-21cm. A small Nearctic nightjar, rather palish and distinctively short-tailed. Sexually dimorphic, although only marginally so. **At rest** Large-headed. Upperparts greyish-brown or -white, speckled and barred brown, crown boldly spotted blackish-brown. No obvious collar around the hindneck. Wing-coverts pale greyish-brown, streaked and barred blackish-brown, tipped buffish. Scapulars pale greyish-buff or -white, with broad, almost star-shaped, blackish-brown centres. No supercilium, but the sides of the crown are often thinly edged white. Thin white (male) or buffish (female) submoustachial stripe, chin and throat dark brown and sides of lower throat whitish. Rest of underparts generally pale greyish-brown or buffish, barred brown. **In flight** Round-winged. Flight moth- or bat-like, often interspersed with short glides. Both sexes lack white markings on the wings, which are brown regularly barred tawny. The male has all but the central pair of tail feathers narrowly tipped white; the female has slightly smaller white tips, often with a buffish subterminal band. **Similar species** None.

VOICE The song is a melodic, treble-noted whistle *poor-will-low* or *poor-we-wow*, occasionally *poor-will-ee*, lasting c. 0.5 second. Singing birds repeat the song phrase for a minute or more, with a slight pause between each set of notes. Sometimes sings at a faster rate, e.g. if another male is singing nearby, or in response to a tape-recording of the song. Sings mainly from the ground, but also from perches such as rocks, posts and low branches, and, occasionally in flight. Will sing from anywhere within its territory, including near the nest. May be heard predominantly at dusk and dawn, and throughout moonlit nights. On overcast evenings, it may commence singing before dusk. Birds flushed from the nest or roost-site during the day occasionally sing briefly before resettling. Tends to sing less in bad or windy weather, or once breeding has begun. In captivity, females have also been know to give the typical *poor-will-low* call.

The alarm calls are soft low clucking *quirk*, *quoit* or *werk* notes, either singly or repeatedly, by both sexes in flight, when taking flight or alighting, when flushed from the nest or during distraction displays. Whilst foraging around the nest-site, the male often gives a softer version of the alarm call. During threat/defence display and when handled, often utters a guttural hissing or growling. May also give high-pitched, mouse-like squeaks. If disturbed, hibernating birds may make odd puffy sounds, but it is not known if these deliberate calls. The chicks utter a variety of cheeps or peeps.

HABITAT Prefers arid or semi-arid country. Occurs in deserts, gravelly flats, open prairie, grassy hillsides with scattered trees or scrub, dry brushy hillsides, boulder-strewn rocky places with scattered trees and brush, rocky canyons, hillsides and plateaus with bushy vegetation, and chaparral. Also found in open woodland, broken forest and clearings in pines and firs. Generally 500–1,000 m, occasionally to 2,500m or more.

HABITS Crepuscular and nocturnal. Roosts on the ground, sometimes on rocks or low branches. Roost-sites are often amongst or 'backed' by shrubs, bushes, tall weeds or rocks. Usually changes roost-sites from day to day. In hot temperatures, roosting birds pant and gular-flutter to keep cool. If flushed from its roost, flies only a short distance before re-alighting. When active, often returns to a roosting site for short periods.

Commonly sits on roads and tracks at night, and often alights on perches such as rocks, logs, posts and electricity poles. In flight, occasionally wing-claps (see Breeding). In cold or bad weather, birds may become torpid for periods of up to 12 hours or more; they often enter torpor towards the end of twilight, occasionally earlier in poorer weather, e.g. before dusk. Breeding birds are rarely found torpid (see Breeding). In a torpid posture, birds may rest with the head pointing downwards, the bill nestling amongst the breast feathers. During the winter, may enter prolonged torpor or 'hibernation', for periods of up to 88 days, choosing rock crevices, ground squirrel holes, insides of rotten logs, bases of tree-stumps or ploughed furrows? as suitable hibernation sites. Has also been found under a leaf of an agave plant close to the ground. May become active briefly in warmer tem/peratures and during the day, leaving the hibernation site to bask in the sun. Remains faithful to the hibernation site, returning if colder weather resumes.

Few data available on predation. Northern Harriers *Circus cyaneus*, Coyotes *Canis latrans*, American Badgers *Texidea taxus* or Great Horned Owls *Bubo virginianus* may be a threat.

Occasionally drinks from still water, by fluttering low over the surface, with wings in a slight V above its back, and dipping its bill into the water. Either repeats this action several times or keeps its bill in the water and 'trawls' for distances of up to 0.5m. Occasionally lands in water very briefly, c. 0.5 second, before flying off and alighting on nearby dry ground, where it may bob its head up and down several times before preening. Forages in brief sallies from the ground, rocks, posts or low branches, often rising almost vertically up to 3m in the air to catch food before gliding back down. Also hawks for food in flight and around lights. Occasionally flutters close to vegetation to pick off insects and may occasionally take food from the ground.

FOOD Mainly beetles and moths (including Noctuidae), but also takes cicadas, bugs, locusts, grasshoppers, flying ants and flies. No further data available.

BREEDING Breeding season probably late May–September in north of range, March–August in the south.

Monogamous, possibly pairing for just one breeding season. Breeding territories may be up to 0.5 km apart. Courtship behaviour unknown. Territorial behaviour not studied but males may wing-clap whilst investigating intruders inside their territory.

No nest is constructed; the eggs are laid on pine needles, bare ground, rotten logs, gravel or flat rocks. Nest-sites are usually beneath overhanging foliage and are often in log-strewn clearings. Nests are positioned in partial shade of logs, rocks and rock shards, or in full sun. Clutch 2. Eggs elliptical or oval, smooth and slightly glossy, creamy white faintly tinged pinkish, unmarked or faintly spotted around the blunt end, 22.1-28.9 x 17.0-21.6mm. They are laid on consecutive days and incubation begins with the first egg. Double-brooded (see below). Replacement clutches are often laid if the first is lost. Incubation is shared by both sexes, but, unlike most other nightjar species, tends to be more often by the male during the day. Changeovers occur from dusk to dawn. During the day in hot weather, the incubating bird often gular-flutters to keep cool. If flushed from the nest, the adult flies off and alights nearby on the ground, a log or a boulder. Often performs a distraction display by fluttering wings and calling (see Voice). When returning to the nest, often lands close to the nest-site, sways from side to side for a short while then waddles onto the nest. Whilst walking to the nest, often stops and pauses for a short while before continuing. When the eggs are fresh, the male may perform a defence display whilst remaining on the eggs, by spreading his wings and tail, bringing his head back onto his shoulders, gaping and hissing (see Voice). He may also raise his wings vertically and vibrate them. During incubation, adults have been recorded moving the eggs up to 3m away from the original nest-site. The incubation period is about 20-21 days, the eggs hatching asynchronously, usually in the early morning. Soon after hatching, the eggshells are removed or possibly eaten by the adults.

If left unattended during the day, a newly hatched chick rests with head outstretched on the ground and eyes closed. The semi-precocial young are brooded by both adults, but more often by the female. If flushed from the nest, the adult alights nearby on the ground or on a log and either performs a distraction display by fluttering its wings, gaping and calling (see voice), or simply swaying from side to side. Occasionally, it also repeatedly protrudes and retracts its tongue. Alternatively, it may perform an injury-feigning distraction display along the ground. In different circumstances, the adult may adopt a defensive posture by facing the potential threat, stretching its wings out and forward, and freezing. A further reaction to danger is to make repeated short flights into the air and closely approach the intruder, landing nearby on the ground, on a log or on a boulder, constantly giving the alarm call (see Voice). With this behaviour, the adult often escorts or leads the intruder away from the nest-site. After danger subsides, the adult may rise suddenly into the air and drop back down to the ground in a zigzagging manner, before walking quietly back to the nest.

The adults usually change brooding duties at dusk. The incoming bird alights near the nest and waddles towards the brooding bird, which flies off suddenly, or it approaches in a series of short hops, before waddling up to the chicks. A more elaborate changeover involves the relieving bird landing a few feet from the nest, where it remains motionless whilst facing the incubating bird. It then looks around before rapidly bobbing its head up and down, displaying its white throat-patches, and waddling up to the nest. The brooding bird again flies off suddenly.

The adults forage up to 500m from the nest-site and the chicks are fed by regurgitation. During each visit to the nest-site, an adult will feed both chicks several times. The brooding bird may leave the chicks to forage briefly, then return and feed them. The male may sometimes catch insects around the nest-site, circle over the nest calling

(see Voice), then alight and waddle up to the nest. Food is then passed to the brooding female and the male departs.

The chicks often move short distances, usually towards cover, but tend to remain within 3m of the nest-site. Longer movements, of up to 10m per day, are possibly caused by disturbance. The young fledge at 20-23 days of age. Occasionally double-brooded, the female often laying the second clutch within 100m of the first nest. The male continues to feed the first brood whilst the female is incubating the second clutch. The young may associate with the male for up to 10 days after fledging. It is not known if the same nest-sites are used year after year, but birds tend to return to the same location and have been know to nest 1 km away from a previous nest.

Torpor is rare in breeding birds, but incubating males may enter torpor just after sunrise in bad weather, and in late summer adults and chicks may become torpid, but this may also be rare.

DESCRIPTION *P. n. nuttallii* **Adult male** Forehead, crown and nape greyish-white or -brown, speckled and barred brown, central crown boldly spotted blackish-brown. Hindneck slightly browner, feathers intricately marked blackish-brown and broadly tipped pale brownish-buff, but patterning and colour forms no obvious collar. Mantle, back, rump and uppertail-coverts greyish-white or -brown, speckled and barred blackish. Wing-coverts pale greyish-brown speckled brown, streaked and barred blackish-brown, washed buff on tips of outerwebs. Scapulars and tertials greyish-white or pale greyish-buff, speckled brown, with broad blackish-brown, almost star-shaped centres. Primaries and secondaries brown broadly barred tawny, and broadly tipped with greyish-brown mottling. Tail brown, indistinctly barred pale tawny, often on outerwebs only; R5-R2 tipped white, c. 17mm, across both webs; central pair (R1) broadly barred with greyish-white or greyish-brown mottling. Lores and ear-coverts dark brown speckled buff. Thin white submoustachial stripe. Chin and throat dark brown speckled buff. Sides of lower throat white, with the lower feathers broadly tipped blackish-brown. Breast pale brownish-buff or pale greyish-brown, thinly barred brown. Belly and flanks buff or buffish-white barred brown. Undertail-coverts buff. Underwing-coverts buff, barred brown along the marginal coverts and lesser underwing-coverts. **Adult female** Similar to the male, but has a buffish submoustachial stripe. R5-R2 with smaller white tips, c. 10mm, often with a buff subterminal band. **Immature** Similar to the adults. **Juvenile** Dull buffish-white speckled greyish; lacks the blackish-brown spotting on the crown, with buffish (not white) patches on the sides of the lower throat and less distinct blackish-brown markings, especially on the underparts. **Chick** At hatching, covered in pale buff or greyish-buff down, often tinged vinaceous. **Bare parts** Iris dark brown; bill blackish; legs and feet brownish-pink or purplish-grey.

MEASUREMENTS Wing (male) 129-145, (female) 129-139; tail (male) 79-88, (female) 79-88; bill (male) c. 14.3, (female) c. 14.3; tarsus (male) 15-18, (female) 15-18. Weight (male) 31.5-57.5g, (female) 36.7-58.0g.

MOULT Few published data available. Juveniles moult their body plumage towards the end of the breeding season (around August).

GEOGRAPHICAL VARIATION Five races are currently recognised, although all subspecies overlap with the nominate race and the validity of some might therefore be questionable.

P. n. nuttallii Described above.

P. n. californicus (Dusky Poorwill) Darker and browner than the nominate with more black on the underparts. Wing (male) 140-146, (female, one) 137; tail (male) 82-86, (female, one) 82. Weight (male) 36.6-57.7g, (female) 38.8-58.2g.

P. n. hueyi (Desert Poorwill) Like a pale form of the nominate. Upperparts pinkish-tan, underparts paler, with less black on the lower throat and narrower brown barring on the belly and flanks. Wing (male) no data, (female one) 140; tail (male) no data, (female one) 84. Weight (male) no data, (female) 40.8-42.3g.

P. n. dickeyi (San Ignacio Poorwill) Similar to *californicus* but smaller, with smaller black markings on the crown, scapulars and breast. Underparts darker than the nominate with heavier brown barring on the lower belly. Often has broader white tips to R5-R2. Wing (male) 129-133, (female) 129-133; tail (male) 79-83, (female) 79-83. Weight (male) 31.7-44.7g, (female) 33.2-43.7g.

P. n. adustus (Sonoran Poorwill) Similar to the nominate but paler and browner. Wing (male) 138-146, (female) 133-146; tail (male) 80-85, (female) 80-92. Weight no data.

DISTRIBUTION AND MOVEMENTS Widely distributed throughout the western half of North America and northern Mexico.

P. n. nuttallii CS British Columbia, SE Alberta, SW Saskatchewan, North Dakota, South Dakota and Nebraska, south through E Washington, C and E Oregon and California to N Mexico (S Sonora east to Tamaulipas, south to N Jalisco and N Guanajuato), and east to E Kansas, NW Oklahoma and C Texas. Sedentary and partially migratory. After breeding, northern populations move south, leaving by late September (October–November in the south) to winter throughout the southern parts of its range, from SE California and S Texas to C Mexico. Returning birds arrive in the southern parts of its North American breeding range during February–March, and by late April–mid-May further north.

P. n. californicus W California and NW Baja California.

Migratory, but sedentary in the south of its range.

P. n. hueyi SE California (Lower Colorado Valley), SW Arizona? and N Baja California. Sedentary.

P. n. dickeyi Baja California (south of latitude 30°N). Sedentary.

P. n. adustus Extreme S Arizona, south to C Sonora (to at least latitude 29°45'N). Birds of this race have also been recorded in Nevada and Texas. Presumably sedentary.

In some parts of its range, some populations may undertake altitudinal movements outside the breeding season.

A possible vagrant (this species?) has been recorded in early May on Garden Key, Dry Tortugas National Park, Monroe County, Florida.

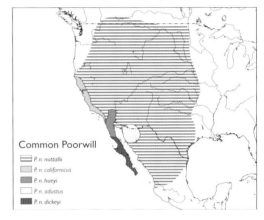

Common Poorwill

- ▤ P. n. nuttallii
- ▨ P. n. californicus
- ▥ P. n. hueyi
- ▢ P. n. adustus
- ▩ P. n. dickeyi

STATUS In North America, possibly uncommon in the north and east of its range, locally common in the southwest (California, Arizona, New Mexico and Colorado). Fairly common to common in N and C Mexico.

REFERENCES Aldrich (1935), Bayne & Brigham (1995), Bent (1940), Brigham (1991), Brigham & Barclay (1992), Csada & Brigham (1992, 1994a,b), Csada *et al.* (1992), Fears (1975), Howell & Webb (1995), Jaeger (1948, 1949), Kissner & Brigham (1993), Orr (1948), Wang *et al.* (1995).

SIPHONORHIS

Siphonorhis Sclater, 1861, Proc. Zool. Soc. London, p. 77. Type by original designation and monotypy, *Caprimulgus americanus* Linnaeus 1758.

Two small species, endemic to islands in the Caribbean, one on Hispaniola, the other on Jamaica and now generally regarded as being extinct. Both species have broad, flat bills with strongly decurved tips, prominent, tubular nostrils and long, unfeathered tarsi. A small amount of sexual dimorphism is shown by both species. Almost nothing is known about the Jamaican species, the other breeds and generally roosts on the ground, constructs no nest and is an aerial feeder.

S. americana

S. brewsteri

49 JAMAICAN POORWILL
Siphonorhis americana Plate 12

Other name: Jamaican Pauraque

Caprimulgus americanus Linnaeus, 1758, *Syst. Nat.* ed. 10, 1, p.193 (America Calidiore = Jamaica); *Siphonorhis* is feminine, *fide* Olson, 1985, *Proc. Biol. Soc. Wash.* 98, p.526

Forms a superspecies with Least Poorwill, with which it was formerly considered conspecific.

IDENTIFICATION Length 23-25cm. A medium-sized, long-legged, variegated nightjar, endemic to Jamaica. Sexually dimorphic, but not greatly so. **At rest** Upperparts rufous-brown streaked blackish-brown, crown more broadly streaked blackish. Indistinct collar on hindneck rufous or rufous-buff. Wing-coverts rufous-brown, distinctly marked with patches of blackish-brown and small, pale buff spots with brown centres. Large white throat-patch. Underparts rufous-brown, boldly spotted whitish on upper belly, becoming buff barred brown towards the tail. **In flight** Both sexes have short, rounded wings without white markings and regularly spotted tawny-buff. Round-tailed. The male has all but the central pair of tail feathers narrowly tipped white; the female has yellowish-buff tips. **Similar species** Least Poorwill (50) of Hispaniola is smaller with greyish-brown upperparts and whiter underparts.

VOICE Unknown.

HABITAT Unknown. Possibly occurs (or occurred) in dry limestone forest, semi-arid woodland or open country.

HABITS No information.

FOOD No data available.

BREEDING No information.

DESCRIPTION Adult male Forehead, crown and nape rufous-brown, broadly streaked blackish-brown. Indistinct rufous-buff collar on hindneck. Mantle and back rufous-brown streaked blackish-brown, rump and uppertail-coverts the same but streaking thinner. Wing-coverts rufous washed buffish, speckled brown and distinctly marked with patches of blackish-brown and small, pale buff spots with pale brown centres. Scapulars pale buff heavily speckled brown, with broad blackish-brown centres and rufous edges to the innerwebs. Primaries brown, regularly spotted buff along the outerwebs, barred tawny-buff on the innerwebs. Secondaries similar, becoming paler, more regularly barred towards the inner feathers. Tertials almost sandy or greyish-white. Tail rufous-brown, flecked and thinly barred brown; R5-R2 narrowly (7-10mm) tipped white. Lores and ear-coverts rufous speckled dark brown. Chin and upper throat rufous, lower throat entirely white. Breast rufous, thinly and faintly barred brown. Belly and flanks buffish barred brown, boldly spotted whitish. Lower belly and undertail-coverts buff barred brown. Underwing-coverts buff barred brown. **Adult female** Similar to the male but perhaps slightly less rufous, with broader streaking on the crown and more extensively white-spotted underparts; R5-R2 narrowly (c. 5mm) tipped yellowish-buff. **Immature** and **Juvenile** Unknown. **Chick** Unknown. **Bare parts** Undescribed.

MEASUREMENTS Wing (male) 133-145, (female, one) 135; tail (male) 117-131, (female, one) 118; bill (male) 13.5-16.5, (female, one) 13.9; tarsus (male) 22.5-23.6, (female) no data. Weight no data.

MOULT One male (museum specimen) taken in September was in wing and tail moult. No further data available.

GEOGRAPHICAL VARIATION Monotypic.

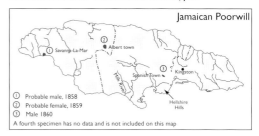

DISTRIBUTION AND MOVEMENTS Endemic to Jamaica. The species is known only from four museum specimens, a male (no data) taken in 1844?, a female (but probably a male) taken at Savanna-la-Mar (Bluefields area), Westmoreland, in August 1858, a male (but probably a female) taken at Freeman's Hall, near Albert Town in Trelawney, in September 1859, and a male taken near Linstead, St Thomas-in-the-Vale (Worthy Park area of St Catherine = near Spanish Town?), in November 1860? Birds seen recently at Milk River and in the Hellshire Hills may possibly have been this species.

STATUS Not positively recorded since the last specimen was taken near Spanish Town in November 1860 and now often considered to be extinct.

REFERENCES Collar *et al.* (1992).

50 LEAST POORWILL
Siphonorhis brewsteri Plate 12

Other name: Least Pauraque

Microsiphonorhis brewsteri Chapman, 1917, *Bull. Amer. Mus. Nat. Hist.* 37, p.329 (Túbano, Province of Azua, Dominican Republic)

Forms a superspecies with Jamaican Poorwill, with which it was formerly considered conspecific.

IDENTIFICATION Length 18-21cm. A small, long-legged, variegated nightjar endemic to Hispaniola. Sexes similar. **At rest** Upperparts greyish-brown streaked blackish-brown, crown broadly streaked blackish. Broad buff collar around the hindneck. Wing-coverts greyish-brown, boldly spotted white. Underparts brown, boldly spotted white on breast becoming white, barred and vermiculated brown on belly. **In flight** The short, round wings give it a very erratic, floppy, 'moth-like' flight. Both sexes lack white markings on the wings, which are brown, heavily spotted buff. The male has all but central pair of tail feathers narrowly tipped white; the female is similar?, or may have the tips washed pale buff. **Similar species** Jamaican Poorwill (49) is larger, more rufous brown and endemic to Jamaica, but widely regarded as extinct.

VOICE The song is a rising whistle *toorrrrri* or a more warbled *tworrrrri*, heard chiefly at dusk and dawn?, and occasionally during the day in the breeding season. Calls are a short, whistled *toorric* or shorter *to-ic*. When disturbed, utters rapid *kaweck-weck-weck-weck-weck* notes. Also gives scratchy notes similar to a small ground-dove.

HABITAT Prefers arid or semi-arid lowlands, especially scrubby woodland. Also occurs in broadleaf, pine or mixed forest. 0–800m.

HABITS Crepuscular and nocturnal? Roosts on the ground or perched lengthways on a horizontal branch, up to 2m above ground. When flushed, it flits a short distance and alights on the ground or a small bush. Floppy, erratic flight in and out of trees is reminiscent of a giant moth. No further information available.

FOOD No data available.

BREEDING Breeding season is April?–June?
No nest is constructed; the eggs are laid on the ground. Nest-sites may be on narrow ridges in or beside burnt areas. Eggs elliptical, dull white, spotted pale purplish-grey and mottled and scrawled buff and pale brown, 23.0-25.2 x 17.5-19.0mm. When an adult is flushed from the nest, it may give a distraction display by quivering its wings. No further information available.

DESCRIPTION Adult male Forehead, crown and nape greyish-brown, broadly streaked blackish-brown. Broad buff collar on hindneck, streaked brown. Mantle, back, rump and uppertail-coverts brown or greyish-brown, streaked blackish-brown. Lesser coverts brown barred cinnamon. Rest of coverts brown speckled and barred buff, many broadly tipped or spotted white. Scapulars blackish-brown tipped and edged pale whitish-buff, inner edge more rufous. Primaries brown, spotted buff along outerwebs of P10-P7; inner primaries, secondaries and tertials brown spotted buff along both webs, spots becoming paler, even whitish, towards tertials. Tail brown; R5-R2 indistinctly barred greyish-brown, narrowly (c. 3-5mm) tipped white; central pair (R1) slightly paler, heavily speckled greyish-brown. Sides of crown from bill, over eye and along base of crown above hindcollar whitish spotted and minutely speckled brown. Lores and ear-coverts rufous speckled brown. Chin and upper throat buff, lower throat entirely white. Indistinct malar stripe brown spotted whitish-buff. Breast brown, boldly spotted white, and spotted cinnamon (139) on sides. Belly and flanks white or whitish, barred and vermiculated brown, undertail-coverts buffish. Underwing-coverts buff barred brown. **Adult female** Similar to the male, perhaps slightly browner. White tips to R5-R2 occasionally washed pale buffish. **Immature** Not known. **Juvenile** Similar to the adults but belly and flanks pale buff faintly barred brown. Some feathers on upperparts pale buffish-brown finely peppered brown, distinctly spotted blackish-brown at tips. **Chick** Not known. **Bare parts** No data.

MEASUREMENTS Wing (male) 118-123, (female) 112-120; tail (male) 97-100, (female) 85-107; bill (male) 13.0-16.2, (female) 13.9-14.9; tarsus (male) 23.2-26.3, (female) 22.0-24.8. Weight no data.

MOULT No data available.

GEOGRAPHICAL VARIATION Monotypic.

DISTRIBUTION AND MOVEMENTS Endemic to Hispaniola. Recorded from C and W Dominican Republic and Haiti, including Ile de la Gonâve. Sedentary.

Least Poorwill

STATUS Rare, but possibly under-recorded.

REFERENCES Bond (1928a), Dod (1979), Wetmore & Swales (1931).

NYCTIPHRYNUS

Nyctiphrynus Bonaparte, 1857, Riv. Contemp., 9, p. 215. Type by subsequent designation, *Caprimulgus ocellatus* Tschudi 1844 (Oberholser, 1914, Bull. U.S.Nat. Mus. No. 86, p. 8, note 5).

Four small, Neotropical species. Species within this genus have prominent, tubular nostrils, elongated, decurved rictal bristles around the gape, dense crown feathers that protrude at the sides to form a rim above the eyes (where they are fringed with hair-like bristles), unfeathered tarsi and slightly rounded tails with all but the central pair, or two pairs of feathers, narrowly tipped white. All species breed and generally roost on the ground, construct no nests and are aerial feeders.

One species, *Nyctiphrynus rosenbergi*, appears to differ from the other members of the genus in several respects. It has less elongated rictal bristles around the gape, the crown feathers are less dense and do not appear to protrude above the eyes, and all the tail feathers are narrowly tipped white.

51 EARED POORWILL
Nyctiphrynus mcleodii   Plate 13

Otophanes mcleodii Brewster, 1888, *Auk* 5, p.88 (Sierra Madre of Chihuahua, Mexico)
Nyctiphrynus mcleodii rayi (Miller, 1948), *Condor* 50, p.224 (Chilpancingo, Guerrero, Mexico)

IDENTIFICATION Length 20-21cm. A small, rather plainish nightjar endemic to western Mexico. Sexes similar. **At rest** May show small 'ear-tufts' at rear of crown. Upperparts greyish or rufescent-brown with large blackish spots on the scapulars and smaller white spots on the wing-coverts. Very narrow, well-defined buffish-white collar on hindneck. Conspicuous white band around throat. Underparts greyish or rufescent-brown becoming buff lightly spotted white on belly. **In flight** Round-winged and round- and dark-tailed. Both sexes lack white markings on the wings, which are regularly barred tawny. Central tail feathers greyish or rufescent-brown, fractionally longer than rest of tail. Outer four tail feathers uniformly dark brown, narrowly tipped white. **Similar species** Yucatan Poorwill (52) is shorter-winged, with upperparts heavily streaked blackish-brown, not plainish, and narrow collar on hindneck less well-defined; underparts more heavily spotted buffish and white.

VOICE The song (perhaps call) is a loud, abrupt *peeyo* or *peejo*. Also gives a descending, tremulous *teu-uu-uu*. Sings from the ground, from rocks or from a low perch in trees, especially pines and oaks. Several birds together may all call at once. When calling, opens gape wide. May be heard mostly at dusk and throughout the night, especially when there is plenty of moonlight. Also calls just before dawn. Apparently both sexes call. Sharp *gwik* or *wuik* call notes are also given. When together, pairs utter low *chuck* notes. Females occasionally make a short, trilled churring when disturbed.

HABITAT Prefers pine woods, open oak woodland and pine-oak association in semi-arid, mountainous country. Also occurs along woodland edges, on oak hillsides below cloud-forest and seasonally? in overgrown fields with scattered trees or in wooded gullies. 600–2,500m.

HABITS Crepuscular and nocturnal. Roosts on the ground, roost-sites often being amongst rocks. When flushed, it may fly up to c. 40m before re-alighting on the ground or a perch, e.g. on rocks or boulders. In trees, it perches lengthways along branches. Feeds by fluttering up from the ground after insects. Also feeds by making sallies from perches in trees. No further information available.

FOOD Beetles and other insects. No further data available.

BREEDING Breeding season probably April–June.
    No nest is constructed; the eggs are laid on the ground, or on pine needles. Nest-sites have been recorded in short grass at the base of a cliff and in clumps of pines *Pinus teocote*. Clutch 2. Eggs ivory-white, unmarked, 25.1-25.8x18.9-19.0mm. No further information available.

DESCRIPTION *N. m. mcleodii* **Adult male** Forehead and sides of crown greyish-brown, minutely speckled buff. Central crown darkish brown speckled rufous. Crown feathers very dense, extending out at sides to form a ridge above the eye; behind the eye, erectile feathers are slightly longer and may show as 'ear-tufts'. Well-defined, very narrow pale buff collar on hindneck. Collar is edged blackish and extends around neck to throat-patch. Rest of nape, mantle and back brown washed and speckled rufous. Rump and uppertail-coverts brown speckled greyish-white. Wing-coverts rufescent-brown, sparsely spotted white. Scapulars rufescent-brown speckled buffish-white with large blackish-brown spot bordered buff along upper edge, on distal half of outerweb. Primaries and secondaries brown regularly barred tawny. Tertials brown speckled rufous. Tail uniformly dark brown, occasionally with some very faint buff barring; R5-R2 narrowly (c. 10mm) tipped white; central pair (R1) fractionally longer than rest of tail and paler, being brown minutely speckled greyish-white. Lores and ear-coverts dark buff minutely speckled brown. Chin and throat rufescent-brown speckled buff. Pure white band around lower throat. Breast

and upper belly rufescent-brown, minutely speckled buff. Belly and flanks buffish, tinged rufous, lightly spotted white. Lower belly and undertail-coverts buff faintly barred brown. Underwing-coverts buff barred brown. **Adult female** Similar to male, occasionally having tawnier upperparts. **Immature** and **Juvenile** Not described. **Chick** Not described. **Bare parts** Iris dark brown; bill dusky or flesh with black tip; legs and feet pale pinkish-drab or greyish.

MEASUREMENTS Wing (male) 127-130, (female) 128-135; tail (male) 102-110, (female) 106-108; bill (male) 11.5-13.2, (female, one) 15.9; tarsus (male) c. 16, (female) c. 16.5. Weight (male, one) 30.8g, (female, one) 24.5g.

MOULT Few data available. Primaries are moulted descendantly. Probably undertakes a complete moult in late summer. One female of *N. m. rayi* (museum specimen) in primary and tail moult in early August.

GEOGRAPHICAL VARIATION Two races are currently recognised, although the validity of *rayi* has been questioned by some authorities.
    N. m. mcleodii Described above.
    N. m. rayi Generally greyer and darker than the nominate, with smaller white spots on the wing-coverts, and more tawny-buff belly and undertail-coverts. Wing (male, one) 126, (female, one) 128; tail (male, one) 111, (female, one) 111. Weight (male) 35.9-36.4g, (female) 31.7-35.3g.

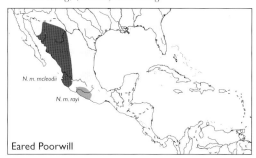
Eared Poorwill

DISTRIBUTION AND MOVEMENTS Endemic to W Mexico.
    N. m. mcleodii S Sonora? Chihuahua, Sinaloa, Jalisco and Colima. Sedentary.
    N. m. rayi Guerrero. Sedentary but perhaps subject to some local movement, e.g. casual in Oaxaca.

STATUS Poorly known, but possibly not uncommon within most of its range.

REFERENCES Howell & Webb (1995), Miller (1948), Schaldach & Phillips (1961).

52   YUCATAN POORWILL
Nyctiphrynus yucatanicus   Plate 13

Caprimulgus yucatanicus Hartert, 1892, *Cat. Bds. Brit. Mus.* 16, p.525 (in key) (Tizimin, Yucatán)

IDENTIFICATION Length 19.5-22cm. A small, brownish and rather streaked Central American nightjar. Sexes similar. **At rest** Upperparts brown streaked blackish-brown, lightly spotted buffish-white on wing-coverts. Narrow, indistinct buffish collar on hindneck. Large white throat-patch. Underparts brown narrowly streaked blackish-brown on breast, becoming brown or brownish-buff spotted white on belly. **In flight** Round-winged and -tailed. Both sexes lack white markings on the wings, which are regularly barred tawny. Outer four tail feathers narrowly tipped white. **Similar species** Eared Poorwill (51) is longer-winged, with well-defined narrow collar on hindneck, rather plain upperparts (but large blackish-brown spots along scapulars) and plainer underparts with smaller white spots on belly.

VOICE The song is a repetitive *weeo weeo weeo*, very similar to the that of Eared Poorwill. Sings from trees. Also gives liquid clucking sounds. The flight (perhaps alarm) call is a series of *week week week* notes.

HABITAT Prefers scrubland, deciduous forest and open woodland, in arid and semi-arid lowlands. Also occurs in farmland, fields, second growth and thorny woods. 0–250m.

HABITS Crepuscular and nocturnal. Arboreal, often occurring high up in trees. Forages from trees and from the ground. No further information available.

FOOD No data available.

BREEDING Breeding season April–June in Guatemala. No data available from other localities.

No nest is constructed; the eggs are laid on leaf-litter on the ground. Eggs elliptical, glossy, buffish speckled brown, 24.8-25.0 x 15.2-18.6mm. If flushed from the eggs, the incubating adult performs an injury-feigning distraction display by fluttering about on the ground and leading the danger away from the nest. No further information available.

DESCRIPTION Adult male Forehead, crown and nape brown speckled greyish-white, streaked blackish-brown. Crown feathers quite dense, and at sides they extend out to form slight ridge above the eye. Narrow, indistinct buffish collar on hindneck. Mantle, back, rump, uppertail-coverts, tertials and wing-coverts brown speckled greyish-white, streaked blackish-brown. Small buffish-white spots on tips of 3-5 median coverts. Scapulars rufous-brown on outerwebs, buffier on innerwebs, with pronounced, pointed blackish-brown centres. Primaries and secondaries brown, regularly barred tawny. Tail brown, indistinctly barred with rufous mottling, becoming plainer towards tip; R5-R2 narrowly (c. 10mm) tipped white. Lores and ear-coverts brown minutely speckled buff. Chin brown speckled greyish-white. Large white patch across lower throat. Breast and upper belly brown speckled greyish-white, streaked blackish-brown. Belly and flanks brown tinged rufous, spotted white on belly. Undertail- and underwing-coverts buff barred brown. **Adult female** Similar to male but occasionally paler and more rufous. **Immature** and **Juvenile** Not known. **Chick** Not known. **Bare parts** Iris dark brown; bill blackish; legs and feet brown.

MEASUREMENTS Wing (male) 110-117, (female) 109-114; tail (male) 101-108, (female) 91-108; bill (male) 12.7-13.8, (female) 13.6-14.7; tarsus (male) 16.2-17.5, (female) c. 16.0. Weight (male, one) 21.3g.

MOULT One female (museum specimen) in primary and tail moult in early August, suggesting a complete post-breeding moult strategy. No further data available.

GEOGRAPHICAL VARIATION Monotypic.

Yucatan Poorwill

DISTRIBUTION AND MOVEMENTS Endemic to Central America, occurring in SE Mexico (Yucatán Peninsula in Yucatán, Campeche and Quintana Roo), N Guatemala (Petén) and N Belize (south of San Ignacio). Sedentary.

STATUS Fairly common to common throughout range.

REFERENCES Hardy & Straneck (1989), Howell *et al.* (1992), Howell & Webb (1995), Land (1970), Paynter (1955), van Tyne (1935).

---

53   OCELLATED POORWILL
Nyctiphrynus ocellatus   Plate 13

Caprimulgus ocellatus Tschudi, 1844, *Arch. f. Naturg.* 10, Bd. 1, p.268 (Peru)
Nyctiphrynus ocellatus lautus Miller and Griscom, 1925, *Amer. Mus. Novit.* 159, p.1 (Peña Blanca, north-eastern Nicaragua)

Formerly considered conspecific with Choco Poorwill.

IDENTIFICATION Length 20-25cm. A small, dark, rather plainish Neotropical forest nightjar. Sexes similar. **At rest** Upperparts and wing-coverts almost uniformly dark greyish-brown. No collar on hindneck. Scapulars and some wing-coverts with large blackish-brown spots, bordered rufous or buffish. White band around throat. Underparts dark greyish-brown, spotted white on belly. **In flight** Round-winged. Both sexes lack white markings on the wings, which are lightly spotted tawny. The outer three, sometimes four, tail feathers are narrowly tipped white. **Similar species** Choco Poorwill (54) is greyish-brown, washed cinnamon, more heavily spotted blackish-brown, with two or three prominent white spots on the inner greater coverts and all tail feathers narrowly tipped white.

VOICE The song is a trilled *preeeo*, repeated roughly once every five seconds 20 times or more. Sings from a low perch in forest interiors or along forest edges. Also sings, less often, from a higher perch or from the ground. May be heard chiefly at dusk. The call is a soft, guttural *wah wah wah*, given from the ground.

HABITAT Prefers small, shady clearings and open understorey in humid and wet lowland forest. Also occurs in evergreen rainforest and dense second growth of mainly small trees and vines. 0–1,350m.

HABITS Crepuscular and nocturnal? Tends not to sit on tracks and roads at night, or at least does so much less often than other nightjars. Feeds by making short sallies from a perch, 2-5m above ground. Also forages in open forest and in clearings. No further information available.

FOOD Moths, beetles, cockroaches (including Blattidae), katydids (including Tettigoniidae) and fireflies (including Lampyridae). No further data available.

BREEDING March?–April? in Costa Rica and Nicaragua; March–? in Colombia and October–November in Peru and E Paraguay. No data available from other regions. No nest is constructed; the eggs are laid on leaf-litter. Nest-sites may be in open areas, on paths, and are often below overhanging foliage. Clutch two. Eggs elliptical, off-white to pinkish-white, unmarked or faintly spotted reddish, 25.2-28.0 x 19.0-20.5mm. No further information available.

DESCRIPTION *N. o. ocellatus* **Adult male** Forehead, crown and nape dark greyish-brown, minutely speckled chestnut (32). Crown feathers very dense, extending out at sides to form ridge above the eye. No collar on hindneck. Mantle, back, rump and uppertail-coverts dark greyish-brown, minutely speckled chestnut. Wing-coverts dark greyish-brown minutely speckled chestnut or rufous, occasionally with some small blackish-brown, whitish or buff spots edged rufous or buffish. Scapulars dark greyish-brown finely speckled greyish-white, with large blackish-brown spot thinly edged rufous on tips. Primaries and tertials brown, spotted tawny along the outerwebs. Secondaries brown speckled tawny. Tail brown, faintly barred tawny or rufous on upper half, distal half plainer; R5-R3 narrowly (4-7mm) tipped white; R2 occasionally with small white spot at centre of tip; central pair (R1) dark brown narrowly barred blackish-brown. Lores and ear-coverts tawny-buff speckled brown. Chin and upper throat dark greyish-brown. Pure white band around lower throat. Breast, belly, flanks and undertail-coverts dark greyish-brown speckled greyish-white, liberally spotted white on belly only. Underwing-coverts rufescent-brown barred brown. **Adult female** Similar to male but generally paler and rather rufous. Primaries and secondaries more heavily spotted tawny. **Immature** and **Juvenile** Not known. **Chick** Not described. **Bare parts** Iris dark brown; bill blackish; legs and feet dark brown.

MEASUREMENTS Wing (male) 129-136, (female) 122-138; tail (male) 112-130, (female) 103-128; bill (male) 10.2-12.3, (female) 10.0-12.0; tarsus (male) c. 18, (female) c. 18. Weight (male) 35.0-43.0g, (female) 29.0-43.5g.

MOULT No data available.

GEOGRAPHICAL VARIATION Two races are currently recognised.
    N. o. ocellatus Described above.
    N. o. lautus Similar to the nominate but smaller, with fewer and smaller black spots on the scapulars, less spotting on the underparts and narrower white tips to the outer tail feathers. Wing (male, one) 118, (female, one) 116; tail (male, one) 98, (female, one) 103. Weight no data.

DISTRIBUTION AND MOVEMENTS Central and South America.
    N. o. ocellatus SW Colombia (Putumayo), E Ecuador (Pastaza), E Peru (Madre de Dios), N and E Bolivia (Pando, Beni, La Paz and Santa Cruz), C, E and SE Brazil (Amazonas east to Pernambuco, south to Rio Grande do Sul), Paraguay (Deptos. Alto Paraná, Caaguazú, Central and Canindeyú) and NE Argentina (Misiones). Sedentary.
    N. o. lautus NE Nicaragua (Peña Blanca, Depto de

Jinotega) and NW Costa Rica (S and SE of Brasilia, Prov. Alajuela). A sight record from the canal zone, Panama, requires confirmation. Sedentary.

STATUS Generally not uncommon throughout most of its range and possibly under-recorded.

REFERENCES Hilty & Brown (1986), Madroño N. & Esquivel (1997), Miller & Griscom (1925), Ridgely & Gwynne (1989), Stiles & Skutch (1989).

---

54 CHOCÓ POORWILL
Nyctiphrynus rosenbergi   Plate 13

Caprimulgus rosenbergi Hartert, 1895, *Bull. Brit. Orn. Club* 5, p x [bis.] (Rio Dagua, Colombia)

Formerly considered conspecific with Ocellated Poorwill.

IDENTIFICATION Length 19.5-21cm. A small, darkish Neotropical nightjar, restricted to the Chocó faunal region of western Colombia and extreme north-western Ecuador. Sexes similar. **At rest** Upperparts and wing-coverts darkish brown washed cinnamon, rather heavily spotted blackish-brown, with two or three large, prominent white spots on the inner greater coverts. No collar on hindneck. Large white throat-patch. Underparts darkish brown, washed cinnamon on breast, greyish-white on belly. **In flight** Fairly short-winged? Both sexes lack white markings on the wings, which are brown spotted tawny. The tail is fairly rounded and narrowly tipped white. **Similar species** Ocellated Poorwill (53) is generally plainer, without the prominent white spots on the inner greater coverts, although the belly is more heavily spotted white; the white tips to the tail feathers are broader but occur on outer 3-4 pairs only (central pair not tipped white).

VOICE The song is a resonant, rhythmic *kwor kwor kweeé* lasting 1.5-2 seconds. Each song phrase comprises 2-5 *kwor* notes with the final *kweeé* being whistled. The song is repeated at either short or long intervals for up to several minutes. May be heard predominantly at dusk and dawn.

The call is a *whee whurrrr* or *kwee whurrr*, rising in pitch on the first note, the second note trilled and descending.

HABITAT Prefers interiors and edges of primary forest, but also occurs in adjacent secondary forest. 0–900m.

HABITS Crepuscular and nocturnal. Forages by hawking for insects above forests, around isolated tree-tops, or in forest clearings. No further information available.

FOOD Moths and beetles (including Scarabaeidae and Curculionidae). No further data available.

BREEDING Breeding season March–June (chicks found mid-April, Esmeraldas) in Ecuador and May–June (chicks found early June, Chocó) in Colombia. No further information available.

DESCRIPTION Adult male Forehead, crown and nape greyish-brown heavily spotted blackish; spots generally surrounded with rufous wash. No collar on hindneck. Mantle and back greyish-brown speckled cinnamon and rufous. Rump and uppertail-coverts dark brown speckled greyish-white. Wing-coverts dark brown barred, spotted and speckled cinnamon and rufous. Large white spot on tip of inner two greater coverts; occasionally smaller white spot, edged buff, on tip of inner third greater covert. Scapulars brown heavily washed cinnamon and rufous, with large irregularly shaped blackish-brown spot in centres. Primaries brown with very small tawny spots along outerwebs of P10-P7; Inner primaries and secondaries dark brown spotted tawny. Tertials brown mottled cinnamon and rufous. Tail brown barred tawny, narrowly (c. 2-3mm) tipped white on all feathers (R5-R1). Lores, ear-coverts and chin dark brown speckled cinnamon. Large white patch across throat. Breast brown, washed or densely speckled and barred cinnamon, with irregularly shaped blackish-brown spots. Belly and flanks blackish-brown, densely and narrowly barred greyish-white, very sparsely spotted white. Undertail-coverts blackish-brown barred greyish-white, broadly tipped white. **Adult female** Similar to the male. **Immature** and **Juvenile** Similar to the adults but markings on upperparts and breast more chestnut. Lacks white spots on inner greater coverts. **Chick** Not described. **Bare parts** Iris dark brown; bill either grey with black tip or blackish; legs and feet greyish or purplish-brown.

MEASUREMENTS Wing (male) 124-127, (female) 125-131; tail (male) 100-105, (female) 95-100; bill (male) 10.6-12.4, (female) 10.3-11.2; tarsus (male) c. 17, (female) 17.6-19.1. Weight (female, one) 52g.

MOULT No data available.

GEOGRAPHICAL VARIATION Monotypic. Very little colour variation noted, although one male (museum specimen) from northern Ecuador is rather blackish.

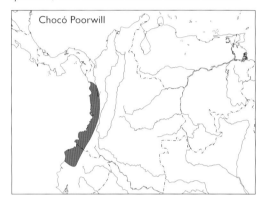

Chocó Poorwill

DISTRIBUTION AND MOVEMENTS Extreme NW South America, in W Colombia (Chocó, Cauca? Valle and Nariño) and NW Ecuador (Esmeraldas, Carchi?).

STATUS Fairly common locally, within its limited range.

REFERENCES Robbins & Ridgely (1992).

CAPRIMULGUS

Caprimulgus Linnaeus, 1758, Syst. Nat., ed. 10, 1, p. 193. Type by tautonymy, *Caprimulgus europaeus* Linnaeus 1758 (*Caprimulgus*, pre-binomial specific name in synonymy).

The largest and most cosmopolitan genus, with 57 species worldwide. Although some species are migratory, a small percentage greatly so, the distribution of the genus based upon general breeding range may be classified as Nearctic (2 species), Neotropical (19 species), Palearctic (5 species), Afrotropical (20 species), Madagascar (2 species), Oriental (8 species) and Australasia (1 species). Of these, 5 species are known to have breeding populations in two faunal zones.

This genus contains the typical or 'true' nightjars that have rictal bristles around the gape, long, rather pointed wings, generally feathered tarsi and a pectinated middle toe. Most species have a variegated plumage and show sexual dimorphism, mainly in the presence or size of the white markings on the outer primaries and tail feathers. Most species generally roost and breed on the ground, none build nests and all are aerial feeders.

One Neotropical species, *Caprimulgus candicans*, may actually belong in the genus *Eleothreptus* G. R. Gray, 1840 and one Afrotropical species, *Caprimulgus binotatus*, was formerly placed (and probably belongs) in a separate genus, *Veles* Bangs, 1918. The genus *Veles* may well prove to be valid, as the sole species previously placed within it has several morphological characteristics which differentiate it from other *Caprimulgus* species; these differences are just as great as those used to separate other genera.

55 CHUCK-WILL'S-WIDOW
Caprimulgus carolinensis   Plate 15

Caprimulgus carolinensis Gmelin, 1789, *Syst. Nat.* 1, pt. 2, p.1028 (Virginia and Carolina = South Carolina, ex Catesby)

May form a superspecies with Rufous Nightjar.

IDENTIFICATION Length 27-34cm. A large, variegated North American nightjar, wintering in the southern United States, Central America and the northern parts of South America. Has two distinct colour phases, brown and greyish-brown. Sexually dimorphic. **At rest** Upperparts brown, broadly streaked blackish-brown. Narrow, indistinct tawny-buff collar on hindneck. Wing-coverts brown, heavily spotted buff and buffish-white; scapulars boldly spotted blackish. Narrow white or buffish-white band around lower throat. Underparts brown, speckled and spotted tawny and buff, becoming buff barred brown on belly. At very close range the adults' rictal bristles prove to have lateral filaments on the basal half. **In flight** Round-tailed and fairly round-winged. Both sexes lack white markings on the wings, which are blackish-brown, densely spotted or barred tawny. The male has white innerwebs to the outer three tail feathers, the outerwebs being tawny, speckled or barred blackish. Females lack white markings on the tail. **Similar species** Rufous Nightjar (56) is generally smaller and darker, ruddier brown, the male with smaller areas of white on the innerwebs of the three outer tail feathers and smaller amounts of generally unmarked tawny on the outerwebs; at very close range the rictal bristles are smooth. Whip-poor-will (63) is much smaller and more variegated, less heavily spotted, the male having broad white tips to the outer three tail feathers, the female narrower, buff tips.

VOICE The song is a loud *chuck weeo weeo*, repeated continuously with c. 2.5 seconds pause between each set of notes. Sings in either short or long bursts, e.g. up to 834 times in succession, changing its song perches whilst doing so. Birds move their heads noticeably when singing. May also deliver song at a faster rate, with a 0.5-1 second pause between each set of notes. Other variations are a higher-pitched song and a muted song with a less forceful first *chuck* note. During this latter variation, song phrases are repeated after a pause of 4-11 seconds. The song is similar to that of Rufous Nightjar but slower and lower-pitched. Sings from song-posts, such as trees, fence-posts, etc. Moves regularly from song-post to song-post, or remains at one song-post and changes position to sing in all directions. May be heard mainly at dusk and dawn and throughout moonlit nights. Will sing in drizzle but not in moderate to heavy rain. Occasionally sings during the day, especially when overcast? As with other nightjars, tends to sing less during the breeding season after the eggs have hatched. Sings in short bursts prior to migration.

In flight, both sexes give a variety of clucking or growling calls. Single birds utter a guttural *chuck* and a soft, low growl, repeating notes after a slight pause. Notes may be even or descending in pitch. When two birds are together, clucks and growls are uttered continuously, e.g. two males in territorial pursuit or contact courtship calls of pair. Foraging birds usually give the growl only. Another commonly given call is a deep *quok* (perhaps an alarm note), which may be similar to the clucking notes (see

above). This call is often, but not always, uttered singly and is generally given in flight. Also calls when taking flight, when flushed or on arrival at song-post. During threat/defence display gives throaty hiss, which is also given when bird is handled. Chicks give thin peep when distressed.

Generally silent during migration and on wintering grounds.

HABITAT Prefers deciduous woods and forests, pine–oak woodland and live-oak groves. Also occurs in suburban habitats, e.g. open country with pastureland, and is occasionally found in coniferous forests. During migration and in winter, may be found in thick woods, open woodland, scrub and palmetto thickets, tangled riverside growth, tall hedgerows, forests, second growth and sub-urban habitats, e.g. in Panama (Panama City) noted in residential areas with large trees. 0–2,600m.

HABITS Crepuscular and nocturnal. Roosts on the ground, on mossy logs and low branches. Occasionally also roosts in natural cavities or hollows. In winter, roosts on the ground or on a large horizontal branch high up in trees. Roost-sites often used for several days or more. If disturbed, does not necessarily change to a new roost-site, unlike other nightjar species. When flushed, flaps and glides away, often re-alighting near the original roost-site; occasionally then mobbed by small passerines.

In trees, perches along or across branches, and also sits crossways on perches out in the open. Migrating birds may occur on ships, where they will perch out in the open, e.g. crossways on rigging. Occasionally when a migrant bird leaving a ship has been seen to alight on the water, possibly through tiredness. Wing-claps in flight, especially during the breeding season, by striking its wings together above the body. Often sits on sandy roads at night.

Forages low over the ground, along woodland edges and over open fields. Also feeds by flycatching from a perch for up to 10-15 minutes at a time, during which it may make 20-30 sallies. In late summer, when in heavy moult, birds may feed by scuttling about on the ground. Will also deliberately swallow pebbles and small stones. Feeding birds may also pursue and catch small birds in flight, especially whilst on migration, e.g. near ships at sea or close to coasts.

FOOD Moths, flying ants, crickets, grasshoppers, damsel-flies, dragonflies, beetles (including Carabidae, Ceram-bycidae, Elateridae and Scarabaeidae), bugs (including Cicadidae), flies, bivalves (1)? and small birds (including Emberizidae, Trochilidae and Hirundinidae).

BREEDING Breeding season generally mid-April–July, although begins early March in south of range, mid-May in the north. Territorial; the male pursues intruding males in close, erratic flight, calling (see Voice) and wing-clapping. The chasing male often fans his tail to display the white markings. The male also wing-claps when investigating other singing males, or when approaching a female. During the courtship display, the male sidles up to a female in rapid, jerky movements, with wings drooped and tail fanned. He also fluffs out his feathers and is extremely vocal (see Voice). After the display, if courtship is successful, the pair perch side-by-side. The male may also dart about on the ground, moving his head from side to side whilst continuously raising his crown feathers. He also occasionally flicks out one wing, or repeatedly leaps 0.3-0.6m in the air. He may then fly off towards a female.

No nest is constructed; the eggs are laid on leaf-litter or pine needles on the ground. Nest-sites are usually out in the open, away from undergrowth, and may be used year after year. Clutch 2; eggs laid on consecutive days. Eggs oval or elliptical, glossy cream, pinkish-cream or white, blotched, marbled and spotted with brown, tawny, lilac, grey and purple, 32.5-40.1 x 23.1-28.2mm. Usually single-brooded. May lay a replacement clutch if the first is lost, although perhaps only in more southerly latitudes. Incubation is usually by the female during the day. If flushed from eggs, the female returns to the nest unobtrusively, e.g. she may alight 1.3m from the eggs, sit motionless for up to five minutes, then waddle back onto the eggs. If found, unattended eggs may be eaten by predators such as Striped Skunks *Mephitis mephitis*.

The incubation period is c. 20 days, and the eggs hatch asynchronously. The semi-precocial young may leave the nest-site within the first day or so, moving up to 3m every two days. They may take refuge under vegetation. If flushed whilst brooding the young, the female may either fly to a prominent perch, such as a fence-post, or perform a distraction display by fluttering about on the ground, gaping and hissing (see Voice). When older, chicks will hop away from an intruder with their wings held above their backs. Chicks fledge after about 16 days but may remain dependent on the adults for a further 14 days.

DESCRIPTION Adult male Forehead, crown and nape brown or greyish-brown, broadly streaked blackish-brown. Indistinct tawny or tawny-buff collar on hindneck. Mantle, back, rump and uppertail-coverts brown or greyish-brown, streaked blackish-brown. Wing-coverts brown or greyish-brown, speckled and heavily spotted pale tawny, buff and pale buff. Scapulars brown or greyish-brown, speckled tawny and buff, very boldly spotted blackish-brown. Primaries and secondaries dark brown, regularly barred tawny and tipped with pale tawny or buff speckling. Tertials brown or greyish-brown, profusely speckled pale buff and greyish-white, streaked blackish-brown along feather-shafts. Tail dark brown, densely flecked with tawny bars or chevrons; R5-R3 largely white on innerwebs, c. 65-80mm; outerwebs tawny, speckled or barred blackish-brown. Lores and ear-coverts tawny, often tinged rufous, speckled dark brown. Chin and throat buff, narrowly barred brown. Narrow buffish-white or pale buff band around lower throat. Breast darkish brown, speckled and heavily spotted tawny, buff and pale buff. Belly, flanks and underwing-coverts buff barred brown. Undertail-coverts buff, less densely barred brown. **Adult female** Similar to the male. Lacks white in the outer tail feathers. R5-R3 often very narrowly tipped pale tawny or buffish, densely speckled brown. **Immature** Similar to the adult female. **Juvenile** Similar to the adult female but generally buffier. **Chick** At hatching, covered in golden-brown or yellowish-ochre down. **Bare parts** Iris dark brown; bill dusky flesh with black tip; legs and feet dull flesh.

MEASUREMENTS Wing (male) 206-225, (female) 201-217; tail (male) 133-151, (female) 130-144; bill (male) 15.4-17.2, (female) 16.5-17.0; tarsus (male) 17.5-20.8, (female) 17.0-20.6. Weight (male) 94.5-137.3g, (female) 113.7-117.9g.

MOULT Primaries are moulted descendantly, the secondaries ascendantly in two series, beginning when the primary moult reaches P6 or P7. Secondaries begin with S1 and S6-S9. Tail moult generally commences with the innermost feathers and ends with the fourth outermost,

e.g. R1, R2, R3, R5, R4. Tail moult may be quite rapid and begins when the primary moult reaches P6-P8.

Adults? undertake one complete moult per year, usually in middle-late summer. Primary moult may begin whilst the bird is still incubating, especially in more northerly latitudes. Occasionally a few body feathers may be retained for more than one year. Moult is usually completed before migration, although some moult has occasionally been noted on birds moving south through Mexico. Rarely moults in winter, although one immature male was in primary moult in February. Juveniles begin body moult before they can fly. Remiges and rectrices are retained until the following summer.

GEOGRAPHICAL VARIATION Monotypic.

Chuck-will's-widow
▮▮▮ breeding range
▮ wintering range
northern limit of wintering range
southern limit of wintering range not known

DISTRIBUTION AND MOVEMENTS North America.
E Kansas, S Iowa, C Illinois, C Indiana, extreme S Ontario, C and E Ohio, C West Virginia, Maryland, New Jersey, S New York (Long Island) and S Massachusetts south to SC and SE Texas, Gulf Coast and S Florida (including Florida Keys). Also occurs in N Bahamas? (one record, Andros). Sporadically found further north, to S Wisconsin, S Michigan and Pennsylvania. Casual (perhaps vagrant) to Maine, New Brunswick and Nova Scotia. Migratory, arriving in northerly parts of range in mid- to late March. Males generally arrive ahead of females. Return migration commences in early September.

Winters from SE Texas and Louisiana south through Central America (not recorded Belize) to northern South America; and from N Florida south through Bahamas to Greater Antilles (east to Virgin Islands). Adults appear to show a preference for wintering in the Greater Antilles, with a higher proportion of immatures wintering in Central and South America.

STATUS Generally common throughout North American breeding range, which is possibly expanding northwards. Fairly common migrant in eastern Mexico, uncommon to fairly common winter visitor from southern Mexico south to Costa Rica. Widespread but uncommon passage migrant and winter visitor (October - April) in Costa Rica and Panama; rare winter visitor (late November - mid February) in Colombia; casual in Venezuela. Few data available from other regions.

REFERENCES Bent (1940), Bjorklund & Bjorklund

(1983), Cooper (1981), Ficken *et al.* (1967), Hilty & Brown (1986), Holden (1964), Howell & Webb (1995), Hoyt (1953), Mengel (1976), Mengel *et al.* (1972), Mengel & Jenkinson (1971), Meyer de Schauensee & Phelps (1978), Ridgely & Gwynne (1989), Rohwer (1971), Slud (1964), Stiles & Skutch (1989), Wetmore (1968).

56   RUFOUS NIGHTJAR
Caprimulgus rufus   Plate 15

Caprimulgus rufus Boddaert, 1783, *Table Pl. Enlum.* p.46 (Cayenne, ex Daubenton pl.735)
Caprimulgus rufus minimus Griscom and Greenway, 1937, *Bull. Mus. Comp. Zool.* 81, p.424 (Panama City, Panama)
Caprimulgus rufus otiosus (Bangs, 1911), *Proc. Biol. Soc. Wash.* 24, p.188 (St Lucia, West Indies)
Caprimulgus rufus rutilus (Burmeister, 1856), *Syst. Uebers. Th. Bras.* 2, p.385 (Brazil, restricted to south-eastern Brazil by Griscom and Greenway, *antea*)
Caprimulgus rufus saltarius Olrog, 1979, *Acta. Zool. Lill.* 33, 2, p.6 (Confluence of Ríos Bermejo and Tarija, Department Orán, Salta, Argentina)

May form a superspecies with Chuck-will's-widow.

IDENTIFICATION Length 25-30cm. A large, reddish-brown or brownish, variegated Neotropical nightjar. Sexually dimorphic. **At rest** Upperparts rufescent-brown, broadly streaked blackish-brown. Narrow, very indistinct tawny-buff collar on hindneck. Lesser coverts dark brown, speckled rufous or tawny. Rest of wing-coverts rufescent-brown, speckled rufous and buff, boldly spotted blackish-brown. Scapulars boldly spotted blackish-brown. Narrow white or buffish-white band around lower throat. Underparts rufescent-brown, barred brown, speckled and spotted cinnamon, buff and white, becoming buff barred brown on undertail-coverts. At very close range the adults' rictal bristles prove to be smooth and lack lateral filaments on the basal half. **In flight** Fairly round-winged. Both sexes lack white markings on the wings, which are blackish brown narrowly barred tawny. The male has a large white spot on the innerwebs of the three outer tail feathers; the outerwebs are tawny and generally unmarked. Females lack white markings on the tail. **Similar species** Chuck-will's-widow (55) is generally larger and paler, the male with the innerwebs of the three outer tail feathers entirely white, the outerwebs tawny, speckled or barred blackish-brown; at very close range the adults' rictal bristles show lateral filaments on the basal half.

VOICE The song is a loud *chuck wee wee weeo*, repeated every few seconds and occasionally delivered at a faster rate, especially by the St Lucia race *otiosus*; similar to that of Chuck-will's-widow but generally faster and higher-pitched. Sings from branches, sometimes 10-20m above ground, just inside woodland edge. Also sings from other perches, such as rocks, and may sing from the ground. May be heard chiefly at dusk and dawn, and throughout the night during breeding season. Has a guttural croaking call. No further information available.

HABITAT Occurs in a wide variety of habitats. May be found in rainforest, gallery forest, second growth, open woodland, forest edges, scrubland and savanna thickets. Also occurs in large suburban gardens, e.g. hotel grounds

on the outskirts of Maracay, Venezuela. In Trinidad, prefers scrubland and deciduous woodland; on St Lucia prefers arid brush country. 0–1,000m, in Colombia to 1,800m.

HABITS Crepuscular and nocturnal. Roosts on the ground or on a low perch. Roost-sites are often amongst thicket undergrowth. When flushed, flies low for a short distance before disappearing into cover or re-alighting on a log or low vine. Often perches crossways on branches. Sits on roads and tracks infrequently at night. Forages from a low perch, usually within forests, but may also hawk from fence-posts, returning to the same post after each foray. No further information available.

FOOD Insects. No further data available.

BREEDING Breeding season January–May in Panama?; late June on St Lucia; February–May in Trinidad; mid-April–May in Colombia and November?–December? in N Argentina. No data available from other localities. No nest is constructed; the eggs are laid on bare ground or on leaf-litter. Nest-sites are usually under vegetation or by fallen logs. Clutch 1-2. Eggs elliptical, creamy white blotched light brown and dull lilac, 29.1-34.0 x 22.0-26.6mm. Incubation is usually by the female during day. If flushed from the nest, the female may alight on nearby perch or log. Distraction display as yet unrecorded. No further information available.

DESCRIPTION *C. r. rufus* **Adult male** Forehead, crown and nape rufescent-brown or cinnamon-rufous broadly streaked blackish-brown. Indistinct tawny-buff collar on hindneck. Mantle, back rump and uppertail-coverts brown tinged cinnamon-rufous, streaked and speckled blackish-brown. Wing-coverts rufescent-brown, speckled rufous and buff, boldly spotted blackish-brown; lesser coverts plainer and darker. Scapulars brown, boldly spotted blackish-brown, although the upper parts of the feathers (usually hidden) are white speckled brown. Primaries blackish-brown, spotted tawny along the outerwebs, barred pale tawny along the innerwebs. Secondaries blackish-brown barred tawny. Tertials rufescent-brown mottled greyish-brown and pale tawny. Tail dark brown, densely flecked with tawny and buff bars or chevrons; R5-R3 with very large white spot (c. 33-44mm) on tips of innerwebs, extending to inner half of outerwebs on R4 and R3; white spots broadly bordered plainish tawny, except along inner edge. Lores and ear-coverts rufous, thinly barred brown. Chin and throat rufescent-brown, barred brown. Narrow buffish-white or pure buff band around lower throat. Breast brownish, washed cinnamon-rufous. Belly and flanks paler and buffier, barred brown, loosely spotted whitish. Undertail-coverts dark buff barred brown. Underwing-coverts buff barred brown. **Adult female** Similar to the male but perhaps slightly more rufous. Tawny barring on wings more pronounced. Lacks white on the outer tail feathers, R5-R3 very narrowly tipped pale buffish. **Immature** Not known. **Juvenile** Paler than the adults, with crown, scapulars and some wing-coverts pale buff or whitish, distinctly spotted black. **Chick** Not known. **Bare parts** Iris dark brown; bill dusky with blackish tip; legs and feet brownish-flesh.

MEASUREMENTS Wing (male) 167-186, (female) 166-185; tail (male) 116-120, (female) 111-137; bill (male) c. 18, (female) 18.2-18.9; tarsus (male) c. 18.5, (female) 18.4-19.3. Weight (male) no data, (female, one) 89g, unsexed (one) 95g.

MOULT No data available.

GEOGRAPHICAL VARIATION Five races are currently recognised; *minimus*, *otiosus* and *saltarius* are considered to be separate species by some authorities. In addition, *C. r. saltarius* is sometimes considered to be a race of Silky-tailed Nightjar, or a synonym of *C. r. rutilus*.

C. r. rufus Described above.

C. r. minimus (Ruddy Nightjar) Less rufescent than the nominate and darker-breasted. The collar on the hindneck is tawnier, the chin and throat paler. White spots on R5-R3 of male, 49-53mm. Wing (male) 175-184, (female) 170-182; tail (male) 113-121, (female) 102-120. Weight no data.

C. r. otiosus (St Lucia Nightjar) Longer-winged, lightly larger and less rufescent than the nominate. White spots on R5-R3 of male larger (c. 57mm) than those of nominate. Wing (male) 183-193, (female) 187-194; tail (male) 122-131, (female) 120-129. Weight no data.

C. r. rutilus Paler than the nominate and less rufescent. The collar on the hindneck often has some white; the tawny spotting on the primaries is more extensive and the undertail-coverts are occasionally plainish buff. White spots on R5-R3 of male 28-48mm. Wing (male) 183-189, (female) 184-196; tail (male) 119-132, (female) 132-135. Weight (male, one) 87.8g, (female, one) 98.0g.

C. r. saltarius (Salta Nightjar) Greyer than the nominate. White spots on R5-R3 of male larger (c. 65mm) than those of nominate. Wing (male, one) 180; tail (male, one) 135. Weight no data.

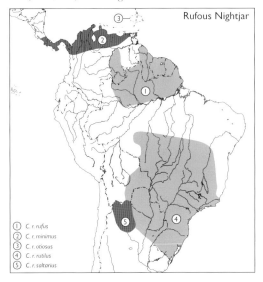

① C. r. rufus
② C. r. minimus
③ C. r. otiosus
④ C. r. rutilus
⑤ C. r. saltarius

DISTRIBUTION AND MOVEMENTS Central and northern South America.

C. r. rufus S Venezuela (W Amazonas and W Bolívar), Guyana, Surinam, French Guiana and N Brazil (upper tributaries of the Rio Negro, Amazonas, south to tributaries on the south bank of the Rio Amazonas). Sedentary.

C. r. minimus S Costa Rica, Panama (including Isla de Coiba), N Colombia, W and N Venezuela (from NW Zulia south to Mérida, east to Sucre) and NW Trinidad (including Bocas Islands). Sedentary.

C. r. otiosus Lesser Antilles (St Lucia). Sedentary.

C. r. rutilus Brazil (Mato Grosso east to Rio de Janeiro, south to Rio Grande do Sul), E Bolivia (Santa Cruz, Chuquisaca? and Tarija?), Paraguay and N Argentina (Santiago del Estero east to Corrientes). Sedentary and partially migratory. Argentinian populations move north after breeding and may winter (May–August) as far afield as Venezuela.

C. r. saltarius NW Argentina (Tucumán? Salta and Jujuy) and SE Bolivia? (Tarija? and Chuquisaca?). Sedentary and partially migratory?

Populations in C Brazil (Pará?, Goiás and Bahia), Peru (Junín and San Martín) and S Ecuador (S Zamora-Chinchipe) have yet to be named or identified subspecifically.

STATUS Fairly common but under-recorded throughout much of its range, probably rarer and more local at the limits of its distribution.

REFERENCES ffrench & O'Neill (1991), Haverschmidt & Mees (1994), Hilty & Brown (1986), Meyer de Schauensee & Phelps (1978), Nores & Yzurieta (1984), Ridgely & Gwynne (1989), Robbins & Parker (1997), Slud (1964), Stiles & Skutch (1989), Wetmore (1968), Wetmore & Phelps (1953).

57 CUBAN NIGHTJAR
Caprimulgus cubanensis Plate 15

Other name: Greater Antillean Nightjar

Antrostomus cubanensis Lawrence, 1860, *Ann. Lyc. Nat. Hist. N.Y.* 7, p.260 (Ciénaga de Zapata and coast of Manzanillo, Cuba)

Caprimulgus cubanensis insulaepinorum Garrido, 1983, *Auk* 100, p.989 (Between Cabo Pepe and Cocodrilo, Isle of Pines, Cuba)

May form a superspecies with Hispaniolan Nightjar, with which it was formerly considered conspecific.

IDENTIFICATION Length 25-29.5cm. A large, dark Caribbean nightjar, endemic to Cuba and the Isle of Pines. Sexually dimorphic. **At rest** Upperparts blackish-brown, speckled greyish-brown, greyish-white and pale buff; crown broadly streaked blackish. No collar around the hindneck. Wing-coverts blackish-brown, speckled and spotted pale buff. Scapulars buffish-white speckled brown, boldly spotted blackish-brown. Buffish-white submoustachial stripe. Broad pale buff band around the lower throat. Underparts buffish-white, speckled and spotted blackish-brown, becoming buff vermiculated brown on the undertail-coverts. **In flight** Both sexes lack white markings on the wings, which are narrowly barred tawny. The male has white tips to the three outer tail feathers; the female has narrower buff tips. **Similar species** Hispaniolan Nightjar (58) is extremely similar, but has heavier streaking on the crown, a narrower, indistinct cinnamon-buff band around the lower throat, plain buffish undertail-coverts, and broader white (male) or buff (female) tips to the three outer tail feathers.

VOICE The song is a short, evenly pitched, trilled whistle *terrrrrrro*. During distraction displays, adults may give 1–3 squeals or screeches. No further information available.

HABITAT Prefers open woodland and the edges of swamps. On the Isle of Pines it also occurs in dense woodland and scrubland.

HABITS Crepuscular and nocturnal. Surprisingly little is known about this large nightjar.

FOOD No data available.

BREEDING Breeding season March–June? on Cuba and the Isle of Pines.

No nest is constructed; the eggs are laid on leaf-litter on the ground. Nest-sites may be in thickets at the edges of clearings within dense scrub. Clutch 1-2. Eggs elliptical, dull white often tinged pinkish-buff, marked and spotted brown, brownish-buff and greyish-purple, 29.1-29.8 x 21.7-22.6mm. Both sexes incubate. If flushed from the eggs, adults may fly off and alight up to 12m away. As they land, they turn to face the intruder, call (see Voice), spread their wings, and fluff out their feathers. The incubation period is c. 19 days. If flushed from the nest, the male may fly a short distance, alight on a branch and perform a distraction display by repeatedly shaking his wings and body. If flushed from the nest, the female also performs a distraction display, often by injury-feigning on the ground. Both adults occasionally roost at the nest-site with their offspring. No further information available.

DESCRIPTION *C. c. cubanensis* **Adult male** Forehead, crown and nape dark brown, speckled greyish-white and pale buff, broadly streaked blackish-brown. No collar around the hindneck. Mantle, back and rump dark brown, speckled greyish-brown. Uppertail-coverts similar but speckling whitish. Wing-coverts dark brown, speckled and spotted pale buff. Scapulars buffish-white speckled dark brown, boldly spotted blackish-brown on tips. Primaries brown, spotted tawny or pale tawny along outerwebs, faintly and indistinctly barred tawny or pale tawny along innerwebs; inner primaries and all secondaries brown, indistinctly and faintly mottled buffish-brown. Tertials brown, densely mottled pale buff and broadly streaked blackish-brown. Tail brown; R5-R3 evenly tipped white (c. 18-27mm) across both webs; R2 narrowly tipped pale buff speckled brown; central pair (R1) greyish-brown, speckled and barred dark brown. Lores and ear-coverts tawny speckled dark brown. Buffish-white submoustachial stripe. Chin and throat dark brown speckled cinnamon. Broad pale buff band around lower throat. Breast dark brown, speckled and spotted buffish-white. Belly and flanks buffish-white, speckled and spotted dark brown. Lower belly buffish-brown barred brown. Undertail-coverts buff vermiculated brown. Underwing-coverts brown barred buff. **Adult female** Similar to the male, although the outer primaries are more lightly spotted tawny, and R5-R3 are narrowly tipped buff, c. 15mm. **Immature** and **Juvenile** Not described. **Chick** Not described. **Bare parts** Iris brown; bill blackish; legs and feet brownish.

MEASUREMENTS Wing (male) 177-185, (female) 174-183; tail (male) 127-140, (female) 117-134; bill (male) 17.7-19.1, (female) 17.6-20.6; tarsus (male) 19.1-19.6, (female) 18.0-19.5. Weight (male) 68-80g, (female) 50-70g.

MOULT No data available.

GEOGRAPHICAL VARIATION Two races are currently recognised. Variation is apparently clinal, with intermediates in size and colour occurring on the Zapata Peninsula in southern Cuba.

C. c. cubanensis Described above. Some males have rather cinnamon underparts.
C. c. insulaepinorum Smaller and darker than the nominate. Wing (male) 168-182, (female) 175-176; tail (male) 121-130, (female) 122-125. Weight no data.

Cuban Nightjar

DISTRIBUTION AND MOVEMENTS A Caribbean species, endemic to Cuba and the Isle of Pines.
C. c. cubanensis Cuba. Sedentary.
C. a. insulaepinorum The Isle of Pines. Recorded from south of Ciénaga de Lanier; between Cabo Pepe and Cocodrilo; between Cocodrilo and Rincón del Guanal, and from Rincón del Guanal itself. Probably occurs throughout the island. Sedentary.

STATUS A poorly known species, with very little data available. On Cuba, the introduced Small Indian Mongoose *Herpestes auropunctatus* may be a serious predator of eggs and young, and chicks may also be at risk from birds of prey. On the Isle of Pines, commoner in the south and around Ciénaga de Lanier.

REFERENCES Bond (1934), Garcia (1985), Garrido (1983), Garrido & Reynard (1994).

---

58   HISPANIOLAN NIGHTJAR
Caprimulgus ekmani   Plate 15

Antrostomus ekmani Lönnberg, 1929, *Ark. Zool.* 20B, No 6, p.1, f.1 (near Jérémie, Haiti)

May form a superspecies with Cuban Nightjar, with which it was formerly considered conspecific.

IDENTIFICATION Length 26-30cm. A large, dark, Caribbean nightjar endemic to Hispaniola. Sexually dimorphic. **At rest** Upperparts and wing-coverts blackish-brown, speckled greyish-white, greyish-brown and buff. Crown broadly streaked blackish. No collar on hindneck. Narrow, indistinct band of cinnamon-buff spots across lower throat. Underparts dark brown, speckled and spotted buffish-white. Undertail-coverts plain buff or tawny-buff. **In flight** Both sexes lack white markings on the wings. The male has very broad white tips to the three outer tail feathers; the female has buffish tips. **Similar species** Cuban Nightjar (57), endemic to Cuba and the Isle of Pines, is extremely similar but has less streaking on the crown, a broad pale buff band across the lower throat, buff undertail-coverts generally barred or vermiculated brown, and no white (or buff) markings in the wing; the male has narrower white tips to the three outer tail feathers, the female narrower buff tips.

VOICE The song consists of a short *click* or *tuc* followed by a trilled whistle, rising in pitch before trailing off, e.g. *tuc terrreo*. It is occasionally delivered at a faster rate, rising in pitch and not trailing off, *tuc terrrrr*. The call is a soft *quat*. Also gives a deep, crow-like *gaaw*.

HABITAT Pine forest. No further information available. 0?–1,500m.

HABITS Crepuscular and probably nocturnal. Roosts on branches near the ground. Roost-sites are usually in areas of dense growth. No further information available.

FOOD Insects. No further data available.

BREEDING Breeding season June–July.
No nest is constructed; the eggs are laid on the ground. Clutch generally 2. Eggs pale greenish-white, spotted brown. No further information available.

DESCRIPTION Adult male Forehead, crown and nape dark brown, speckled pale buff and greyish-white, broadly streaked blackish-brown. No collar on hindneck. Mantle, back and rump dark brown, finely speckled greyish-brown. Uppertail-coverts similar but speckling whitish. Wing-coverts dark brown finely speckled and lightly spotted pale buff. Scapulars buffish-white speckled brown, boldly spotted blackish-brown on tips. Primaries brown, spotted tawny or pale tawny along outerwebs; faintly and indistinctly barred tawny or pale tawny on innerwebs; inner primaries and all secondaries indistinctly mottled buffish-brown. Tertials brown densely mottled pale buff, centres broadly streaked brown. Tail brown; R5-R3 broadly (35-63mm) tipped white or white-tinged buff, usually more so on outerwebs; R2 sometimes narrowly tipped with some white; central pair densely mottled with very broad greyish-brown chevrons. Lores and ear-coverts tawny speckled dark brown. Chin and throat dark brown, finely speckled cinnamon. Narrow, indistinct band of cinnamon-buff spots across lower throat. Breast dark brown, finely speckled buffish-white with large buffish-white spots. Belly and flanks dark brown speckled and spotted buffish and greyish-white. Undertail-coverts plain buff or tawny-buff. Underwing-coverts buff barred brown. **Adult female** Similar to the male but R5-R3 broadly (c. 30mm) tipped buff. Buff tips often with brown streak through centre, along feather-shaft. **Immature** and **Juvenile** Not known. **Chick** Not known. **Bare parts** Iris brown; bill blackish; legs and feet brown.

MEASUREMENTS Wing (male) 176-177, (female) 177-181; tail (male) 137-140, (female) 131-145; bill (male) 18.2-20.0, (female) 18.8; tarsus (male) 17.1-18.8, (female) 17.1. Weight no data.

MOULT No data available.

GEOGRAPHICAL VARIATION Monotypic.

Hispaniolan Nightjar

DISTRIBUTION AND MOVEMENTS A Caribbean species, endemic to Hispaniola.

In Haiti, recorded from Terrier Rouge and near Jérémie. In the Dominican Republic, recorded from Santo Domingo, San Juan, La Vega and Pouton. Sedentary.

STATUS Local and possibly not common throughout Hispaniola.

REFERENCES Garrido & Reynard (1994), Wetmore & Swales (1931).

---

59   TAWNY-COLLARED NIGHTJAR
Caprimulgus salvini   Plate 16

Other names: Chip Willow

Caprimulgus salvini Hartert, 1892, *Ibis*, p.287 (Mirador, Vera Cruz, is accepted as the type locality)

Forms a superspecies with Silky-tailed and Yucatan Nightjars, with which some authorities consider it to be conspecific.

IDENTIFICATION Length 23-25.5cm. A dark, medium-sized nightjar, endemic to eastern Mexico. Sexually dimorphic. **At rest** Upperparts blackish-brown boldly streaked and spotted blackish. Tawny or buff collar on hindneck. Wing-coverts blackish-brown, lightly spotted and speckled cinnamon. Narrow white or buffish-white band around lower throat. Underparts blackish-brown heavily spotted white, becoming buff barred brown on undertail-coverts. **In flight** Both sexes lack white markings on the wings, which are brown spotted tawny (male) or buff (female). Round-tailed. The male has broad white tips to the three outer tail feathers, the female has narrower white tips or very narrow buffish tips. **Similar species** Yucatan Nightjar (60) is extremely similar, although occasionally much paler, more greyish-brown, and the underparts are usually paler and whiter; often has a more conspicuous, tawny or tawny-buff collar on the hindneck. Silky-tailed Nightjar (61) is also extremely similar, but is larger and the male has narrower white tips to the three outer tail feathers; occurs only in central South America.

VOICE The song is a rather rapid *chip willow* or *yip willow*. Also gives a faster *chip wow*. Sings from trees or bushes. May be heard mainly at dusk and dawn. No further information available.

HABITAT A lowland species, preferring semi-desert and dry, open woodland with scrub. Also occurs in more humid areas, e.g. farmland with fields and thickets, forest edges and clearings. 0–500m.

HABITS Crepuscular and nocturnal. Forages from trees, bushes and possibly the ground. No further information available.

FOOD Insects. No further data available.

BREEDING Breeding season April–August. Clutch 2. Eggs whitish with brown and grey markings. No further information available.

DESCRIPTION Adult male Forehead, crown and nape blackish-brown, heavily spotted blackish. Tawny or buff collar on hindneck. Mantle, back, rump and uppertail-coverts blackish-brown, finely peppered light brown and broadly streaked blackish. Wing-coverts blackish-brown, spotted and speckled cinnamon. Scapulars are half-whitish (generally hidden), half blackish-brown, with a large, almost star-shaped, blackish spot and small cinnamon spot dorsally on each web. Primaries brown, spotted (outerwebs) and barred (inner-webs) tawny. Secondaries brown with paler tawny markings. Tertials blackish-brown. Tail dark brown, faintly barred tawny along outerwebs of R5-R2; R5-R3 broadly (30-40mm) tipped white, edged buff; extent of white greater on outerwebs; central pair (R1) broadly barred with greyish-brown mottling. Lores and ear-coverts dark rufous barred brown. White submoustachial stripe. Chin and throat blackish-brown. Narrow whitish band around lower throat. Upper breast blackish-brown, heavily spotted white. Lower breast blackish-brown, speckled and barred true cinnamon. Belly and flanks blackish-brown heavily spotted white. Undertail-coverts buff barred brown. Underwing-coverts tawny or buff, barred brown. **Adult female** Similar to the male but tawny spotting and barring on wings paler and band around lower throat paler and buffier. R5-R3 narrowly (5-10mm) tipped whitish or buff. **Immature** and **Juvenile** Not known. **Chick** Not known. **Bare parts** Iris dark brown; bill blackish; legs and feet blackish-brown.

MEASUREMENTS Wing (male) 167-173, (female) 166-172; tail (male) 124-127, (female) 116-125; bill (male) 16.3-19.2, (female) 16.2-18.4; tarsus (male) c21, (female) 17.3-19.0. Weight, no data.

MOULT No data available.

GEOGRAPHICAL VARIATION Monotypic.

Tawny-collared Nightjar

DISTRIBUTION AND MOVEMENTS Endemic to E Mexico (Nuevo León and S Tamaulipas south through E San Luis Potosi and Veracruz to N Oaxaca? and Chiapas?). Sedentary, but some of the population may undertake local movements with birds recorded December–February in southern Veracruz and northern Oaxaca.

A bird (museum specimen) taken from Nicaragua in April, is considered by some authorities to be this species (see Yucatan Nightjar).

STATUS A little known species, but possibly fairly common throughout breeding range.

REFERENCES Hardy & Straneck (1989), Howell & Webb (1995), Land (1970).

60   YUCATAN NIGHTJAR
Caprimulgus badius   Plate 16

Antrostomus badius Bangs and Peck, 1908, *Proc. Biol. Soc. Wash.* 21, p.44 (Toledo district, British Honduras)

Forms a superspecies with Tawny-collared and Silky-tailed Nightjars, with which some authorities consider it to be conspecific.

IDENTIFICATION Length 25-25.5cm. A generally dark, medium-sized, large-headed and short-tailed Central American nightjar, endemic to the Yucatan Peninsula. Sexually dimorphic. **At rest** Upperparts greyish-brown, spotted and speckled greyish-white, heavily spotted and streaked blackish-brown. Broad tawny or tawny-buff collar on hindneck. Wing-coverts greyish-brown, spotted and speckled greyish-white, cinnamon, buff and tawny. Broad buffish-white band around lower throat. Underparts brownish heavily spotted white, becoming buff barred brown on undertail-coverts. **In flight** Both sexes lack white markings on the wings, which are brown spotted tawny. Tail rounded. The male has broad white tips to the three outer tail feathers, the female narrow tawny-buff tips. **Similar species** Tawny-collared Nightjar (59) is extremely similar but generally darker, with duller underparts and often a less conspicuous tawny or buff collar on hindneck. Silky-tailed Nightjar (61) is larger and darker, occurring only in central South America.

VOICE The song is a melodious undulating *wheo wee-a wee-a* or *ree-o reé reé*, similar to that of Silky-tailed Nightjar. May be heard mainly at dusk and dawn. The call is a series of chuck notes. No further information available.

HABITAT Little information available. Appears to prefer open lowland woodland and forest edges.

HABITS Crepuscular and nocturnal. No further information available.

FOOD No data available.

BREEDING Breeding season April?–August? Clutch 2. Eggs elliptical, white, sparsely flecked and blotched brown and purplish-grey, 30.0 x 21.5mm. No further information available.

DESCRIPTION Adult male Forehead, crown and nape greyish-brown, speckled and spotted greyish-white, boldly spotted blackish-brown. Broad tawny or tawny-buff collar on hindneck. Mantle, back, rump and uppertail-coverts greyish-brown, speckled pale buff and cinnamon, broadly streaked blackish-brown. Wing-coverts greyish-brown, finely speckled cinnamon, pale tawny and greyish-white, spotted buffish-white or cinnamon. Scapulars greyish-brown, heavily speckled pale buff, greyish-white and cinnamon, with large irregularly shaped blackish-brown spot. Primaries brown, spotted (outerwebs) and faintly barred (innerwebs) tawny. Secondaries brown, mottled pale tawny and pale cinnamon. Tertials greyish-brown speckled buffish and greyish-white, broadly streaked blackish-brown along feather-shafts. Tail brown faintly barred tawny; R5-R3 broadly (c. 45mm) tipped white, R2 narrowly (c. 8mm) tipped white, especially on outerweb; central pair (R1) broadly barred with greyish-brown mottling. Lores and ear-coverts tawny speckled blackish-brown. Chin and throat dark brown, thinly barred cinnamon. Broad white band around lower throat;

immediately below is a broad buff band, which may be a continuation of the collar on hindneck. Breast brown, speckled pale buff and cinnamon, heavily spotted white. Belly and flanks blackish-brown, speckled cinnamon and barred brown, boldly spotted white. Undertail-coverts buff or buff barred brown. Underwing-coverts buff barred brown. **Adult female** Similar to the male but R5-R3 narrowly (c. 10mm) tipped buff. **Immature** and **Juvenile** Not known. **Chick** Not known. **Bare parts** Iris dark brown; bill blackish; legs and feet blackish-brown.

MEASUREMENTS Wing (male) 167-172, (female) 167-174; tail (male) 120-128, (female) 112-125; bill (male) 17.4-18.1, (female) 16.6-18.3; tarsus (male) c. 18, (female) 18.0-18.2. Weight (male, one) 65.5g, (female, two) 51.2-55.7g.

MOULT No data available.

GEOGRAPHICAL VARIATION Monotypic.

Yucatan Nightjar
■ Winter range of part of the population
X vagrant

DISTRIBUTION AND MOVEMENTS Endemic to the Yucatán Peninsula, SE Mexico (Yucatán, Quintana Roo, Isla de Cozumel and the northern half of Campeche). Mainly sedentary, although some of the population moves south in the winter, with birds recorded December to February in Belize, northern Honduras (near Tela) and Half Moon Cay.

A bird (museum specimen) taken from Matagalpa, Nicaragua in April, is considered to be Tawny-collared Nightjar by some authorities.

STATUS A little-known species, but fairly common within its breeding range.

REFERENCES Hardy & Straneck (1989), Howell & Webb (1995), Paynter (1955).

---

61 SILKY-TAILED NIGHTJAR
Caprimulgus sericocaudatus Plate 16

Antrostomus sericocaudatus Cassin, 1849, *Proc. Acad. Nat. Sci. Phila.* 4, p 238 (South America. Restricted to vicinity of Rio de Janeiro, Brazil by Dickerman, 1975, *Bull. Brit. Orn. Club* 95, p.18)
Caprimulgus sericocaudatus mengeli Dickerman, 1975, *Bull. Brit. Orn. Club* 95, p.19 (Instituto Veterinario de Investigaciones Tropicales y de Alturas, 59km east of Pucaupa,

Loreto Department, Peru)

Forms a superspecies with Tawny-collared and Yucatan Nightjars, with which some authorities consider it to be conspecific.

IDENTIFICATION Length 24-30cm. A large, dark, long-winged Neotropical nightjar. Sexually dimorphic. **At rest** Upperparts dark greyish-brown, broadly streaked and spotted blackish-brown. Very broad, indistinct tawny-buff collar on hindneck. Wing-coverts brown, spotted buff and cinnamon. Large buff or buffish-white patch on lower throat. Underparts brown, boldly spotted whitish. **In flight** Both sexes lack white markings in the wings, which are brown spotted tawny. Tail rounded. The male has whitish tips to the three outer tail feathers; the female has narrower buff tips. **Similar species** Tawny-collared Nightjar (59) of eastern Mexico is extremely similar but smaller with different vocalisations; the male has broader white tips to the three outer tail feathers. Yucatan Nightjar (60) of the Yucatan Peninsula, Central America, is smaller, generally paler and always shows a narrower, more conspicuous, tawny or rufescent collar on hindneck; the male has broader white tips to the three outer tail feathers.

VOICE The song is an almost mournful, undulating *doh wheo eeo*, repeated for three minutes or more with only a very brief pause between each set of notes. Sings from a low perch and may be heard chiefly at dusk and dawn, all year round in some regions, e.g. Misiones, Argentina. The call is a treble-noted *gawrr a gawrr*, or a longer *gawrr a gawrr*. The song of the smaller race *mengeli* is a more melodious, drawn-out, higher-pitched *doh wheeeo weeeo*.

HABITAT Prefers forest edges, especially with thickets, bamboo understorey or second growth, and clearings. Occurs in subtropical evergreen forest (nominate race) or tropical rainforest (race *mengeli*).

HABITS Crepuscular and nocturnal. Roosts on or near the ground. At night, perches on branches, snags and stumps, up to 9m above ground. Often flies around and across forest clearings, 2-3m above the ground (perhaps a territorial flight). No further information available.

FOOD Beetles, crickets, grasshoppers and ants. No further data available.

BREEDING Very little information available. No nest is constructed; the eggs are laid on leaf-litter. Eggs elliptical, 28.0-31.0 x 21.0-23.0mm.

DESCRIPTION *C. s. sericocaudatus* **Adult male** Forehead, crown and nape brown, profusely speckled greyish-white, buff and cinnamon, broadly streaked blackish-brown. Very broad, indistinct collar on hindneck tawny-buff barred brown. Mantle, back, rump and uppertail-coverts brown, lightly barred and speckled cinnamon. Wing-coverts brown, spotted buff and cinnamon. Scapulars brown and buff, boldly spotted blackish-brown, with two small cinnamon spots on feather-tips. Outer primaries brown, spotted tawny on outerwebs, barred tawny on innerwebs; inner primaries and all secondaries brown barred tawny. Tertials brown mottled greyish-white, buff and cinnamon. Tail dark brown, faintly and indistinctly barred tawny; R5-R3 tipped (c. 20mm) white, edged buff, extent of white greater on outerwebs; R2 very narrowly tipped buff; central pair (R1) densely barred with greyish-brown mottling. Lores and ear-coverts rufous speckled dark brown. Chin and throat brown barred buff. Large buff patch across lower throat. Breast brown, spotted buff and white. Belly and flanks buff, densely barred brown and heavily spotted white. Undertail-coverts buff, lightly barred or vermiculated brown. Underwing-coverts buff barred brown. **Adult female** Similar to the male, but perhaps slightly browner and paler. R5-R3 narrowly (5-10mm) tipped buff. **Immature** and **Juvenile** Similar to the adults, but white or buff tips to the three outer tail feathers narrower. **Chick** Not known. **Bare parts** Iris dark brown; bill blackish; legs and feet blackish-brown.

MEASUREMENTS Wing (male) 177-186, (female) 167-190; tail (male) 140-148, (female) 130-152; bill (male) 16.0-18.2, (female) 16.4-18.0; tarsus (male) 16.9-19.8, (female) 17.0-18.7. Weight (male, one) 83g, (female) no data.

MOULT No data available.

GEOGRAPHICAL VARIATION Two races are currently recognised.
> **C. s. sericocaudatus** Described above.
> **C. s. mengeli** Length 24-27cm. Smaller and darker than the nominate. Wing (male) 157-163, (female, one) 157; tail (male) 124-127, (female) 118-120. Weight (male, one) 62g, (female) 53-66g.

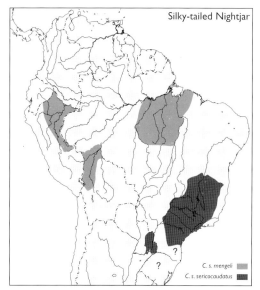
Silky-tailed Nightjar

C. s. mengeli
C. s. sericocaudatus

DISTRIBUTION AND MOVEMENTS South America. Known range is extremely fragmented but species is probably under-recorded.
> **C. s. sericocaudatus** SE Brazil (Minas Gerais, São Paulo, E Paraná and possibly Santa Catarina and Rio Grande do Sul), E Paraguay (Deptos Caazapá, Canendiyú, Caaguazú, Itapúa and Alto Paraná) and extreme NE Argentina (N and C Misiones). Sedentary.
> **C. s. mengeli** N Brazil (Pará), N Peru (Loreto) and NW Bolivia (Pando and La Paz). Sedentary.

STATUS Locally uncommon to fairly common throughout its range, but poorly known.

REFERENCES Dickerman (1975), Hardy & Straneck (1989), Schulenberg & Remsen (1982).

62   BUFF-COLLARED NIGHTJAR
Caprimulgus ridgwayi   Plate 14

Other name: Ridgway's Whip-poor-will

Antrostomus ridgwayi Nelson, 1897, *Auk* 14, p.50 (Tlalkisala, Guerrero)
Caprimulgus ridgwayi troglodytes Griscom, 1930, *Auk* 47, p.85 (Progreso, Guatemala)

IDENTIFICATION Length 21.5-24.5cm. A medium-sized, greyish-brown and variegated Central America nightjar. Sexually dimorphic. **At rest** Upperparts greyish-brown streaked blackish-brown; crown boldly spotted blackish-brown. Broad tawny or buff collar around the hindneck. Wing-coverts greyish-brown, streaked and spotted blackish-brown, speckled and spotted greyish-buff and buff. Scapulars greyish-brown, boldly spotted blackish-brown edged tawny or cinnamon. Narrow buffish-white supercilium and moustachial stripe. Broad buffish-white band around lower throat, merging with the hindneck collar on sides of head. Underparts greyish-brown tinged cinnamon, streaked and speckled brown, becoming pale buff barred brown on belly and flanks. **In flight** Both sexes lack white markings on the wings, which are brown, regularly barred and spotted tawny. The male has very broad white tips to the three outer tail feathers, the female narrower, buffish tips. **Similar species** Whip-poor-will (63) has darker upperparts and a narrower, less distinct tawny-buff collar around the hindneck.

VOICE The song is an accelerating series of 7-18 notes, ascending slightly in pitch, *cuk cuk cuk cuk cuk chuka-cheea* or *tok tok tek tek tek teeka-teea*. Sings from the ground, rocks or from perches in trees. May be heard at dusk and dawn, and for brief periods throughout the night. The call is a descending series of deep, guttural *tuk* notes. May also give *quirr* notes.

HABITAT Prefers arid or semi-arid open woodland, scrubland and rocky places. Occurs in deciduous forest, pine-oak forest, second growth, brushy woodland, fields and thickets. Also inhabits rocky hillsides with scattered trees and shrubs, ravines, washes, canyons and stony scrubland. Avoids dry areas where rocks, boulders and vegetation are absent. 0–3,000m.

HABITS Crepuscular and nocturnal. Roosts on the ground. Roost sites are usually beneath vegetation, and are frequently on sloping terrain, with the roosting bird facing down the slope. Often sits on roads and tracks at night, and frequently perches in scrubby vegetation, up to 2m above ground. Also perches on stumps and posts, often resting in a rather vertical posture. Generally solitary, although in winter it may be loosely semi-colonial, with up to 30 birds occurring in the same area. Hunts by making short flycatching sallies from perches or from the ground, and also forages low down over open ground. Flight extremely buoyant, with frequent twists, turns, climbs and dives, often interspersed with long glides. In winter, foraging flights may begin from vegetation on top of vertical cliffs. No further information available.

FOOD Beetles and moths. No further data available.

BREEDING Breeding season April–August in Mexico. No data available from other regions.
    Territorial. Males patrol the edges of their territories, and frequently stop to sing from favoured perches (see

Voice). Intruding males are chased away in aerial pursuits. After a pair bond has been formed, copulation may take place on the ground. No nest is constructed; the eggs are laid on leaf-litter on rocky ground. Nest-sites may be partly shaded by vegetation. Clutch 2. Eggs elliptical or sub-elliptical, buff blotched brown and lilac, 21.0-29.6 x 18.9-20.9mm. If flushed from the nest, adults perform an injury-feigning distraction display. Chicks semi-precocial. Towards the end of the breeding season, family parties of 3 or 4 birds may occur together. No further information available.

DESCRIPTION *C. r. ridgwayi* **Adult male** Forehead, crown and nape greyish-brown thinly streaked blackish-brown; central feathers boldly spotted blackish-brown with cinnamon edges. Broad tawny or buff collar around hindneck. Mantle, back, rump and uppertail-coverts greyish-brown streaked blackish-brown, faintly barred brown. Wing-coverts greyish-brown with irregularly shaped blackish-brown centres, speckled and spotted greyish-buff and buff. Primary coverts brown, barred or spotted tawny. Scapulars greyish-brown with bold, irregularly shaped blackish-brown centres edged tawny or cinnamon. Primaries and secondaries brown, regularly barred and spotted tawny, tipped with greyish-brown mottling. Tertials greyish-brown mottled brown and buff. Tail brown, broadly barred with greyish-brown and pale tawny-buff mottling; R5-R3 broadly tipped white, 40-58mm on R5, less so on R4 and R3, with white almost restricted to innerweb on R3. Lores and ear-coverts brown speckled buffish. Chin and throat greyish-brown speckled brown. Lower throat has broad buffish-white band, feathers with blackish-brown tips or subterminal bands, merging with hindcollar. Breast greyish-brown tinged cinnamon, streaked and speckled brown. Belly, flanks and undertail-coverts pale buff barred brown. Underwing-coverts buff barred brown. **Adult female** Similar to the male but with narrow (c. 12mm) buffish tips to R5-R3. **Immature** and **Juvenile** Similar to the adults although some may retain juvenile secondaries, which are more heavily tipped buff or cinnamon. Males have R5 and R4 tipped buffish-white, c. 40mm, R3 less so. **Chick** Not described. **Bare parts** Iris brown; bill brown or blackish; legs and feet black or brownish.

MEASUREMENTS Wing (male) 146-161, (female) 155-162; tail (male) 106-125, (female) 110-121; bill (male) 15.7-17.4, (female) 14.6-15.0; tarsus (male) 17.0-19.8, (female, three) 15.0-19.4. Weight (male) 44.7-53.7g, (female) 45.0-52.8g, unsexed 39.8-61.0g.

MOULT Adults probably undertake a complete post-breeding moult. Immatures possibly also undergo a complete post-breeding moult, although some may retain a few inner secondaries until after the following breeding season. No further data available.

GEOGRAPHICAL VARIATION Two races are currently recognised.
    C. r. ridgwayi Described above.
    C. r. troglodytes Smaller than the nominate, often with the scapulars more boldly spotted cinnamon or tawny. Wing (male) 146-149, (female, one) 151; tail (male) 97-111, (female, one) 108. Weight (male, one) 51.0g, (female) no data.

DISTRIBUTION AND MOVEMENTS A little-known species, generally restricted to Central America.
    C. r. ridgwayi W Mexico (E Sonora, W Chihuahua, Sinaloa and E Durango, south along the Pacific side

to C Chiapas). Sedentary in the south of its range, partially migratory in the north. A few birds summer, mid-April to mid-May–August in the extreme SW USA (Pima, Santa Cruz, Pinal and Cochise Counties in SE Arizona, and Hidaldo and Dona Ana Counties in SW New Mexico). Part of population possibly moves to lower altitudes during non-breeding season.
    A vagrant, probably of this race, recorded at Boskovich Farms, near Oxnard, California, on 8 June 1996.
C. r. troglodytes C Guatemala, C Honduras and C Nicaragua. Sedentary.

Buff-collared Nightjar
▮▮▮ *C. r. ridgwayi*
▮▮▮ *C. r. troglodytes*

STATUS Frequent to common in Mexico, rare to uncommon in Guatemala and Honduras. Range possibly expanding northwards, and noted as a rare summer visitor to SW USA from 1958 onwards, with less than 10 singing males occurring annually. Birds are occasionally killed by traffic on roads, and a bird once found in a poor state of health after preying upon a dobsonfly *Corydalis cornuta*, a mandible from the fly having broken off and pierced the oesophagus, trachea and breast muscle. Habitat loss is also a potential threat.

REFERENCES Alvarez del Toro (1949), Bowers & Dunning (1997), Howell & Webb (1995), Land (1970), Monroe (1968).

---

63   WHIP-POOR-WILL
Caprimulgus vociferus   Plate 14

Caprimulgus vociferus Wilson, 1812, *Amer. Orn.* 5, p.71, pl.41, figs 1-3 (Pennsylvania)
Caprimulgus vociferus arizonae (Brewster, 1881), *Bull. Nuttall Orn. Club* 6, p.69 (Chiricahua Mountains, Arizona)
Caprimulgus vociferus setosus van Rossem, 1934, *Bull. Mus. Comp. Zool.* 77, p.408 (Galindo, Tamaulipas, Mexico)
Caprimulgus vociferus oaxacae (Nelson, 1900), *Auk* 17, p.260 (Near city of Oaxaca, Oaxaca)
Caprimulgus vociferus chiapensis (Nelson, 1900), *Auk* 17, p.261 (Valley of Comitan, Chiapas)
Caprimulgus vociferus vermiculatus (Dickey and van Rossem, 1928), *Proc. Biol. Soc. Wash.* 41, p.130 (Los Esesmiles, Dept. of Chalatenango, El Salvador)

May form a superspecies with Puerto Rican Nightjar, with which it was formerly considered conspecific.

IDENTIFICATION Length 22-27cm. A medium-sized, greyish-brown, variegated nightjar occurring throughout much of North and Central America. Sexually dimorphic. **At rest** Upperparts greyish-brown streaked blackish-brown, broadly so on crown. Indistinct tawny-buff collar on hindneck. Wing-coverts greyish-brown, speckled and spotted tawny, buff, greyish-white and blackish-brown. Shows a row of large blackish spots along the scapulars and across the upper forewing. May show a thin buffish moustachial stripe and an indistinct white malar stripe. White or buffish-white band around lower throat. Underparts brownish, heavily spotted whitish, greyish-white and cinnamon, becoming buff barred brown on belly and flanks. **In flight** Both sexes lack white markings on the wings, which are brown, heavily and regularly spotted tawny. The male has very broad white tips to the three outer tail feathers, the female narrower buff tips. **Similar species** Chuck-will's-widow (55) is much larger and has a more spotted appearance, the male with a distinctive tail pattern (the three outer tail feathers entirely white on the innerwebs and tawny-buff mottled blackish-brown on the outerwebs), the female having indistinct, pale tips to the three outer tail feathers (no white or buff markings on the tail). Buff-collared Nightjar (62) has paler upperparts and a broader, more distinct tawny collar around the hindneck. Dusky Nightjar (65) is darker, blacker-brown, less variegated, and found only in Costa Rica and western Panama, south of the Whip-poor-will's known range. Puerto Rican Nightjar (64) is smaller and darker and occurs only on Puerto Rico.

VOICE The song is a distinctive, treble-noted whistle *whip pr-will* or *whip pr-weeea*, the last note usually rising in pitch at the end, occasionally rising then descendig before trailing off. The song is extremely variable and may be delivered very quickly or rather slowly. It is often preceded by or interspersed with several short, sharp *quit* notes, e.g. *quit, whip poor-will*. The song of the western race *arizonae* is more liquid and melodious, and is also variable with slower and faster versions. Sings from branches, boulders, stone walls, buildings and the ground, regularly moving around its territory to sing from favoured song-posts. Raises head slightly whilst singing. May be heard chiefly at dusk and dawn, and throughout moonlit nights. Tends not to sing during moderate to heavy rain. Males disturbed from their roost-sites during the day may sing or call briefly, although this is quite rare. Successfully breeding birds sing less after the hatching of their young, whilst unmated males continue to sing strongly throughout the season. Sings briefly during migration.

Immediately after the song, the males may utter a loud, whirring, whistling call lasting for c. 30 seconds or more. This type of call may be unusual and has, apparently, been noted only at dawn. In flight, birds of the race *arizonae* repeatedly give a *hu-whip* call when in close contact with each other. This is probably a contact call, although it is not known whether it is between a male and female or between birds of the same sex. An alarm call, given from a perch or the ground, is a short *couk* note.

A variety of calls are given during courtship and at the nest-site. When together, both sexes utter soft *coo* notes. The male also gives a musical *coo-eu* or *coo-eu-ah*. During the courtship display, the female gives a guttural chuckle or *cur cur cur*. During a changeover at the nest-site, both sexes give single or repeated *couk* notes, or a low *cur cur cur*. If flushed from the eggs, the female gives several *chuck* or *couk* notes, often whilst flying around the intruder, or a soft *quirt-quirt* from a perch. Distress notes given at the nest-site by both sexes, especially the male, are subdued *whip* calls; the male also gives a subdued *whip-will*. The male calls the chicks to him with a low *cur cur cur*, the female using a low, guttural *ca-ruck cruuur*. At the nest, the

chicks utter a piping *kwee*, uttered constantly when no adult is present. When answering an adult's call, the chicks give a more plaintive *kwee-uh* or *kwee-a*. When feeding the young, the female gives the low *cur cur cur* calls. During threat/defence displays, adults utter a throaty hiss, also given when birds are handled.

HABITAT Occurs in all types of forests, woods and open woodlands, especially oaks and pine–oak associations. It tolerates both arid and more humid conditions and may be found from lowlands through to montane country. It also occurs in suburban habitats. On migration in E Mexico, it occurs in coastal scrub. The western race *arizonae* ranges through lowland oak woods and oak–sycamore forests, high yellow pinelands, aspen woods and Douglas firs up to spruce forest at the summits of moun-tains. 0–3,000m.

HABITS Crepuscular and nocturnal. Roosts on the ground, in thickets or on low branches. When flushed from its roost, flies a short distance before re-alighting on the ground or on a perch. When alarmed, it spreads and lowers its tail, half opens its wings and calls (see Voice), bowing at each note. Frequently sits on roads and tracks at night, and occasionally dust-bathes. Forages in short sallies from a perch, in open spaces, clearings, parks, etc. Also feeds in more sustained flight amongst treetops; whilst foraging, its buoyant, wheeling flight includes sharp swerves, sudden rises and dives, and sweeping glides on level wings. Frequently hovers (see also Breeding). Often feeds close to running water. Also said to feed on the ground, turning over leaves? May eat grit, perhaps to aid digestion. Migrates at night, often in small groups of up to c. 30 birds. No further information available.

FOOD Moths (including Sphingidae and Noctuidae), beetles, grasshoppers, crickets, mosquitoes, caddisflies, locusts, worms? and ants. No further data available.

BREEDING Breeding season May–July in North America; mid-March–July in Mexico and late February–May? in El Salvador.

Territorial. Readily hovers when investigating intruders in its territory or at its nest-site. Courtship behaviour by both sexes can be quite variable. A singing male may attract a female which alights near him, calling (see Voice), whereupon the male stops singing, faces her and slowly walks to her in an undulating manner by raising his body to its fullest height with each step. The female 'bobs' slowly while the male circles her, one or perhaps both birds continually calling (see Voice) and 'purring'. If display is unsuccessful, the female flies off. Alternatively, after re-alighting near a singing male, she lowers her head and trembles, the male sidles up to her, touches bills and moves first to one side, then the other. Another form of display involves the female landing on the ground below a male singing from a low branch: she spreads her wings and tail, lowers her head and moves first to one side, then to the other. Such displays can last 10-15 minutes.

Breeding is often synchronised with the lunar phase. No nest is constructed; the eggs are laid on leaf-litter on the ground, often near or beside a fallen log. Nest-sites may be in small clearings, along edges of trees or woods, near open glades or under bushes. In more arid conditions, nest-sites of the western race *arizonae* may also be below overhanging rocks, in rocky, forested ravines, and on outcrops, escarpments or steep hillsides. The same nest-sites may be used year after year. Clutch 1-2. Eggs elliptical, slightly glossy, white or pale cream, and either unmarked, faintly marked pinkish and brownish or blotched and irregularly spotted brown, purple and lilac, 25.8-32.7 x 19.3-23.5mm. The eggs are laid on consecutive days, and incubation begins with the first egg. Double-brooded (see below), beginning second clutch c. 33 days after the first.

Incubation is usually by the female during the day, the male roosting close by, or up to 400m away. Changeover takes place at or just after dusk. The male lands close to the nest, calling (see Voice) and wags tail and body from side to side. The female leaves and the male walks to the eggs, often turning them with his bill before incubating. He may leave the eggs at times, incubating only for short spells. The female returns during the night and both sexes then share incubation duties until the female takes over for the last time, later in the night. She sits very tight when danger approaches. If flushed from the eggs during the day, soon after laying, she tends not to perform a distraction display but flies off a short distance and disappears into cover. When returning to the nest, she frequently hovers and alights on the ground before moving onto the eggs; she does not appear to walk to the eggs. If flushed during the latter stages of incubation, she may fly to a tree-stump or a low branch and call (see Voice). The adults frequently hover close to an intruder at or near the nest-site. Incubation usually takes 19-21 days.

After hatching, the eggshells are often left at or near the nest-site. The young are able to move in short hops soon after hatching, often in response to a calling adult (see Voice), and may move up to 30m from the nest-site during the first 10 days. The chicks are fed at night by both adults. They grip the adult's bill and the adult arches its back, spreads its wings and regurgitates food. If the female is flushed from the chicks during the day, the chicks move a short distance, often in opposite directions and 'freeze' as the female performs a distraction display. She may fly around the nest-site repeatedly giving alarm calls (see Voice), or injury-feign by fluttering about on the ground, calling (see Voice), shivering her wings and shaking her body. She may also fly up and perch across a branch, continually changing position to sit lengthways, then back again. Old records of females carrying chicks between their legs are possibly erroneous. Chicks fledge at c. 15 days of age and are usually independent after c. 30 days, but will still accept food from their parents.

For pairs that are double-brooded, the male appears to brood the chicks at the first nest while the female lays and incubates the second clutch. A changeover occurs when the male relieves the female and incubates the second clutch whilst she attends the first brood. During ringing studies, females have been recorded at both nests.

DESCRIPTION *C. v. vociferus* **Adult male** Forehead, crown and nape greyish-brown, minutely speckled brown and streaked blackish-brown; central feathers broadly streaked blackish-brown. Indistinct collar on hindneck pale tawny to pale buff, barred brown. Mantle, back, rump and uppertail-coverts greyish-brown, minutely speckled greyish-white and pale buff, streaked blackish-brown. Wing-coverts greyish-brown, speckled and spotted greyish-white, tawny, buff and pale buff. Scapulars greyish-brown mottled buff, distal third with large, irregularly shaped blackish-brown spots, edged with smaller tawny or cinnamon spots. Primaries brown, heavily spotted (outerwebs) and barred (innerwebs) tawny; inner two primaries and all secondaries brown barred tawny on innerwebs. Tertials greyish-brown, heavily mottled and

flecked pale buff, tawny and greyish-white. Tail dark brown, spotted tawny on outerwebs; R5-R3 broadly tipped white, R5 40-45mm, R4 50-55mm, R3 c. 60mm, R2-R1 broadly and densely mottled and flecked with pale buff and greyish-brown bars or chevrons. Thin, buffish moustachial stripe; broad, indistinct white malar stripe. Lores and ear-coverts rufous, buff or tawny, speckled dark brown. Chin and throat dark brown, speckled or indistinctly barred buff or pale tawny. White spot on either side of lower throat or whitish or buffish-white band around lower throat. Breast dark brown, heavily spotted or scalloped white, greyish-white or cinnamon; spots and scallops with brownish speckling. Belly and flanks buff, speckled and indistinctly barred brown. Undertail-coverts buff, tinged whitish, barred brown. Underwing-coverts buff or tawny barred brown. **Adult female** Similar to male, although the band around the lower throat is thinner and buffier. R5-R3 tipped buff flecked brown, 12-15mm. **Immature** Probably similar to the adults. **Juvenile** Similar to the adults but buffier. Crown spotted blackish. Scapulars, tertials and median coverts deep brownish-buff with large blackish spot. Lesser coverts blackish, barred and mottled reddish-brown. **Chick** At hatching, covered in cinnamon, pale brown or buff down, fading to yellowish-tan within a few days. **Bare parts** Iris dark brown; bill dark brown or blackish; legs and feet brownish.

MEASUREMENTS Wing (male) 149-169, (female) 147-163; tail (male) 113-133, (female) 105-123; bill (male) 15.4-16.0, (female) 14.5-15.0; tarsus (male) 15.5-19.7, (female) 16.0-19.2. Weight (male) 49.1-68.8g, (female) 53.9-67.7g.

MOULT Few published data available. Juveniles moult their body feathers and most wing-coverts during the post-breeding moult, July–September.

GEOGRAPHICAL VARIATION Six races are currently recognised, although *arizonae* is considered a separate species by some authorities.

C. v. vociferus Described above.

C. v. arizonae (Stephen's, Western or Southern Whip-poor-will) Supposedly larger than the nominate race, with longer rictal bristles. Differences in plumage minimal and apparently not consistent. The lores and ear-coverts are more tawny-ochraceous, the undertail-coverts are only lightly barred brown, and the male has slightly smaller white tips to the outer tail feathers (R5 c. 38mm, R4 c. 47mm). Wing (male) 155-165, (female) 155-165; tail (male) 107-123, (female) 107-123. Weight (male) 43.9-61.9g, (female) 47.5-56.7g.

C. v. setosus Apparently the largest race. The male has narrower? white tips to the outer tail feathers (R5 c. 29mm), the female narrower buff tips (R5 c10mm). Wing (male) 163-172, (female) 160-167; tail (male) 118-127, (female) c. 121. Weight no data.

C. v. oaxaca Similar to *setosus* but back darker, blackish spots on the scapulars larger, upperparts spotted and mottled reddish-brown heavily streaked blackish-brown, tawny hindneck collar coarsely barred blackish, breast and flanks coarsely and irregularly spotted reddish- and greyish-brown. Wing (male) c. 163, (female) c. 162; tail (male) c. 123, (female) c. 119. Weight (male) 47.6-56.0g, (female) 43.9-59.0g. Possibly synonymous with *setosus*.

C. v. chiapensis The darkest race. Upperparts spotted and barred rufous-brown, underparts blackish, coarsely marked dull buff, undertail-coverts often

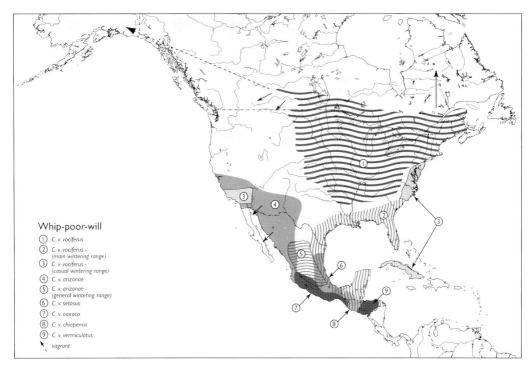

Whip-poor-will

1. *C. v. vociferus*
2. *C. v. vociferus -* (main wintering range)
3. *C. v. vociferus -* (casual wintering range)
4. *C. v. arizonae*
5. *C. v. arizonae -* (general wintering range)
6. *C. v. setosus*
7. *C. v. oaxaca*
8. *C. v. chiapensis*
9. *C. v. vermiculatus*

↘ vagrant

unmarked, white tips to R5 on male c. 40mm. One museum specimen noted as being almost identical to Dusky Nightjar (65). Wing (male) 160-169, (female) 152-155; tail (male) 122-127, (female) 104-112. Weight (male) 42.0-50.5g, (female) 53-61g.

C. v. vermiculatus Similar to *chiapensis* but paler, more reddish, with smaller and fewer blackish markings on the scapulars. Measurements, no data.

DISTRIBUTION AND MOVEMENTS Widely distributed throughout south-eastern Canada, USA and Central America, as far south as Honduras and El Salvador.

C. v. vociferus SC and SE Canada (NC Saskatchewan and S Manitoba east through S Ontario and S Quebec to New Brunswick and Nova Scotia) and EC and E USA (NE Montana? east to Maine, and south to NE Oklahoma, extreme NE Texas, N Louisiana, N Mississippi, N Alabama, N Georgia, EC North Carolina and E Virginia). Presumed casual visitor to SW and C Canada (S Alberta, SW Saskatchewan and N Quebec). Accidental SE Alaska (Kupreanof Island). Migratory, arriving on the southern breeding grounds in late March, and on the northern breeding grounds by early May. Departs September?– November? Winters from the lowlands of South Carolina and the Gulf States (including S Texas) south through E Mexico (September–April) to Guatemala, S Belize, El Salvador and Honduras. It may also casually winter in S California, Cuba, Costa Rica (rare? on the Pacific slope mid-November to late March) and W Panama (two records? W Chiriquí). Also occasionally winters along the east coast of the USA, as far north as New Jersey. ***C. v. arizonae*** SW USA (S California, S Nevada, C Arizona, C New Mexico and extreme W Texas) south through the mountains to C Mexico (Durango and Jalisco). Casual in Baja California. Migratory, arriving on the breeding grounds in late April and departing

again by late September. Winters in C Mexico. May be an altitudinal migrant in parts of its Mexican range. ***C. v. setosus*** E Mexico (C Tamaulipas south to S Veracruz and N Oaxaca). Presumably sedentary. ***C. v. oaxaca*** SW Mexico (Michoacán south to Oaxaca and adjacent parts of Chiapas). Sedentary. ***C. v. chiapensis*** SE Mexico (Chiapas) and the highlands of Guatemala. Presumably sedentary. ***C. v. vermiculatus*** Highlands of Honduras and El Salvador. Presumably sedentary.

STATUS Generally fairly common to locally abundant, but apparently decreasing in some regions in the north of its breeding range.

REFERENCES Bent (1940), Blackford (1953), Fowle & Fowle (1954), Howell & Webb (1995), Mills (1986, 1987), Raynor (1941), Ridgely & Gwynne (1989), Stiles & Skutch (1989), Thurber & Serrano (1987), Wetmore (1968).

64   PUERTO RICAN NIGHTJAR
Caprimulgus noctitherus   Plate 14

Other name: Puerto Rican Whip-poor-will

Setochalcis noctitherus Wetmore, 1919, *Proc. Biol. Soc. Wash.* 32, p.235 (Puerto Rico, type from Bayamón)

May form a superspecies with Whip-poor-will, with which it was formerly considered conspecific.

IDENTIFICATION Length 22-22.5cm. A medium-sized, brownish, variegated Neotropical nightjar, endemic to the island of Puerto Rico. Sexually dimorphic, although not strongly so. **At rest** Upperparts greyish-brown tinged rufous and streaked blackish-brown, broadly so on crown.

Indistinct tawny-buff collar on hindneck. Wing-coverts greyish-brown, speckled and spotted buff, tawny and greyish-white. Shows a row of large blackish spots across the upper forewing and along the scapulars. White or buffish-white band around lower throat. Underparts brownish, heavily spotted greyish-white and cinnamon, becoming buff barred brown on belly and flanks. **In flight** Both sexes lack white markings on the wings, which are brown, heavily and regularly spotted buff. The male has broad white tips to the three outer tail feathers; the female has narrower, buffish tips. **Similar species** Whip-poor-will (63) is larger and paler but does not occur on Puerto Rico (for full description, see that species).

VOICE The song is a rapid burst (2-15) of short, liquid, whistled *whlip* notes, e.g. *whlip whlip whlip whlip whlip*, often preceded by a few faint *quert* notes. Sings from favoured perches, such as the tops of small trees, throughout the territory. May be heard chiefly at dusk and dawn, but also throughout the night. Sings throughout the year, but tends to sing less towards the end of the breeding season, in poor weather, during periods of a new moon or on moonless nights. The flight calls are short *quert* notes, which may also be given from a perch, from the ground or when approached. Also utters growls and *gaw* notes. During aerial territorial disputes, males call hoarsely or utter loud growling sounds. During courtship display, males and females both make soft, clucking sounds. Whilst displaying at the nest-site and during the changeover of incubation duties, both sexes give soft, guttural calls. During threat/defence displays, adults make a guttural hissing. Adults call their chicks to them with soft, clucking notes.

HABITAT Prefers dry, limestone forests of semi-deciduous, hardwood trees and an open understorey, with little or no ground vegetation. Also occurs in dry, open scrubby secondary growth, xeric or dry scrubland, open scrub forest and forest with tangled, thorny undergrowth. A few birds have been found in *Eucalyptus robusta* plantations. Avoids riparian forest and, except where the canopy is intact, disturbed areas. 0–230m.

HABITS Crepuscular and nocturnal. Roosts on the ground, low branches or tree-stumps. When active, often flies with wings held in a V above its body. Hovers quite readily. Frequently perches across and along branches, c. 3-6m above ground, and has favourite perches which it uses night after night. Feeds by making sallies from perches 2.5-6m above ground, usually returning to the same perch; forages beneath the canopy. Smaller prey items are probably consumed in flight but larger insects are carried in the bird's bill, back to the perch. On alighting, the birds holds its head upright, and shakes and swallows its prey. Also feeds on insects attracted to artificial lights, e.g. at lamp-posts. At such food sources, birds often fly through the insect swarms with their gapes open, or land on the ground with their wings outstretched, to pick up beetles.

Towards the end of the breeding season, immature birds feed by making short sallies from the ground. They may also forage on the ground itself. No further information available.

FOOD Beetles (including Scarabaeidae), moths and other insects. No further data available.

BREEDING Breeding season late February–July (mainly April–June). Territorial (perhaps permanently so), exhibiting strong site fidelity from year to year. At the boundaries of adjoining territories, males often sing against each other. If two singing males are close to each other, e.g. less than 10m apart, disputes may erupt with both males suddenly flying up above the canopy, calling (see Voice) and grabbing bills in mid-air. These disputes may last 5-10 seconds, after which each male usually flies back to one its song-posts. Occasionally, both males tussle and flutter to the ground, calling constantly (see Voice), and continue the dispute on the forest floor. Courtship behaviour occurs in the early hours of the night, 2-7 days before the first egg is laid and usually within 30m of the eventual nest-site: the male and female sit parallel on a branch, c. 50cm apart, the male singing for up to 30 seconds, then fanning his tail, drooping his wings, vibrating his body and walking slowly towards the female, both sexes calling (see Voice); he may then fly up to 2m away and resume singing. Mating has not yet been documented. At the beginning of the breeding cycle, females often roost on the ground within 10m of the chosen nest-site, the first egg being laid up to three days later. Breeding appears to be influenced by the lunar phase, with nests being started in periods of low moonlight and hatching occurring in high moonlight.

No nest is constructed; the eggs are laid on leaf-litter on the ground. Nest-sites are usually beneath scrub vegetation in woodland with a canopy height of 4-6 m, or at the base of a small tree offering partial shade. Clutch 1-2. Eggs elliptical, buffish-brown blotched and spotted purple, markings denser around the blunt end.

Incubation is shared by both sexes, although males incubate during the day more often than females. If a female incubates by day, the male occasionally roosts close by. Incubation commences when the first egg is laid. The female usually relieves the male at dusk, and during the changeover both sexes display to each other. The incubating male becomes restless at dusk, especially if nearby males start singing, and shifts position on the eggs. The female flies in silently and alights on a low branch. Both sexes call (see Voice) and the male stands and displays in front of the nest, by spreading his wings and raising and spreading his tail. The female then flies to the nest and both birds face each other for 10-15 seconds, during which the male vibrates his body and ruffles his feathers and the female droops her wings and spreads her tail. The male then flies off and the female walks to the eggs and begins to incubate. Such changeover displays may last for up to 90 seconds. Occasionally, if the female does not relieve the male, he may leave the eggs unattended while he flies off to a song perch and sings. The nest may be unattended for an hour or more before one of the adults arrives to incubate. A male will occasionally return to the nest shortly after dusk and display to the female. The female usually continues to incubate and the male flies off again. Males usually return to their nests at dawn and display to the females, who then fly off silently. If flushed from the eggs, the adult flies a short distance and alights on the ground, often spreading its wings and tail and vibrating its body. If danger persists, the adult flies another short distance, re-alights and remains there. The incubation period is 18-21 days and the eggs hatch asynchronously.

The semi-precocial young can leave the nest-site soon after hatching and move short distances of up to 50cm in response to a calling parent (see Voice). Newly emerged chicks occasionally fall prey to ants but older nestlings may be moved out of harm's way by the adults. The chicks are fed by regurgitation by both parents but mainly by the male. The young are brooded mainly by the male. Occasionally both adults may be present at the nest-site. If flushed from the chicks, the adult performs a distraction display. It flies a short distance, alights on the ground, and then either injury-feigns by flapping its wings and spreading its tail, or gapes, vibrates its wings rapidly and spreads its tail, repeating these actions if the danger persists. It may also perform a different display by flying to a branch to perch with its wings drooped and tail spread, gaping and bill-snapping repeatedly and calling loudly or uttering a throaty hissing (see Voice). When the chicks are c. 7-14 days old, the distraction displays of the adults become more intensive, and during them the chicks quickly move to dense cover. At night, unattended chicks often forage on the ground in their immediate surroundings.

The chicks can fly short distances at c. 14 days old. At this age, they are not brooded by their parents but merely roost next to them. If disturbed, the adults fly off without performing a distraction display and the young fly up and perch in the nearest tree. Towards the end of the breeding season, juveniles often forage on the ground alongside paths or in clearings (see Habits). At this age, whilst they are still weak flyers, the young birds may be preyed on by Short-eared Owls *Asio flammeus*. Breeding nightjars and their eggs and young may also be predated by Pearly-eyed Thrashers *Margarops fuscatus*, fire-ants, feral cats or mongooses *Herpestes auropunctatus*. Immatures may remain within their parents' territory for up to 1 month after fledging.

Possibly double-brooded.

DESCRIPTION Adult male Forehead, crown and nape greyish-brown, speckled brown and streaked blackish-brown; central feathers broadly streaked blackish-brown with rufous edges. Broad, indistinct tawny-buff collar on hindneck. Mantle, back, rump and uppertail-coverts greyish-brown tinged rufous, streaked blackish-brown. Wing-coverts greyish-brown, speckled and spotted tawny, buff, greyish-white and blackish-brown. Scapulars greyish-brown mottled buffish, very broadly tipped with an irregularly shaped blackish-brown spot edged with smaller tawny or cinnamon spotting. Primaries brown, heavily spotted (outerwebs) and barred (innerwebs) buff; inner two primaries and all secondaries brown barred buff on innerwebs. Tertials greyish-brown heavily mottled pale buff, tawny and greyish-white. Tail dark brown spotted tawny on outerwebs; R5-R3 broadly (22-25mm) tipped white, R2-R1 with broad bars or chevrons of densely mottled and flecked pale buff and greyish-brown. Lores and ear-coverts buffish or tawny, speckled dark brown. Chin and throat brownish, speckled or indistinctly barred buff and pale tawny. Narrow buffish-white band around lower throat. Breast brownish, distinctly spotted and scalloped greyish-and cinnamon-white. Belly and flanks buff, spotted whitish or buffish-white and indistinctly barred brown. Undertail-coverts buffish-white lightly barred brown. Underwing-coverts buff barred brown. **Adult female** Similar to male but R5-R3 narrowly (c. 6mm) tipped buffish. **Immature** and **Juvenile** Paler than the adults. **Chick** At hatching, covered in reddish-buff or cinnamon down. **Bare parts** Iris dark brown; bill blackish; legs and feet blackish-brown.

MEASUREMENTS Wing (male) 132-138, (female, one) 133; tail (male) 110-120, (female, 105-112); bill (male)

11.7-15.0, (female) 14.3-16.3; tarsus no data. Weight (unsexed) 34.9-36.6g.

MOULT No published data available.

GEOGRAPHICAL VARIATION Monotypic.

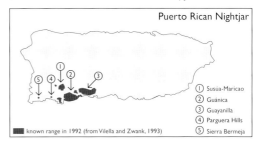

known range in 1992 (from Vilella and Zwank, 1993)

① Susúa-Maricao
② Guánica
③ Guayanilla
④ Parguera Hills
⑤ Sierra Bermeja

DISTRIBUTION AND MOVEMENTS Endemic to the island of Puerto Rico in the West Indies, where it is now confined to the arid south-west. Guánica-Bermeja (Guánica forest and the adjacent private lands at Ensenada) Guayanilla-Peñuelas (Guayanilla forest) and Susúa-Maricao (Susúa forest and the adjacent private lands to Susúa and Maricao forests). Also occurs in the Parguera hills and Sierra Bermeja (c 10km west of Parguera). Sedentary.

STATUS Thought likely to be extinct, until it was rediscovered in 1961. The current population (1984 figures) was estimated at between 670-800 pairs. In Guánica forest, census work located c. 324 pairs at densities of c. 1 pair per 8 hectares at altitudes above 75m and c. 1 pair per 18.8 hectares between 25-75m. In Susúa forest there were approximately 68 pairs at densities of 1 pair per 8.1 hectares north of Carretera del Bosque and 1 pair per 24.5 hectares south of Carretera del Bosque. In the Guayanilla hills there were thought to be c. 263 singing males.

Studies in 1985–1987, 1989–1990 and 1992 produced 347 singing males in the Guánica area, 177 singing males in the Susúa-Maricao area and 188 singing males in the Guayanilla area, a total of 712 singing males in 9,839 ha. It has been suggested that altogether 1,400–2,000 individuals may exist in the c. 10,000ha of coastal dry and cordillera forest in south-western Puerto Rico.

Deforestation and feral cats are possible reasons for its current, restricted range. The introduction of the mongoose is also blamed for the restriction in nightjar numbers, although different habitat preferences of the two species suggest little overlap in their ranges.

REFERENCES Collar *et al.* (1992), Kepler & Kepler (1973), Noble (1988), Noble *et al.* (1986a,b), Reynard (1962), Vilella (1989, 1995), Vilella and Zwank (1987, 1993a,b), Wetmore (1919).

65   DUSKY NIGHTJAR
Caprimulgus saturatus   Plate 14

Other name: Sooty Nightjar

Antrostomus saturatus Salvin, 1870, *Proc. Zool. Soc. London* p.203 (Volcán de Chiriquí, Panama)

IDENTIFICATION Length 21-25cm. A small to medium-sized, generally dark Neotropical nightjar, endemic to western Panama and the central highlands of Costa Rica. Sexually dimorphic. **At rest** Upperparts and wing-coverts blackish-brown, heavily spotted tawny and buff. No collar on hindneck. Indistinct pale buffish band around lower throat. Underparts blackish-brown heavily spotted tawny, becoming dark buff barred brown, spotted whitish on belly and flanks. Females are often paler than males and occasionally much more rufous. **In flight** Both sexes lack white markings on the wings, which are dark brown regularly spotted tawny. Round-tailed. The male has broad white tips to the three outer tail feathers, the female narrower tawny-buff tips. **Similar species** Whip-poor-will (63) is paler, greyer-brown and more variegated, with a whiter, more distinct band around the lower throat. Occurs further to the north, only reaching as far south as Honduras.

VOICE The song is a trilled, double-noted whistle *prurrrr prurree* or *prurrrr prruwhip*, the first note evenly pitched, the second rising at the end. This song ig!3lower, more drawn out than the triple-noted whistle of the Whip-poor-will. Sings from perches and possibly also from the ground. May be heard chiefly after dusk and before dawn, and occasionally throughout clear nights. The flight call is a scratchy *wheer*.

HABITAT Prefers open, humid, montane woods and forests where it inhabits clearings, woodland edges and second growth. Also occurs in highland pastures with scattered tall trees. 1,500–3,100m.

HABITS Nocturnal. Roosts on the ground or on low branches. Roost-sites are usually in thickets, often along the edges of woods and forests. Often perches on fallen logs. Forages from branches, feeding over open spaces adjacent to woods and forests. Very little appears to have been documented on the behaviour of this species.

FOOD Moths and beetles. No further data available.

BREEDING Breeding season is possibly February–April (juveniles found in April). No nest is constructed; the eggs are laid on leaf-litter or grass, on the ground. Nest-sites may be amongst tall grass and ferns, in clearings with scattered tall trees. Clutch 1? Egg elliptical, dull or glossy white, 28.6-21.6mm. No further information available.

DESCRIPTION Adult male Forehead, crown and nape blackish-brown, heavily spotted tawny and buff. No collar on hindneck. Mantle, back and rump blackish-brown, heavily spotted tawny and buff, becoming slightly paler towards uppertail-coverts. Wing-coverts and scapulars blackish-brown heavily spotted tawny. Primaries blackish-brown, regularly spotted tawny along outerwebs. Secondaries blackish-brown, regularly barred tawny along outerwebs. Tertials blackish-brown, spotted and barred tawny. Tail blackish-brown; R5-R3 thinly barred tawny along outerwebs, broadly tipped white, c. 25mm; R2-R1 broadly and indistinctly barred tawny, speckled blackish-brown. Lores and ear-coverts blackish-brown spotted tawny. Chin and throat blackish-brown spotted tawny and buff. Lower throat feathers tipped pale buff and pale tawny, forming indistinct band around lower throat. Breast and upper belly blackish-brown heavily spotted tawny, with some buff and white spots admixed. Belly, flanks and undertail-coverts dark buff barred brown, irregularly spotted buff, cinnamon and white. Underwing-coverts dark brown, faintly barred tawny. **Adult female** Similar to the male, perhaps slightly paler and occasionally much

more rufous. R5-R3 tipped tawny-buff. **Immature** and **Juvenile** Similar to the adults but even paler and more rufous. **Chick** Not known. **Bare parts** Iris dark brown; bill blackish; legs and feet greyish or dark brownish.

MEASUREMENTS Wing (male) 149-160, (female) 147-161; tail (male) 100-122, (female) 104-126; bill (male) 14.0-15.5, (female) 15.0-15.3; tarsus (male) 14.0-17.1, (female) 15.2-17.4. Weight (male, one) 52.9g, (female, one) 51g.

MOULT No data available.

GEOGRAPHICAL VARIATION Monotypic.

Dusky Nightjar

DISTRIBUTION AND MOVEMENTS Confined to montane forests and woodlands in the southern parts of Central America, in Costa Rica (central highlands, including the Cordillera Central, the mountains along the southern edge of the central plateau and the Dota mountains) and western Panama (Volcán Barú region, W Chiriquí). Sedentary.

STATUS Locally common in the central highlands of Costa Rica, uncommon in western Panama.

REFERENCES Marin & Schmitt (1991), Ridgely & Gwynne (1989), Slud (1964), Stiles & Skutch (1989), Wetmore (1968).

---

66 BAND-WINGED NIGHTJAR
Caprimulgus longirostris   Plates 17/18

Caprimulgus longirostris Bonaparte, 1825, *J. Acad. Nat. Sci. Phila.* 4, pt. 2, p.384 (South America)
Caprimulgus longirostris ruficervix (Sclater, 1866), *Proc. Zool. Soc. London* p.139 (in key), p.140, pl.14 (Bogotá, Colombia, and Quito, Ecuador)
Caprimulgus longirostris roraimae (Chapman, 1929), *Amer. Mus. Novit.* 341, p.2 (Philipp Camp, Mt Roraima, Venezuela)
Caprimulgus longirostris decussatus Tschudi, 1844, *Arch. f. Naturg.* 10, Bd. 1, p.268 (Peru)
Caprimulgus longirostris atripunctatus (Chapman, 1923), *Amer. Mus. Novit.* 67, p.2 (Acobamba, Junín, Peru)
Caprimulgus longirostris bifasciatus Gould, 1837, *Proc. Zool. Soc. London* p.22 (Valparaiso, Chile)
Caprimulgus longirostris patagonicus Olrog, 1962, *Acta Zool. Lilloana* 18, p.115 (Estancia El Tranquito, 250 km northwest of San Julian, Department of Magallanes, Santa Cruz, Argentina)

IDENTIFICATION Length 20-27cm. A medium-sized Neotropical nightjar that occurs in two forms depending on subspecies group, greyish-brown and blackish-brown.

Sexually dimorphic. **At rest** Upperparts greyish-brown streaked blackish-brown, or blackish-brown mottled tawny, buff and greyish-white. Broad tawny or buffish collar around hindneck. Wing-coverts greyish-brown or blackish-brown, boldly spotted buff, pale buff or greyish-buff. Scapulars blackish-brown, boldly spotted buff. Large white (male) or buffish (female) patch around lower throat. Underparts brownish barred and spotted buff, becoming buff barred brown on belly and flanks. **In flight** The male has a white band towards the wing-tip across the four outer primaries, broad white tips to the three (or four) outer tail feathers and a white bar across the upper half of the innerwebs of the three (or four) outer tail feathers. The female has a narrow buffish or buffish-white band across the four outer primaries, and either lacks white on the tail or has an indistinct whitish spot on the innerwebs of the outer one or two tail feathers. **Similar species** In the Pantepui of southern Venezuela, Blackish Nightjar (73) and Roraiman Nightjar (74) are quite similar to the dark race *roraimae* but are, on average, slightly smaller and blacker. They both differ in wing and tail markings (see those species) and lack a tawny or buff collar around the hindneck.

VOICE The song is a variable, high-pitched whistle, *seeeeeert sweeeeert seeeet*, repeated every 1-3 seconds. The song note may rise slightly, descend or be evenly pitched. Sings from a low perch or from the ground. May be heard mainly at dusk and dawn. The flight call is a thin, high-pitched *cheeet*, usually given during the breeding season. Occasionally utters a nasal *tchree-ee* when flushed.

HABITAT Prefers forest edges, woodland borders, open woodland, clearings, arid bush and campos. Also occurs in open areas with low vegetation, shrubby páramos, puna grassland, deserts and stony semi-deserts, steppe country and grassy slopes in semi-arid elfin forest. It may also be found in towns and cities, especially during migration periods. 0–4,200m.

HABITS Crepuscular and nocturnal. Roosts on the ground. Roost-sites are usually beneath thickets or bushes and are often in ravines or gorges, beside road cuttings or on rocky slopes. If flushed from its roost, flies with jerky, irregular wingbeats and drops suddenly to the ground a short distance away. Often sits on roads and tracks at night. In towns, often perches on roofs and walls of buildings. Forages by making short sallies from the ground or from a low perch. Also feeds on insects attracted to street lamps, building lights and illuminated windows. No further information available.

FOOD Moths, beetles and termites. No further data available.

BREEDING Breeding season February?–September? in W Venezuela; February–November in Colombia; ?–late July–? in Ecuador; November–? in Chile and C Argentina and September–October in SE Brazil (Rio de Janeiro). Breeding seasons not fully documented and no published data available from other regions.

No nest is constructed; the eggs are laid on bare ground, on leaf-litter or on bare rock. Nest-sites may be amongst regenerating vegetation on burnt ground, beside logs in open ground, beside roads, at the bases of small cliffs, amongst vegetation in semi-arid country and on the roofs of old buildings. Clutch 1-2. Eggs elliptical or subelliptical, pinkish, creamy pink or whitish, spotted and scrawled brown, lilac and grey, or unmarked, 25.0-32.8 x 18.2-22.0mm.

During one form of display (possibly distraction or male courtship) the bird flutters low over the ground with its tail held vertically downwards, occasionally showing its white tail spots. No further information available.

DESCRIPTION *C. l. longirostris* **Adult male** Forehead, crown and nape greyish-brown speckled brown, central feathers broadly streaked blackish-brown, sides of forehead and crown often white or greyish-white. Broad collar around hindneck tawny-buff, barred or spotted blackish-brown. Mantle and back dark greyish-brown, speckled and spotted blackish-brown. Rump and uppertail-coverts greyish-brown, speckled and barred blackish-brown. Lesser coverts blackish-brown speckled buffish, primary coverts brown, boldly spotted tawny with brown speckling. Alula and adjacent marginal wing-coverts white. Rest of wing-coverts brown speckled greyish-brown, boldly spotted buff with brown speckling. Scapulars blackish-brown, boldly spotted buff with brown speckling. Primaries and secondaries brown, P10-P7 with a broad (c. 15mm) white band, almost midway along feather, the outerwebs of which are occasionally narrowly edged buff, P6-P1 and secondaries boldly spotted and barred tawny with brown speckling. Tertials greyish-brown mottled brown. Tail brown; R5-R3 (occasionally R2) broadly (c. 40-50mm) tipped white, with a white bar c. 10mm wide across the upper half of the innerweb (occasionally with an extra white spot or bar on the innerweb, above the white bar, and often the white tips are edged buff, speckled brown and restricted to the innerwebs only on R3 and R2); R5-R3 also barred buff or pale tawny along outerwebs, above white tips; R2 mottled greyish-brown or buffish-brown; central pair (R1) greyish-brown, mottled and barred brown. Lores and ear-coverts blackish-brown, barred or speckled buff. Chin and upper throat buff barred brown. Large white patch, often edged buff, across lower throat, lower feathers of which are also tipped or spotted blackish-brown. Breast greyish-brown or brown, speckled and barred buff. Belly, flanks and underwing-coverts buff barred brown. Undertail-coverts buff. **Adult female** Similar to the male but with a buffish throat, a narrow tawny-buff, buff or buffish-white band across P10-P7 and either no white on the tail or an indistinct whitish spot towards the tip of the innerweb of R5 and sometimes R4. **Immature** and **Juvenile** Similar to the adults but plainer, with a narrow tawny band across P10-P7. **Chick** Apparently not described. **Bare parts** Iris brown; bill blackish; legs and feet blackish-brown.

MEASUREMENTS Wing (male, three) 162-163, (female, three) 163-167; tail (male, three) 117-128, (female, three) 117-121; bill (male) c. 16-19.4, (female) 15-19.7; tarsus (male) 20.7-22, (female) 18.2-21. Weight (male) 44.5-50.0g, (female) 42.0-56.6g.

MOULT No published data available.

GEOGRAPHICAL VARIATION Seven races are currently recognised in two distinct groups, the blackish, spotted forms *ruficervix*, *roraimae* and *atripunctatus* (north and west of range, in uplands) and the greyish-brown or streaked greyish forms *longirostris*, *bifasciatus*, *patagonicus* and *decussatus* (lower-lying regions in middle, east and south of range). All races are extremely variable in coloration and markings. The race *ruficervix* is occasionally considered a separate species, although there appears to be no published evidence to support this view.

    C. l. longirostris Described above. Some birds are heavily tinged cinnamon, others have broader, tawnier collars around the hindneck.

    C. l. ruficervix (Rufous-naped Nightjar) Darker and more heavily spotted than the nominate. Some birds are more heavily spotted and ocellated tawny on the upperparts and wing-coverts, giving them a somewhat rufous appearance; some have pale buff, almost whitish, spotting on the wing-coverts. Males have on average a narrower white band (c. 5-10mm) across P10-P7, and smaller white tail spots (c. 30-40mm). Wing (male) 152-161, (female) 152-161; tail (male) 103-112, (female) 103-112. Weight (male) no data, (female, one) 54.0g.

    C. l. roraimae Similar to *ruficervix* but larger and darker, with fewer white markings on the upperparts and breast. Males have a narrow white band (c. 5-10mm) across P10-P8, a vestigial white mark on P7, and the white spot on R5 is 30-35mm and often restricted to the innerweb only. Females often lack tawny on the wings and white or buff markings on the outer tail feathers. Wing (male) 167-177, (female) 165-168; tail (male) 110-125, (female) 110-124. Weight (male) no data, (female, one) 54.0g.

    C. l. decussatus The smallest and palest race. Males have the smallest white tail spots (c. 20-30mm). Possibly intergrades with *atripunctatus* in the east of its range. Wing (male) 136-139, (female, one) 142; tail no data. Weight (male) 28.5-35.0g, (female, one) 32.0g.

    C. l. atripunctatus Paler and greyer than *ruficervix* and more heavily ocellated buffish on the upperparts. The male also has a broader white band (c. 10-15mm) across P10-P6. Probably intergrades with *decussatus* in the west of its range. Wing (male) 151-167, (female) 152-163; tail (male) 112-119, (female) 112-122. Weight (male) 36.8-48.0g, (female, one) 71.0g.

    C. l. bifasciatus Paler than the nominate, larger than *decussatus*. The white band of the male across P10-P7 is c. 15mm, the white tail spots are large (c. 40-50mm). Probably intergrades with *patagonicus* in the south-east of its range. Wing (male) 158-167, (female) 158-166; tail (male) 119-124, (female) 117-124. Weight no data. Birds on Mocha Island appear to be larger and darker than those on the mainland and have a narrower tawny-buff collar around the hindneck. Wing (male, one) 171; tail (male, one) 136.

    C. l. patagonicus A large, small-billed race, described as similar to *bifasciatus* and other forms but separated by its dark coloration, dominated by black markings on a clear grey background. One male (museum specimen) from Chubut, Argentina, is silvery-grey with blackish markings on the upperparts, so appears much paler than both *bifasciatus* and the nominate race. Probably intergrades with *bifasciatus* in the south-west of its range. Wing (male) 161-178, (female, one) 162; tail (male, two) 130-148, (female) no data. Weight no data.

DISTRIBUTION AND MOVEMENTS Widely distributed over much of north-eastern, central and southern South America.

    C. l. longirostris SE Brazil (S Bahia, Minas Gerais, Espírito Santo, Rio de Janeiro, São Paulo, Paraná, Santa Catarina and Rio Grande do Sul), NW and C

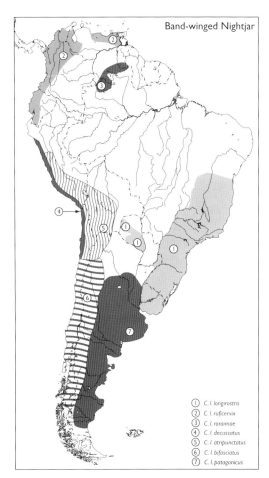

Band-winged Nightjar

1. *C. l. longirostris*
2. *C. l. ruficervix*
3. *C. l. roraimae*
4. *C. l. decussatus*
5. *C. l. atripunctatus*
6. *C. l. bifasciatus*
7. *C. l. patagonicus*

Paraguay (Nueva Asunción and Presidente Hayes), NE Argentina and Uruguay. Apparently sedentary in the north of its range, migratory in the south, thus birds (presumably this race) in Paraguay in late May to late August are probably migrants from the south.

    C. l. ruficervix W and N Venezuela (Zulia, Mérida, Táchira and W Barinas, and N Carabobo, Aragua, Distrito Federal to Monagas), Colombia (temperate zone of the Andes from Magdalena south-west to W Nariño and east to Cundinamarca) and Ecuador (temperate zone of the Andes). Presumably sedentary.

    C. l. roraimae Confined to the Pantepui of S Venezuela (SE and S Bolívar and C and S Amazonas). Presumably sedentary.

    C. l. decussatus SW Peru (arid littoral from Lambayeque to Tacna) and lowlands in extreme N Chile (Tarapacá and Antofagasta). Presumably sedentary.

    C. l. atripunctatus Middle Andes from C and S Peru, C and SW Bolivia (La Paz, Cochabamba, W? Santa Cruz, Oruro and Potosi?), NW Argentina (Jujuy) and N Chile (Tarapacá to Antofagasta). Presumably sedentary.

    C. l. bifasciatus Chile (Atacama south to Magallanes, including Guaitecas Islands and Mocha Island) and W Argentina (Salta south along the Andes to Mendoza and then at lower altitudes south to W Santa Cruz). Partially migratory, southern birds moving north to winter in the chaco of northern Argentina. The birds on Mocha Island merit further taxonomic study (see Geographical Variation).

C. l. patagonicus C and S Argentina (Santa Fe and Córdoba south to Santa Cruz). Partially migratory, southern birds moving north to winter from Buenos Aires north to Formosa.

STATUS Generally not uncommon throughout much of its breeding range.

REFERENCES Fjeldså & Krabbe (1990), Hilty & Brown (1986), Johnson (1967), Kiff *et al.* (1989), Meyer de Schauensee & Phelps (1978), Sick (1985), Straube (1990).

---

67   WHITE-TAILED NIGHTJAR
Caprimulgus cayennensis   Plate 18

Caprimulgus cayennensis Gmelin, 1789, *Syst. Nat.* 1, pt. 2, p.1031 (Cayenne)
Caprimulgus cayennensis albicauda (Lawrence, 1875), *Ann. Lyc. Nat. Hist. N.Y.* 11, p.89 (Talamanca, Costa Rica)
Caprimulgus cayennensis apertus (Peters, 1940), *Check-list of the birds of the world* 4, p.201 (San Antonio, Western Andes above Cali, Colombia)
Caprimulgus cayennensis insularis (Richmond, 1902), *Proc. Biol. Soc. Wash.* 15, p.159 (Curaçao)
Caprimulgus cayennensis leopetes Jardine and Selby, 1830, *Ill. Orn.* 2, pl.87 and text (Tobago)
Caprimulgus cayennensis manati (Pinchon, 1963), *Oiseau et R.F.O.* 33, p.107 (Martinique)

IDENTIFICATION Length 20-22.5cm. A small, variegated Neotropical nightjar. Sexually dimorphic. **At rest** Upperparts greyish-brown, streaked blackish-brown. Broad tawny-buff collar around hindneck. Wing-coverts greyish-brown, heavily spotted white, buff and pale buff. Male has a thin whitish line across forewing. Supercilium buffish or white, often indistinct, submoustachial stripe buffish or white. Male has a large white throat-patch, buffish breast heavily spotted white and white underparts; the female has a buffish throat and is generally darker and buffier. Tail slightly forked. **In flight** The male shows a well-defined white band towards the wing-tip across the four outer primaries, and a largely white tail. The female lacks white on the wings and tail. **Similar species** Little Nightjar (70) has a less distinct collar around the hindneck, no supercilium and a squarer tail; in flight, males show darker underparts, a large white spot on the four outer primaries and a white spot on the tips of all but the central pair of tail feathers; females lack white markings on the wings and only very rarely show a small amount of white on the tips of the three outer tail feathers. Spot-tailed Nightjar (69) has a broader, more pronounced supercilium, a darker crown and no white markings on the wings, which are heavily and regularly spotted tawny; the male has broadish white tips to all but the central pair of tail feathers, while the female shows no white on the tail. See also Scrub Nightjar (71).

VOICE The song is a series of short, high-pitched whistles *pt-cheeeeeee*, which descend slightly in pitch as they trail off. Sings from low perches, e.g. fence-posts, grass stems and rocks. May be heard chiefly at dusk and dawn. The flight calls are high *see-see* notes. When flushed, often utters soft, staccato *tic-tic* or soft *wut* notes. After alighting near the

nest, the female utters a soft *wut-wut-wut* as she approaches her chicks.

HABITAT Prefers open grassland and savanna with scattered bushes and thickets, scrubland and forest edges. Also occurs on grassy or eroded hillsides with scattered bushes, in pastures and in large clearings, e.g. airstrips. 0–3,200 m?

HABITS Crepuscular and nocturnal. Roosts on the ground or across low branches in bushes. Roost-sites are often in or under low shrubs, or amongst grass tussocks. Sits on roads and tracks at night. Forages by making short sallies from the ground and also hunts amongst animals in corrals and low over scrubby vegetation. No further information available.

FOOD Moths, beetles (including Geotrupidae and Curculionidae), bugs, damselflies, crickets and grasshoppers. No further data available.

BREEDING Breeding season February–June in Costa Rica; March–July in Colombia; April?–June? in Venezuela; February–December in Surinam; January–June in Trinidad; February–June in Tobago; and late January–July in Martinique. No published data available from other localities.

Very little appears to have been published on the breeding habits of this species. During the courtship display, birds wing-clap and also make 'whirring' sounds with their wings. No nest is constructed; the eggs are laid on the ground. In Trinidad, nest-sites are often in rough grass or occasionally on gravel with nearby vegetation. In Surinam, they may be on sand amongst sparse, low vegetation and in Martinique on bare, stony ground at the base of a tree or out in the open on close-cropped savanna. Clutch 1-2. Eggs elliptical, pinkish-buff or creamish, scrawled, blotched or spotted lilac, grey and reddish-brown, markings denser around the blunt end, 23.9-28.5 x 18.7-20.8mm. Incubation is by the female, at least during the day. Chicks can move short distances within a few days of hatching. If flushed from the chicks, the female performs an injury-feigning distraction display (not described). At night, when returning to the nest, she alights nearby, calls (see Voice) and runs with her wings held up towards her chicks. No further information available.

DESCRIPTION *C. c. cayennensis* **Adult male** Forehead, crown and nape greyish-brown, speckled brown and streaked blackish-brown, central feathers broadly streaked blackish-brown, edged tawny. Broad tawny-buff collar on hindneck. Mantle, back, rump and uppertail-coverts greyish-brown streaked blackish-brown. Wing-coverts greyish-brown, speckled and heavily spotted tawny, buff and pale buff. Upper median coverts broadly tipped white, occasionally tinged buffish, which shows as a white line across the forewing. Marginal wing-coverts white. Scapulars blackish-brown broadly edged buff or buffish-white on outerwebs. Primaries brown, with narrow, well defined white band, almost midway along the feather, across both webs of P10-P7, and a small white spot above white band P9-P7; vestigial white spot on innerweb of P6; P3-P1 tipped white. Secondaries brown broadly tipped white, with two large white spots on the innerwebs. Tertials greyish-brown speckled brown, streaked blackish-brown along feather-shafts, with buff spot on tip of outerweb. Tail slightly forked, feathers becoming shorter towards central pair, and patterning extremely variable; R5 white, with one dark brown bar across innerweb, halfway along feather; R4-R2 white, broadly tipped and outerwebs edged brown with one broad brown bar across innerwebs, halfway along feathers; central pair (R1) greyish-brown, speckled and broadly barred blackish-brown. Supercilium and submoustachial stripe white or buffish. Lores and ear-coverts rufous barred brown. Chin and throat white, often tinged pale buff. Breast buff tinged cinnamon, barred brown and boldly spotted white. Belly and flanks white, washed pale buff. Undertail-coverts white or very pale buff. Underwing-coverts white barred brown. **Adult female** Darker than the male, with a buffish throat, brownish breast and buff underparts barred brown. No white on the wings, the outer primaries brown heavily spotted tawny or buff. Tail brown with palish tips, alternately barred dark brown and buff/tawny; central pair (R1) as male. **Immature** and **Juvenile** Not described. **Chick** Not described. **Bare parts** Iris dark brown; bill blackish; legs and feet blackish-brown.

MEASUREMENTS Wing (male) 136-155, (female) 132-157; tail (male) 110-130, (female) 91-107; bill (male) 15.4-16.2, (female) 13.2-13.6; tarsus (male) 16.8-18.3, (female) 15.4-17.0. Weight (male) 30.0-40.0g, (female) 25.6-46.0g.

MOULT No data available.

GEOGRAPHICAL VARIATION Six races are currently recognised, although the validity of some is questionable.
    C. c. cayennensis Described above. Can be quite variable in colour, ranging from very dark greyish-brown to pale, light brown.
    C. c. albicauda The male has the belly, flanks and undertail-coverts heavily tinged buff, the female dark brownish-buff underparts. Supposedly longer-tailed than the nominate race. Wing (male) 134-150, (female) 129-141; tail (male) 106-122, (female) 97-108. Weight no data.
    C. c. apertus Similar to *albicauda*? but the female, at least, has darker upperparts and deeper buff underparts. Supposedly longer-winged, longer-tailed and larger-billed than the nominate. Wing (male) 137-138, (female) 138-149; tail (male) 106-112, (female) 104-108; bill (male) no data, (female) 12-13. Weight no data.
    C. c. insularis Paler than the nominate with more buff on the upperparts, especially on the crown and wing-coverts; supposedly also smaller with darker undertail-coverts. Wing (male) 130-144, (female, one) 136; tail (male) 113-127, (female, one) 96. Weight no data.
    C. c. leopetes The male has tawnier upperparts than the nominate, especially on the crown and wing-coverts, a richer, more defined hindneck collar, and darker buff edges to the outerwebs of the scapulars. The underparts are darker, more heavily washed buff. The female has paler, browner upperparts and a brighter, more defined hindneck collar. Wing (male) 139-145, (female) 137-140; tail (male) 111-118, (female) 100-106. Weight (male) 31-34g, (female) no data.
    C. c. manati Generally darker than the nominate. The male has a narrower white band across the four outer primaries and slightly less white on the tail. No mensural data available to the author.

DISTRIBUTION AND MOVEMENTS A generally common species, widely distributed throughout the northern parts of South America, somewhat less common in southern Central America.

    C. c. cayennensis C and NE Colombia (Norte de Santander south, east of the Andes, to Huila and S Meta, east to E Vichada), Venezuela (Zulia south to NE Barinas and E Apure, east through Guárico and Aragua to Monagas and Delta Amacuro, and throughout Bolívar and W and C Amazonas), Guyana, Surinam, French Guiana and probably N Brazil (Roraima and Amapá). Sedentary.
    C. c. albicauda Costa Rica (Pacific slope, from N Guanacaste south), Panama (Pacific slope, from Chiriquí and Veraguas through Coclé and E Panamá to W Darién) and NW Colombia (Córdoba? and Bolívar north through Atlántico and Magdalena to Santa Marta region). The southern limits of this race in Colombia are not clear. Sedentary.
    C. c. apertus W Colombia (subtropical zone of the Western Andes, east to Santander) south to N Ecuador? (Imbabura). The northern limits of this race in Colombia are not clear. Sedentary.
    C. c. insularis Extreme NE Colombia (Guajira), NW Venezuela (coast of Falcón, including the Paraguaná Peninsula), Margarita Island and the islands of Curaçao, Aruba and Bonaire. Sedentary.
    C. c. leopetes Trinidad, Tobago, Bocas Islands and Little Tobago. Sedentary.
    C. c. manati Martinique. Sedentary.
This species (race unknown) has occurred as a vagrant (sight record) on Puerto Rico.

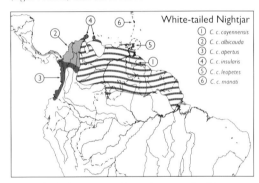

STATUS Fairly common throughout much of its range, although locally uncommon in Panama and scarce on Aruba, Curaçao and Bonaire.

REFERENCES ffrench & O'Neill (1991), Haverschmidt & Mees (1994), Hilty & Brown (1986), Meyer de Schauensee & Phelps (1978), Pinchon (1963), Ridgely & Gwynne (1989), Stiles & Skutch (1989), Voous (1965), Wetmore (1968).

---

68   WHITE-WINGED NIGHTJAR
Caprimulgus candicans   Plate 19

Stenopsis candicans Pelzeln in Sclater, 1866 (1867), *Proc. Zool. Soc. London* p.588 (Irisanga, São Paulo)

IDENTIFICATION Length 19-21cm. A small, pale, greyish-brown Neotropical nightjar. Sexually dimorphic. **At rest** The male's outermost primaries often curve slightly upwards. Upperparts and inner wing-coverts pale greyish-brown, often tinged cinnamon, speckled, barred and streaked brown, boldly spotted blackish on crown. No collar around hindneck. Outer wing-coverts white, edged brown and boldly spotted blackish. Scapulars greyish-brown boldly marked blackish, outerwebs generally buffish. Broad pale buff submoustachial stripe. Ring of buffish spots around lower throat. Breast greyish-brown tinged chestnut and tawny, barred and speckled brown, rest of underparts white. The female lacks white in the plumage, with the scapulars more boldly marked blackish and buffish underparts. **In flight** Broad and round-winged, the outer primaries curving slightly inwards. The male has whitish wings, the outer primaries being broadly tipped brown, and a largely white tail. The female has browner wings, broadly barred tawny-buff, and a brown tail, broadly barred buffish. **Similar species** The male is unmistakable and the following possibly only applies to females and immatures. Sickle-winged Nightjar (119) is generally browner and less cinnamon (females only), and boldly spotted whitish on the upperparts (immatures only); the underparts are more heavily spotted and barred brown, the primaries are more thickly and densely barred tawny, and at rest the wing-tips fall short of the tip of the tail.

VOICE During territorial chases, males utter a short, whistled *tshere-she-shew* which undulates in pitch. Males on the ground may also give this call when startled. Females may utter a sharp *eek* when alarmed. Males also produce a variety of sounds probably made with their wings (see Habits and Breeding). No further information available.

HABITAT A lowland species that prefers open grasslands with scattered trees and bushes. Occurs in dry, open savannas and open cerrado or grasslands with scattered bushes, prostrate palms *Butia*, termite mounds and anthills. Also inhabits regenerating grasslands that have been burnt in previous years. Avoids tall grass. 0–210m.

HABITS Crepuscular and nocturnal. At night, often sits on small patches of open bare ground, or perches on clumps of grass, termite mounds or prostrate palms *Butia* up to c. 1m above ground. When hunting, flight is slow and interspersed with frequent glides. Forages low over hillsides and hilltops in climax cerrado with scattered shrubs and dwarf jatai palms *Butia*, often flying 1-2m above the grass, and occasionally hunts over burnt cerrado. Also flycatches by making short sallies from an elevated perch, at the beginning of which, males may produce a mechanical *grrrrt* sound. No further information available.

FOOD Beetles and moths. No further data available.

BREEDING Breeding season late September?–November? in E Paraguay and C Brazil.

Territorial, males defending their territories by chasing away intruding males. Territories may measure up to 60m in diameter, are often open areas with few palms on the upper slopes of ridges, and usually contain 1-3 display areas that each have a vertical perch and a small anthill, 2-3m apart. The vertical perches are 0.4-0.6m high and often protrude above the grassland; the anthills are always lower than the vertical perch, 0.3-0.5m in height. During moonlit nights, males perform courtship display flights from elevated perches, by flying in a gentle arc with fluttering, 'butterfly-like' wingbeats and the wings held back, after which they alight briefly on top of an anthill before flying with deep wingbeats directly back to and past the elevated perch. As they pass the perch, they loop around and re-settle on it. Mechanical sounds produced during these displays include a sharp *tk* as they alight on top of an anthill and a strong, toad-like *grrrrt*, probably made with the wings, as they fly back to the first perch or as they alight. Males sometimes start their display flights from the top of an anthill. No further information available.

DESCRIPTION Adult male Forehead, crown and nape pale greyish-brown, speckled white and brown and occasionally tinged cinnamon, central feathers boldly spotted or streaked blackish, sides of crown whitish forming a stripe above eye, and sides of nape boldly streaked or spotted buffish. No collar on hindneck. Mantle, back and rump pale greyish-brown, occasionally tinged cinnamon, faintly barred and speckled brown and thinly streaked dark brown. Uppertail-coverts very pale greyish-brown, speckled and vermiculated brown. Inner lesser, median and greater coverts pale greyish-brown, often tinged cinnamon and buff, speckled and vermiculated brown, boldly streaked and spotted pale buff at feather-shafts. Outer lesser coverts and alula white, often broadly edged brown on outerwebs. Primary coverts white, broadly edged brown or dark brown on outerwebs, and boldly tipped with dark brown 'tear-drop' shaped spots. Scapulars pale greyish-brown, boldly spotted, streaked or marked blackish, speckled brown on innerwebs and largely buff or cinnamon-buff on outerwebs. Primaries white proximally, dark brown or blackish distally, the amount of white increasing on each primary towards the body, with P4-P1 largely white, edged (outerweb only) and tipped dark brown or blackish (P2-P1 occasionally all white). Secondaries white, thinly edged brown on outerwebs. Tertials greyish-brown tinged cinnamon and buff, speckled and streaked dark brown. Tail generally white; R5 white, thinly edged (outerweb only) and tipped buff; R4-R2 white, broadly edged buff speckled brown on outerwebs, thinly tipped buff; central pair (R1) pale greyish-brown, speckled or thinly barred brown, feather-shafts occasionally dark brown. Lores and ear-coverts chestnut, speckled or barred dark brown. Broad pale buff or whitish submoustachial stripe. Chin pale buff, throat tawny-chestnut barred and speckled brown. Row of buffish spots around lower throat. Breast greyish-brown tinged tawny and chestnut, barred and speckled brown. Belly, flanks, undertail- and underwing-coverts white. **Adult female** Unknown, (but see Immature and Juvenile, also below). **Immature** and **Juvenile** (sex unknown, but possibly female) Similar to the adult male, but slightly browner and less greyish, and lacks white on the wings, underparts and tail. The undertail-coverts are pale buff and unmarked, the scapulars more boldly marked with blackish 'inverted Christmas tree' patterns. The primaries and secondaries are brown, broadly and regularly barred tawny-buff. The tail is brown, broadly and boldly barred buffish, with central feathers (R1) greyish-brown, speckled and thinly barred dark brown. **Chick** Unknown. **Bare parts** Iris reddish-brown or chestnut; bill generally blackish with flesh-coloured bases; tarsus grey or greyish-flesh.

One other plumage, not seen by me, is known (possibly of an immature male). Head similar to the male, but sides of crown greyish, finely speckled black and white. Upperparts and wing-coverts light clay, with cinnamon and drab markings. Scapulars blackish, edged cinnamon on outerwebs. P10 dark greyish-brown, tipped with small, white spots, P9-P7 dark greyish-brown, regularly spotted cinnamon, tipped with small, whitish spots, P6-P1, secondaries and tertials dark greyish-brown, regularly spotted cinnamon. Tail dark brown barred cinnamon, central feathers (R1) dark brown barred tawny. Lores, ear-coverts, chin and throat dark cinnamon-rufous. Narrow white submoustachial stripe. Breast and flanks cinnamon, speckled whitish and finely barred brownish, belly and undertail-coverts whitish.

MEASUREMENTS Wing (male) 133-154, (female, one) 148; tail (male) 95-107, (female, one) 90; bill (male, three) c. 14-19, (female, one) c. 16; tarsus (male) 20.9-25.8, (female, one) 20.0. Weight (male) 46-51g, (female) no data.

MOULT The type specimen, a male taken in southern Brazil in early January, appears to have been nearing the end of a complete moult. On both wings P1-P6 appear new, P7 is nearly half grown and P8-P10 appear old. This suggests that the primaries are moulted descendantly. The tail moult appears to be centrifugal. No further data available.

GEOGRAPHICAL VARIATION Monotypic.
The male (museum specimen) from Bolivia is slightly smaller than birds from Brazil and Paraguay, has blackish scapulars narrowly edged pale buff on the outerwebs, a brownish breast with buff spotting, and the white tail feathers edged brown not buff.

White-winged Nightjar

possible range

DISTRIBUTION AND MOVEMENTS A little-known South American species.
C and SW Brazil (near Cuiabá in southern Mato Grosso, Irisanga = Orissanga in western São Paulo, and Emas National Park in south-western Goiás), E Paraguay (Aguará-Ñu in Depto Canindeyú) and Bolivia (near Estancia El Provenir, in Prov. Yucuma, Depto Beni). Apparently sedentary and partially migratory, i.e. may be migratory in parts of its range.

STATUS Thought not to be uncommon in the 1980s, at Emas National Park in Brazil, but possibly only recorded there once since 1990. Considered to be fairly common at Reserva Natural del Bosque Mbaracayú–Aguará-Ñu in eastern Paraguay, with up to 20 pairs possibly present in suitable habitat during September–December 1995.

REFERENCES Collar *et al.* (1992), Davis & Flores (1994), López Lanús *et al.* (in prep.), Lowen *et al.* (1996a,b, 1997).

---

69   SPOT-TAILED NIGHTJAR
Caprimulgus maculicaudus   Plate 20

Other name: Pit-sweet

Stenopsis maculicaudus Lawrence, 1862, *Ann. Lyc. Nat. Hist. N.Y.* 7, p.459 (Pará)

IDENTIFICATION Length 19-21.5cm. A small, variegated or occasionally heavily spotted Neotropical nightjar. Sexually dimorphic. **At rest** Crown blackish-brown spotted buff or tawny. Upperparts brown or greyish-brown, barred and vermiculated dark brown, buff and tawny. Distinct buff or tawny collar on hindneck. Wing-coverts brown heavily speckled pale buff, with three rows of large buff or cinnamon spots. Broad buffish line along scapulars. The combination of a thickish buff supercilium, thin buff submoustachial stripe and very broad, triangular, blackish malar stripe is unique amongst small nightjars within its range. Small buff or cinnamon-buff patch on throat. Breast brownish, spotted buff, cinnamon-buff, or buffish-white. Distinct cinnamon-rufous band, thinly barred brown, on lower breast and upper belly. Rest of underparts buff with some indistinct brown barring, becoming plain buff towards undertail-coverts. **In flight** Both sexes lack white markings on the wings, which are brown heavily and regularly spotted tawny. May show a thinnish buff trailing edge to the inner wing. The male has broadish white tips, distally washed cinnamon/pale buff, speckled brown, to all but the central pair of tail feathers. There are also three widely spaced white spots along the innerwebs of the four outer tail feathers, some of which may only be noticeable if the tail is fanned. The female has no white markings on the tail. **Similar species** White-tailed Nightjar (67) has a paler crown, less pronounced supercilium and, in flight, no buffish trailing edge to the inner wing; males show a white band on the four outer primaries and largely white tails, females have wings less densely spotted tawny. Little Nightjar (70) has an indistinct collar around the hindneck, a large white throat-patch, no supercilium, no thickset blackish malar stripe and, in flight, no buffish trailing edge to the inner wing; males show white spots on four or five of the outer primaries and white spots on the tips of the four outer tail feathers, usually on the innerwebs only; females have wings less densely spotted tawny. See also Least Nighthawk (32).

VOICE The song is a thin, high-pitched single *t-seet* or *t-sweet*, occasionally *t-tsuwee* or *t-t-swee*. Another variation is a slower *pt swee-i*. May sing continuously for up to one hour or more at a time. Sings from the ground or a perch, e.g. low shrubs in grassy areas. May be heard chiefly at dusk, often commencing earlier than other nightjar species. Tends to sing less once breeding has commenced. Calls given in flight or whilst perched include a rapid series of *t-seet* notes, an accelerating *t-seet seet-seet* and a shriller *seeu* or *see-ee-eeii*. Whilst calling in flight, it often makes a triple fluttering noise with its wings.

HABITAT Prefers savanna and grassland, with scattered low trees and thickets, plus bushy pastures, open marshy places, clearings, second growth and along woodland edges. In Brazil it also inhabits buriti palm groves, in Honduras and north-eastern Nicaragua pine savanna, and in Venezuela possibly rainforest. 0–500m.

HABITS Crepuscular and nocturnal. Roosts on the ground

or low branches. Roost-sites are usually in thickets, but may sometimes be out in the open or in low bushes in marshy vegetation. Outside the breeding season, semi-colonial roosting, in large numbers, sometimes occurs. Often sits on roads, tracks and in open spaces at night. In trees, perches crossways on branches. Repeatedly hunts by flycatching from the ground, always returning to the same spot. No further information available.

FOOD Beetles (including Carabidae, Scarabaeidae, Curculionidae, Elateridae, Hydrophilidae, Staphylinidae and Tenebrionidae), moths (including Noctuidae), flies, bugs (including Reduviidae), Orthoptera (including Blattodea and Gryllidae) and damselflies.

BREEDING Breeding season late March–July in Mexico; October–April in Surinam and possibly late February–May in Colombia. No data available from other countries. No nest is constructed; the eggs are laid on the ground. Nest-sites are usually in open, grassy areas, often close to a low bush. Clutch 2. Eggs buff or creamy pink, spotted or flecked reddish-brown and pale lilac, markings heavier at blunt end, 23.1-26.1 x 16.5-19.6mm. The chicks can move short distances within a few days of hatching.

If flushed from her chicks, a female may fly off low over the ground for up to 30m and re-alight on the ground facing the intruder. If the danger continues to approach her, she flies off again. A male when flushed (from the nest?) may jump into the air, fluttering his wings with rapid, shallow beats, spread his tail to reveal the white mark-ings and sing (see Voice). No further information available.

DESCRIPTION Adult male Forehead and crown blackish-brown spotted buff or tawny. Nape blackish-brown barred tawny and buff. Buff, tawny or cinnamon-rufous (40) collar around hindneck. Mantle and back brown, regularly and thinly barred tawny, becoming paler on rump and uppertail-coverts. Wing-coverts brown, heavily speckled pale buff, with large buff or cinnamon spots on tips of outerwebs. Primary coverts brown spotted tawny. Scapulars blackish-brown on innerwebs, mostly buffish or cinnamon-buff on outerwebs. P10-P8 brown with large tawny spots along the upper two-thirds of the feather; rest of primaries brown, regularly spotted tawny. Secondaries brown, broadly tipped pale tawny and regularly spotted tawny, spots becoming paler and buffer on inner secondaries. Tertials brown, mottled and spotted buff and greyish-brown. Tail (R5-R2) dark brown, spotted or barred tawny along the outerwebs, with two or three widely spaced white spots along the innerwebs, spots becoming larger towards the central feathers; R5-R2 are also broadly (10-15mm) tipped white, the white tips having the distal half washed cinnamon/pale buff, speckled brown; central pair (R1) greyish-brown, speckled and thinly barred brown, and slightly longer than the others. Broad buff supercilium, lores and ear-coverts tawny or rufous, densely speckled dark brown. Thin buff submoustachial stripe, blackish malar stripe broad and triangular. Chin, throat and breast cinnamon-buff or buff, feathers with brown tips. Distinct cinnamon-rufous band with regular thin brown barring around lower breast and upper belly. Belly and flanks buff, indistinctly barred brown. Undertail-coverts buff. Underwing-coverts buff barred brown. **Adult female** Similar to the male but without white markings on the tail, R5-R2 being dark brown indistinctly barred pale tawny or buff and tipped buffish-brown speckled brown. **Immature** and **Juvenile** Similar to the adult (female?) but

all primaries and secondaries narrowly tipped pale buffish. **Chick** At hatching, covered in blackish down with brownish-buff markings. **Bare parts** Iris brown; bill blackish; legs and feet greyish.

MEASUREMENTS Wing (male) 127-146, (female) 122-137; tail (male) 87-114, (female) 88-105; bill (male) 10.6-16.5, (female) 10.6-13.1; tarsus (male) 14.8-17.2, (female) 14.0-15.5. Weight (male) 28.3-35.2g, (female) 26.0-39.0g.

MOULT No data available.

GEOGRAPHICAL VARIATION Monotypic. Some birds are more rufous than others.

DISTRIBUTION AND MOVEMENTS Central and South America. SE Mexico (S Veracruz, NE Oaxaca, Tabasco and N Chiapas), the Mosquitia of E Honduras? and NE Nicaragua, Panama?, Colombia (Córdoba, NW Chocó, Boyacá, Meta, SE Guainía and W Vaupés), Venezuela (Barinas, Miranda, Bolívar and S Amazonas), Guyana, Surinam, French Guiana (Mana), Brazil (Amazonas, Pará, São Paulo and Rio de Janeiro), Paraguay (Canendiyú), N and EC Bolivia (Beni, Cochabamba and Santa Cruz) and SE Peru (Cuzco). Sedentary throughout most of its range in South America, migratory in Central America. Occurs in SE Mexico as a breeding summer visitor, arriving by late March and departing in July or August, wintering in South America. Recorded in C Honduras (Lake Yojoa) as a migrant only.

STATUS Fairly common, locally so in Mexico and parts of Brazil (e.g. Marajó, Pará) and uncommon in Colombia. No data from other localities.

REFERENCES Blake (1949), Haverschmidt & Mees (1994), Hilty & Brown (1986), Howell & Webb (1995), Lowen *et al.* (1997), Meyer de Schauensee & Phelps (1978), de Urioste (1994), Zimmerman (1957).

70   LITTLE NIGHTJAR
Caprimulgus parvulus   **Plate 20**

Caprimulgus parvulus Gould, 1837, *Proc. Zool. Soc. London* p.22 (near Santa Fé, Rio Paraná, Argentina)
Caprimulgus parvulus heterurus (Todd, 1915), *Proc. Biol. Soc. Wash.* 28, p.81 (La Tigrera, Santa Marta, Colombia)

Formerly considered conspecific with Scrub Nightjar.

IDENTIFICATION Length 19-21cm. A small, variegated Neotropical nightjar. Sexually dimorphic. **At rest** Upperparts greyish-brown streaked blackish brown, broadly so on the crown. Broad but indistinct buff or tawny-buff collar around hindneck. Wing-coverts greyish-brown, barred, spotted and speckled buff, tawny, rufous and whitish. Scapulars blackish-brown, broadly edged buff or pale buff on outerwebs. No supercilium. Large white throat-patch. Underparts greyish-brown spotted pale buff and greyish-white, thinly barred light brown, becoming buff barred brown on belly and flanks. **In flight** Has a rapid, fluttery flight action. The male has a large white spot towards the wing-tip on the four outer primaries (innerweb only on the outermost), occasionally a smaller white spot on the fifth outermost and a white spot on the tips of all but the central pair of tail feathers. These tail spots are always restricted to innerwebs of the second and third outer feathers, occasionally so on the two outermost. The female generally lacks white markings on the wings and tail. Very rarely, some females may show a very small white spot on the tips of the innerwebs of the three outer tail feathers. **Similar species** Spot-tailed Nightjar (69) has a rufous collar around the hindneck, a distinct buffish supercilium, a thick black malar stripe and a small cinnamon-buff patch on the throat; in flight, both sexes lack white markings on the wings, which are heavily spotted tawny, and may show a thinnish buff trailing edge to the inner wing; the male has broadish white tips (both webs) to all but the central pair of tail feathers. White-tailed Nightjar (67) has a more distinct buff or tawny collar around the hindneck, an indistinct buffish-white supercilium and a very slightly forked tail; in flight, males show a thinner, more defined, white band across the four outer primaries, largely white tails and much whiter underparts, while females have darker underparts, buffish (not white) throats and lack white markings on the wing and tail. Scrub Nightjar (71), confined to western Ecuador and north-west Peru, is very similar at rest but has a different scapular pattern (see that species), a smaller white throat-patch, and less distinctly barred underparts; in flight, males show a white band across the five outer primaries and entirely white innerwebs to the two outer tail feathers, while females have smaller white spots on the primaries and much less white on the tail, usually restricted to distal two-thirds of the innerweb of the outermost. See also under Pygmy Nightjar (75). See also Least Nighthawk (32).

VOICE The song is a very distinctive, warbled series of 4-8 notes which descend in pitch *dop dro-dro-dro-dro-dro*. Sings from perches such as tree-stumps. May be heard chiefly at dusk and dawn. Also sings throughout the night, including moonless nights, and very rarely in mid-morning. The song of the north-western race *heterurus* is a deeper, even-pitched *pik gobble-gobble-gobble-gobble*.

HABITAT Occurs in open woodland and forests, lightly wooded country, savannas, thickets, open country with scattered bushes, pastures and weedy fields, espinilho and eucalyptus groves. In Venezuela, the race *heterurus* prefers slightly hilly terrain, and also occurs in suburban parkland. 0–1,000m.

HABITS Crepuscular and nocturnal. Roosts on the ground. When flushed from its roost, it flies up to c. 20 m before re-alighting on the ground, often behind a tree or bush. Often sits on roads and tracks at night. No further

information available.

FOOD Moths and beetles (including Curculionidae). No further data available.

BREEDING Breeding season late October–? in Colombia; October–November in Paraguay and November–? in south-western Brazil. No further information available.

No nest is constructed; the eggs are laid on the ground. Nest-sites are often near or under a thick bush. Clutch 2. Eggs elliptical, creamy white to buffish-white, blotched and scrawled brown, with underlying patches of lavender-grey, 24.0-28.8 x 18.2-21.0mm. No further information available.

DESCRIPTION *C. p. parvulus* **Adult male** Forehead, crown and nape greyish-brown finely speckled light brown and thinly streaked blackish-brown, central feathers very broadly streaked blackish-brown. Broad, indistinct buff or tawny-buff collar around hindneck. Mantle, back, rump and uppertail-coverts greyish-brown, speckled light brown and thinly streaked blackish-brown. Lesser coverts dark brown indistinctly barred buff. Greater coverts and some median coverts brown, spotted buff and tipped whitish. Primary coverts and rest of median coverts brown, spotted and barred rufous. Scapulars blackish-brown, broadly edged buff or pale buff on feather. Primaries brown; large white spot, almost midway along feather, on innerweb of P10 and across both webs of P9-P7; P6 with either no white, vestigial white mark or small white spot speckled brown around edges. Secondaries brown, barred tawny on outerwebs and buff on innerwebs. Tertials greyish-brown, speckled brown and broadly streaked blackish-brown. Tail brown, indistinctly barred buff or pale tawny; R5 and R4 with white spot (10-15mm across) on tips, either on both webs or on innerwebs only; R3 and R2 with white spot on tips of innerwebs; central pair (R1) greyish-brown speckled and barred brown. Lores and ear-coverts rufous speckled dark brown. Whitish submoustachial stripe. Chin buffish. Large, triangular white patch on throat, the lower feathers of which are tipped blackish-brown, with a buff sub-terminal band. Breast greyish-brown, thinly barred brown, spotted pale buff. Belly, flanks and underwing-coverts buff barred brown. Undertail-coverts buff or buff barred brown. **Adult female** Similar to the male but lacks white spots on the primaries and usually on the tail. The primaries are brown, irregularly spotted buff or pale tawny. Rarely, some females have a very small white spot on the innerwebs of R5-R3. **Immature** and **Juvenile** Similar to the adult female but the primaries and secondaries are narrowly tipped buff or buffish-white. **Chick** Not described. **Bare parts** Iris dark brown; bill blackish; legs and feet brownish- or greyish-olive.

MEASUREMENTS Wing (male) 133-144, (female) 128-141; tail (male) 90-105, (female) 85-105; bill (male) 13-14.5, (female) 12.5-13.3; tarsus (male) 13.2-17.4, (female) 16.3-17.2. Weight (male) 25.0-42.6g, (female) 36.0-46.5g.

MOULT The primaries are moulted descendantly. Fresh plumage, e.g. moult completed, noted on birds (museum specimens) from eastern Peru (October) and Paraguay (January). No further data available.

GEOGRAPHICAL VARIATION Two races are currently recognised.

   C. p. parvulus Described above.
   C. p. heterurus Similar to the nominate but with much wider white band across the five outer primaries, slightly darker underparts and slightly larger white

spots (14-20mm) on the tips of all but the central two tail feathers. The song is also slightly different (see Voice). Wing (male) 135-147, (female) 134-144; tail (male) 87-99, (female) 87-100. Weight no data.

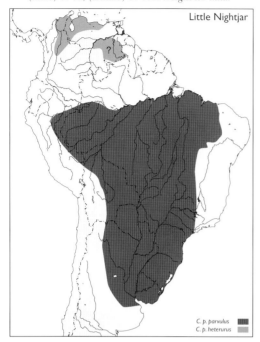

Little Nightjar

C. p. parvulus
C. p. heterurus

DISTRIBUTION AND MOVEMENTS Widely distributed in generally open, lightly wooded country throughout much of South America. Two distinct populations occur, separated by a large gap between c. 7.5°N and the Amazon River.

C. p. parvulus E Peru, N, E and SE Bolivia (Beni, Santa Cruz, Chuquisaca and Tarija), Brazil south of the Amazon (Amazonas east to Pará, Maranhão, Goiás, Piauí and Bahia, south through São Paulo and Mato Grosso to Rio Grande do Sul), Paraguay, Uruguay, N Argentina (Catamarca south-east through Córdoba to N Buenos Aires) and N Chile? Sedentary and partially migratory, although movements are poorly understood. Occurs as a migrant from E Peru eastwards to N Brazil (Pará). In E Brazil, large numbers occur in Minas Gerais in October, and it is a summer visitor only to S Brazil (Rio Grande do Sul) from late October to mid-February.

C. p. heterurus N and C Venezuela (Distrito Federal, Aragua, Miranda, Mérida, Zulia and Bolívar) and N Colombia (Magdalena, Norte de Santander, Santander and Cundinamarca). Presumably sedentary.

STATUS Surprisingly poorly known, but apparently common to locally abundant in many parts of its range.

REFERENCES Belton (1984), Hilty & Brown (1986), Meyer de Schauensee & Phelps (1978), Schwartz (1968).

71 SCRUB NIGHTJAR
Caprimulgus anthonyi   Plate 20

Other name: Anthony's Nightjar

Setopagis anthonyi Chapman, 1923, *Amer. Mus. Novit.* 67, p.4 (Portovelo, Ecuador)

Formerly considered conspecific with Little Nightjar.

IDENTIFICATION Length 18-21cm. A small, variegated Neotropical nightjar, confined to western Ecuador and the extreme north-west of Peru. Sexually dimorphic. **At rest** Upperparts greyish-brown speckled buffish and streaked blackish-brown. Crown broadly streaked blackish-brown. Broad indistinct collar on hindneck tawny-buff barred brown. Wing-coverts greyish-brown, speckled brown and buffish, heavily spotted buff and pale buff. Scapulars with large, irregularly shaped blackish-brown centres and broad buff edges to the outerwebs. White patch across the lower throat. Underparts greyish-brown or brown broadly barred buff and pale buff, becoming buff indistinctly barred brown on belly. **In flight** The male has a white band towards the wing-tip, across the five outer primaries, and entirely white innerwebs to the two outer tail feathers. The female has a thinner, less defined white band across the outer primaries and a whitish innerweb, distally, to the outermost tail feather only. **Similar species** Little Nightjar (70), not known to overlap with Scrub Nightjar, is very similar at rest but has a different scapular pattern (see that species) and a larger white throat-patch; in flight, males show a large white spot on the four outer primaries and a white spot on the tips of all but the central two tail feathers; the female generally lacks white markings on the wings and tail, but sometimes has a very small white spot on the tips of the innerwebs of the three outer tail feathers. White-tailed Nightjar (67) has a more distinct buff or tawny-buff collar around the hindneck, an indistinct buffish-white supercilium and a very slightly forked tail; in flight, males show a well-defined white band across the four outer primaries, largely white tails and much whiter underparts; females have darker underparts, buffish (not white) throats and lack white markings on the wing and tail.

VOICE The song is a short, whistled *wheeeeo* or *t-wheeeeo*, repeated several times at 1-2 second intervals. Sings from the ground and low perches. May be heard chiefly at dusk and dawn. The flight call is a soft *tuk tuk tuk*. Another call is a rolling *quaqrrr*, which rises in pitch from the beginning and again from the middle. This call is usually given from a perch, e.g. the low fork in a bush.

HABITAT Prefers arid scrubland with scattered bushes and trees, dry, open, grassy country, and the borders and edges of deciduous woodland. Also occurs along roadsides in dry deciduous forest, in brushy mesquite woodland, second growth mesquite thickets in farmland, fallow farmland, wet pastures and damp grassy meadows. 0–775m.

HABITS Crepuscular and nocturnal? Roosts on the ground. Roost-sites may be in bushy areas in desert scrubland, or in clearings. Hawks for insects low over the tops of bushes. No further information available.

FOOD Moths, grasshoppers and beetles (including Scarabeidae). No further data available.

BREEDING Breeding season appears to be December?–March?, coinciding with the arrival of the rains, which are highly irregular. In Ecuador, nests with eggs have been found in February (e.g. at Santa Elena).

Possible courtship behaviour involves the male chasing the female in broad loops to heights of c. 10m above the ground. No nest is constructed; the eggs are laid on leaf-litter on the ground. Nest-sites may be in small clearings in fairly dense vegetation along the edges of thickets and beneath trees. Clutch 1-2. Eggs elliptical, pinkish-buff heavily speckled and scrawled brown, reddish-brown and grey, 24.4-25.0 x 19.1-19.6mm. Possibly double-brooded in years of prolonged rains but may not breed in years with little or no rain. No further information available.

DESCRIPTION Adult male Front of forehead above bill tawny barred dark brown. Rest of forehead, crown and nape greyish-brown, speckled brown and broadly streaked blackish-brown. Indistinct collar on hindneck tawny-buff barred brown. Mantle, back, rump and uppertail-coverts greyish-brown, speckled buffish and streaked dark brown. Wing-coverts greyish-brown, speckled and heavily spotted buff and pale buff. Scapulars brown speckled buff on innerwebs, with large, irregularly shaped blackish-brown centres and broadly edged buff on outerwebs. Primaries brown; large white spot, almost midway along feather, on P10-P6, often washed buff on P10; vestigial white mark on P5; rest irregularly spotted and barred pale tawny or buff. Secondaries brown, barred and tipped tawny-buff. Tertials greyish-brown heavily mottled brown and blackish-brown. Tail brown; R5-R4 entirely white on innerwebs; R3-R2 faintly and indistinctly barred pale tawny-buff; central pair (R1) heavily mottled greyish-brown. Lores and ear-coverts tawny-buff, barred and speckled dark brown. Chin and upper throat tawny-buff, barred and speckled dark brown. White patch across lower throat, the lower feathers of which are tipped pale buff. Breast greyish-brown, broadly barred buff and pale buff. Belly and flanks buff or pale buff, indistinctly barred brown. Undertail-coverts buff. Underwing covers buff barred brown. **Adult female** Similar to the male but white spots on P10-P6 smaller, often washed tawny on the outerwebs. White on tail usually restricted to distal two-thirds of innerweb of R5 only. **Immature** and **Juvenile** Similar to the adults but has buff or tawny-buff spots on the outer primaries, pale buff tips to the primaries and secondaries, and generally pale, dirty buff innerwebs to the outermost tail feathers (R5). Throat-patch buff or buffish-white. **Chick** Not known. **Bare parts** Iris dark brown; bill blackish; legs and feet pinkish grey-brown.

MEASUREMENTS Wing (male) 132-136, (female) 135-142; tail (male) 97-100, (female) 90-101; bill (male) 14.6-15.7, (female) 12.9-14.2; tarsus (male) 16.8-17.9, (female) 16.4-18.6. Weight (male) 32.3-39.5g, (female) 31.0-42.0g.

MOULT The primaries are moulted descendantly. The tail appears to be moulted irregularly with the central pair (R1) first, followed by the outermost (R5). No further data available.

GEOGRAPHICAL VARIATION Monotypic. No colour variations have so far been recorded within its restricted range.

DISTRIBUTION AND MOVEMENTS Confined to the dry lowlands and adjacent foothills in western Ecuador (Esmeraldas, Manabi, Guaya, El Oro, Azuay and Loja) and the extreme north-west of Peru (Las Pampas, Depto

Lambayeque; northern end of the upper Rio Marañón valley, Bagua, Depto Amazonas, and near Jaén, Depto Cajamarca). Sedentary and partially nomadic, perhaps moving seasonally with the rains.

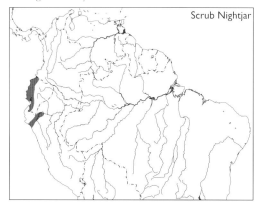
Scrub Nightjar

STATUS Locally common in suitable habitat, e.g. common and widespread on the Santa Elena Peninsula, Ecuador. May be increasing in some areas of Ecuador, as a result of continuing deforestation.

REFERENCES Robbins *et al.* (1994), Schwartz (1968).

72   CAYENNE NIGHTJAR
Caprimulgus maculosus   Plate 17

Nyctipolus maculosus Todd, 1920, *Proc. Biol. Soc. Wash.* 33, p 74 (Tamanoir, Cayenne)

IDENTIFICATION Length 22.5cm. A small, brown, variegated Neotropical nightjar. Known only from a single specimen, a male. **At rest** Upperparts greyish-brown, broadly streaked blackish-brown on crown and nape. Narrow, indistinct tawny collar on hindneck. Wing-coverts greyish-brown heavily spotted buff; scapulars blackish-brown, broadly edged buff. Large white patch either side of lower throat. Underparts buff heavily barred brown. **In flight** Wings rather pointed with a small white spot, towards the wing-tip, on the four outer primaries, and a vestigial white mark on the fifth outermost. The outer three tail feathers are rather broadly tipped white (innerweb only on outermost). **Similar species** Blackish Nightjar (73) is darker and blacker with a more spotted appearance, round-winged in flight, when the male shows a small white spot on three of the four outer primaries (never on the outermost) and small white tips to the second and third outer tail feathers; the female lacks white markings on the wings and tail.

VOICE Unknown.

HABITAT Unclear. The only known specimen was taken near the lower reaches of a river with numerous boulder-strewn rapids, in an area of thick forest and open spaces containing sandy or stony riverbanks, large boulders and savanna-like clearings.

HABITS No information available.

FOOD No data available.

BREEDING No information available.

DESCRIPTION Adult male Forehead, crown and nape greyish-brown, spotted cinnamon, broadly streaked blackish-brown. Very narrow, indistinct collar on hindneck tawny barred brown. Mantle and back greyish-brown spotted true cinnamon. Rump and uppertail-coverts greyish-brown spotted buff. Lesser coverts dark brown speckled and spotted chestnut; rest of wing-coverts brown heavily spotted buff and cinnamon. Scapulars blackish-brown, outerwebs broadly edged buff. Primaries and secondaries brown; small white spot, almost midway along feather, on innerweb of P10 and across both webs of P9-P7; vestigial white mark on both webs of P6; inner primaries and secondaries barred and spotted tawny along feather-edges. Tertials brown, mottled greyish-brown, buff and tawny. Tail dark brown indistinctly barred tawny, broadly tipped white on innerweb of R5 and both webs of R4-R3; central pair (R1) mottled greyish-brown, barred blackish-brown. Lores and ear-coverts chestnut speckled dark brown. Chin, throat and upper breast buff tinged chestnut and barred brown. Large white patch either side of lower throat. Belly, flanks and undertail-coverts buff barred brown. Underwing-coverts buff and true cinnamon, barred brown. **Adult female** Not known. **Immature** and **Juvenile** Not known. **Chick** Not known. **Bare parts** Iris dark brown?; bill blackish; legs and feet dark brown.

MEASUREMENTS (one male only) Wing 144; tail 115; bill 13.1; tarsus 18.4. Weight, no data.

MOULT No data available.

GEOGRAPHICAL VARIATION Monotypic.

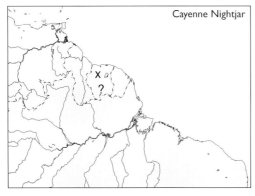

Cayenne Nightjar

DISTRIBUTION AND MOVEMENTS Extreme N South America. The only known specimen was taken at Saut Tamanoir (5°09'N 53°45'W) on the Fleuve Mana, c. 10km above its confluence with Rivière Cockioco, French Guiana, on 24 April 1917. A bird caught at Saül airstrip (3°35'N 53°12'W), French Guiana, in September 1982, may have been a female of this species.

STATUS Known only from the type specimen.

REFERENCES Collar *et al.* (1992), Todd (1920).

73   BLACKISH NIGHTJAR
Caprimulgus nigrescens   Plate 17

Caprimulgus nigrescens Cabanis, 1848, in Schomburgk, *Reisen Brit. Guiana* 3, p.710 (Lower Essequibo River, British Guiana)

Forms a superspecies with Roraiman Nightjar.

IDENTIFICATION Length 19.5-21.5cm. A small, dark and rather spotted Neotropical nightjar. Sexually dimorphic. **At rest** Upperparts blackish, heavily mottled tawny, cinnamon, buff and greyish-white. No collar around the hindneck. Wing-coverts blackish, speckled and spotted buff, tawny, cinnamon and greyish-white; scapulars blackish-brown spotted tawny, occasionally bordered buff on outerwebs. Small white patch on either side of the lower throat. Underparts dark brown, barred and spotted buff, buffish-white, tawny and cinnamon, becoming buffish barred brown on lower belly and flanks. **In flight** Round-winged. The male has a small white spot, towards the wing-tip, on the second, third and fourth outermost primaries (often innerwebs only), and white tips to the second and third outermost tail feathers, occasionally extending to the innerweb of the outermost and outerweb of the fourth outermost. The female lacks white markings on the wings and tail. **Similar species** Roraiman Nightjar (74), occurring at higher levels and very locally in the Pantepui of eastern Venezuela, is extremely similar but slightly larger, with a larger white throat-patch and bold white spots on the tertials and inner wing-coverts; the male has a narrow white bar, towards the wing-tip, across the three outer primaries, and broad white tips on the innerwebs of the second and third outermost tail feathers; the female has a very thin tawny bar on the three outer primaries and a small white spot on the tips of the second and third outermost tail feathers. Band-winged Nightjar (66) of the race *roraimae* is slightly larger and browner, with a broad tawny collar around the hindneck and different wing and tail markings (see that species). Cayenne Nightjar (72), known only from a single male, is browner and more variegated. Wing tips rather pointed. Has a small white spot on the four outer primaries, a vestigial white mark on the fifth outermost primary, and the outer three tail feathers are broadly tipped white (inner web only on outermost).

VOICE The song is a soft, purring *pru-r-r-r-t* or *qu-r-r-r-t*, repeated 2-5 times in quick succession. Sings from rocks, bushes and trees, and may be heard throughout the night, from dusk onwards. The alarm call is a short sharp *ptink* or *prek*. During threat, defence and distraction displays, utters a guttural hissing.

HABITAT Prefers open, stony country with little vegetation, granite outcrops scattered with low vegetation, and stony places in and along rivers. Occurs in rainforests, second growth and open savannas with scattered bushes. Away from rocky areas, it may also be found along trails, in clearings or on recently burnt ground. 100–1,100m.

HABITS Crepuscular and nocturnal. Roosts on the ground or rocks. Roost-sites may be shaded, partly shaded or out in the open, but prefers to roost close to, and facing away from, low vegetation. If danger approaches, a roosting bird adopts a flattened posture, with eyes shut. If danger persists, the bird sits upright and opens its eyes, 'bobs' up and down and gives an alarm call (see Voice), then leaves the roost-site in a series of short hops or flights, whilst 'bobbing' and alarming. Flies only a short distance before re-alighting, and often returns to the original roost-site when danger has passed. Roost-sites are often used for several days in succession, and are characterised by an accumulation of droppings. Changes roost-site if disturbed repeatedly at any one location. During the breeding season, two or three birds often roost close together (usually pairs or family groups), often within less than 0.5m of each other.

Becomes restless just before dusk and leaves the roost-site in a series of short flights. If a pair are roosting together, the female generally flies off first, and alights further away from the roost-site than the male. Often sits on roads and tracks at night, and frequently rests on rocks between bouts of feeding. Forages over rocky outcrops and neighbouring canopy. At dawn, returns to its roost-site by alighting nearby, and then approaches it in a series of short flights or runs.

FOOD Moths and beetles (including Elateridae). No further data available.

BREEDING Breeding season May?–August? in Guyana (chicks June and August); February–March and August–November (coinciding with dry season) in Surinam (although eggs found in all months except May and December); September–October in Bolivia and August–November in W Brazil. No data available for other regions.

No nest is constructed; the egg is laid on bare ground, sandy soil or leaf-litter, or in shallow depressions, 20-30mm deep, on bare granite rock. Nest-sites are often close to vegetation, and may be in forest clearings and burnt areas, alongside forest roads, trails and riversides, on granite outcrops or on exposed rocks on islands in rivers. Clutch 1. Egg elliptical, slightly glossy, creamish-buff, pinkish-buff or reddish-brown, spotted and blotched brown and grey, 23.2-27.6 x 16.9-20.3mm. Incubation is shared by both adults. At some nests, the male relieves the female in the early afternoon, and incubates until dusk; at others he incubates for much of the day. Eggs laid on open rock may become lethally overheated if left unattended for long periods. Eggs laid in shallow depressions in rock may become partly or totally immersed in rainwater during showers. The adults will continue to incubate an immersed egg, as water evaporates quickly from warm rock, and the egg will often hatch normally. If flushed from its egg, the adult performs an injury-feigning distraction display by flapping about on the ground with drooped wings. It may also fly around the intruder, land and press its breast on the ground whilst 'bobbing' its rear body and tail up and down. The incubation period is possibly c. 17 days.

The semi-precocial young are able to move distances of several metres by hopping towards a calling parent. If flushed from its chick, the adult may perform an injury-feigning distraction display by flapping along the ground for a short distance before flying off. The chicks fledge at c. 14 days and leave the nesting area at 16-18 days.

Normally double-brooded, but replacement clutches may be laid if one is unsuccessful.

DESCRIPTION Adult male Forehead, crown and nape blackish-brown, spotted tawny, greyish-white and cinnamon. No collar around hindneck. Mantle, back, rump and uppertail-coverts blackish-brown, spotted tawny, greyish-white and cinnamon; wing-coverts the same but also with buff spots. Scapulars blackish-brown spotted tawny, broadly

edged buff on outerwebs. Primaries dark brown; small white spot, almost midway along feather, on edge of innerweb of P9, on innerweb or both webs of P8, and on both webs of P7; inner primaries barred buffish along edges of innerwebs. Secondaries dark brown, barred buffish along edges of innerwebs. Tertials blackish-brown, flecked and spotted greyish-white. Tail dark brown, R5-R3 indistinctly and faintly barred pale buff, R4 and R3 tipped (c. 10mm) white, R5 (innerweb only) and R2 occasionally tipped white also; R2 and R1 indistinctly barred with greyish-brown and buffish mottling. Lores and ear-coverts blackish-brown, barred and spotted buff and cinnamon. Chin and upper throat blackish-brown. Lower throat white, or small white patch on either side of lower throat. Breast dark brown, barred buffish-white, buff and tawny. Belly and flanks buffish, barred brown, greyish-buff and pale cinnamon. Undertail-coverts buff. Underwing-coverts dark brown, faintly barred cinnamon and pale buff. **Adult female** Similar to the male, but lacks white markings on the wings and tail. **Immature** and **Juvenile** Similar to the adults, but often has rather vinaceous upperparts and cinnamon underparts. The primaries are narrowly tipped greyish-brown. The male has a small, dull white spot on P8 and P7, and smaller, duller white tips to R4 and R3. **Chick** At hatching, covered in pale greyish down. **Bare parts** Iris dark brown; bill blackish; legs and feet dark brown.

MEASUREMENTS Wing (male) 139-152, (female) 134-154; tail (male) 88-104, (female) 87-103; bill (male) 13.2-13.9, (female) 11.0-13.6; tarsus (male) 15.9-17.0, (female) 15.0-17.0. Weight (male) 32.5-42.0g, (female) 32.0-50.0g.

MOULT Both adults and immatures possibly undertake a complete post-breeding moult. In southern Venezuela, complete moult noted in February. The primaries are moulted descendantly. No further data available.

GEOGRAPHICAL VARIATION Monotypic, although birds from Colombia and Ecuador are possibly browner, and therefore paler, than birds from the Guianas and Peru.

Blackish Nightjar

DISTRIBUTION AND MOVEMENTS A widespread tropical species, occurring throughout the Amazon basin in South America, in E Colombia (Meta, Vaupés and Vichada), E Ecuador, E Peru, C and S Venezuela (south of the Orinoco River), Guyana, Surinam, French Guiana,

N Brazil (south to Mato Grosso, east to Pará and N Maranhão) and Bolivia (Beni and Santa Cruz). Sedentary.

STATUS Common to locally abundant in suitable habitat throughout its range.

REFERENCES Haverschmidt & Mees (1994), Hilty & Brown (1986), Ingels & Ribot (1982, 1983), Ingels *et al.* (1984), Meyer de Schauensee & Phelps (1978), Roth (1985).

74   RORAIMAN NIGHTJAR
Caprimulgus whitelyi   **Plate 17**

Antrostomus whitelyi Salvin, 1885, *Ibis* (5)3, p.438 (Mt Roraima, British Guiana = Venezuela *fide* Phelps 1938, *Bol. Soc. Ven. Cien. Nat.* p.91)

Forms a superspecies with Blackish Nightjar.

IDENTIFICATION Length 21cm). A small, rather dark Neotropical nightjar, known only from the Pantepui, Venezuela. Sexually dimorphic. **At rest** Upperparts blackish spotted cinnamon, buff, greyish-white and tawny. No collar on hindneck. Wing-coverts blackish, spotted cinnamon, tawny and buff. No obvious scapular pattern. Large white patch on either side of lower throat, or extending across whole throat. Underparts dark brown barred buff or buffish-white, becoming buff barred brown on belly. **In flight** The male has a thin white bar towards the wing-tip across both webs of the three outer primaries, and large white spots on the tips of the innerwebs of the second and third outermost tail feathers. The female has a thin tawny bar on the outer primaries and smaller white spots on the tail. **Similar species** Blackish Nightjar (73), occurring at lower altitudes, is extremely similar but slightly smaller, with a smaller white throat-patch and no bold white spots on the tertials and innerwing-coverts; the male has a white spot, not bar, on the second–fourth outermost primaries and narrow white tips (across both webs) to the second and third outermost tail feathers; the female lacks tawny markings on the wings and white markings on the tail. Band-winged Nightjar (66) of the race *roraimae* is slightly larger and browner, with a broad tawny collar around the hindneck and different wing and tail markings (see that species).

VOICE Unknown.

HABITAT Humid forested country on the slopes and summits of the tepuis (tabletop mountains). Prefers open areas, such as clearings and treefalls, with scattered, very dense vegetation. 1,280–1,800m.

HABITS Unknown.

FOOD No data available.

BREEDING Unknown.

DESCRIPTION Adult male Forehead, crown, nape, mantle, back, rump and uppertail-coverts blackish-brown, spotted cinnamon, with some greyish-white intermixed. No collar on hindneck. Wing-coverts blackish-brown spotted cinnamon, tawny and buff. Some coverts, especially innermost greater and inner median coverts, also have a large white spot on the tips of the outerwebs, some of which are partially edged buff. Scapulars blackish-

brown spotted tawny, spots sometimes with dark centres, and occasionally edged buff around tips. Primaries dark brown; thin (c. 5mm) white bar roughly midway across both webs of P10-P8; inner primaries and all secondaries barred buffish along edge of innerwebs. Tertials brown with greyish-white flecking and large white spot on tip of outerwebs. Tail dark brown, R5-R3 faintly and broadly barred very pale buff, R4-R3 with large (c. 20mm) white spot on tips of innerwebs, inner two pairs with bars and chevrons of greyish-brown and buff, broader than on outer feathers. Lores and ear-coverts blackish-brown, spotted and barred cinnamon and buff. Chin and upper throat dark brown. Large white patch, edged pale buff, on either side of lower throat or extending across whole throat. Breast dark brown barred pale buff. Belly and flanks pale buff or buffish-white barred brown. Undertail-coverts buff, generally unmarked but occasionally broadly barred brown. Underwing-coverts buff barred brown. **Adult female** Similar to or browner than the male, with thin tawny bar on edge of innerweb of P10 and across both webs of P9-P8, although not meeting at feather-shaft. Tawny spotting on scapulars often larger, usually with dark brown centres. Spots on tips of tertials and wing-coverts smaller, often buffish not white. White spots on tail smaller (c. 8mm). **Immature** and **Juvenile** Not known. **Chick** Not known. **Bare parts** Iris dark brown; bill blackish; legs and feet dark brown.

MEASUREMENTS Wing (male) 156-163, (female) 155-164; tail (male) 96-108, (female) 92-108; bill (male) 13.5-15.0, (female) 13.5-16.0; tarsus (male) 14.0-16.2, (female) 12.2-16.0. Weight (male) 30-40g, (female) 45-48g.

MOULT No data available.

GEOGRAPHICAL VARIATION Monotypic.

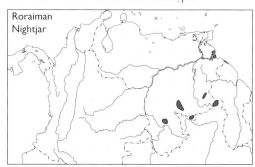

DISTRIBUTION AND MOVEMENTS An endemic species to the Pantepui of SE Venezuela and possibly the adjacent areas of Guyana and N Brazil. Known only from Cerros Roraima, Ptari-tepui, Jaua, Urutaní and Duida. Sedentary.

STATUS No data available but probably not very common within its restricted range.

REFERENCES Dickerman & Phelps (1982), Meyer de Schauensee & Phelps (1978), Phelps (1938).

75 PYGMY NIGHTJAR
Caprimulgus hirundinaceus   Plate 20

Caprimulgus hirundinaceus Spix, 1825, *Av. Bras.* 2, p.2, pl.3, f1 (Rio Solimões, error = Feira de Sant'Anna, Bahia, cf. Hellmayr, 1929, p.400)
Caprimulgus hirundinaceus cearae (Cory, 1917), *Field Mus. Nat. Hist. Publ. Zool. Ser.* 12, p.4 (Quixada, Ceará, Brazil)
Caprimulgus hirundinaceus vielliardi Ribon, 1995, *Revta. Bras. Zool.* 12 (2), p.334 (Colatina, Espírito Santo, Brazil)

IDENTIFICATION Length 16-20cm. A small, greyish Neotropical nightjar which often looks rather pale, small-headed and large-eyed. Sexually dimorphic. **At rest** Upperparts and wing-coverts brown, densely speckled greyish-white. Either no collar on hindneck or an indistinct buff collar. No obvious scapular pattern. Thin, indistinct whitish supercilium and indistinct buff submoustachial stripe. Large white patch on throat, with broad cinnamon-buff band below. Underparts brown, densely spotted and barred pale buff and greyish-white, becoming buff barred brown on belly and flanks. **In flight** Has short, broad wings, with slightly pointed wing-tips. Square-tailed. The male has a white spot towards the wing-tip on the four outer primaries and white tips to the two outer tail feathers (innerweb only on outermost). The female has smaller white spots on the four outer primaries and lacks white on the tail. **Similar species** Least Nighthawk (32) is usually browner (but more variable in colour and sometimes greyish) with a smaller white patch on the throat, paler, whiter underparts, slender, more pointed wings and slightly forked tail; the male has a more defined white band across the four outer primaries, a buffish-white trailing edge to the inner wing and white tips to the innerwebs of the second to fourth outer tail feathers; the female has a slightly thinner white band across the four outer primaries, a duller, buffier trailing edge to the inner wing and smaller white tips to the tail feathers. Little Nightjar (70) is browner, more variegated, with blackish-brown scapulars broadly edged buff, a broad but indistinct collar on the hindneck, a large white patch on the throat, no super-cilium and often a stubby-winged look; males have larger white spots on the four outer primaries and white tips (often innerwebs only) to all but the central pair of tail feathers; females lack white on the wings and (usually) the tail.

VOICE The song is a short single-noted whistle, *wheeo* or *wheo*, and is often preceded by a rapid series of 3-4 *wha* notes, e.g. *wha wha wha wheeo*. The *wha* calls are also given in flight. The alarm calls are liquid *prrip* notes.

HABITAT Prefers woodland, but also occurs in cleared areas. The newly described population at Colatina in Espírito Santo, inhabits rocky areas. No further information available.

HABITS Crepuscular and nocturnal. Frequently sits on tracks and dirt roads at night. Also rests on sand and stones in clearings. Forages in open, disturbed areas. No further information available.

FOOD No data available.

BREEDING Breeding season not documented. Nest-sites may be beside dirt roads. Eggs 24.1-24.7 x 17.4-18.3mm. No further information available.

DESCRIPTION *C. h. hirundinaceus* **Adult male** Forehead, crown and nape brown, profusely speckled greyish-white and cinnamon. Generally no collar on hindneck, although occasional buff feathers on nape may show as an indistinct collar. Mantle, back, rump and uppertail-coverts brown, densely speckled greyish-white and cinnamon. Wing-coverts brown, densely speckled greyish-white, buff and cinnamon, and spotted greyish-white, greyish-brown and buff. Scapulars brown speckled greyish-white, with greyish-brown or buff spot on tip of outerwebs. Primaries brown; white spot, almost midway along feather, on innerweb of P10, on innerweb or across both webs of P9 and across both webs of P8-P7, although feather-shafts are always brownish; inner primaries, P1-P4, narrowly tipped dirty buff. Secondaries brown, barred buff on innerwebs. Tertials brown, densely speckled greyish-white, buff and cinnamon. Tail brown, R5 with white spot (c. 15mm across) on tip of innerweb, R4 with white tip (c. 15-18mm) across both webs, R3 and R2 indistinctly barred greyish-white, central pair (R1) broadly barred with greyish-white mottling. Supercilium white, thin and indistinct; thin submoustachial stripe buffish. Lores and ear-coverts brown speckled greyish-white and buff. Chin and upper throat white barred brown. Large, triangular white patch on throat, merging into broad cinnamon-buff brown-spotted band on upper breast. Breast brown, spotted and barred pale buff and greyish-white. Belly and flanks buff barred brown. Undertail-coverts buff, lightly barred brown. Underwing-coverts buff barred brown. **Adult female** Similar to the male but slightly paler. The spots on the four outer primaries are smaller. The tail is brown, speckled and indistinctly barred tawny-buff. **Immature** Paler than the adults, and often heavily tinged cinnamon. The primaries are broadly tipped buffish. **Juvenile** Not known. **Chick** Not known. **Bare parts** Iris dark brown; bill blackish-brown; legs and feet blackish-brown.

MEASUREMENTS Wing (male) 119-130, (female) 121-129; tail (male) 77-94, (female) 88-93; bill (male) c. 11, (female) c. 12; tarsus (male, one) 16.5, (female, one) 15.6. Weight no data.

MOULT The primaries are moulted descendantly. Primary moult (museum specimens) noted in March (*C. h. cearae*), late June, late November and early December. Tail moult (museum specimens) noted late June and late November. No further data available.

GEOGRAPHICAL VARIATION Three races of this little known species are currently recognised.
  C. h. hirundinaceus Described above. Possibly intergrades with *cearae* in the north-west of its range (S Piauí), where slightly paler birds sometimes occur.
  C. h. cearae Similar to the nominate but paler. The breast, belly and undertail-coverts are less heavily barred brown, the latter even sometimes plain. The male has larger white spots on the four (or five) outer primaries, including the feather-shafts which are wholly or partly white, and broader white tips to the innerweb of R5 and both webs of R4, c. 20mm. Wing (male) 110-127, (female) 115-129; tail (male) 75-95, (female) 79-93. Weight no data.
  C. h. vielliardi Known only from one, or perhaps two, museum specimens, and only recently described to science. The type specimen, a male, is darker and longer-winged than the other two races and has smaller white spots on the four outer primaries. The inner four primaries are boldly spotted buff on the

upper half of the outerwebs (perhaps this race only). Wing (male, one) 137, (female) no data; tail (male, one) 91, (female) no data. Weight no data. The status of this form may be worthy of further study.

Pygmy Nightjar

- C. h. cearae
- C. h. hirundinaceus
- C. h. vielliardi

DISTRIBUTION AND MOVEMENTS Confined to northeastern Brazil, where it was thought to be endemic to the xeric caatinga region, although a new population has now been discovered to the south (see below).

> *C. h. hirundinaceus* E Brazil (southern Piauí, southeast across Bahia, and east to Alagoas). Presumably sedentary.
> *C. h. cearae* Extreme NE Brazil (Ceará south through eastern Piauí to the extreme north of Bahia). Presumably sedentary.
> *C. h. vielliardi* CE Brazil (a newly discovered population, known only from Colatina, Espírito Santo). Presumably sedentary.

STATUS Poorly known and probably not very common, although apparently not rare in some regions, e.g. Capivara National Park, southeastern Piauí.

REFERENCES Cory (1917), Hellmayr (1929), Olmos (1993), Ribon (1995).

---

76   BROWN NIGHTJAR
Caprimulgus binotatus   Plate 25

Caprimulgus binotatus Bonaparte, 1850, *Consp. Av.* 1, p.60 (Ashanti, type from Dabocrom, Gold Coast)

Previously placed in a separate genus, *Veles* Bangs 1918, *Proc. New Eng. Zool. Club* 6, p.92. Has several morphological characteristics that differentiate it from other Afrotropical nightjars (see text).

IDENTIFICATION Length 21-23cm. A small to medium-sized, darkish brown Afrotropical nightjar, occurring only in rainforest. Sexes similar. **At rest** Upperparts and wing-coverts dark brown, densely mottled and flecked tawny and chestnut-brown. At close range, crown feathers protrude slightly over the eye, and may show very small 'ear-tufts' at rear of crown. No collar on hindneck. Small but distinctive white spot on either side of lower throat. Rictal bristles rather short and weak. Underparts dark

brown, mottled and barred tawny and chestnut-brown. Tail unique amongst African nightjars, being rather stiff with 'tented' structure. **In flight** Both sexes have uniquely curved outer primaries and lack white markings on the wings and tail. **Similar species** None. The only other African rainforest species, Bates's Nightjar (108), is much larger, darker and more variegated. The male has a very small white spot on the outer four primaries and broad white tips to the outer two tail feathers.

VOICE The song is a repetitive series of up to 60 or more *twoh* or *kliou* notes, with a brief pause between each note. Sings from perches, up to c. 20m above ground, and occasionally from roads and tracks and in flight. May be heard mainly at dusk and dawn. No further information available.

HABITAT Prefers lowland primary rainforest. In northern Congo it occurs in semi-evergreen forest with a fairly open canopy and thick understorey, especially where Marantaceae and Zingiberaceae are plentiful. In south-western Central African Republic it has also been recorded at the edges of *Raphia* swamps in dense, semi-deciduous rainforest. Tends to avoid closed-canopy forest.

HABITS Crepuscular and probably nocturnal. Roosts above ground, e.g. on loops of creepers hanging from trees, possibly on palm leaves. Feeds at dusk by flycatching from perches such as vine-clad stumps in trees, up to c. 20m above ground, always returning to the same perch. During sallies, hawks for insects beneath, in, or just above the forest canopy. Also forages up to c. 30m above ground, over roads, tracks or rivers. When threatened, it may perform a defence display by 'gaping' at the potential danger. No further information available.

FOOD Insects. No further data available.

BREEDING Breeding season January–March? in Liberia; February–March? in Central African Republic; and May–June? in Cameroon.

Breeding habits unknown. Possibly territorial, territories 500–1,000m apart. Nest-sites are possibly off the ground, e.g. on arched *Raphia* leaves. No further information available.

DESCRIPTION Adult male Forehead, crown, nape, mantle, back, rump and uppertail-coverts dark brown, finely flecked and barred chestnut-brown and/or tawny. No collar on hindneck. Wing-coverts dark brown, finely barred chestnut-brown. Scapulars pronounced, having proximal half buff and distal half dark brown, speckled chestnut around edges. Primaries brown with evenly spaced small tawny spots along edge of outerwebs. Secondaries brown, heavily speckled cinnamon on outerwebs. Tertials brown, speckled and mottled buff and pale tawny. Tail dark brown, densely mottled chestnut-brown and tawny. Lores and ear-coverts dark brown, finely flecked and barred chestnut-brown and tawny. Chin and throat as rest of head but a shade paler. Small white spot on either side of lower throat. Breast dark brown, mottled and barred chestnut-brown and tawny. Breast feathers long and fairly loose. Belly and flanks dark brown barred chestnut-brown, bars broader and paler than on breast, becoming buffier towards undertail-coverts. Underwing-coverts dark brown. **Adult female** Similar to the male but fractionally paler on the upperparts. Scapulars paler and less distinct. Primaries with larger tawny spotting along outerwebs; tail dark brown, broadly barred tawny.

Immature Not known. **Juvenile** Similar to the adults, but scapulars and inner coverts pale greyish-buff spotted dark brown. **Chick** Not known. **Bare parts** Iris brown; bill blackish; legs and feet dark brown.

MEASUREMENTS Wing (male) 142-156, (female) 147-152; tail (male) 90-102, (female) 95-101; bill (male) 12.6-13.5, (female) 13.5-14.0; tarsus (male) 10-12, (female) 10-12. Weight unsexed (one) 63g.

MOULT Few data available. In N Congo, an adult noted in wing moult mid-May. The primaries are moulted descendantly.

GEOGRAPHICAL VARIATION None. monotypic.

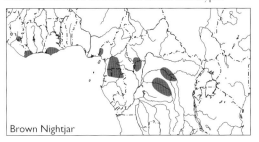

Brown Nightjar

DISTRIBUTION AND MOVEMENTS Extremely fragmented distribution in the rainforests of Western and Central Africa: Liberia (Mt Nimba), SW Ivory Coast (south of Tai), S Ghana (Dabocrom, Nini-Suhien National Park and Atlanta Forest Reserve), S Cameroon (Efulen, Meret, Bitye), W Cameroon (Korup National Park, near Mundemba), N Gabon, N Congo (Nouabalé-Ndoki National Park), S Central African Republic and C Zaire. Sedentary.

STATUS A rather rare species throughout its range but possibly under-recorded.

REFERENCES Brosset & Erard (1986), Carroll & Fry (1987), Dowsett-Lemaire & Dowsett (1998), Fry *et al.* (1988).

---

77   RED-NECKED NIGHTJAR
Caprimulgus ruficollis   Plate 23

Caprimulgus ruficollis Temminck, 1820, *Man. d'Orn.* ed. 2, 1, p.438 (Algeciras, Spain)
Caprimulgus ruficollis desertorum Erlanger, 1899, *J. Orn.* 47, p.521, pl.11, upper f (Tunisia, no holotype designated; the specimen figured is from Djebel el Meda, near Gabes)

IDENTIFICATION Length 30-32cm. A large, variegated, western Palearctic nightjar, wintering in West Africa. Sexually dimorphic. **At rest** Large-headed. Upperparts greyish-brown streaked blackish-brown. Broad buff or tawny-buff collar around the hindneck. Wing-coverts greyish-brown boldly spotted buff. Scapulars blackish-brown, broadly bordered buff on the outerwebs. Prominent white or buffish-white submoustachial stripe. Large white patch on lower throat. Underparts greyish-brown, speckled greyish-white barred brown, becoming buff barred brown on belly and flanks. **In flight** Long-winged and long-tailed. Flight slow and deliberate. The male has a large white spot towards the wing-tip on the

three outer primaries (usually on innerwebs only) and broad white tips to the two outer tail feathers (but see also Description). The female has smaller whitish spots on the three outer primaries and smaller, dirtier white tips to the two outer tail feathers. **Similar species** European Nightjar (79) is smaller, shorter-winged and generally browner, with a distinct buffish line across the forewing at rest, and a faster, more buoyant flight; the male has smaller white spots, closer to the wing-tip, on the three outer primaries and smaller white tips to the two outer tail feathers; the female lacks white markings on the wings and tail.

VOICE The song is a series of loud *cut-ock* notes repeated continuously for up to two minutes or more, occasionally speeding up towards the end. The song may be preceded by a rapid series of short *quot* notes, chuckling or gurgling sounds. Sings from perches in trees and on posts or, more rarely, in flight. May be heard chiefly at dusk, at dawn and between c. 01h30–04h30, but also sings throughout the night. Tends to sing less strongly in poor weather, when cloudy or in periods of low moonlight. Also sings less after breeding has commenced, especially after the chicks have hatched. Roosting males flushed during the day may sing briefly before finding a new roost-site. Males sometimes sing on the wintering grounds in Africa, e.g. Mali in January (this species?). The winter song is slower and lower-pitched than the summer, territorial song.

In response to the playback of the song, males fly towards the source, calling at twice the normal speed and wing-clapping; females utter a continuous, low *tuk tuk tuk tuk*, usually from a perch. The flight call is a single or double-noted *cutow*, although this has yet to be accurately described. Whilst incubating, an adult (possibly the female) may utter a continuous series of knocking notes which start slowly then gradually accelerate. During threat/defence display, utters a throaty hissing, which is also given when the bird is handled.

HABITAT Prefers lowlands and hillsides with scattered vegetation and areas of bare soil or sand. Also occurs in pine woodland, coastal forests, coastal dunes with scattered vegetation, *Eucalyptus* or olive plantations, vineyards, cork oak *Quercus suber* scrub, open scrubland with prickly pear *Opuntia* and scattered trees, and dense thickets of broom, gorse, bramble *Halimium*, tree heath *Erica arborea* up to 3m tall, or pistachio *Pistacea lentiscus*. Also found in semi-desert conditions and on arid hillsides with dwarf vegetation. In north-eastern and eastern-central Tunisia, also occurs in cactus plantations. Throughout its breeding range, avoids treeless country and sand-dunes. 0–1,500m.

HABITS Crepuscular and nocturnal. Roosts on leaf-litter or stones on the ground and lengthways along branches. Roost-sites are usually in woods or amongst scrub. Often sits on roads and tracks at night.

Hunts over open ground, including marshland, often at heights of up to 30m above ground. During the breeding season, usually feeds outside the nesting territory. Forages in a slow, wheeling and floating flight, with sudden erratic twists and turns and occasional hovers. Usually feeds alone, although sometimes several may forage together, also with European Nightjars, presumably in areas where food is plentiful. May also forage on the ground and amongst animal droppings. When hunting, food is apparently stored in the extended pharyngeal cavity and digested later when the bird is resting. No further information available.

FOOD Moths (including Noctuidae and Thaumetopoeidae) and moth larvae, locusts and locust nymphs, mosquitoes, flies, grasshoppers, beetles and caterpillars. Also known to ingest small seeds, earth and grains of sand but this material may be taken accidentally.

BREEDING Breeding season early May to late August in Spain and Portugal; mid-May to August? in C Morocco, Algeria and Tunisia. Has also bred in southern France.

Probably monogamous. Territorial, territory sizes as small as 0.18 to 0.34ha where there is a lack of suitable nesting habitat. Males defend their territories in flight and often chase off intruding males, especially at the beginning of the breeding season, and will also chase away a calling (perhaps migrant) European Nightjar. Whilst defending their territories, males call (see Voice) and wing-clap by snapping their wings together above the back. During territorial disputes, both males may alight and sing strongly at each other, often from perches only 1-2m apart. Both sexes frequently hover whilst investigating intruders in their territory.

During courtship display flight the male pursues a female in rapid direct flight and wing-claps up to 15 times in succession. In a different display, perhaps after pairing, the male and female fly beside each other slowly, tails fanned and wings either held in a V above their backs or lowered in an inverted V.

Usually nests solitarily but in Tunisia, birds may breed in loose groups of up to 12 pairs with nests 2-20m apart. No nest is constructed; the eggs are laid on the ground, usually on leaf-litter or pine needles. Nest-sites may be out in the open, beneath or amongst low bushes, beside fallen logs and branches or under trees. In coastal southern Portugal, also nests amongst driftwood at very high (possibly storm) tide marks on large sandbanks. Clutch usually 1-2. Eggs elliptical, glossy white or creamy white, marbled and blotched grey and brown, 28.5-34.0 x 21.0-25.0mm. Incubation is usually by the female, at least during the day. The male often incubates for short periods at dusk and dawn, sometimes approaching the nest in late afternoon and hovering above the sitting female, although changeover may not occur. During the night, the female may leave the nest unattended for up to 20 minutes while she feeds nearby. In hot weather during the day, the incubating adult often gular-flutters to keep cool. Clutches are occasionally moved up to 20m from the original nest-site by the adults. In south-western Spain, nests may be predated by lizards, e.g. *Lacerta lepida*, and nests in vineyards may suffer as a result of agricultural activities. The incubation period is generally 14-19 days and the eggs hatch asynchronously.

The semi-precocial young may leave the nest-site soon after hatching, although an adult sometimes calls them back. Chicks that do leave the nest-site may move up to c. 1m during the first day, up to 4m in 3-4 days and up to c. 10m within six days of hatching. A returning adult searches for its offspring with short hovers and darting flights and eventually broods the chicks at their new location. Both adults brood their young, although the female usually broods by day, with the male often roosting close by. The male may occasionally brood the chicks during the day. At dusk, the female will often leave the chicks unattended for up to 20 minutes. During the night, the chicks are brooded and fed by both adults. Males tend to be away from the nest for longer periods than the female, the males' absences averaging 18-19 minutes, the females' 5-

6 minutes. At changeover the returning adult alights beside the nest and the brooding bird silently flies off. The newly arrived bird then shuffles onto the nest and feeds the young. To be fed, the chicks peck and grab at the adults' bill, the adult then holding its head down vertically and feeding the young in a series of jerking movements, during which its bill appears to remain almost closed; the adult then settles down and broods the chicks until the next changeover.

If flushed from the chicks, the female either flies off a short distance and alights on the ground, or performs an injury-feigning distraction display by flapping about on the ground or on a bush, fanning her tail, gaping and hissing (see Voice). Alternatively, she may repeatedly fly off a short distance and hover briefly with her tail fanned. When returning to the nest, the adult alights close by, wing-clapping, and runs to the nest. From 2-3 days of age, chicks, if threatened, perform a defence display by gaping at intruders. Chicks make their first short flights when about 16-18 days old and become independent after 4-5 weeks. Family parties often stay together for a short while immediately after breeding.

Single- or double-brooded. The male takes over the care of the first brood if the female lays a second clutch. Second nests may be as close as c. 2m to the first nest.

DESCRIPTION *C. r. ruficollis* **Adult male** Forehead, crown and nape greyish-brown speckled brown, central feathers broadly streaked blackish-brown. Broad buff or tawny-buff collar around hindneck. Mantle, back, rump and uppertail-coverts greyish-brown speckled brown, streaked blackish-brown. Wing-coverts greyish-brown speckled brown on innerwebs, outerwebs blackish-brown boldly spotted buff on feather-tips. Scapulars largely blackish-brown, broadly edged buff on outerwebs. Primaries brown, P10-P7 barred tawny on upper half, with large white spot towards the tip of the feather on innerwebs of P10-P8, and buffish-white or buffish mark on inner half of outerwebs of P9 and P8; vestigial brownish-white mark on P7, although older birds may have a more pronounced white spot; inner primaries, P7-P1, regularly barred tawny, tipped buffish. Secondaries brown barred tawny, tipped buffish. Tertials greyish-brown speckled brown, streaked blackish-brown along feather-shafts. Tail brown, R5-R2 barred pale tawny on outerwebs, R5 and R4 broadly tipped white, c. 37mm, R3 occasionally tipped white (perhaps older birds only), central pair (R1) greyish-brown, mottled and barred brown. Lores and ear-coverts rufous-buff barred brown. Distinct white or buffish-white submoustachial stripe. Chin and throat buff, thinly barred brown. Large white patch across lower throat, the lower feathers of which are broadly tipped blackish-brown. Breast greyish-white, speckled and barred brown. Belly and flanks buff or tawny-buff, barred brown. Undertail-coverts buff barred brown and tipped whitish. Underwing-coverts buff barred brown. **Adult female** Similar to the male but white spots on the three outer primaries smaller, the inner spot often tinged buffish. Has narrower white tips, 15-25mm, to the two outer tail feathers. **Immature** and **Juvenile** Similar to the adults but paler. The spots on the three outer primaries are buffish and the two outer tail feathers have pale (buffish-brown?) tips. **Chick** At hatching, covered in brownish-buff down. **Bare parts** Iris dark brown; bill blackish-brown; legs and feet greyish-brown.

MEASUREMENTS Wing (male) 196-217, (female) 198-

218; tail (male) 149-168, (female) 141-162; bill (male) 10.5-12.7, (female) 9.7-12.0; tarsus (male) 20.8-24.3, (female) 16.1-25.3. Weight (male) 70-102, (female) 81-86, (unsexed) 60?-119g.

MOULT Adults undertake a complete post-breeding moult, immatures a partial or occasionally a complete? post-breeding moult, which usually commences on the breeding grounds (late June to late August) and is continued on the wintering grounds (see below). The primaries are usually moulted descendantly. The sequence of secondary moult is not clear, at least in adults, but immatures may have a centripetal moult, commencing with the outermost (S1) proceeding ascendantly and the innermost (S13) proceeding descendantly, the moult converging on the inner secondaries. The sequence of tail feather replacement is also unclear.

Immatures usually undertake a near-complete post-breeding moult, which commences on the breeding grounds with the head and body feathers and, rarely, the innermost 1-4 secondaries. The moult is then continued on the wintering grounds before being suspended, with many birds apparently retaining the outermost 1-8 primaries (nearly always the outermost, P10), some central secondaries and some tail feathers (usually T3 and T4).

Towards the end of the following breeding season (July onwards), second-year birds undertake another near-complete post-breeding moult, which commences with the head and body feathers, some primaries and often some secondaries and tail feathers. The primary and secondary moults usually resume at the points at which they were suspended the previous winter, and the moult is continued on the wintering grounds before being suspended again, birds retaining 2-6 outer primaries.

Adults undertake a complete or near-complete post-breeding moult, which again commences on the breeding grounds, is continued on the wintering grounds and is then suspended, many birds retaining some primaries, usually in the middle of the feather tract. The primary moult resumes at the point at which it was suspended the previous winter and proceeds descendantly, the outermost 2-6 unmoulted primaries being replaced first, followed by the inner primaries, commencing at P1. Occasionally, some birds may exhibit serially descendant primary moult, arrested moult or even aberrant moult. The sequence of secondary moult is unclear. The sequence of tail moult is also poorly understood, but adults appear to begin by replacing feathers not renewed during the previous moult, e.g. R3 and R4.

GEOGRAPHICAL VARIATION Despite its rather limited breeding range, two distinct forms are recognisable.

C. r. ruficollis Described above. No real colour variation is evident, although some birds are occasionally paler.
C. r. desertorum Much paler, more sandy-buff, than the nominate, and often heavily tinged rufous, with narrower blackish-brown streaking on the crown and a broader hindneck collar. The male has broader? (37-48mm) white tips to the two outer tail feathers. Wing (male) 198-214, (female) 198-210; tail (male) 153-171, (female) 146-167. Weight no data.

DISTRIBUTION AND MOVEMENTS Has a rather restricted breeding range in the western Palearctic, wintering in West Africa.

C. r. ruficollis Spain, Portugal and N Morocco. Migratory. Leaves the breeding grounds by late October or November. Recorded as a regular autumn migrant on Gibraltar and along coastal Morocco, and in western and central Mauritania October–November. Winters in West Africa, although the exact range remains unknown. Some may winter in Morocco (e.g. Chichaoua and Agadir) December–January. Recorded in N Senegal, late November and January; in Gambia late October to late January; common and widespread C and S Mali, October–March. Migrates from its wintering grounds on a broad front in March to early May, across Mauritania, Western Sahara, Morocco and W Algeria, usually arriving in Tunisia and the Iberian peninsula in late April and May.

Recorded as a vagrant, but has also bred, in S France.
C. r. desertorum NE Morocco, N Algeria (south to the Great Atlas Mountains) and N Tunisia. Migratory, some birds perhaps sedentary. Movements to and from the breeding grounds are probably similar to those of the nominate race, as are the winter quarters. Recorded in late November in N Senegal, November in E Gambia, and March in Mali, Ivory Coast in February and March, and N Ghana (Gambaga) in March. Vagrants, probably of this race, have been recorded in Britain and Libya.

Birds of unspecified race have also been recorded from Ivory Coast in November, January, February and March. Vagrants of unspecified race have also been recorded in Denmark, the Balearic Islands (Ibiza), Sicily, Malta, Yugoslavia? Turkey? Madeira and, possibly, the Canary Islands. The origin of a specimen being offered for sale in Jerusalem, Israel, is questionable.

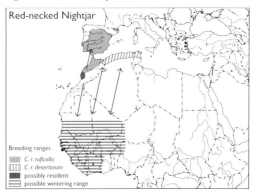

Red-necked Nightjar

Breeding ranges
▨ *C. r. ruficollis*
▥ *C. r. desertorum*
■ possibly resident
▤ possible wintering range

STATUS Quite common in Spain and locally common in Portugal, the total population in the mid 1990s being estimated at between 103,000 and 136,000 birds. Locally common in Tunisia and uncommon in Morocco, but no data available from Algeria. Declines noted in the Algarve region of Portugal, and in Morocco. An increase in road traffic is a potential cause for decline, whilst in some breeding areas, habitat destruction and changes in farming practices, including the use of agrochemicals, is also a threat.

REFERENCES Aragonés (1997), Beven (1973), Copete & Gustamante (1992), Cramp (1985), Cuadrado & Domínguez (1996), Fry *et al.* (1988), Fuller (1995), Gargallo (1994), Hagemeijer & Blair (1997), Salewski (1997), Snow & Perrins (1998), Tomas (1991).

Other name: Grey Nightjar

Caprimulgus indicus Latham, 1790, *Index Orn.* 2, p.588 (India)
Caprimulgus indicus hazarae Whistler and Kinnear, 1935, *J. Bombay Nat. Hist. Soc.* 38, p.37 (Abbottabad, Hazara, Himalayas)
Caprimulgus indicus kelaarti Blyth, 1851, *J. Asiatic Soc. Bengal* 20, p.175 (Ceylon)
Caprimulgus indicus jotaka Temminck and Schlegel, 1847, Siebold's *Fauna Jap., Aves* p.37, pl.12 and 13 (Japan)
Caprimulgus indicus phalaena Hartlaub and Finsch, 1872, *Proc. Zool. Soc. London* p.91 (Palau Islands)

IDENTIFICATION Length 28-32cm. A large, greyish-brown, variegated, Oriental and eastern Palearctic nightjar. Sexually dimorphic. **At rest** Upperparts greyish-brown streaked blackish-brown, broadly so on crown. Indistinct pale buff or tawny-buff collar on hindneck. Lesser coverts brown, speckled greyish-white, buff or tawny. Rest of wing-coverts greyish-brown boldly spotted greyish-white, pale buff or pale tawny, spots distinctly smudged or vermiculated brown. Scapulars blackish-brown, broadly edged greyish-white vermiculated brown. Buffish-white submoustachial stripe. Large white patch either side of lower throat. Underparts greyish-brown finely barred greyish-brown or pale buff, becoming buff barred brown on belly and flanks. **In flight** The male has a large white spot towards the wing-tip on the four outer primaries (innerweb only on outermost) and white tips (distally washed brown) to all but the central pair of tail feathers. The female has brownish-tawny or tawny spots on the four outer primaries and brownish-white or brownish-buff tips to all but the central pair of tail feathers. **Similar species** Indian Nightjar (96) is slightly smaller and has a broad buff or tawny hindneck collar; the male has smaller white spots on the four outer primaries and broad white tips to the two outer tail feathers, while the female has smaller buff spots on the four outer primaries and white tips to the two outer tail feathers. Large-tailed Nightjar (87) and Jerdon's Nightjar (88) lack the bold greyish-white, tawny or buffish spotting on the wing-coverts; the males have broad white tips to the two outer tail feathers, the females buff or buffish-white tips. Philippine Nightjar (89) lacks the bold spotting on the wing-coverts and shows a buffish line across the forewing and white tips to the two outer tail feathers. Savanna Nightjar (102) is slightly smaller and is less boldly spotted on the wing-coverts; the male generally has the two outer tail feathers entirely white, the female lacks white on the tail. European Nightjar (79), race *unwini*, winters in small numbers in the extreme north-west of the Jungle Nightjar's range, but is much paler and greyer, and has the wing-coverts less heavily spotted; the male has a white spot on the three outer primaries and white tips to the two outer tail feathers, while the female lacks white on the wings and tail.

VOICE The song is a rapid series of loud, ringing, *tucktucktucktuck* notes. Sings for minutes on end, in bursts of up to 16 notes (3-4 per second), with a slight pause between each set of notes. Also gives a monotonously repeated *tuckoo tuckoo tuckoo* or *chuckoo chuckoo chuckoo*, lasting for up to 15 minutes or more and occasionally ending with a hollow, fading *wowowowow*. Sings from stumps and rocks, whilst perched lengthways on a high branch, from the ground and in flight. May be heard chiefly at dusk and dawn and throughout the night, especially when there is plenty of moonlight. Migratory races occasionally sing briefly on the wintering grounds. Also utters a fast, deep *quor-quor-quor* (possibly female only). In courtship flight, gives a rapid series of low, soft *you-you-you* calls. In Sri Lanka, male has *hóó hóó hóó hóóteter* flight call which may be the same as the above.

HABITAT Prefers forest and wooded country. Occurs in open woodland, dry or moist deciduous forest, pine forest, mixed bamboo forest, forest glades, thick brushwood jungle, open scrubland, farmland, cultivated land, mandarin orange orchards and teak plantations. In the Himalayas it also inhabits ravines sparsely vegetated with scrub and jungle-clad hillsides. In Sri Lanka, also occurs on stony fields. May also occur in large cities during winter/passage, e.g. Kuala Lumpur, Malaysia. 0–3,300m.

HABITS Crepuscular and nocturnal. Roosts on leaf-litter on the ground, or perched lengthways on a branch. Roost-sites are usually shaded, and may be amongst rocks or stones, along forest edges, in woodland clearings beneath shrubs or bushes, or amongst coffee bushes. Occasionally roosts in the open, e.g. at the edge of a dry paddyfield. When active, often claps wings in flight (see Breeding). Frequently sits on roads and tracks at night. When on the ground, can shuffle or run short distances. Forages with a buoyant, sailing flight, frequently twisting and turning after prey. Hunts low over the ground in clearings and glades, or high up over tree tops. Also feeds on insects attracted to lights. No further information available.

FOOD Moths, beetles (including Scarabaeidae), bugs, flying ants, cicadas, grasshoppers, locusts and small wasps. Tree seeds are possibly ingested accidentally. No further data available.

BREEDING Breeding season late May to early August in Russia and Japan; March–June (mainly April and May) in the Himalayas; late April–July in Pakistan; February–May (mainly March and April) in India; late February–August in southern India; and February–July in Sri Lanka. No data available for other regions.

During the courtship flight, the male glides with his wings held in a V above his back, his tail fanned and angled, and calls (see Voice). Frequently wing-claps.

No nest is constructed; the eggs are laid on leaf-litter, on bare ground or on earth or ashes after vegetation has been burnt. Nests may be shaded or in full sun. Nest-sites may be close to or on rocks, beneath bushes or tufts of grass, in thickets, on stony slopes or in ravines. Clutch 1-2. Eggs elliptical, creamy white, spotted and marbled grey, brown and umber, 26.8-34.4 x 20.0-24.4mm. Incubation is generally by the female, with the male incubating for short periods just after dusk and just before dawn. If flushed from the nest, the female often flies up into a tree. The incubation period is usually 16-19 days. The semi-precocial chicks fledge at c. 17 days. No further information available.

DESCRIPTION *C. i. indicus* **Adult male** Forehead, crown and nape greyish-brown streaked blackish-brown, broadly so on central crown. Very indistinct pale buff or tawny-buff collar on hindneck. Mantle, back, rump and uppertail-coverts greyish-brown, speckled and faintly barred pale brown, streaked blackish-brown. Lesser coverts brown, speckled pale buff, tawny or greyish-white. Rest of wing-coverts greyish-brown mottled pale buff or greyish-white on innerwebs, outerwebs brown boldly spotted pale buff, pale tawny or greyish-white on tips; spots smudged or vermiculated brown. Scapulars blackish-brown, broadly edged greyish-white vermiculated brown. Primaries brown; large white spot, almost midway along feather, on innerweb of P10 and across both webs of P9-P7, P10 often spotted buff along edge of outerweb; P9-P7 regularly spotted tawny above white spot; inner six primaries regularly barred tawny. Secondaries brown tipped with greyish mottling, regularly barred tawny, barring becoming paler on inner secondaries. Tertials brown densely mottled greyish-brown. Tail brown, indistinctly barred pale tawny or greyish-brown; R5-R2 tipped white (17-30mm), distally speckled or washed brown, often broadly so; central pair (R1) greyish-brown, mottled and barred brown. Lores and ear-coverts brown, speckled pale buff or pale tawny-buff. Submoustachial stripe buffish-white. Chin and throat brown barred buff. Large white patch either side of lower throat, lower feathers of which are tipped dark brown, with a buff or pale tawny subterminal band. Breast greyish-brown, finely barred brown and pale buff. Belly, flanks, undertail- and underwing-coverts buff barred brown. **Adult female** Similar to the male. P10-P7 with small tawny or pale tawny spot, often heavily washed brown on innerweb. R5-R2 narrowly tipped brownish-white or brownish-buff. **Immature** Similar to the adult female. Primaries and secondaries narrowly tipped pale tawny or cinnamon. **Juvenile** Similar to the immature but paler. **Chick** At hatching, covered in brown and buff down. **Bare parts** Iris dark brown; bill brownish or blackish; legs and feet brownish.

MEASUREMENTS Wing (male) 174-200, (female) 181-195; tail (male) 121-136, (female) 117-135; bill (male) 15.2-19.4, (female) 15.3-17.5; tarsus (male) 17.6-18.2, (female) 16.5-18.2. Weight no data.

MOULT Few published data available. Birds of the migratory race *jotaka* may undertake a complete moult on the wintering grounds, since a female was noted in primary moult during early April, Thailand.

GEOGRAPHICAL VARIATION Five races are currently recognised.
    C. i. indicus Described above. A generally brownish race and not too variable in colour, although greyish birds with whiter markings do occur.
    C. i. hazarae (Himalayan Jungle Nightjar) Slightly larger and darker brown than the nominate. The markings on the back are heavier, the barring on the tail is broader and the throat-patches are tawnier. Wing (male) 196-215, (female) 187-208; tail (male) 124-146, (female) 121-137. Weight (male, one) 67.8g, (female, one) 78.6g.
    C. i. kelaarti Slightly smaller than the nominate and darker grey with whiter markings. The barring on the tail is heavier. Wing (male) 168-180, (female) 174-190; tail (male) 111-126, (female) 116-120. Weight no data.
    C. i. jotaka (Japanese Nightjar) Larger, darker and darker-breasted than the nominate. Wing (male) 207-226, (female) 195-226; tail (male) 124-136 (142?), (female) 115-138. Weight (male) 60-108g, (female) 65-91.5g.
    C. i. phalaena Smaller than the nominate, and perhaps more rufous-brown. Wing (male) 161-163, (female)

160-163; tail (male) 115-121, (female) 116-117. Weight no data.

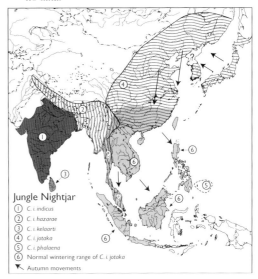

Jungle Nightjar
1. *C. i. indicus*
2. *C. i. hazarae*
3. *C. i. kelaarti*
4. *C. i. jotaka*
5. *C. i. phalaena*
6. Normal wintering range of *C. i. jotaka*
↖ Autumn movements

DISTRIBUTION AND MOVEMENTS Widely distributed across the Oriental faunal zone and the south-eastern Palearctic.
    C. i. indicus India south of the Himalayas, although absent from W Rajasthan and Kutch. Sedentary and locally migratory, movements possibly altitudinal.
    C. i. hazarae NE Pakistan (Hazara) east across the Himalayas, including N India, Nepal and Bhutan, to NE India (Sikkim, Assam, Nagaland, Manipur and Mizoram), Bangladesh and S China (Yunnan), south through Burma and the Malay Peninsula (passage migrant and winter visitor only?). Sedentary and locally migratory, movements probably altitudinal.
    C. i. kelaarti Sri Lanka. Sedentary.
    C. i. jotaka SE Siberia, E, C and S China, Japan (Hokkaido, Honshu, Shikoku, Kyushu) and S Korea. Also occurs (perhaps only occasionally) on Miyake-jima. Migratory. Leaves the breeding grounds September–November, moving south through eastern China, and across the South China Sea?, to winter in S China, Indochina, Malaysia, Sumatra, Java, Borneo and the Philippines. The Japanese population appears to migrate across the Sea of Japan rather than the East China Sea, e.g. rare on Okinawa. In Japan, recorded on Kyushu twice in winter (December and February). Return migration probably March–May. Vagrants have been recorded in the Moluccas (Halmahera), NW New Guinea (a male on Palau Island) and the Aleutians (a female on Buldir Island).
    C. i. phalaena Palau Islands. Presumably sedentary.

STATUS Locally common to fairly abundant in many parts of its breeding range.

REFERENCES Ali & Ripley (1970), Brazil (1991), Legge (1880), Roberts (1991).

Other name: Common Nightjar

Caprimulgus europaeus Linnaeus, 1758, *Syst. Nat.* ed. 10, 1, p.193 (Sweden)
Caprimulgus europaeus meridionalis Hartert, 1896, *Ibis* (7)2, p.370 (Parnassus, Greece)
Caprimulgus europaeus sarudnyi Hartert, 1912, *Vög. pal. Fauna* 2, p.849 (Tarbagatai Mountains)
Caprimulgus europaeus unwini Hume, 1871, *Ibis* (3)1, p.406 (Agrore Valley)
Caprimulgus europaeus plumipes Przewalski, 1876, *Mongol. i strana Tangut* 2, p.22 (Northern bend of the Huang Ho)
Caprimulgus europaeus dementievi Stegmann, 1949, *Ochrana prirody* 6, p.109 (Orok Nor, Outer Mongolia)

Forms a superspecies with Rufous-cheeked Nightjar and Sombre Nightjar.

IDENTIFICATION Length 24.5-28cm. A medium-sized, greyish-brown, variegated Palearctic nightjar. Sexually dimorphic. **At rest** Upperparts greyish-brown streaked blackish-brown, broadly so on central crown. Indistinct pale buff collar around the hindneck. Lesser coverts brown, finely speckled cinnamon, tawny or buff. Rest of wing-coverts greyish-brown spotted buffish. Shows a distinct buff line across the forewing and a buff line along the scapulars. Broad buffish-white submoustachial stripe. White patch either side of lower throat, occasionally extending across whole of lower throat. Underparts greyish-brown barred brown, spotted buff and pale buff, becoming buff barred brown on belly and flanks. **In flight** Wings fairly pointed. Flight extremely buoyant and often rather rapid. The male has a white spot, towards the wing-tip, on the three (rarely four) outer primaries and white tips to the two outer tail feathers. The female lacks white markings on the wings and tail. Some females have small tawny brown-speckled spots on the three outer primaries and narrow tawny-brown tips to the two outer tail feathers, but these features are rarely noticeable in the field. **Similar species** Red-necked Nightjar (77) is larger, longer-winged and greyer-brown, with slower, more deliberate flight, larger white spots on the three outer primaries and broader white tips to the two outer tail feathers. Rufous-cheeked Nightjar (81), a migratory southern African species which may overlap in November–April, has a narrow buff or tawny-buff hindneck collar and heavily spotted wing-coverts, the male in flight showing a white spot on the four outer primaries and white tips to the two outer tail feathers, the female smaller white spots on the four outer primaries and narrow brownish-buff tips to the two outer tail feathers. Sombre Nightjar (80), sympatric in East Africa roughly from October to April, is darker, more heavily spotted, with a broad buff or tawny-buff hindneck collar, the male in flight showing a large white spot on the four outer primaries and very broad white tips to the two outer tail feathers, the female smaller white spots on the four outer primaries and narrow brownish-buff tips to the two outer tail feathers. Egyptian Nightjar (82), likely to be confused only with the pale, sandy-buff race *plumipes* on its Turkestan breeding grounds or on passage through the Middle East, is paler and more uniform with no obvious scapular pattern, usually appears bulkier and slightly larger in flight, and generally lacks white markings on the wings and tail (but see that species). Jungle (78), Savanna (101), Indian (96) and Large-tailed Nightjars (87) occur in north-western India where small numbers of the pale, greyish eastern race *unwini* winter. For descriptions, see those species. See also Vaurie's Nightjar (84).

VOICE The song is a sustained churring (up to 10 minutes without pause), which frequently changes for a few seconds to a faster, lower pitch. Often flies around territory and sings from a wide variety of perches, including trees and bushes, horizontal branches, exposed branch-top or tree stem, tops of wooden pylons or telephone poles, pylon cross-supports, overhead wires and cottage roofs. Also sings from low tree-stumps and the ground. In lower Sind, Pakistan, favourite song-posts are the tops of *Euphorbia caducifolia* cactus stumps. May be heard throughout the night but chiefly at dusk and dawn. Sings less in poor weather, e.g. in rain or strong winds. Also tends to sing less after breeding has commenced but unmated males probably sing strongly throughout the breeding season. Roosting males flushed during the day may sing for a few seconds before settling down again. Sometimes sings on spring migration or on the wintering grounds, e.g. in Zimbabwe. The churring song often ends with a bubbling trill and much wing-clapping, possibly in response to the approach of a female. Bubbling trills (possibly by male only) are frequently given throughout the breeding season, usually in interaction with a female, e.g. on approaching the nest-site.

   The flight contact call, given by both sexes, is a short *co-ic*, *quoik* or *quaw-eek*, often repeated several times. This call is also given just before taking flight or landing, when flushed during the day, in aerial displays, whilst chasing potential predators (see Habits) or by the male when moving from roost-site to perch or between perches/ song-posts, or when chasing an intruding male from his territory. During copulation, the male may make a murmuring sound, the female *kwik-wik-wik-wik* notes. Alarm calls (given by both sexes in flight, from the ground or whilst perched) include a variety of *chuk*, *chek* or clucking notes and, occasionally, a double-noted *chek-ek*. Also gives *chunk*, *chink*, *chik* or *dack* notes, similar to the calls given by Blackbird *Turdus merula* or Great Spotted Woodpecker *Dendrocopos major*, usually when birds are excited, e.g. during aerial pursuits.

   At the nest-site, both sexes often make low-pitched, grunting *wuff* or *schut* sounds, or utter gruff *wuk wuk wuk* notes. The female also gives loud quack-like calls. If disturbed at the nest, both sexes utter muffled *oak oak* or *uok uok* notes. If flushed whilst brooding chicks, the male may alight nearby and repeatedly utter short churrs. Calls given by males trying to locate their offspring consist of drawn-out, plaintive *ko-iiiek* notes. During threat/defence displays, adults make guttural hissing sounds, also given when a bird is handled. Guttural hissing is also given during distraction displays, e.g. from a female on a perch near the nest-site.

   When calling for food, chicks give a soft *brüh brüh*. Unattended chicks give *treub* or *treep* calls. Older chicks, not yet fledged, also give a guttural hiss during threat/ defence display, similar to that given by adults (see above). When flushed, immatures occasionally utter a muffled chirp. Immature males may attempt to churr briefly after they have fledged.

HABITAT Prefers dry, open country, occurring on lowland heaths with scattered trees and bushes (preferably under 3m in height), on commons and moorland, in all types of forest and woodland, inhabiting glades, clearings, margins and edges, recently felled woodland, open woodland and new forestry plantations. Also inhabits chalk downland, industrial waste tips, wooded or scrubby steppes, sparsely forested or vegetated hillsides, stony hillsides, sides of ravines, oak scrubland, sandy woodland, shingle, sand-dunes, semi-deserts and deserts. It is occasionally found in dense coppices. Avoids urban areas. 0–2,800m.

For breeding, generally avoids mountains, true steppes, unwooded plains, dense forest interiors, mature plantations, cultivation, reedbeds and tall grasslands, but often leaves breeding sites to feed in atypical habitats such as orchards, gardens, grassland, arable land, water-meadows, marshes, wet heaths, streams and reedbeds.

On the African wintering grounds the species occurs in all types of wooded country, including savanna, mopane and miombo woodland and riparian formations. It is also found in dry acacia steppe near coasts, clearings in wet, evergreen forest, open sandy country (possibly *plumipes* only) and highlands. 0–5,000m.

HABITS Crepuscular and nocturnal. Roosts on pine needles or leaf-litter on the ground, on or beside dead branches lying on the ground or on low perches such as tree-stumps, piles of logs and roots, or in trees, on branches up to c. 10m or more above ground. Occasionally roosts on discarded man-made materials such as cardboard or sacking. Also roosts within mature plantations (trees over 5m in height). Prior to breeding, females apparently prefer to roost alone in trees outside the territory, but quite often they will also roost alone or beside their mate inside the territory. Territorial males occasionally roost semi-colonially (see Breeding). Roost-sites are usually part-shaded and may be used for long periods, but are usually changed after being disturbed. Roosting birds often shift position to face the sun, presumably to reduce the amount of shadow they cast, or occasionally move away from shadow to sunbathe. If danger approaches, a roosting bird flattens itself with its head held down and forward, and its eyes almost closed. If flushed from its roost it flies low, either silently or calling (see Voice) and wing-clapping, and re-alights up to c. 40m away. It may also fly off with jerky wingbeats, return and land near the roost-site, then fly off again. On the wintering grounds, generally roosts on the ground but in trees, on branches 5-20m above ground. Winter roost-sites are used regularly and several birds may roost close together.

When leaving the roost-site, it may be mobbed by birds or bats, and during the night it may be mobbed or chased by other nocturnally active birds such as Red-necked Nightjar (77) or Woodcock *Scolopax rusticola*, or by bats, e.g. Pipistrelle *Pipistrellus pipistrellus*. Both sexes mob and chase potential predators such as Tawny Owl *Strix aluco*, Little Owl *Athene noctua* and Fox *Vulpes vulpes*, often wing-clapping, calling (see Voice) or hovering whilst they do so. Bats may also rarely be chased.

Often sits on roads, tracks and paths at night. When active, both sexes frequently wing-clap, e.g. when moving form one perch to another (see also Breeding) and often hovers, when feeding or investigating intruders in territory, e.g. humans or large animals such as deer. Usually hovers with body held nearly vertical but also with fluttering wingbeats and body held more horizontally.

Drinks in flight by flying low over the surface of water, raising its wings and tail slightly and lowering its head, briefly dipping its bill into the water. Also slows slightly, lowers its tail and feet and leans forward with bill fully open. Drinks several times before flying off. Forages in agile, buoyant flight with sudden twists, turns, wheels, rises and descents, or flaps and glides with wings held in a V above its body. Also flycatches in short flights of c. 10-15 m, from the ground or a low perch, or hovers for c. 3 seconds close to the tree canopy, taking food from amongst foliage, repeating the action every 5-20m. Occasionally hovers and swoops down after prey. Rarely feeds on the ground, but does so by darting forward to take food.

Forages over open heathland or in forests and woodland, usually in clearings and open spaces or along edges and borders, glades and rides. Often leaves breeding sites, travelling up to 6km or more to feed in gardens and orchards, wetlands, meadows and farmland, especially around grazing animals, and over stagnant ponds (see also Habitat). Usually feeds solitarily but loose flocks of up to 15 birds may occur at favourable feeding sites. Also hawks after insects around street lights, building lights and mercury vapour moth-traps. May forage diurnally on overcast days, usually late afternoons, on both breeding and wintering grounds. In poor feeding conditions, birds may fall into a lethargic state with a reduced body temperature, pulse and breathing rate, but possibly does not enter complete torpor. Migrating birds often live off fat reserves.

Usually migrates at night, singly or in loose flocks of up to 20+ birds. Occasionally migrates diurnally, but only in low numbers, 1-3 birds.

FOOD Moths (including Hepialidae, Cossidae, Pyralidae, Arctiidae, Lymantriidae, Geometridae, Noctuidae, Cymatophoridae, Drepanidae, Lasiocampidae, Notodontidae, Sphingidae and Tortricidae), beetles (including Carabidae, Dytiscidae, Scarabaeidae, Geotrupidae, Elateridae, Copridae, Coccinellidae, Cerambycidae, Curculionidae, Chrysomelidae, Silphidae, Lucanidae, Anthicidae and Melolonthidae), mantises, mayflies, dragonflies, Orthoptera (including Tettigoniidae, Gryllidae, Acrididae and Gryllotalpidae), cockroaches, bugs (including Corixidae, Miridae, Cercopidae, Jassidae, Ledridae and winged Aphidoidea), Hymenoptera (including Ichneumonidae and various Formicidae), antlions (Myrmeleontidae), lacewings (including Hemerobiidae and Chrysopidae), caddisflies (including Hydropsychidae, Phyrganeidae, Leptoceridae and Limnophilidae) and flies (including Tipulidae, Culicidae, Anisopodidae, Limnobiidae, Cecidomyiidae, Scatophagidae, Tachinidae and Empididae). Occasionally takes butterflies and flightless glow-worms, and also feeds on spiders and mites, the latter probably taken with other prey items. Grit and small stones are also ingested, and vegetable matter is probably taken accidentally. Chicks c. 5-6 days old have been recorded eating their own faeces.

BREEDING Breeding season generally late May–August over much of Palearctic range, occasionally earlier in some regions, e.g. April–July in W Pakistan, or May–July? in NW Africa.

Generally monogamous (but see below). Territorial, territory sizes apparently ranging from 1.5–32ha. Maximum breeding density possibly 20 pairs per km, according to location and availability of suitable habitat.

Males arrive on the breeding grounds first and establish territories. Females follow up to c. 20 days later. Males generally drive off intruding males, especially early in the season, with much wing-clapping and calling (see Voice). Males patrol their territories in a gliding flight, with wings held in a V above their backs and tails fanned at an angle. At boundary disputes, males may alight and sing, swaying from side to side with tail fanned. Fights between males may occur on the ground or in flight. On the ground, males face each other with wings drooped and tails slightly raised, and make short leaps at one another until one leaves. If a neighbouring territory is vacated, e.g. after a failed breeding attempt, a male may expand his territory by singing from new song-posts within the empty territory.

Typical gliding flight of territorial male.

During the courtship display flight, the male glides with his wings held in a V above the body and his tail fanned at an angle, frequently wing-claps and follows the female around in circles, calling (see Voice). The female remains silent. During this display, the pair often rise c. 25m up into the air, circle rapidly, then descend in a fast glide. After pair formation the female follows the male to the ground for copulation and/or nest-site selection? After landing, the male may continue to display to the female, by flying up and circling in a fluttering flight with rapidly quivering wing-tips, before landing again. The male usually lands opposite the female and both sexes sway from side to side. The female then stops and the male bobs up and down with wings held partly open, and jerks his tail up and down. This bobbing movement becomes faster, then stops, and the tail is then fanned. The female may stand with her wings open and her tail spread, and the male then glides onto the female's back, and copulation takes place. The male occasionally lands beside the female before displaying and copulating. During copulation, the male lowers his head and raises and quivers his wings. Copulation usually occurs on the ground but may occasionally taken place on a variety of perches, e.g. song-posts, overhead power cables or wires, and dead trees. The female usually perches across wires or branches and the male hovers above her with fluttering or flickering wingbeats, then circles up to 6m distant, before returning and hovering again. The female may lean forward and the male alights on her back and copulation takes place (alternatively, he may perch beside her before copulation takes place). He then usually flies off, but if the females remains he may return before both depart.

Breeding is often influenced by the lunar phase, but unlike some other species this is not the only factor. Once a pair-bond has been formed, both birds often roost together inside their territory. Where neighbouring territories are occupied, pairs often roost at the boundaries, following interactions between the neighbouring pairs during the night. One or two days before the first egg is laid, the female usually roosts alone at the chosen nest-site. No nest is constructed; the eggs are laid on the ground, on leaf-litter, pine needles, or bare soil. Nest-sites may be out in the open, beneath trees, bushes or shrubs, within upturned tree-roots or amongst vegetation. Occasionally nests inside mature plantations (e.g. trees over 5m in height), often up to 10m away from clearings or tracks. Nest-sites may sometimes be used for several years in succession. Clutch 1-2; those of 3-4 eggs possibly involve a second female. Eggs elliptical, smooth and fairly glossy, whitish, greyish-white or cream, spotted and blotched yellowish-brown, dark brown and grey or densely scrawled brown and grey. The eggs are rarely unmarked. 27.0-37.0 x 20.0-25.0mm. The eggs are laid at 36-48 hour intervals. Incubation begins when the first egg is laid, and is mainly by the female. The male often roosts within a few metres of the nest-site but occasionally up to 200m away even outside the territory and inside another's. Occasionally, 2-4 breeding males may roost semi-colonially (sometimes within c. 10m of each other), in favoured areas outside their territories, e.g. small, sheltered clear-fells in forests (see also below). These males may return to roost inside their territories if a second clutch is laid, but then go back to the other roost-site after the first brood has become independent. The incubating adult occasionally gapes or 'yawns' widely. The male relieves the female at dusk and dawn and incubates for short periods of up to c. 15 minutes. At the changeover the male usually approaches the nest wing-clapping and calling (see Voice), lands with its wings raised, then folds his wings and walks to the nest. The relieved bird leaves abruptly, before its partner has landed. The nest may be left unattended for short periods during the night. Whilst incubating at night, the female may fly up to catch an insect, then return to the nest and resettle onto the eggs. If disturbed at the nest-site, the adult may move the eggs a short distance, by nudging them with its bill. During heavy rains, incubating females may leave their eggs to shelter under nearby vegetation, and clutches are often deserted afterwards. Large slugs near unattended eggs are known to prevent females from returning to them. If found, unattended or deserted eggs may be predated by foxes, domestic dogs, hedgehogs *Erinaceus europaeus*, weasels *Mustela nivalis*?, crows *Corvus* sp., Magpies *Pica pica* or Jays *Garrulus glandarius*. After a clutch has failed, a female may resume roosting with her mate. The incubation period is generally 17-18 days, but may be as long as 21 days, especially if the nest-site is subject to disturbance. The eggs hatch asynchronously.

The young are generally semi-precocial and can move up to 25m away from the nest-site before fledging. After their chicks have hatched, neighbouring males may roost close to one another in a separate area away from their territories. The chicks are brooded by the female for at least the first 10-16 days, then by the male if the female lays a second clutch (see below). After c. 10 days, if they have not laid a second clutch, females often roost away from their nest-site. Rarely, both adults may roost at the nest-site with their offspring. Both adults feed the young, up to c. 10-11 times per night, one chick being fed per visit. The chick calls (see Voice) and grabs at or tugs the adult's bill or rictal bristles, the adult opens its bill and a saliva-enveloped food ball is then fed to the chick. During feeding, the heads of both the chick and adult move up and down, the chick trembles, opens its wings and may hold them over the adult's head. As the chicks grow older, males may hunt for food at greater heights above ground, although this may only occur when hawking around trees or in wooded country.

If flushed from the chicks, the female performs an injury-feigning distraction display on the ground, with wings and tail spread. She may stop, shake her wings and waggle her tail from side to side, gaping and hissing (see Voice), sometimes running or hopping a short distance to resume the performance. Alternatively, the female may fly to an exposed branch or vertical tree stem, perch crossways with wings drooped and tail fanned, and utter a deep, guttural hissing (see Voice). Other displays on the ground involve the female rolling from one side to another and shaking one wing at a time, or just lying still on her side for up to c. 5 minutes. Brooding adults (presumably either sex) may also injury-feign in flight by flapping their wings violently to give the impression of slow, impeded flight, after which they flutter to the ground. If approached, they take flight again and repeat the display, gradually drawing the intruder away from the nest. If the brooding female is flushed, with the male roosting close by, only the female performs an injury-feigning distraction display, whilst the male takes flight and circles around the intruder before flying off. Less commonly, when flushed from the nest, the adult flies off, often in a series of glides with wings held in a V above its back, circles around the nest-site, calls (see Voice) and occasionally alights on the ground with wings outstretched and calls again (see Voice). Although this latter display is more often reported for the male, it is not clear whether it occurs during the night or day or when the nest contains eggs or young. An older, feathered but unfledged chick performs a threat/defence display if danger approaches, raising its head by extending its neck in a spiralling movement, opening and raising its wing, gaping and hissing (see Voice); if the danger persists, it may flutter away across the ground but, if followed, it may stop and repeat the threat/defence display. The young fledge at 16-17 days of age, and after c. 19 days they may follow one of their foraging parents. Family parties of 2-4 birds are often evident in late summer. The young become independent at c. 32 days old.

Early breeders may be double-brooded, late breeders are single-brooded. If a second clutch is laid, the female leaves the first brood when the chicks are 10-16 days old (see above). The male may then brood the chicks for a further 5-8 days, after which they may be left unattended, although the male often roosts close by. After leaving the first brood, the female usually lays the second clutch within 1-2 days; the second nest-site may be up to 100m from the first. If the female does not lay again, or the second clutch fails, she may return to the first brood and both parents may then roost at the nest-site, the male brooding one chick, the female the other. If the second clutch is close to the first and the male dies, the chicks of the first brood may join the female at the second nest-site. At a successful nest, the male leaves the first brood at dusk and relieves the female incubating the second clutch, enabling her to forage for food. When the male leaves the second clutch, usually when the female returns, he returns to the first brood to feed the young.

Pairs that have started a second clutch often allow an additional male within their territory, usually within the vicinity of the first brood; the second male may attempt to sing within the territory but he is usually chased away by the breeding male, but later in the season, especially when the breeding male is with the chicks of the first brood, the second male may sing strongly from one of the established song-posts. Both males will join forces to chase off any other males that stray into the territory. When the breeding male relieves the female at the second nest, the second male will visit the first brood, although it is not known if he broods and feeds the young. During the day, when the chicks are older, the two males may roost close to one another. After the chicks of the first brood have fledged, they may join the two males in aerial displays during which all four birds call to one another (see Voice). If the breeding male relieves the female at the second nest, the juveniles of the first brood will often stay with the second male. The young from the first brood may occasionally roost with the female at the second nest-site.

A female may occasionally pair (breed?) with a second male for her second brood, laying the eggs up to c. 400m away from the first brood. Her first mate will continue to tend the first brood and usually has nothing to do with the second.

Although rare, dominant males may display to and breed with two females, the two nest-sites being up to 40m apart. The two clutches may be laid up to 14 days apart. The chicks of the first clutch to hatch usually grow normally, as the male helps to feed them in the normal way. The second brood of chicks grow more slowly because the male can only help feed them sporadically. The male may mate again with one of the females later in the season and a second brood (the male's third) may be reared.

DESCRIPTION *C. e. europaeus* **Adult male** Forehead, crown and nape greyish-brown streaked blackish-brown, broadly so on central feathers. Indistinct pale buff collar around hindneck. Mantle, back, rump and uppertail-coverts greyish-brown streaked blackish-brown. Lesser coverts dark brown, minutely speckled cinnamon, tawny or buff. Median coverts brown broadly tipped buff or pale buff, forming buff line across the closed forewing. Rest of wing-coverts greyish-brown, densely speckled greyish-white and pale buff, and spotted buff and pale tawny. Scapulars blackish-brown, speckled rufous or pale tawny on innerwebs, broadly edged buff on outerwebs. Primaries brown, broadly tipped with greyish-brown mottling, regularly spotted or barred buff or tawny; large white spot, towards tip of feather, on innerwebs of P10-P8 (rarely, on P7 also). Secondaries brown, regularly barred buff or tawny, tipped greyish-brown. Tertials greyish-brown, speckled and mottled brown, broadly streaked blackish-brown along feather-shafts. Tail brown, R5 and R4 broadly but indistinctly barred buff and pale tawny, broadly (22-37mm) tipped white, R3 and R2 broadly barred greyish-brown speckled brown, often tinged buffish, central pair (R1) greyish-brown, speckled and thinly barred brown. Lores and ear-coverts tawny-buff speckled brown. Broad buffish-white submoustachial stripe. Chin buff or pale buff. Throat buff, cinnamon-buff or tawny-buff, barred brown. Large white patch on either side or occasionally extending across whole of lower throat, the lower feathers of which are tipped dark brown with a buff subterminal band. Breast greyish-brown barred brown, spotted buff and pale buff. Belly and flanks, underwing- and undertail-coverts buff barred brown, latter often washed or tipped whitish. **Adult female** Similar to the male but lacks white markings on the wings and tail. Usually has a buffish or tawny spot speckled brown towards the wing-tip on the innerwebs of P10-P8, and narrow (less than 20mm) tawny or buff tips speckled brown on R5 and R4. **Immature** and **Juvenile** Similar to the adult female, perhaps slightly paler. **Chick** At hatching, covered in dark brown and creamy buff down. **Bare parts** Iris dark brown; bill blackish; legs and feet brown or flesh-brown.

MEASUREMENTS Wing (male) 184-213, (female) 184-211; tail (male) 129-146, (female) 129-144; bill (male) 8.0-13.7, (female) 7.5-14.0; tarsus (male) 16.1-20.5, (female) 16.3-18.9. Weight (male) generally 55-87g, may increase to 101 g prior to migration, (female) 67-95g.

MOULT Adults undertake a complete post-breeding moult which usually (but not always) commences on the breeding grounds (July–September) with the head and body feathers and tertials. Very rarely, the innermost primary, P1, is also moulted on the breeding grounds. Moult is usually suspended prior to or during migration and recommences on the wintering grounds between late September and December, completing between early January and March. Data from East Africa (Ngulia, Kenya) suggest that some birds may restart (or continue?) their moult during migration. The primaries are moulted descendantly, the secondary moult is centripetal, moulting ascendantly from S1, and descendantly from S12 (S13), converging on S7-S8. The tail moult is generally centrifugal, although the outermost tail feather, R5, is often moulted before R4, the sequence therefore being R1, R2, R3, R5, R4.

Immatures undertake a complete moult during their first winter. Birds fledged from early broods may begin moulting on the breeding grounds and complete, as adults do, on the wintering grounds, while birds from late broods often begin their moult only after arrival on the winter quarters. Immatures tend to commence and finish their moult later than adults. Occasionally, some adults and immatures may arrest primary or secondary moult, retaining some old feathers throughout the following breeding season.

GEOGRAPHICAL VARIATION Six races are possibly recognisable. However, there is much clinal variation and intergradation; the validity of *meridionalis* and *sarudnyi* is often questioned, and *dementievi* needs to be re-examined critically.

C. e. europaeus Described above. Variation is clinal, birds becoming smaller southwards, smaller and greyer eastwards. Intergrades with *meridionalis* in Europe and possibly with *sarudnyi* in Asia.

C. e. meridionalis Smaller and paler than the nominate, generally being more silvery-grey. The male has slightly larger white spots on the three outer primaries. Variation is clinal, birds becoming smaller and paler eastwards. Wing (male) 175-192, (female) 176-189; tail (male, one) 126, (female) 124-134. Weight (male) 52-71g, (female, one) 55g.

C. e. sarudnyi Paler than the nominate. The male has larger white spots on the three outer primaries and whiter undertail-coverts. This race is extremely variable in size and colour and its characteristics are apparently not consistent. In the west it is intermediate between the nominate and *unwini*, different authors describing it as closer to either the nominate, *meridionalis* or *unwini*. In fact it probably intergrades with the nominate in the north, *meridionalis* in the

west and *unwini* in the south. In the east it is generally buffier-brown, presumably where it intergrades with *plumipes*. Wing (male) 171-196, (female) 171-196; tail (male) 135-143, (female, one) 122. Weight no data.

C. e. unwini (Hume's Nightjar) Paler, greyer and plainer than the nominate, with more narrowly streaked blackish-brown upperparts, a sometimes whiter hindneck collar, often larger white patches on either side of the lower throat, and unmarked or more sparsely barred undertail-coverts. The male has larger white spots on the three outer primaries, often extending across the outerwebs of P9 and P8. Wing (male) 176-192, (female) 180-184; tail (male) 115-137, (female) 122-130. Weight (male) 51-61g, (female) 70-74g.

C. e. plumipes Paler and sandier than the nominate, being sandy-buff or cinnamon-buff all over, with buffish spots on the tertials, median coverts and breast, broad buff or white edges to the outerwebs of the scapulars, and more completely feathered tarsi. The male has larger white spots on the three outer primaries. In the west it intergrades with *sarudnyi*. Wing (male) 180-195, (female) 182-196; tail (male) 134-137, (female) 131-137. Weight (male) 54-66g, (female) 58-72g.

C. e. dementievi A pale race, greyer and more heavily vermiculated than both *unwini* and *plumipes*. No mensural data available.

DISTRIBUTION AND MOVEMENTS A widespread and highly migratory Palearctic species, wintering mainly in Africa, with smaller numbers overwintering in north-western India and Pakistan.

C. e. europaeus N and C Europe (from Britain and France in the west, north to 63-64°N in Scandinavia, east to Russia), east through N Asia (south of c. 60°N?) to the Lake Baikal region. The southern limits of the breeding range are not clearly defined, as southerly populations intergrade with *meridionalis* in Europe and *sarudnyi* in Siberia. Migratory. Leaves breeding grounds in late July–November (mainly late August–October), western populations moving south on a broad front across Europe, the Mediterranean and northern Africa, eastern populations moving south-west on a broad front through the Middle East (mid-August to early December) and East Africa. Winters from late September to early April mainly in eastern and southern Africa, although small numbers may winter in West Africa, e.g. SW Mauritania, NW Senegal (presumably this race), W Gambia, Guinea Bissau, Sierra Leone, Mali, Ivory Coast, Ghana (rare, two records) and E Nigeria. Occasionally a few birds may overwinter as far north as Morocco (January records from Marsa). In spring, returning birds move north or north-east, March–June, the bulk of the population arriving back on the breeding grounds April–May.

C. e. meridionalis NW Africa (N Morocco, N Algeria, NW and NE? Tunisia) and Iberia, east through southern Europe, the Mediterranean, Crimea, the Caucasus and Ukraine?, to NW Iran and the Caspian Sea. The northern limits of the breeding range are unclear, as it intergrades with nominate *europaeus*. Migratory. Leaves the breeding grounds about the same time as the nominate, moving south on a broad front across the Mediterranean, the northern parts of the Middle East and North Africa. Winters mainly

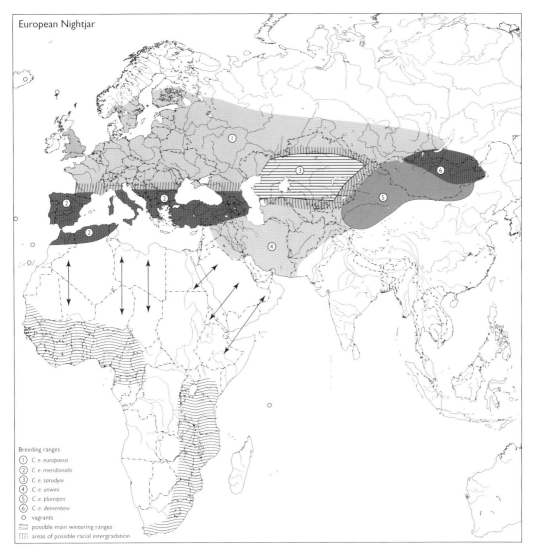

European Nightjar

Breeding ranges
1. *C. e. europaeus*
2. *C. e. meridionalis*
3. *C. e. sarudnyi*
4. *C. e. unwini*
5. *C. e. plumipes*
6. *C. e. dementievi*
○ vagrants
▱ possible main wintering ranges
▥ areas of possible racial intergradation

in Central? and southern Africa, although smaller numbers may winter in West Africa, from NW Senegal (rare, one record), Gambia and Guinea Bissau to Cameroon (except in the east) and N Gabon? Return movements north probably take place at the same time as those of the nominate race.

C. e. sarudnyi Kazakhstan, from the Caspian Sea east to Kyrgyzstan, Tarbagatay and Altay. The northern, eastern and southern limits of its breeding range are unclear owing to its intergradation with adjacent races. Migratory. Autumn movements are probably much the same as those of the Asian populations of the nominate race. Possibly winters mainly in eastern and south-eastern Africa. Returning birds move north-east through the Arabian Peninsula, late February?–May?

C. e. unwini SW Asia (Iraq, Iran except the north-west, east to W Tien Shan and Kasthigaria, north to S Turkmeniya and Uzbekistan). The northern limits of its breeding range are unclear, where it intergrades

with *sarudnyi*. Migratory. Leaves the breeding grounds August?–September?, moving south-eastwards on a broad front across the Middle East. Winters mainly in eastern and south-eastern Africa, although occasionally small numbers overwinter in Israel, Pakistan and NW India? Return movements in the spring apparently take place further to the north.

C. e. plumipes N China (Sinkiang and E Tien Shan eastwards) and NW and S Mongolia. In the west it intergrades with *sarudnyi*. Migratory. In the autumn, it moves south-west on a broad front, wintering mainly in south-eastern Africa (Zimbabwe, Mozambique and eastern South Africa), generally at altitudes below 500m. Return movements probably north-easterly.

C. e. dementievi NE Mongolia and S Transbaikalia. Migratory, probably wintering in eastern or south-eastern Africa.

Vagrants of unidentified race have been recorded on Iceland (probably nominate), Faeroes (probably nominate), Azores, Madeira, Canary Islands and Seychelles.

237

STATUS Locally common to very common in suitable habitat throughout much of its breeding range, although it is decreasing in range and numbers in many European countries. The breeding population in Europe is currently estimated at between 290,000 and 830,000 pairs, with numbers apparently remaining stable only in Sweden, France, Andorra (3–5 pairs), Portugal, Hungary, Poland, Slovakia, Slovenia, Cyprus (very small population), Belarus, Lithuania and Russia. The main reasons for decline are probably habitat loss, increasing disturbance at breeding sites, the use of pesticides, and increasing traffic on roads. In some countries, forestry management may possibly be responsible for a slight increase in range and numbers in recent years, e.g. in Britain, national surveys in 1981 and 1992 show an increase of singing males from 2,100 to 3,400. The stronghold of this species appears to be in the vast expanses of the former Soviet Union, where up to half a million pairs or more may be present.

REFERENCES Alexander & Cresswell (1990), Ali & Ripley (1970), Bowden & Green (1994), Cramp (1985), Cresswell (1986, 1987, 1990, 1992, 1993, 1996), Cresswell & Alexander (1990, 1992), Fry *et al.* (1988), Hagemeijer & Blair (1997), Kenyon (in press), Lack (1929, 1930a,b, 1932, 1957), Roberts (1991), Snow & Perrins (1998), Tucker & Heath (1994), Vaurie (1960b).

---

80   SOMBRE NIGHTJAR
Caprimulgus fraenatus   Plate 23

Caprimulgus fraenatus Salvadori, 1884, *Ann. Mus. Civ. Genova* 21, p.118 (Daimbi, Shoa)

Forms a superspecies with Rufous-cheeked Nightjar, with which it was formerly considered conspecific, and European Nightjar.

IDENTIFICATION Length 25cm. A medium-sized, darkish and rather spotted Afrotropical nightjar. Sexually dimorphic. At rest Upperparts dark brown speckled greyish-white and streaked blackish-brown. Broad buff or tawny-buff collar on hindneck. Wing-coverts dark brown, heavily spotted tawny and buff. Distinct row of large, irregularly shaped blackish spots along the scapulars. Central tail feathers thickly barred brown. White sub-moustachial stripe contrasts markedly with dark plumage. White spot on either side of lower throat or white patch cross whole of lower throat. Underparts dark brown spotted buff, becoming buff barred brown on belly and flanks. In flight The male has a large white spot towards the wing-tip on the four outer primaries (innerweb only on outermost) and very broad white tips to the two outer tail feathers. The female has smaller white spots, usually tinged buffish, on the four outer primaries, and pale buff tips to the two outer tail feathers. Similar species Rufous-cheeked Nightjar (81), a migratory species yet to be recorded in the range of Sombre Nightjar, is greyer and paler, streaked rather than spotted on the upperparts, less heavily spotted on the wing-coverts and breast, with a generally thinner and less prominent hindneck collar, and more thinly barred central tail feathers; the male has narrower white tips to the two outer tail feather, the female smaller white spots (washed tawny not buffish) on the four outer primaries, and narrower pale buff tips to the two

outer tail feathers. European Nightjar (79), sympatric in October–December and February?–April?, is similar to Rufous-cheeked Nightjar in having streaked rather than spotted upperparts, but is browner (nominate), greyer and paler (*unwini*) or paler and buffier (*plumipes*), with an indistinct hindneck collar and a prominent buff line across the forewing; the male has a small white spot on the three outer primaries and white tips to the two outer tail feathers, while the female lacks white in the wing and tail. Fiery-necked Nightjar (93) of the nominate race *pectoralis* (only in southern Africa) can be extremely similar but has a whistled song, females having smaller white spots on the four outer primaries and white tips to the two outer tail feathers.

VOICE The song is a low, evenly pitched, rapid churr, lasting for several minutes or more and occasionally interrupted with *kik-wow*, *a-whoop* or liquid *kow* notes. Song also often commences with one or two *kik-wow* notes and occasionally ends with three or four *kow* notes, descending in pitch. Sings from branches in trees, up to c. 5m above ground, possibly also from the ground. May be heard chiefly at dusk and dawn. The flight call is a liquid *quik* note. During threat/defence display, utters a throaty hiss, which is also given when the bird is handled.

The song of this species is extremely similar to that of Rufous-cheeked Nightjar.

HABITAT Prefers open bush and scrub country, usually on stony or rocky ground. Also occurs in grassland, thin sage bush, *Dodonaea* scrub and more recently in *Eucalyptus* plantations. 0–3,200m.

HABITS Crepuscular and nocturnal. Roosts on the ground, roost-sites being used for several weeks at a time. When flushed, calls (see Voice) and flies only a short distance before re-alighting on the ground, always facing the potential danger. On settling, it is at first alert with head and neck raised and eyes open. If not approached, it then settles down with eyes closed. It is often found in small groups outside the breeding season. Feeds at night by hawking for insects. No further information available.

FOOD Moths, grasshoppers, bugs and beetles (including Scarabaeiade and Cerambycidae). No further data available.

BREEDING Breeding season May–July? in NW Somalia; February–May and November in W Kenya; January–March and September–November in Ethiopia, C and S Kenya and NE Tanzania; and June in SW Somalia? and coastal Kenya?

Probably monogamous. No nest is constructed; the eggs are laid on bare earth or on sandy ground. Nest-sites are usually amongst grass, often partly under bushes and may be on flat ground, flat stones, or gently sloping terrain, e.g. the sides of rocky ridges. Clutch 1-2. Eggs elliptical or elliptical-ovate, pinkish-white, -buff or glossy white? faintly spotted and blotched brown, lilac and grey, markings denser around the blunt end, 23.5-30.5 x 18.0-21.2 (25?)mm. Incubation is usually by the female, at least during the day. If flushed from the nest after the eggs have hatched, the female gives a distraction display by feigning injury. If danger passes, she returns to the nest within c. 10 minutes. No data available for incubation and fledging periods but the chicks can leave the nest-site after approximately 12 days. No further information available.

DESCRIPTION Adult male Forehead, crown and nape greyish-white finely speckled and streaked brown; central feathers broadly spotted dark brown. Broad buff or tawny-buff collar on hindneck. Mantle, back, rump and uppertail-coverts brown speckled greyish-white and thickly streaked dark brown. Lesser coverts brown speckled greyish-white, buff and pale tawny, rest of wing-coverts similar but heavily spotted buff and pale tawny. Scapulars boldly and irregularly spotted blackish-brown, broadly edged (outerweb) and tipped buff. Primaries brown; large white spot, towards feather-tip, on innerweb of P10 and both webs of P9-P7, inner primaries barred tawny and tipped pale greyish-brown. Secondaries brown barred tawny, tipped pale greyish-brown. Tertials greyish-brown mottled brown, spotted pale buff and tawny. Tail brown, R5 and R4 broadly (35-52mm) tipped white, R3 and R2 faintly barred pale brown, central pair (R1) greyish-brown mottled brown, thickly barred brown. Lores and ear-coverts brown speckled buff or rufous. Prominent white submoustachial stripe. Chin buff, throat buff barred brown. White spot on either side of lower throat or white patch across whole of lower throat, the lower feathers of which are broadly tipped dark brown with a buff subterminal band. Breast darkish brown, thinly barred and heavily spotted buff. Belly, flanks and underwing-coverts buff barred brown. Undertail-coverts buff, occasionally whitish, barred brown or unmarked. **Adult female** Similar to the male but the white spots on the four outer primaries are smaller, washed buff on the outerwebs of P9 and P8, and entirely so on P7. Lacks white on the outer tail feathers, R5 and R4 being narrowly tipped pale buff mottled brown. **Immature** and **Juvenile** Similar to the adults but browner and paler. **Chick** Not described. **Bare parts** Iris dark brown; bill black; legs and feet brown.

MEASUREMENTS Wing (male) 159-174, (female) 153-171; tail (male) 104-122, (female) 94-123; bill (male) 16.2-17.2, (female) 13.6-18.9; tarsus (male) 20.0-22.3, (female) 20.4-24.5. Weight (male) 55.2-71.2g, (female) 46.0-67.5g.

MOULT Few published data available. The primaries are generally moulted descendantly, the secondaries ascendantly. Tail moult is variable with no obvious consistent pattern.

GEOGRAPHICAL VARIATION Monotypic. No colour variation noted.

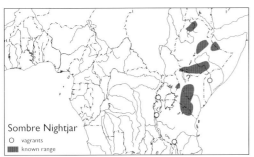

Sombre Nightjar
○ vagrants
▓ known range

DISTRIBUTION AND MOVEMENTS An East African (Rift Valley?) species occurring discontinuously from northern Ethiopia south to northern Tanzania. N, C and S Ethiopia, SE Sudan, NW Somalia, C and SW Kenya, NE Uganda and NE Tanzania. Sedentary and locally migratory. Occurs as a breeding visitor only (May–October) in NW Somalia, moving to Ethiopia for the winter. Also recorded SW Somalia and N and E Kenya, and as a possible vagrant in Zaire (Rwenzori), Burundi (Bujumbura) and S

Tanzania (Njombe highlands).

STATUS Few data available, but may be locally common in suitable habitat.

REFERENCES Archer & Goodman (1961), Fry *et al.* (1988), Jackson (1938), Lewis & Pomeroy (1989).

81   RUFOUS-CHEEKED NIGHTJAR
Caprimulgus rufigena   Plate 23

Caprimulgus rufigena A. Smith, 1845, *Illustr. Zool. South Africa, Aves* pl.100 and text (Eastern Cape Province, South Africa)
Caprimulgus rufigena damarensis Strickland, 1852, in Jardine's *Contr. Ornith.* p.123 (Damaraland. Restricted to Omaruru by Clancey, 1965, *Durban Mus. Novit.* 7, p.344)

Forms a superspecies with Sombre Nightjar, with which it was formerly considered conspecific, and European Nightjar.

IDENTIFICATION Length 23-24cm. A medium-sized, greyish-brown Afrotropical nightjar. Sexually dimorphic. **At rest** Upperparts greyish-brown, streaked blackish-brown. Narrowish buff or tawny-buff collar around hindneck. Wing-coverts greyish-brown, heavily spotted tawny and buff. Broad buffish line along scapulars. Central tail feathers thinly barred brown. White spot on either side of lower throat or white patch across whole of lower throat. Underparts greyish-brown spotted buff, becoming buff barred brown on belly and flanks. **In flight** The male has a large white spot towards the wing-tip on the four outer primaries (innerweb only on the outermost) and white tips to the two outer tail feathers. The female has smaller white spots, usually tinged tawny, on the four outer primaries, and pale buff tips to the two outer tail feathers. **Similar species** European Nightjar (79), which penetrates part of its range in winter, possesses an indistinct or no hindneck collar and a prominent buff line across the forewing; the male has a small white spot on the three outer primaries and white tips to the two outer tail feathers, while the female lacks white markings on the wings and tail; race *unwini* is paler and greyer, *plumipes* generally paler and buffier. Sombre Nightjar (80) of East Africa is browner and darker, spotted rather than streaked on the upperparts, more heavily spotted on the wing-coverts and breast, with thick brown bars on the central tail feathers and generally a broader, more prominent hindneck collar; the male has broader white tips to the two outer tail feathers, the female larger white spots (washed buff, not tawny) on the four outer primaries, and broader pale buff tips to the two outer tail feathers.

VOICE The song, extremely similar to that of Sombre Nightjar, is a continuous, evenly pitched churr, lasting for up to three minutes or more without pause. It often commences with *a-whoop* notes and shorts churrs, and often ends with 3-15 low-pitched *kow* notes. Sings from the ground, occasionally from trees. May be heard mostly at dusk and dawn. The flight call is a series of *chuck* notes. The alarm/ distress call is a slow *chuck chuck chuck*, e.g. given by female alighting on a branch after being flushed from a chick.

HABITAT Prefers open wooded savannas, miombo

woodland, woodland edges and clearings, semi-arid acacia scrubland and gravelly semi-deserts. Also occurs in plantations and on sparsely vegetated hillsides. 0–1,600m.

HABITS Crepuscular and nocturnal. Roosts on the ground, roost-sites often being close to or beneath bushes. If approached, a roosting bird adopts a flattened posture by lowering its head to the ground. If flushed from its roost, it flies a short distance before suddenly re-alighting on the ground or sometimes a low branch. Usually occurs singly or in pairs. Often sits on roads and paths at night. Outside the breeding season up to c. 50 birds may occur together, e.g. when feeding around lights at game park waterholes. No further information available.

FOOD Moths and beetles. No further data available.

BREEDING Breeding season September–November in Angola and Zambia; September–January in Botswana; and September–December in Zimbabwe and South Africa.

Monogamous and territorial. Probably courtship display commences with the male, perched on the ground, calling and making little leaps into the air. If a female is attracted, then possibly both sexes make short, low flights, during which the white wing spots are strikingly evident. Males clap their wings in flight during courtship displays, or when pursuing intruding males in their territory. No nest is constructed; the eggs are laid on bare earth, often near twigs and sticks, but avoids dense leaf-litter. Nest-sites are either in the shade of nearby vegetation or out in the open, with no shade or cover. Nests in burnt areas and dry woodlands, also occasionally in damp vleis, recently felled areas and open agricultural land. Clutch 1-2. Eggs elliptical, glossy, whitish, buffish or pale pinkish-cream, faintly but densely spotted and blotched brown, grey and lilac, occasionally unmarked, 23.9-30.0 x 18.4-21.6mm. Incubation begins when the first egg is laid and lasts 15-17 days. The chicks fledge within 18-20 days. No further information available.

DESCRIPTION *C. r. rufigena* **Adult male** Forehead, crown and nape greyish-brown, speckled and streaked brownish; central feathers broadly streaked blackish-brown edged rufous. Broadish buff or tawny-buff collar on hindneck. Mantle, back, rump and uppertail-coverts greyish-brown, speckled brownish and streaked dark brown. Lesser coverts brown speckled greyish-white, buff and pale tawny. Rest of wing-coverts similar but heavily spotted buff and pale tawny. Scapulars blackish-brown, broadly bordered buff on outerwebs. Primaries brown; large white spot, towards feather-tip, on inner web of P10 and both webs of P9-P7; inner primaries and secondaries brown barred tawny, indistinctly tipped pale greyish-brown. Tertials greyish-brown, mottled brown and spotted pale buff or tawny. Tail brown; R5 and R4 tipped white, 21-33mm; R3 and R2 faintly barred pale brown; central pair (R1) mottled greyish-brown, thinly barred brown. Lores and ear-coverts brown speckled buff or rufous. Chin buff, throat buff barred brown. White spot on either side of lower throat or white patch across whole of lower throat, the lower feathers of which are broadly tipped dark brown with a buff subterminal band. Breast brownish, spotted and thinly barred buff. Belly, flanks and underwing-coverts buff barred brown. Undertail-coverts buff, often tipped whitish, barred brown or unmarked. **Adult female** Similar to the male but the white spots on the four outer primaries are smaller, washed tawny on P7 and the outerwebs of P8-P9. Lacks white on the outer tail feathers, R5 and R4 narrowly

tipped pale buff mottled brown. **Immature** and **Juvenile** Similar to the adults but paler. **Chick** At hatching, covered in greyish-white and rufous down. **Bare parts** Iris brown; bill blackish; legs and feet brownish-flesh.

MEASUREMENTS Wing (male) 157-180, (female) 156-171; tail (male) 111-136, (female) 113-125; bill (male) 8-13, (female) 8-11; tarsus (male) 11.0-19.9, (female) 11-18. Weight (male) 48.0-65.3g, (female) 46.0-66.0g.

MOULT Few published data available. Adults undertake a complete post- breeding moult, which commences on the breeding grounds with the body plumage. The wing and tail moult is also begun and is then suspended prior to or during the northward migration, before being completed on the wintering grounds. The primaries are moulted descendantly, the secondaries ascendantly. Tail moult appears to be centrifugal.

The moult of immature birds is as yet undescribed. One bird (museum specimen, age uncertain) taken on the wintering grounds, exhibited serially descendant wing moult.

GEOGRAPHICAL VARIATION Two subspecies are currently recognised.

C. r. rufigena Described above.

C. r. damarensis Upperparts paler and greyer with thinner brown streaks and a generally paler, more buffish hindneck collar. Little colour variation noted but one male (museum specimen) from Namibia is rather sandy-buff overall. Wing (male) 158-168, (female) 154-167; tail (male) 114-124, (female) 110-123. Weight no data.

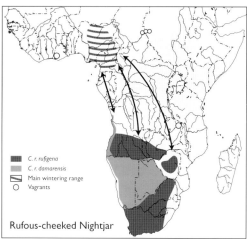

- ▨ *C. r. rufigena*
- ▨ *C. r. damarensis*
- ◩ Main wintering range
- ○ Vagrants

Rufous-cheeked Nightjar

DISTRIBUTION AND MOVEMENTS Occurs over much of southern and south-western Africa, moving north after breeding to winter in parts of Central and West Africa.

C. r. rufigena South Africa (W Cape Province east to Orange Free State and Transvaal, but absent from much of the east), Zimbabwe (central plateau), S Zambia, S Mozambique? and S Angola? (as far north as N Bihe). Migratory (see below).

C. r. damarensis NW South Africa (N Cape Province), Namibia (except coastal region), Botswana and coastal W Angola. Migratory (see below).

Both populations appear to winter mainly in Cameroon (April–August) and less commonly so in Nigeria (May–August). They may also winter in the west of the Congo basin. Occurs as a passage migrant in Zimbabwe (middle Zambezi? and SE lowveld?), Zaire (entire country on northward migration, western parts on southward migration), N Zambia, N Angola, Congo and Gabon. Rare or vagrant? in Central African Republic and W Sudan (Darfur).

STATUS Frequent to locally common in suitable habitat during the breeding season. In the northern wintering grounds, frequent but sparsely distributed in wooded country.

REFERENCES Fry *et al.* (1988), Stresemann & Stresemann (1966), Tyler (1992).

---

82 EGYPTIAN NIGHTJAR
Caprimulgus aegyptius   Plate 24

Caprimulgus aegyptius Lichtenstein, 1823, *Verz. Doubl. Zool. Mus. Berlin* p.59 (Upper Egypt)
Caprimulgus aegyptius saharae Erlanger, 1899, *J. Orn.* 47, p.525, pl.12, upper f (Oued Beshima, Tunisia)

IDENTIFICATION Length 24-26cm. A medium to large, rather uniform sandy-grey Palearctic nightjar. Marginally sexually dimorphic. **At rest** Upperparts sandy-grey or greyish-buff, lightly spotted blackish-brown. Indistinct buff collar around hindneck. Wing-coverts sandy-grey or greyish-buff, speckled and vermiculated brown and blackish brown, boldly spotted buff. No obvious scapular pattern. Buffish-white submoustachial stripe. White patch across lower throat or on either side of lower throat. Underparts sandy-grey or greyish-buff, spotted buff and barred brown, becoming buff barred brown on belly and flanks. **In flight** Long and broad-winged. Flies with deep, powerful wingbeats and frequently glides with its wings held level to the body. From above, both sexes generally have dark brownish wing-tips; from below, the wings are largely white. Uncommonly may show a small white spot, towards the wing-tip, on the upperside of the three outer primaries. The male has narrow whitish tips to the two outer tail feathers, the female narrower, pale buffish tips. **Similar species** Sykes's Nightjar (83) is smaller, both sexes showing a broad white band across the three outer primaries; the male has broad white tips to the two outer tail feathers, the female buffish-white tips larger and more defined than female Egyptian. European Nightjar (79) of the eastern race *plumipes* is pale, buffish-brown, more streaked, showing a distinct scapular pattern (see that species) and a buffish line across the forewing at rest, and in flight appearing less bulky and even slightly smaller; the male has a white spot on the three outer primaries and white tips to the two outer tail feathers, while the female lacks white markings on the wing and tail. Vaurie's Nightjar (84), known by a single female from Western Sinkiang (western China), is buffier and much smaller, with broad, blackish-brown streaking on the rear of the crown and nape. Golden Nightjar (86) occurs throughout the sahelian wintering grounds, but is smaller, more tawny-buff, with shorter, slightly rounded wings and (both sexes) large white spots on the four outer primaries and broad white tips to the two outer tail feathers.

VOICE The song is a rapid series of purring *kowrr* or *powrr* notes (3-4 notes per second), lasting for up to several minutes. Often sings at a faster rate, uttering shorter *kow* notes. Sings from the ground. May mostly be heard at dusk and dawn. Also gives a rapid series of croaking *toc* notes interspersed with short churrs e.g. *toc toc toc toc churrrrrr toc toc toc*. In flight, from the ground or when flushed, utters *tuk-l tuk-l* notes, a growling *owk* or croaking *toc* (perhaps the same as above). Also gives *chuc chuc* calls. Birds on the ground, running and seeking shelter, often make grumbling sounds.

HABITAT Prefers deserts and semi-deserts, often being found close to water. Also occurs in sandy, sparsely vegetated country, low-lying, arid sand and clay plains with scattered scrub and tamarisk and dry waste ground near water. In Afghanistan, also inhabits desolate lowland regions. In Sudan, wintering birds also occur in long grass amongst trees. The north-west African population breeds in deserts, desert-steppe or sandy steppe with outcrops of limestone, and winters in areas with *Salsola*, *Artemisia* and *Tamarix*, dry country and amongst ricefields.

HABITS Crepuscular and nocturnal. Occasionally active during the day, if conditions are overcast or the ground on which it is roosting becomes too hot. Roost-sites are sometimes in the open but often in the shade of trees, bushes, rocks, stones or banks of soil or clay, and are often close to water. In full sunlight and hot temperatures, a roosting bird may adopt a flattened posture, with wings half-open along the ground and head hunched back into its body. If the temperature increases, it may move into the shade of nearby vegetation and resume roosting in a normal posture with its back to the sun. In winter, roosting birds may also occur in long grass amongst trees. Passage and wintering birds often roost in loose flocks. During spring migration, small groups of up to 15 birds may roost together. Prior to or during autumn migration, large numbers (perhaps hundreds) may roost together (e.g. Iraq, August–September). At winter roosts up to c. 50 birds may occur together. If flushed from its roost, it flies or glides a short distance before re-alighting on the ground, after which it may then run to cover.

Frequently sits on roads and tracks at night. Also settles near irrigation ditches and pools of water in wadis. Often claps wings in flight. Forages low over the ground near wells and bushes, over water and amongst nomad encampments and livestock. Also hunts over cultivated land and towns. When feeding, occasionally occurs in small flocks of up to ten birds. Rarely, takes food on the ground. Drinks in flight, by dipping its bill into the surface of water.

Migrates at rather high altitudes, often in small, perhaps single-sex flocks. On the wintering grounds in Sudan, often occurs with Golden Nightjar.

FOOD Beetles (including Scarabaeidae, Elateridae and Carabidae), bugs, moths (including Noctuidae), crickets, grasshoppers, ants, termites and mosquitoes. No further data available.

BREEDING Breeding season mid-March–June (to August in wet years) in Morocco; mid-April to mid-June in Algeria and Tunisia, and mid-May–? in Turkmenistan. No data available from other localities.

No nest is constructed; the eggs are laid on the ground. Nest-sites may be out in the open, amongst stones, beneath low bushes or in depressions in the ground. Clutch 1-2. Eggs elliptical, smooth or glossy, cream or whitish, marbled and blotched pale olive and grey, 27.0-34.5 x 19.1-22.9mm. Incubation begins when the first egg is laid and is mainly by the female, at least during the day, with the male often roosting close by. The incubation period is about 17-18 days, with the eggs usually hatching asynchronously. The chicks are nidicolous or semi-precocial? Soon after hatching, they may be moved away from the nest-site, the adult shuffling along with a chick between its legs. The chicks are brooded only for a few days, after which the adults roost separately. The chicks fledge in c. 4 weeks. Possibly double-brooded. No further information available.

DESCRIPTION *C. a. aegyptius* **Adult male** Forehead, crown and nape sandy-grey, lightly or boldly spotted blackish-brown. Indistinct buffish collar around hindneck. Mantle, back, rump and uppertail-coverts sandy-grey, greyish-buff or brownish-buff, faintly speckled and vermiculated brown. Wing-coverts sandy-grey, greyish-buff or brownish-buff, streaked, speckled and vermiculated brown and blackish-brown, boldly spotted buff or pale buff, the spots being speckled brown. Scapulars sandy-grey or greyish-buff, with blackish-brown 'bat-shaped' spots or T-shaped marks. Primaries brown, broadly tipped greyish-brown; outerwebs regularly but indistinctly spotted buffish, speckled brown, inner webs broadly scalloped white; on some individuals the distal scallop nearest the tip of P10-P8 may extend across to the feather-shaft and show as a white spot on birds in flight. Secondaries and tertials sandy-grey or greyish-buff, mottled brown. Tail sandy-grey, greyish-buff or brownish-buff, mottled and barred brown, R5 and R4 tipped white tinged buffish (18-24mm), the extent greater on R5 than on R4. Occasionally has a thin, indistinct, buffish supercilium behind the eye. Lores and ear-coverts sandy-grey or greyish-buff, speckled or thinly barred brown. Buffish-white submoustachial stripe. Chin and throat pale buff or whitish, barred brown. White patch on either side of lower throat or white patch across whole of lower throat. Breast sandy-grey or greyish-buff, spotted buff and finely barred brown. Belly and flanks sandy-buff barred brown. Undertail-coverts pale buff barred brown. Underwing-coverts buff barred brown. **Adult female** Similar to the male. Often has less white on the inner webs of the primaries. R5 and R4 narrowly tipped pale buffish speckled brown (12-20mm). **Immature** and **Juvenile** Similar to the adults but paler and plainer (juveniles occasionally rather tawny), with less white on the inner webs of the primaries. The upperparts are pale sandy-buff, finely barred and vermiculated light brown; breast pale buffish, finely barred light brown; belly and flanks whitish-buff, very faintly barred brown. **Chick** At hatching, covered in pale buff or sandy-buff down. **Bare parts** Iris dark brown; bill blackish or dark brown; legs and feet blackish, greyish or brownish.

MEASUREMENTS Wing (male) 192-216, (female) 193-216; tail (male) 114-133, (female) 114-132; bill (male) 8.1-12.7, (female) 8.4-12.4; tarsus (male) 19.4-23.4, (female) 20.5-24.6. Weight (male) 68-93g, (female, one) 70g.

MOULT Adults undertake a complete post-breeding moult, commencing early during late April to mid-June (mainly mid-May). The moult is either finished by September/October on the breeding grounds, or is suspended until after migration and then finished in the winter quarters. The primaries are moulted descendantly, the secondaries ascendantly, the tail centrifugally (R1 to R5). Immatures may undertake a partial or complete post-breeding moult.

GEOGRAPHICAL VARIATION Two races are best

recognised, one in Asia and one in north-west Africa. A third race, *arenicolor*, is recognised by some authorities based mainly on size, this form being the largest, with wing lengths greater than 200mm.

C. a. aegyptius Described above. Colour variation is minimal, birds ranging from greyish-buff to brownish-buff.

C. a. saharae Generally sandier, less greyish-buff than the nominate and averages slightly smaller. Wing (male) 186-196, (female) 182-199; tail (male) 106-121, (female) 103-122. Weight (male) no data, (female, one) 81g.

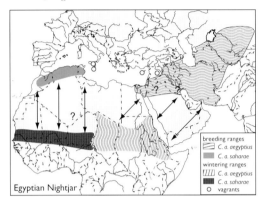

Egyptian Nightjar

breeding ranges
 C. a. aegyptius
 C. a. saharae
wintering ranges
 C. a. aegyptius
 C. a. saharae
 ○ vagrants

DISTRIBUTION AND MOVEMENTS A Palearctic species with two distinct breeding populations, one ranging from the Middle East to parts of southern Asia, the other in north-west Africa. Both populations winter mainly in the sahelian zone of Africa (but see below), possibly inter-mixing in places.

C. a. aegyptius NE Egypt (edge of Nile Delta south to Faiyum), Israel?, Jordan, N Saudi Arabia?, Kuwait?, Iraq, Iran, W Afghanistan, Turkmenistan, Uzbekistan, east to W Tadzhikistan, Kazakhstan (c. 74°E). Migratory and partially sedentary (Egypt). Leaves breeding grounds by September and migrates on a broad front, south-east across the Arabian Peninsula (September–November), occasionally turning up on ships in the Persian Gulf, northern parts of the Arabian Sea and the Gulf of Aden. Small numbers may winter throughout the Arabian Peninsula, but the bulk of the population winters in the sahelian zone of Africa, mainly in the east. Recorded from N and NE Chad, S, C and NE Sudan (October–March), NE Egypt (Nile Delta), SE Egypt (Gebel Elba) and NE Nigeria (Lake Chad; passage only? recorded August–October and again in February). Rarer to the south-east in N and C Ethiopia (December–January) and only one record NW Somalia (December). To the east, birds possibly of this race recorded from E Mali (January–April) and N Togo (vagrant? May–June!). Return migration late February to early June (mainly mid-March to mid-May). Has occurred as an apparent vagrant in Syria.

C. a. saharae C and EC Morocco, N Algeria, occasionally S Algeria (Hoggar Mountains), C Tunisia and NW Libya? Said to occur east to N Egypt (Nile Delta) but no data available. Migratory. Leaves breeding grounds September–October, moving south and south-west. Winters in W Africa, from S Mauritania (September–

February) and N Senegal (December–February) through C and SC Mali (November–February) to N Burkina, SE Niger and NE Nigeria (see nominate above). Return migration March–April. Has occurred as a vagrant in Sicily and Malta.

Passage birds in WC Libya (late October to early November) are of undetermined race. Vagrants of unassigned race have been recorded in Britain, W Germany, Sweden, Italy and Cyprus.

STATUS Widespread but local and often not common in northwest Africa, locally scarce to common in Egypt, scarce in the Middle East and possibly common to locally abundant in central Asia. Widely dispersed throughout wintering range.

REFERENCES Cramp (1985), Fry *et al.* (1988), Robin (1969), Snow & Perrins (1998), Vaurie (1960b).

---

83   SYKES'S NIGHTJAR
Caprimulgus mahrattensis   Plate 24

Other name: Sind Nightjar

Caprimulgus mahrattensis Sykes, 1832, *Proc. Comm. Zool. Soc. London* p.83 (Mahrattas)

IDENTIFICATION Length 23cm. A medium-sized, rather uniform sandy-grey Palearctic nightjar, restricted to the semi-deserts of Iran, Afghanistan and Pakistan. Marginally sexually dimorphic. **At rest** Upperparts sandy-grey, lightly spotted blackish-brown. Indistinct buffish collar on hindneck. Wing-coverts sandy-grey, streaked and vermiculated blackish-brown, boldly spotted buff and pale buff. No obvious scapular pattern. Whitish submoustachial stripe. White patch on either side of lower throat, occasionally extending across whole of throat. Underparts sandy-grey spotted buff, barred brown, becoming buff barred brown on belly and flanks. **In flight** Both sexes have a broad white band towards the wing-tip across the three outer primaries. The male has broad white tips to the two outer tail feathers, the female smaller, buffish-white tips. **Similar species** Egyptian Nightjar (82) is larger, both sexes only very rarely showing small white spots on the three outer primaries in flight, but the underside of the outer primaries is largely white; the male has narrow buffish-white tips to the two outer tail feathers, the female narrower, buffier tips.

VOICE The song is an even-pitched churr, lasting 3-4 minutes without pause. Sings from the ground. May be heard predominantly at dusk and dawn. During display flights, utters soft clucking calls. When flushed from its roost, gives low, soft *chuck-chuck* or *cluck-cluck* notes, which are also given by the male in flight and may be the same as the display flight calls.

HABITAT Prefers semi-deserts with scattered thorn scrub. Also occurs in dry, stony scrubland, on clay or gravel plains, flat, salty ground with tamarisk, and stony wasteland. Occasionally inhabits dry, hilly areas with rocky outcrops and sparsely vegetated sand-dunes in deserts. Tends to avoid well-cultivated or irrigated areas. 0–500m.

HABITS Crepuscular and nocturnal. Roosts on the ground. Roost-sites may be unsheltered, but are more usually close to thorn bushes, tamarisk bushes or clumps

of euphorbia. Occasionally roosts in tall trees (e.g. mango *Mangifera indica*) in forests. On the wintering grounds, often roosts beside grass tussocks. Frequently claps wings in flight. Often sits on canalside roads and open embankments at night, between bouts of foraging. Occasionally walks or shuffles along the ground, with wings held vertically. Forages close to the ground, twisting and turning in flight, with sudden vertical rises. Also feeds over grassy swamps. No further information available.

FOOD Moths and beetles (including Scarabaeidae and Melolonthinae). No further data available.

BREEDING Breeding season February–August (mainly March–May) in Pakistan. No data available from other regions.

Semi-colonial? No nest is constructed; the eggs are laid on bare, stony or salt-encrusted ground. Nest-sites may be in the open, under small clumps of grass or beneath low bushes, such as thick tamarisks or dry bramble. Clutch 2. Eggs elliptical, greyish-white, smeared and blotched grey, 25.5-30.5 x 19.6-22.0mm. Incubation is mainly by the female, at least during the day. The incubation period is c. 17-18 days. The chicks are semi-precocial and may be nidicolous. No further information available.

DESCRIPTION Adult male Forehead, crown and nape sandy-grey, sparsely streaked or spotted blackish-brown edged buff. Indistinct buffish collar around hindneck. Mantle, back, rump and uppertail-coverts sandy-grey or greyish-buff, thinly and faintly barred brown. Wing-coverts sandy-grey or greyish-buff, streaked, speckled and vermiculated brown and blackish-brown, boldly spotted buff or pale buff, spots speckled brown. Scapulars sandy-grey or greyish-buff, with blackish-brown T-shaped marks. Primaries brown, broadly tipped with pale greyish-brown mottling; broad (c. 30mm) white band almost midway along feather, across P10-P8; P7 occasionally with vestigial white mark; inner six primaries are regularly barred pale tawny. Secondaries brown broadly tipped with greyish-buff mottling, regularly barred buffish; inner secondaries and tertials sandy-grey or greyish-buff, speckled and streaked brown. Tail brown; R5 and R4 barred buff, especially along the outerwebs, broadly (c. 35mm) tipped white; R3 and R2 brownish-buff, mottled and barred brown; central pair (R1) sandy-grey or greyish-buff, mottled and barred brown. Supercilium buffish and indistinct. Lores and ear-coverts sandy-grey thinly barred brown. Whitish or buffish-white submoustachial stripe. Chin and throat buff or buffish-white, barred brown. White patch on either side of lower throat or white patch across whole of lower throat. Breast sandy-grey or greyish-buff, spotted buff and finely barred brown. Belly, flanks, undertail- and underwing-coverts buff barred brown. **Adult female** Similar to the male. The white band on P10 (inner web only) to P8 is smaller (c. 25mm) and often washed buffish, especially on P8. R5 ad R4 narrowly tipped buffish-white (c. 20mm). **Immature** and **Juvenile** Paler and plainer than the adults, with much of the plumage lightly vermiculated brown. **Chick** At hatching, covered in grey and black speckled down. **Bare parts** Iris dark brown; bill dark brown; legs and feet pale fleshy-brown.

MEASUREMENTS Wing (male) 165-177, (female) 165-179; tail (male) 99-110, (female) 97-110; bill (male) 18-20, (female) 18-20; tarsus (male) 18.0-23.5, (female) 18.0-24.1. Weight no data.

MOULT No data available.

GEOGRAPHICAL VARIATION Monotypic. Colour variation is slight, with birds occasionally being greyer and more heavily marked, or paler and more sandy-buff.

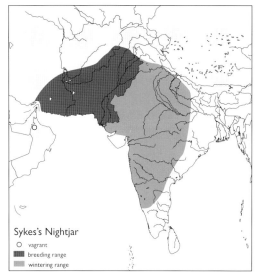

DISTRIBUTION AND MOVEMENTS Its rather limited breeding range is confined to SE Iran, S Afghanistan and Pakistan. Sedentary and partially migratory. In winter, it disperses widely throughout western and central India, and has been recorded from Rajasthan, Kutch, N Gujarat, Saurashtra, W Khandesh, Deccan, Konkan, south to N Mysore.

A probable vagrant occurred at Madah, Oman, on 20 January 1997.

STATUS Locally common in parts of its range.

REFERENCES Ali & Ripley (1970), Roberts (1991).

---

84   VAURIE'S NIGHTJAR
Caprimulgus centralasicus   Plate 24

Caprimulgus centralasicus Vaurie, 1960, *Amer. Mus. Novit.* 1985, p.1 (Goma [or Guma], western Sinkiang [= Xinjiang], western China)

IDENTIFICATION Length 19cm. A small, sandy-coloured Asian nightjar, known only from a single female specimen. **At rest** Upperparts sandy-buff, streaked and vermiculated brown. No collar around the hindneck. Wing-coverts sandy-buff vermiculated brown and spotted pale buff. No obvious scapular pattern. Underparts pale buffish barred brown. **In flight** Lacks white markings on the wings, which are brown barred tawny, broadly tipped pale greyish-brown. The underwing is buffish. The two outer tail feathers are narrowly tipped pale buffish-white. **Similar species** Egyptian Nightjar (82) is larger, slightly greyer, with a more spotted rather than streaked appearance and, in flight, the upperwing is darker, the underwing white. Immatures of the Asian race *plumipes* of European Nightjar (79) may prove to be extremely similar!

VOICE Unknown.

HABITAT Possibly arid plains and sandy foothills covered in low scrub.

HABITS No information available.

FOOD No data available.

BREEDING No information available.

DESCRIPTION Adult male Unknown. **Adult female** (Immature?) Forehead, crown and nape sandy-buff vermiculated brown; rear of crown and nape broadly streaked dark brown. No collar around the hindneck. Mantle, back, rump and uppertail-coverts sandy-buff, finely streaked and vermiculated brown. Primary coverts brown, broadly barred buffish; rest of wing-coverts sandy-buff, vermiculated brown and spotted pale buff. Scapulars sandy-buff, streaked dark brown along feather-shafts. Primaries and secondaries brown barred tawny, broadly tipped pale greyish-brown. Tertials sandy-buff, vermiculated brown and tipped pale buff. Tail sandy-buff, thinly barred brown; R5 and R4 tipped pale buffish-white (c. 7mm). Ill-defined buffish-white supercilium, lores creamy buff and ear-coverts tawny-buff barred brown. Chin and throat pale buff. Small buffish-white spot on either side of lower throat. Breast buffish-white barred brown. Belly and flanks buff barred brown. Undertail-coverts buff. Underwing-coverts pale tawny-buff barred brown. **Immature** and **Juvenile** Not known (unless the only known specimen is immature). **Chick** Not known. **Bare parts** Iris dark brown; bill dark horn; legs and feet fleshy-brown.

MEASUREMENTS (one female) Wing 161; tail 97; bill 13.1; tarsus 14.8. Weight no data.

MOULT The only known specimen was in active primary moult when taken, with P1-P7 new and P8-P10 nearly fully grown, P10 slightly shorter than (and therefore behind) P9 and P8. The primaries are therefore moulted descendantly. No further data available.

GEOGRAPHICAL VARIATION Monotypic. The validity of this species is questionable, as the only known specimen was taken from within the breeding range of one of the Asian races (*plumipes*) of European Nightjar (see that species).

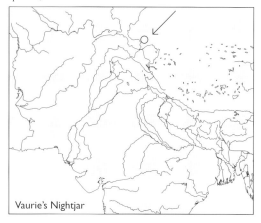

DISTRIBUTION AND MOVEMENTS The only known specimen was taken at 37°31'N 78°17'E from Goma (= Pishan), south-western Xinjiang, western China, on 7 September 1929. If a valid species, it possibly occurs

244

throughout the southern Tarim basin along the Kun Lun.

STATUS Known only from the type specimen.

REFERENCES Vaurie (1960a).

---

85 NUBIAN NIGHTJAR
Caprimulgus nubicus Plate 26

Caprimulgus nubicus Lichtenstein, 1823, *Verz. Doubl. Zool. Mus. Berlin* p.59 (Nubia)
Caprimulgus nubicus tamaricis Tristram, 1864, *Proc. Zool. Soc. London* p.170, 430 (Dead Sea depression, Palestine)
Caprimulgus nubicus torridus Lort Phillips, 1898, *Bull. Brit. Orn. Club* 8, p.23 (Eyk, Haud Plateau, Somalia)
Caprimulgus nubicus jonesi Ogilvie-Grant and Forbes, 1899, *Bull. Liverpool Mus.* 2, p.3 (Dimichiro Valley, Garieh Plain, Socotra Island)

IDENTIFICATION Length 21-22cm. A small, highly variable Afrotropical nightjar, its breeding range extending north-east into parts of the southern Palearctic. Sexually dimorphic. **At rest** Upperparts generally greyish or buffish, thinly streaked blackish-brown. Crown often heavily streaked or spotted rufous. Broad tawny-buff collar on hindneck. Wing-coverts and scapulars lightly spotted buff or heavily spotted tawny and buff. White throat-patch often restricted to a small spot on either side of the lower throat. Underparts buff barred brown. **In flight** Wings are fairly broad and rounded. The male has a large white spot towards the wing-tip on the four outer primaries (inner web only of outermost) and broad white tips to the two outer tail feathers. The female has smaller white spots, edged buffish, on the four outer primaries, and occasionally smaller white tips to the two outer tail feathers. **Similar species** Donaldson-Smith's Nightjar (91) is slightly smaller, less round-winged and generally chestnut or rufous in colour, with smaller white spots on four outer primaries and smaller white tips to outer two tail feathers. Slender-tailed Nightjar (110) lacks bold tawny or buff spotting on the upperparts and has a longer, gradated tail; males have a white trailing edge to the inner wing, a whitish line across the closed forewing and a white edge to the outermost tail feather (white replaced with buffish on females).

VOICE The song is a double-noted *ow-wow* or occasionally treble-noted *ow-wow-wow*, continuously repeated for up to 35 seconds or more and similar to the song of Freckled Nightjar (103). It is occasionally followed by a lower-pitched, four-noted *whow-whow-whow-whow* or a low *bruur* repeated up to eight times. Sings from the ground and whilst doing so the white throat-patch is extremely visible. Said to have a call note similar to that of European Nightjar (79).

HABITAT Occurs in tamarisk thickets, wadis with *Hyphaene* and tamarisk, acacia scrub, often near water, dry riverbeds with pools or short stretches of running water, desert thornscrub, sparsely vegetated sandy areas, saltmarshes? and bushy coastal dunes. In Yemen, also occurs in climax acacia/euphorbia woodland. 0–1,000m (rarely to 1,650m).

HABITS Crepuscular and nocturnal. Roosts on bare ground in the shade of rocks and bushes. On passage, also roosts on hard sand beneath low thorn bushes

amongst coastal dunes. At night, often sits on sandy roads and tracks and in open spaces. When singing, the white throat-patches are extremely visible. Occasionally claps wings when flushed and in flight? In Somalia, moves away from wadis after the rains, out into open bush country, usually to places where water collects. Feeds from dusk onwards by flitting about for insects, often close to water. In Saudi Arabia, it also forages on the ground amongst animal droppings. No further information available.

FOOD Moths, grasshoppers and beetles. No further data available.

BREEDING Breeding season April–July? in Israel; May?–September in Saudi Arabia (juvenile late September); June–August in NW Somalia (juvenile August) and late March–May in S Kenya. No data available from other regions.

No nest is constructed; the eggs are laid on bare soil, sand, or gypsum. Nest-sites may be at the base of small thorn bushes in semi-desert regions or on rocky scarps. Clutch 1-2. Eggs elliptical, ivory white or dull white, marbled or blotched lilac and brown, 25.0-26.0 x 19.0mm. No further information available.

DESCRIPTION *C. n. nubicus* **Adult male** Forehead, crown and nape cinnamon finely speckled brown, central feathers streaked blackish-brown. Broad tawny collar on hindneck. Mantle, back, rump and uppertail-coverts cinnamon finely speckled brown. Lesser and median coverts cinnamon, many of the feathers having large buff or tawny-buff spot covering half the outerweb. Primary and greater coverts dark brown broadly barred tawny. Scapulars either buff on one web, speckled brownish on the other, or blackish-brown broadly edged buff both webs. Primaries and secondaries dark brown; large white spot, almost mid-way along outer wing, on inner web of P10 and both webs of P9-P7; inner six primaries and all secondaries broadly barred tawny. Tertials cinnamon finely speckled brown, thinly streaked and barred blackish-brown and spotted buff. Tail brown; R5-R2 barred and spotted tawny (often outerwebs only); R5 and R4 broadly (34-38mm) tipped white; central pair (R1) brownish-cinnamon speckled and thinly barred dark brown. Lores and ear-coverts cinnamon speckled buff and tawny. Thin white submoustachial stripe. Chin whitish; throat buff barred brown; small white patch on either side of lower throat; occasionally lower throat entirely white. Breast buff barred brown, becoming speckled brown on lower breast. Belly and flanks buff or cinnamon barred brown. Under-tail- and underwing-coverts buff, latter occasionally barred brown. **Adult female** Similar to the male. The white spots on the four outer primaries are smaller, edged buffish. The white tips to the two outer-tail feathers are often smaller, edged or washed buffish. **Immature** and **Juvenile** Similar to the adults but paler and plainer. **Chick** Not known. **Bare parts** Iris dark brown; bill dark brown; legs and feet brownish or greyish.

MEASUREMENTS Wing (male) 145-146, (female) 141-148; tail (male) 102-103, (female) 100-104; bill (male) 10-14.3, (female) 10-14.3; tarsus (male) 18-22, (female) 18-22. Weight no data.

MOULT The race *C. n. tamaricis* possibly undertakes a complete post-breeding moult between June and September, during which the primaries are moulted descendantly. No further data available.

GEOGRAPHICAL VARIATION Four races are currently recognised.

C. n. nubicus Described above.

C. n. tamaricis Greyer than the nominate, with thinner streaking on the crown. The white tips to the two outer tail feathers are larger (c. 34-46mm). Wing (male) 142-157, (female) 142-154; tail (male) 97-115, (female) 96-108. Weight (male, one) 46g, (female) no data.

C. n. torridus The largest race. Greyer than the nominate, with the crown heavily spotted rufous, wing-coverts heavily spotted buff and tawny-buff, scapulars heavily spotted tawny. The white tips to the two outer tails feathers are smaller (c. 24-28mm). Wing (male) 149-161, (female) 147-163; tail (male) 92-105, (female) 96-111. Weight (male) 47-55g, (female, one) 49g.

C. n. jonesi Greyer than the nominate, with broader blackish-brown streaking and some rufous and tawny spotting on the crown. Similar to *torridus* but with smaller tawny spotting on the scapulars and no heavy buff spotting on the wing-coverts. Apparently known only from the male type specimen. Wing 156; tail 104. Weight no data.

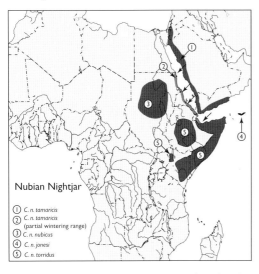

Nubian Nightjar

① *C. n. tamaricis*
② *C. n. tamaricis* (partial wintering range)
③ *C. n. nubicus*
④ *C. n. jonesi*
⑤ *C. n. torridus*

DISTRIBUTION AND MOVEMENTS Israel, Jordan, SW Saudi Arabia, S Yemen, Socotra Island and NE Africa.

C. n. nubicus Central Sudan. Probably sedentary.

C. n. tamaricis Israel, Jordan, SW Saudi Arabia (including one record from Farasan Islands), SW and S Yemen and Eritrea? Sedentary and partially migratory? Recorded throughout the breeding range during winter. Part of the population may move southwest, October–November, wintering in the coastal lowlands of NE Africa from NE Sudan and Eritrea to Djibouti and NW Somalia. Autumn wanderers also noted in NE Saudi Arabia and Oman (mainly October). Spring movements in Israel noted mid-February to late May (mainly March–April).

C. n. torridus Somalia, C Ethiopia, Kenya and possibly NE Uganda (near Moroto). Sedentary and partially migratory?

C. n. jonesi Socotra Island. Probably sedentary.

Two apparent sight records of this species (race unknown) from Merzouga, SW Morocco, are questionable.

STATUS Locally uncommon to common throughout East African range; scarce in Israel, Jordan, SW Arabia and Socotra. In Israel, has declined in numbers in recent years, and this is possibly due to disturbance, change in farming practices, and increased road traffic.

REFERENCES Archer & Godman (1961), Cramp (1985), Fry *et al.* (1988), Peters & Loveridge (1936), Shirihai (1996), Zimmerman *et al.* (1996).

86 GOLDEN NIGHTJAR
Caprimulgus eximius   Plate 24

Caprimulgus eximius Temminck, 1826, *Pl. Col.* livr. 67, pl.398 (Sennar, Sudan)
Caprimulgus eximius simplicior Hartert, 1921, *Novit. Zool.* 28, p.109 (Zinder, Niger)

IDENTIFICATION Length 23-25cm. A small to medium-sized, uniquely coloured Afrotropical nightjar, occurring in semi-desert across the Sahel. Sexes similar. **At rest** Often appears large-headed. Upperparts and wing-coverts tawny or tawny-buff, covered with greyish-white rectangular spots which are edged and densely speckled dark brown. No collar on hindneck. Large white throat-patch. Underparts similar to upperparts on upper breast, becoming paler and unmarked on lower breast and belly. **In flight** Both sexes have a large white spot towards the wing-tip on the four outer primaries, and broad white tips to the two outer tail feathers. Appears rather pale in poor or artificial light. **Similar species** None. Egyptian Nightjar (82) occurs throughout much of the same range during winter (December–March?) but is larger, sandy-grey, with longer, more pointed wings, generally lacking white in the outer primaries and male with only small pale tips to the two outer tail feathers.

VOICE The song is a low pitched churr, which may last up to several minutes. Sings from the ground, and may be heard predominately at dusk and dawn.

HABITAT Prefers grassy semi-desert with scrub, also occurring on sandy, gravelly, stony or rocky terrain, often with clumps of grass and scrub, and on fallow land. In northern Senegal, also occurs in open sandy country with scattered trees. Avoids woodland and areas of dense scrub. 0–600m.

HABITS Crepuscular and nocturnal. Roosts on the ground. Not easily flushed, and may shuffle out of the way of animals rather than take flight. Feeds at dusk, often close to and over water. In Sudan, birds may occur with Egyptian Nightjars. No further information available.

FOOD Grasshoppers, moths, mantises, bugs and beetles (including Elateridae, Scarabaeidae and Cerambycidae). No further data available.

BREEDING Breeding season April–May in N Senegal and Mali; March–April in Sudan.

No nest is constructed; the eggs are laid on bare ground. Nest-sites are usually near vegetation, e.g. clumps of grass. Clutch usually 2. Eggs ovate, greyish-white or greyish-buff, heavily blotched greyish or yellowish-brown over mauve, 28.2-29.5 x 20.6-21.6mm. No further information available.

DESCRIPTION *C. e. eximius* **Adult male** Forehead, crown and nape tawny or tawny-buff, densely spotted greyish-white speckled dark brown. No collar on hindneck. Mantle and back tawny or tawny-buff with fewer and fainter markings than on head and almost unmarked on some individuals. Wing-coverts, tawny-buff on lesser coverts, becoming paler and buffier over median and greater coverts, densely covered in greyish-white rectangular spots, edged and speckled dark brown. Primary coverts tawny, thickly spotted or barred dark brown. Scapulars similar to the wing-coverts but also with dark brown arrowhead or star-shaped markings towards feather-tips. Outer primaries dark brown, barred tawny, pale tawny or greyish-white, speckled brown at tips; large white spot, towards the feather-tip, across both webs of P10-P7; inner primaries and all secondaries tawny, spotted or barred dark brown, bars at feather-tips often greyish-white speckled brown. Tertials similar to rest of upperparts. Tail tawny or tawny-buff, R5 and R4 barred brown, with broad dark brown subterminal bar and broad (32-47mm) white tips; rest of tail barred greyish-white speckled brown. Lores and ear-coverts tawny-cinnamon, generally unmarked. Chin buff. Large white triangular patch covering entire throat, lower feathers of which are narrowly tipped dark brown with buff or pale tawny spot in centre, or broadly tipped tawny. Breast tawny-buff with similar markings to head. Belly and flanks buff, thinly barred brown on upper breast only. Undertail-coverts pale buff or whitish, unmarked. Underwing-coverts buff or whitish, generally unmarked but occasionally faintly vermiculated brown. **Adult female** Similar to the male but the white spots on the four outer primaries are narrowly edged tawny-buff and the white tips to the two outer tail feathers are fractionally smaller, often washed buff or pale tawny. **Immature** and **Juvenile** Similar to the adults but paler and plainer. **Chick** At hatching, covered in rufous-isabelline down. **Bare parts** Iris, bill, legs and feet greyish-black.

MEASUREMENTS Wing (male) 171-187, (female) 174-183; tail (male) 108-125, (female) 113-117; bill (male) 10-13, (female) 10-13; tarsus (male) 20-23, (female) 20-23. Weight (male, one) 66.3g, (female) no data.

MOULT No published data available.

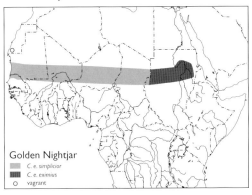

Golden Nightjar
- C. e. simplicior
- C. e. eximius
- O vagrant

GEOGRAPHICAL VARIATION Two races are currently recognised.

   C. e. eximius Described above.

   C. e. simplicior Generally paler and buffier than the nominate, although some birds are often rather tawny. Wing (male) 179-187, (female, one) 173; tail (male) 113-123, (female, one) 119. Weight no data.

DISTRIBUTION AND MOVEMENTS An Afrotropical species, occurring discontinuously throughout the Sahel region.

   C. e. eximius C Sudan. Sedentary.

   C. e. simplicior S Mauritania, N Senegal, C and E Mali, S and SE Niger and C Chad. Generally sedentary, although may undertake local movements outside the breeding season. A vagrant recorded (June) at Guelta du Zemmour, SW Morocco.

STATUS Locally uncommon to fairly common throughout its range, but under-recorded in many regions.

REFERENCES Fry *et al.* (1988), Rothschild & Wollaston (1902).

---

87   LARGE-TAILED NIGHTJAR
Caprimulgus macrurus   Plate 32

Other name: Coffinbird

Caprimulgus macrurus Horsfield, 1821, *Trans. Linn. Soc. London* 13, pt. 1, p.142 (Java)
Caprimulgus macrurus andamanicus Hume, 1873, *Stray Feath.* 1, p.470 (Jolly Boys Island, Andaman Islands)
Caprimulgus macrurus albonotatus Tickell, 1833, *J. Asiatic Soc. Bengal* 2, p.580 (Dampara, Dholbhum, Bengal)
Caprimulgus macrurus bimaculatus Peale, 1848, *U.S. Expl. Exped.* 8, p.170 (Singapore)
Caprimulgus macrurus salvadorii Sharpe, 1875, *Proc. Zool. Soc. London* 99, pl.22, fig. 1 (Labuan Island)
Caprimulgus macrurus johnsoni Deignan, 1955, *Sarawak Mus. J.* 6, p.315 (Puerto Princesa, Palawan Island)
Caprimulgus macrurus schlegelii Meyer, 1874, *Sitzb. Akad. Wiss. Wien* 69, p.210 (no locality = Port Essington, ex Gould, *Birds Austral.* 2, pl.9)

Forms a superspecies, and was formerly considered conspecific, with Jerdon's, Philippine and Sulawesi Nightjars.

IDENTIFICATION Length 25-29cm. A generally large and fairly long-tailed, greyish-brown, variegated nightjar, occurring from South-East Asia to northern Australia. Variable in size and colour. Sexually dimorphic. **At rest** Upperparts greyish-brown streaked blackish-brown, broadly so on crown. Indistinct buff or tawny-buff collar on hindneck. Wing-coverts greyish-brown, spotted buff or tawny-buff, lesser coverts darker. Scapulars blackish-brown, broadly bordered buff on outerwebs. White sub-moustachial stripe, large white patch on throat. Underparts brownish, barred and speckled buff, becoming buff barred brown on belly and flanks. **In flight** Wings fairly pointed, flight erratic and stiff-winged. The male has a large white spot towards the wing-tip on the four outer primaries (inner web only on outermost) and broad white tips to the two outer tail feathers. The female has smaller buff spots on the four outer primaries and narrower buff or buffish-white tips to the two outer tail feathers. **Similar species** Jerdon's Nightjar (88) is extremely similar but has a paler head, less streaking on the crown and a more rufous hindneck, mantle, back and breast, the male with smaller white spots on the four outer primaries, the female with smaller buff spots; it is also smaller and less buffish than the race *albonotatus* in parts of north-eastern India where the ranges of the two species overlap. Philippine Nightjar

(89), endemic to the Philippines except Palawan, is also extremely similar but is smaller with a more speckled and spotted appearance and a distinct buffish line across the forewing, the male having smaller white spots on the outer primaries and narrower white tips to the two outer tail feathers (the outerweb of the outermost often wholly or partly dark brown), the female similar but often with buffier spots on the four outer primaries. Sulawesi Nightjar (90), endemic to Sulawesi and the Sula Islands, has smaller white spots on the four outer primaries and narrower white tips to the two outer tail feathers (generally similar in plumage to Philippine Nightjar). Indian Nightjar (96) is smaller, with a distinct tawny-buff hindneck collar and wing-coverts heavily spotted tawny-buff; the male has smaller white spots on the four outer primaries, the female smaller white spots edged or washed buff. Jungle Nightjar (78) has the wing-coverts heavily spotted greyish-white or buffish, the male with all but the central pair of tail feathers narrowly tipped white or white and brown, the female with brownish-white or brownish-buff tips. Savanna Nightjar (102) is slightly smaller, greyer and less variegated, the male having the two outer tail feathers generally white, the female lacking white on the tail.

VOICE The song is a continuous chopping or knocking sound, consisting of *chock* or *tok* notes repeated at variable rates for minutes on end. It is occasionally preceded by low grunting, croaking or growling notes, given in flight or from the ground. Sings from perches, from the ground and occasionally in flight. At song-posts, often turns around to sing in different directions, and whilst singing the white throat-patch is puffed out and extremely visible. May mostly be heard at dusk and dawn, but sometimes throughout the night and occasionally briefly during the day. The flight call is a treble-noted *chock-a-chock*. During courtship displays, possibly both sexes utter low crooning notes. If flushed, both sexes may utter a deep harsh *chuck* note. The female calls the chicks to her with low croaking sounds. During distraction displays, possibly both sexes give loud croaks or guttural hissing sounds. The chicks beg for food with soft peeps. At night, chicks may utter a weak *chop-chop*.

HABITAT Occurs in a wide variety of habitats. In northern India it may be found in deciduous forests and woods, bamboo forest, forest clearings, secondary growth and scrub, thick bush and coffee estates. In Pakistan it occurs in subtropical dry deciduous forest, especially *Acacia modesta* with an understorey of *Adhatoda vasica* and *Carissa opaca*. In southern China it prefers forested foothills. On the Malay Peninsula it occurs in mangroves, open country, suburban gardens, villages and cultivated land in lowlands, and by roadsides, along broad rivers and in cleared areas in forests. Also occurs near beaches and on offshore islands. In Sumatra it occurs in generally open country such as cultivated lowlands and plantations, including young forests, also often in and around villages. In Borneo it prefers open lowland country and also inhabits gardens. On Palawan it occurs in secondary forest, bamboo forest, mangroves and cultivated areas. In south-eastern Indonesia it prefers woodland, forest edge and cultivation, and on Lombok and Sumbawa it also inhabits grasslands. In New Guinea it occurs along the edges of forests and mangroves, and in large forest clearings, second growth, disturbed habitats, savanna, mid-montane grasslands, gardens and dry streambeds through forest, also on river sandbanks and along roadsides. In northern Australia, it prefers monsoon forest, coastal forest, rainforest edge, bamboo thickets and paperbark woodland and swamps, plus overgrown creeks and open areas along the landward edges of mangroves. 0–2,700m in the northern parts of its range, 0–2,000m in New Guinea, 0–1,200m in Borneo and Wallacea and 0–900m in Sumatra. In N Pakistan, summers at 460–900m. No data available from other localities.

HABITS Crepuscular and nocturnal. Roosts amongst leaf-litter on the ground, amongst roots, or on logs. Roost-sites are usually in shaded or partly shaded places, with or without ground cover. Usually roosts singly but quite often pairs rest close together. In parts of its range it may be loosely gregarious and up to 12 birds may roost in favoured spots. When flushed from its roost, it flies low and erratically, alighting on the ground, low branches or fallen logs. Commonly sits on roads, tracks, bare ground and paths at night. Occasionally shuffles short distances on the ground when active, and often alights across or lengthways on branches and other perches, including slender wire clotheslines. Hovers in flight, although perhaps only occasionally. When perched, continually turns head looking for insects, even whilst singing. Feeds by flycatching from perches or hawking over clearings, glades and open country. Also feeds on the ground, or flies up from roads and tracks and hunts over nearby open ground. In Australia, appears to forage over areas of c. 50ha. Occasionally hovers near grazing animals and feeds on insects disturbed from ground vegetation. No further information available.

FOOD Moths, crickets, grasshoppers, wasps, earwigs, bugs and beetles (including Elateridae, Copridae, Tenebrionidae, Carabidae, Curculionidae, Cantharidae and Scarabaeidae). No further data available.

BREEDING Breeding season March–May in N India and Burma; March–June in N Thailand; March–April on the Andaman Islands; January–June? on the Malay Peninsula; January–May in Sumatra; July on Palawan; ?–April in Sarawak; September–February in Java; October on Flores; September on Bacan; September–January in New Guinea (also July in western highlands), September–November? in New Britain and September–November, occasionally August–January, in N Australia. No data from other localities. Breeding season in some of the areas mentioned is probably longer than described.

Territorial, perhaps permanently so in parts of its range, e.g. Australia. During territorial or courtship displays, males glide with wings raised and tail fanned, revealing the white markings. During aerial courtship, a pair may fly close together in a buoyant flight full of turns, dives and jinks. Both sexes also occasionally hover. Courtship also takes place on the ground. The male and female face each other, sometimes with their wings spread, and touch bills, swaying from side to side, shuffling about and making soft crooning sounds (see Voice). Occasionally, two or three pairs may congregate at these display arenas.

No nest is constructed; the eggs are laid on leaf-litter, bare ground or sand. Nest-sites may be beneath bushes or trees, close to stones, at the foot of banks, on lawns, in open areas, along the edges of forests and woods, on hillsides or on seashores. In parts of its range, e.g. India, several nests may be occupied in the same vicinity and breeding may therefore be loosely colonial. Nest-sites may be used for several years in succession. Clutch 1-2. Eggs elliptical or oval, glossy, whitish, cream, pale pinkish-cream or salmon-buff, indistinctly blotched and spotted grey, pale purplish-brown and lavender, 26.1-34.5 x 19.8-25.3 (33.0?) mm. Both sexes may incubate, but incubation is usually by the female during the day, the male often roosting 20-30m from the nest-site. If flushed from the eggs, the adult performs an injury-feigning distraction display along the ground. The adult (this species?) may also fly a short distance, alight and move around, raising its wings and gaping. The incubation period is c. 16-22 days.

The semi-precocial young can leave the nest-site within the first two days, moving distances of up to 3m. The female calls the chicks to her (see Voice). If the young do not respond, she runs towards them with her wings held above her body. If flushed from the chicks, the adult injury-feigns (see above), or performs a different distraction display by alighting on a nearby perch, drooping its wings, gaping and calling (see Voice). Both sexes incubate and feed the young by regurgitation. When mobile, the chicks run and hop about with their wings held up. They are brooded during the day for 14 days or more and become independent at c. 35 days. The adults and young may remain in loose family groups for another month or two, roosting close to each other during the day.

Probably single-brooded.

DESCRIPTION *C. m. macrurus* **Adult male** Forehead, crown and nape greyish-brown streaked blackish-brown, broadly so on central crown. Indistinct collar around hindneck buff or tawny-buff, barred brown. Mantle, back, rump and uppertail-coverts brown streaked dark brown, faintly barred greyish-brown or pale tawny. Lesser coverts dark brown, minutely speckled rufous, marginal coverts brown barred buff; primary coverts brown barred tawny. Rest of wing-coverts brown speckled tawny and buff, boldly spotted buff. Scapulars either blackish-brown broadly edged buff on the outerwebs or greyish-brown speckled brown, the outerwebs broadly tipped blackish-brown, with a narrow tawny subterminal band. Primaries brown; large white spot towards the feather-tip on P10 (inner web only) and P9, and broad white band across P8 and P7; vestigial white mark on P6; P6-P1 barred and spotted tawny (outer-webs) and buff (innerwebs). Secondaries brown, barred and speckled tawny and tawny-buff. Tertials brown mottled buffish, streaked and spotted blackish-brown. Tail brown, very faintly barred brownish-buff; R5 and R4 broadly (c. 40-50mm) tipped white, with brownish smudges along edges of outerwebs; R5 and R4 also barred buff along outerwebs, above white tips; central pair (R1) broadly but faintly barred greyish-brown tinged buff. Lores and ear-coverts tawny-rufous narrowly barred brown. Chin and throat tawny barred brown. Large white patch on lower throat, the lower feathers of which are broadly tipped blackish-brown with a buff subterminal band. Breast brown, speckled and spotted greyish-buff, buff and tawny. Belly, flanks, underwing- and undertail-coverts buff barred brown, latter broadly tipped buffish-white. **Adult female** Similar to the male, but the spots on the four outer primaries are buff, and R5 and R4 are tipped buffish or buffish-white (17-28mm). **Immature** and **Juvenile** Similar to the adults, but duller and tawnier. **Chick** At hatching, covered in pinkish-buff down, speckled and mottled blackish. **Bare parts** Iris dark brown; bill blackish; legs and feet blackish.

MEASUREMENTS Wing (male) 174-195, (female) 168-194; tail (male) 126-154, (female) 122-140; bill (male) 15.2-15.8, (female) 15.2-15.8; tarsus (male) 15-17, (female) 15-17. Weight (unsexed) 55-77g.

MOULT Adults and immatures probably undertake a complete post-breeding moult. The primaries are moulted descendantly, but the sequence of secondary moult has not been documented. The tail moult is probably centrifugal.

GEOGRAPHICAL VARIATION Seven races are currently recognised, differing mainly in size and overall coloration.

C. m. macrurus Described above.

C. m. andamanicus A dark race with reduced but variable white (male) or buff (female) spots on the four outer primaries. Shorter-tailed than the nominate, with tips to R5 and R4 narrower (31-37mm) in the male, 18-26mm in the female, whose throat is buffish. Wing (male) 176-189, (female) 174-183; tail (male) 113-131, (female) 111-125. Weight no data.

C. m. albonotatus The largest and palest, rather buffish race. The female has tips to R5 and R4 broader (18-44mm) than on the nominate. Wing (male) 197-235, (female) 192-220; tail (male) 142-180, (female) 146-164. Weight (male, two) 74-79g, (female) no data. Intergrades with *bimaculatus* in the east.

C. m. bimaculatus Similar to the nominate but larger. Wing (male) 184-212, (female) 178-210; tail (male) 126-162, (female) 125-163. Weight (male) no data, female (one) 61g, unsexed (one) 90.1g.

C. m. salvadorii Darker than the nominate, with more blackish upperparts, almost white edges to the wing-coverts and less rufous underparts. Wing (male) 178-194, (female) 175-193; tail (male) 124-140, (female) 121-138. Weight no data.

C. m. johnsoni Slightly darker than the nominate. Wing (male) 173-187, (female) 171-179; tail (male) 129-138, (female) 116-125. Weight (male) no data, (female, one) 53g, unsexed (one) 66g.

C. m. schlegelii Similar to the nominate but upperparts slightly darker with less cinnamon, the crown more coarsely speckled. The underparts, especially the breast, are also darker. Tips to R5 and R4 as broad as 34-65mm in the male. Wing (male) 170-196, (female) 170-195; tail (male) 120-154, (female) 118-151. Weight (male) 54-79g, (female) 60-74g.

DISTRIBUTION AND MOVEMENTS Widely distributed from north-eastern India, south-east through Indochina and Indonesia, to northern and north-eastern Australia.

C. m. macrurus Java and Bali. Sedentary.

C. m. andamanicus Confined to the Andaman Islands, but possibly absent from Little Andaman. Sedentary.

C. m. albonotatus NE Pakistan (Murree foothills, Lehtrar Valley and Kahuta), N India (Punjab east to Assam and the Burmese border, south to S Andhra Pradesh), S Nepal, Bhutan and Bangladesh. Sedentary and partially migratory. Summer breeding visitor to Pakistan (Murree foothills around Margalla hills, lower Lehtrar Valley and Kahuta), arriving from mid-to late March and departing in September, when it probably moves eastwards to the Siwaliks. Less frequent October–February in other parts of its range and perhaps subject to some local movements.

C. m. bimaculatus NW India (Assam), Burma, S China (SW Yunnan and Hainan), Vietnam, Laos, Thailand, Cambodia, Malay Peninsula (south to Singapore) and the islands of Phuket, Sireh, Langkawi, Penang, Besar,

Berani, Senang, Ubin, Tekong and Ayer Merbau, Sumatra and the Riau Archipelago (Bulan, Galang, Batam and Bintan). Sedentary. In the north-west of its range, it merges into *C. m. albonotatus*.

C. m. salvadorii W, N and SE Borneo (Sarawak, Brunei, Sabah and Kalimantan Selatan), including Labuan, Balambangan, Banguey and the southern Sulu Islands (Bangao). Sedentary.

C. m. johnsoni Palawan and probably the Calamian Group. Sedentary.

C. m. schlegelii Wallacea, New Guinea and islands and N Australia. Recorded from Buton Island, Salayar Islands, Lesser Sunda Islands (Lombok east to Tanimbar), the Moluccas but not the Sula Islands, western Papuan Islands (Waigeo and Salawati), New Guinea, Geelvink Bay islands, D'Entrecasteaux Archipelago (Goodenough and Fergusson Islands), Louisiade Archipelago (Tagula), Manam Island, Karkar and Bagabag Islands, Bismarck Archipelago (Long, Tolokiwa, Umboi, New Britain, Lolobau, Watom, New Ireland, New Hanover, Tabar and Lihir), N Australia (extreme north of Northern Territory from Port Keats to Yirrkala, and including Melville Island and Groote Eylandt) and NE Australia (NE Queensland from Cape York to Fraser Island). Breeds or has bred Curtis Island. Possibly occurs as a vagrant as far south as the Queensland–New South Wales border). Sedentary but may undertake local movements in parts of its range. Records from SE Australia (Wallis Lake, New South Wales, and Mallee, South Australia) have been questioned by some authorities.

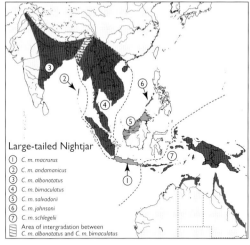

Large-tailed Nightjar
① *C. m. macrurus*
② *C. m. andamanicus*
③ *C. m. albonotatus*
④ *C. m. bimaculatus*
⑤ *C. m. salvadorii*
⑥ *C. m. johnsoni*
⑦ *C. m. schlegelii*
▨ Area of intergradation between
C. m. albonotatus and *C. m. bimaculatus*

STATUS Common to locally abundant throughout much of its range, although scarce or absent from some localities.

REFERENCES Ali & Ripley (1970), Diamond & LeCroy (1979), Higgins (in press), Mees (1977, 1985), Ripley & Beehler (1987), Roberts (1991), Schodde & Mason (1981, 1997).

88   JERDON'S NIGHTJAR
Caprimulgus atripennis   Plate 32

Caprimulgus atripennis Jerdon, 1845, *Illustr. Indian Orn.* pl. 24 (Eastern Ghats to west of Nellore)
Caprimulgus atripennis aequabilis Ripley, 1945, *Bull. Brit. Orn. Club* 65, p.40 (Trincomalee, north-east Ceylon)

Forms a superspecies, and was formerly considered conspecific, with Large-tailed, Philippine and Sulawesi Nightjars.

IDENTIFICATION Length 25.5-27cm. A large, greyish-brown, variegated nightjar, restricted to southern India and Sri Lanka. Sexually dimorphic. **At rest** Often appears rather pale-headed. Crown greyish-brown, central feathers boldly but sparsely spotted or streaked blackish-brown. Rest of upperparts greyish-brown tinged rufous. Collar around hindneck generally rufous and ill-defined, often merging into mantle. Lesser coverts dark brown speckled rufous, rest of coverts greyish-brown, speckled and spotted buff. Scapulars largely blackish-brown, with pale tawny bar across middle of feather. Underparts brownish speckled buff, cinnamon and rufous-buff, becoming buff barred brown on belly and flanks. **In flight** Wings pointed. The male has a white spot towards the wing-tip on the four outer primaries (innerweb only on outermost) and broad white tips to the two outer tail feathers. The female has smaller, buffish spots on the four outer primaries and narrower buff or buffish-white tips to the two outer tail feathers. **Similar species** Large-tailed Nightjar (87) is extremely similar but greyer-brown overall and crown heavily streaked blackish-brown, the male with larger white spots on the four outer primaries, the female with larger buff spots; in parts of north-eastern India where the ranges of the two species overlap, the race *albonotatus* is also larger and paler, more buffish. Indian Nightjar (96) is smaller, with heavier streaking on the crown, a distinct tawny-buff collar around the hindneck and heavier tawny-buff spotting on the wing-coverts; the male has smaller white spots on the four outer primaries, the female smaller buff spots. Jungle Nightjar (78) has the wing-coverts heavily spotted greyish-white or buffish, the male having all but the central pair of tail feathers narrowly tipped white or white and brown, the female brownish-white or -buff tips.

VOICE The song is a loud, liquid *ow-r-r-r*, repeated every three seconds or so for minutes on end. Singing is often preceded by low *grog-grog-grog* notes. Sings from perches, such as branches or low stumps. May mostly be heard at dusk and dawn.

HABITAT Prefers forested country, occurring in evergreen, moist deciduous, dry, and mixed bamboo forest and secondary scrub jungle. Also found in disturbed habitats, such as coffee estates and the vicinity of towns. In Sri Lanka, also occurs in tracts of woodland in semi-cultivated country and in scrubland. 0–2,000m.

HABITS Crepuscular and nocturnal. Roosts on the ground. When active, frequently perches lengthways and across branches and also settles on tops of vertical snags and stumps. At night, often sits on roads and tracks or on bare patches of earth in woodland. When foraging, swooping flight is quite powerful but also glides with wings held vertically. No further information available.

FOOD Beetles, moths and termites. No further data available.

BREEDING Breeding season March–July (mainly March–April) in India; February–May and August–September in Sri Lanka.

No nest is constructed; the eggs are usually laid on sandy ground. Nest-sites are often beneath shrubs and bushes. Clutch 2. Eggs elliptical, cream or buffish, sparsely spotted and speckled brown, dark brown and grey, 28.5-31.3 x 20.4-23.5mm. Both sexes share incubation. The semi-precocial young can leave the nest-site soon after hatching. If danger approaches, chicks may move and hide under vegetation. No further information available.

DESCRIPTION *C. a. atripennis* **Adult male** Forehead, crown and nape greyish-brown speckled pale buff, central feathers sparsely but boldly spotted or streaked blackish-brown. Indistinct collar on hindneck, rufous tinged tawny or buff, streaked and speckled brown, collar often merging into mantle. Mantle, back, rump and uppertail-coverts brown tinged rufous, streaked, speckled and spotted brown. Lesser coverts dark brown speckled rufous. Rest of wing-coverts greyish-brown speckled brown and buff, boldly spotted buff. Scapulars brown speckled greyish-brown, tawny and buff, broadly tipped blackish-brown. Distinct thin tawny bar across middle of feather. Primaries brown; white spot towards the feather-tip on innerweb of P10 and across both webs of P9-P7, spots often edged buffish; inner six primaries spotted and mottled tawny. Secondaries brown, regularly spotted and mottled tawny. Tertials greyish-brown mottled brown and pale tawny. Tail brown, faintly mottled pale tawny and greyish-brown; R5 and R4 broadly (32-56mm) tipped white, tips often edged buffish; central pair (R1) greyish-brown, mottled and barred brown. Lores chestnut or tawny, speckled brown. Ear-coverts tawny or buff, speckled brown. Sides of head, below ear-coverts, buff or tawny-buff, barred brown. Chin and throat rufous or dark buff, speckled brown. White patch across lower throat, the lower feathers of which are broadly tipped dark brown, with a buff subterminal band. Breast brownish, speckled buff, cinnamon or rufous-buff. Belly and flanks buff or dark buff, barred brown. Undertail- and underwing-coverts buff barred brown. **Adult female** Similar to the male. The spots on the four outer primaries are smaller and buffish. R5 and R4 tipped white or buffish-white, 20-32mm (often innerweb only on R5). **Immature** and **Juvenile** Similar to the adults but paler. Crown less heavily spotted. **Chick** Not described. **Bare parts** Iris brown; bill dark brown; legs and feet dark brown.

MEASUREMENTS Wing (male) 173-185, (female) 170-186; tail (male) 120-142, (female) 120-131; bill (male) 13.1-16.8, (female) 15.5-21.5; tarsus (male) 19.5-20.9, (female) 16.0-18.5. Weight (male, one) 55g.

MOULT No data available.

GEOGRAPHICAL VARIATION Two races are currently recognised, although some authorities consider the species to be monotypic.

C. a. atripennis Described above. Little colour variation noted, but paler individuals do occur. Darker birds are rare.

C. a. aequabilis Darker than the nominate, especially on the upperparts. The indistinct collar on the hindneck is narrower, duller and streaked blackish. The breast is greyer, finely patterned black. Tips of R5 and

R4 35-49mm in the male, 22-25mm in the female. Wing (male) 165-181, (female) 166-186; tail (male) 118-135, (female) 114-127. Weight no data.

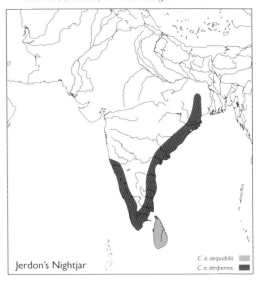

Jerdon's Nightjar

C. a. aequabilis
C. a. atripennis

DISTRIBUTION AND MOVEMENTS Confined to southern and eastern India and Sri Lanka.

C. a. atripennis India, in the Western Ghats (Kerala north to S Maharashtra) and the Eastern Ghats (Tamil Nadu north to Durgapur, West Bengal). Sedentary.

C. a. aequabilis Sri Lanka. Sedentary.

STATUS Reasonably common throughout its range.

REFERENCES Ali & Ripley (1970), Mees (1977, 1985), Ripley & Beehler (1987).

89   PHILIPPINE NIGHTJAR
Caprimulgus manillensis   Plate 32

Caprimulgus manillensis Walden, 1875, *Trans. Zool. Soc. London* 9, Pt. 2, p.159 (Manila ex G. R. Gray, 1848, *List Bds. Brit. Mus., Fissirostres* p.7, where a *nomen nudum*)

Forms a superspecies, and was formerly considered conspecific, with Jerdon's, Large-tailed and Sulawesi Nightjars.

IDENTIFICATION Length 23-26cm. A large, greyish-brown, variegated nightjar, occurring only on the Philippine Islands. Sexes similar. **At rest** Upperparts greyish-brown streaked blackish-brown, broadly so on crown. No collar on hindneck. Lesser coverts dark brown flecked tawny, rest of wing-coverts greyish-brown, spotted blackish-brown, tawny, buff and pale buff. Shows a buffish line across the forewing. Scapulars blackish-brown, broadly bordered buff on outerwebs. White band around throat. Underparts greyish-brown speckled brown, spotted buff, becoming buff barred brown on belly and flanks. **In flight** Wings fairly pointed. Both sexes have a white spot towards the wing-tip on the second, third and fourth outer primaries (innerweb only on second outermost) and white tips to the two outer tail feathers (the outerweb of the outermost often wholly or partly brown). **Similar species** Large-tailed Nightjar (87) is slightly larger, more variegated, with a distinct buffish line across the forewing at rest; the male has larger white spots on the outer primaries and broader, whiter tips to the two outer tail feathers; the female has buffish markings on the wing and tail. Sulawesi Nightjar (90), confined to Sulawesi and the Sula Islands, is extremely similar but both sexes have smaller, whiter tips to the two outer tail feathers and longer, stouter rictal bristles, although this feature is only noticeable at extremely close range. Jungle Nightjar (78) occurs on the Philippines in winter, August–May (see that species). Savanna Nightjar (102) is slightly smaller, with a less spotted appearance; in flight the male has the two outer tail feathers generally white, while the female lacks white on the tail.

VOICE The song is a continuously repeated *took-toor-r-r*, with only a slight pause between each set of notes. May be heard chiefly at dusk and dawn.

HABITAT Occurs in primary forest, secondary forest, pine forest, second growth, scrubland, open areas with clumps of trees, and mangroves. Also inhabits the edges of towns and agricultural areas and may be found near rocky beaches. 0–2,000m.

HABITS Crepuscular and nocturnal. No further information available.

FOOD No data available.

BREEDING Breeding season April–May, possibly longer.
No nest is constructed; the eggs are laid on leaf-litter on the ground. Nest-sites are usually in clearings or beside paths and trails, within forests or woodland. Clutch 1-2. Eggs elliptical or ovate, whitish, heavily blotched and spotted brown, dark brown and grey, 28.4-29.8 x 20.3-21.1mm. No further information available.

DESCRIPTION Adult male Forehead, crown and nape greyish-brown streaked blackish-brown, broadly so on central crown. No collar on hindneck. Mantle, back, rump and uppertail-coverts greyish-brown speckled brown, streaked blackish-brown. Lesser coverts dark brown flecked tawny. Median coverts (or lower lesser coverts?) brownish, broadly tipped buff, forming distinct buffish line across closed forewing. Rest of wing-coverts greyish-brown vermiculated brown on innerwebs, blackish-brown boldly spotted tawny, buff or pale buff on outerwebs. Scapulars blackish-brown, broadly edged buff on outerwebs. Primaries brown, P10 with small tawny spot towards the feather-tip on edge of innerweb, P9 with tawny or buffish mark on edge of outerweb and small whitish or buffish-white spot on innerweb, P8 and P7 with buffish-edged white spot across both webs; inner six primaries and secondaries brown regularly spotted tawny, tipped buffish or cinnamon. Tertials greyish-brown, mottled brown, blackish-brown and buffish. Tail brown; R5 and R4 barred tawny along outerwebs, broadly (23-35mm) tipped white, the outerweb of the white tip on R5 wholly or partly smudged brown; R3 and R2 faintly barred greyish-brown; central pair (R1Ô) mottled greyish-brown, speckled and barred brown. Lores and ear-coverts tawny or rufous, barred brown. Chin and throat brown barred buff. White patch extending around lower throat, the lower feathers of which are tipped blackish-brown, with a buff subterminal band. Breast greyish-brown speckled brown, streaked blackish-brown along feather-shafts. Upper belly greyish-brown, feathers streaked blackish-brown along shafts, broadly tipped buff. Lower belly, flanks, underwing-

and undertail-coverts buff barred brown, latter occasionally tipped whitish. **Adult female** Similar to the male. R5 and R4 tipped white, 15-30mm, the outerweb of R5 wholly or partly smudged brown. **Immature** and **Juvenile** Similar to the adults but browner and paler. **Chick** At hatching, covered in brownish-rufous down. **Bare parts** Iris dark brown; bill blackish; legs and feet blackish.

MEASUREMENTS Wing (male) 162-181, (female) 165-180; tail (male) 105-134, (female) 110-131; bill (male) 14.2-16.1, (female) 14.5-17.5; tarsus (male) 17.0-18.8, (female) 17.5-18.5. Weight (male) 59.9-68.0g, (female) 58.5-80.0g, unsexed 54.0-84.5g.

MOULT No data available.

GEOGRAPHICAL VARIATION Monotypic.

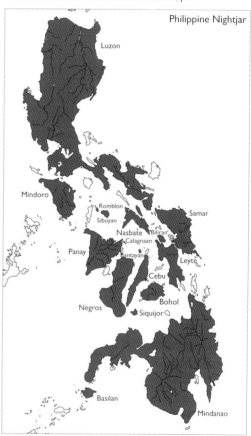

DISTRIBUTION AND MOVEMENTS Confined to the Philippines, but absent from the Palawan group. It occurs on Luzon, Mindoro, Ticao, Masbate, Panay, Negros, Romblon, Sibuyan, Bantayan, Cebu, Siquijor, Leyte, Samar, Biliran, Bohol, Calagnaan, Mindanao and Basilan. It is probably also found on some of the other islands. Sedentary.

STATUS Probably not common throughout its range.

REFERENCES Dickinson *et al.* (1991), Mees (1977, 1985).

Caprimulgus celebensis Ogilvie-Grant, 1894, *Ibis* (6)6, p.519 (Celebes)
Caprimulgus celebensis jungei Neumann, 1939, *Bull. Brit. Orn. Club* 59, p.92 (Taliaboe)

Forms a superspecies, and was formerly considered conspecific, with Jerdon's, Philippine and Large-tailed Nightjars.

IDENTIFICATION Length 24-30cm. A medium to large greyish-brown, variegated nightjar, endemic to Sulawesi and the Sula Islands. Sexes similar. **At rest** Upperparts greyish-brown streaked blackish-brown, broadly so on central crown. Generally no collar on hindneck. Lesser coverts dark brown speckled tawny and buff. Rest of wing-coverts greyish-brown, boldly spotted buff, pale buff and tawny. Scapulars blackish-brown edged buffish. White throat-patch. Underparts greyish-brown, speckled and spotted brown, greyish-white and buff, becoming buff barred brown on belly and flanks. **In flight** Both sexes have a white spot towards the wing-tip, on the second, third and fourth outer primaries (innerweb only on second outermost) and white tips to the two outer tails feathers. **Similar species** Philippine Nightjar (89) is extremely similar but both sexes have broader white tips to the two outer tail feathers (the outerweb of the outermost wholly or partly brown) and, at very close range, shorter rictal bristles. Large-tailed Nightjar (87) is more variegated: the male has larger white spots on the four outer primaries and broader white tips to the two outer tail feathers; the female has buffish spots on the outer primaries and buffish-white or buffish tips to the two outer tail feathers. Savanna Nightjar (102) is slightly smaller with a less spotted appearance; the male has the two outer tail feathers generally white, the female lacks white on the tail. Heinrich's Nightjar (42) is darker, more spotted rather than variegated, has a broad band around the throat, less distinct white spots on the outer primaries and no white on the tail.

VOICE The song is a series of *tok* or *chuck* notes lasting 1.2-1.5 seconds, the later notes softer and trailing off, ie. *tok-tok-tok-tr-tr-tr-tr*. Sings from branches in trees, up to 10m or more above ground. Song posts are often at the edges of fields or coastal bush, or along the edges of roads through forests. May mainly be heard at dusk. No further information available.

HABITAT Occurs in secondary forest, coastal bush and the edges of mangroves. On Taliabu, it frequents lightly logged forests in the lowlands. 0–300m.

HABITS Crepuscular and nocturnal. Often flies with deep, stiff wingbeats and also glides with its wings held in a V above its back. Hawks for insects in fast, erratic flight. Birds may forage over patches of alang-alang *Imperata cylindrica*. No further information available.

FOOD Insects. No further data available.

BREEDING No information available.

DESCRIPTION *C. c. celebensis* **Adult male** Forehead, crown and nape greyish-brown streaked blackish-brown, broadly so on central feathers. Generally no collar on hindneck, although isolated buff feathers on nape may give impression of an indistinct collar. Mantle, back, rump and uppertail-coverts greyish-brown streaked blackish-brown. Lesser coverts dark brown speckled tawny and buff. Rest of wing-coverts greyish-brown speckled tawny, buff and brown, boldly spotted buff and pale buff. Scapulars blackish-brown, edged and speckled buff. Primaries brown, P9-P7 with small white spot towards feather-tips; inner six primaries and secondaries brown regularly spotted tawny, faintly tipped greyish-brown. Tertials greyish-brown mottled brown and blackish-brown. Tail brown indistinctly barred tawny, R5 and R4 tipped white (19-22mm), central pair (R1) greyish-brown, speckled and barred brown. Lores and ear-coverts rufous speckled brown. Chin and throat brown barred buff. White patch on lower throat, the lower feathers of which are tipped blackish-brown, with a buff subterminal band. The white patch extends around the throat, becoming tawny on the sides of the head. Breast greyish-brown, speckled and spotted greyish-white and buff. Belly, flanks, undertail- and underwing-coverts buff barred brown. **Adult female** Similar to the male. R5 and R4 tipped white (c. 22mm). **Immature** and **Juvenile** Not known. **Chick** Not known. **Bare parts** Iris dark brown; bill blackish; legs and feet blackish.

MEASUREMENTS Wing (male) 170-183, (female, one) 170; tail (male) 132-146, (female, one) 138; bill (male) 16.2-17.1, (female, one) 14.6; tarsus (male, one) 20.4, (female) no data. Weight no data.

MOULT No data available.

GEOGRAPHICAL VARIATION Two races are currently recognised.

   C. c. celebensis Described above.
   C. c. jungei Similar to the nominate but has smaller white tips to the two outer tail feathers (male 16-19mm, female c. 14mm). Wing (male) 175-176, (female, one) 172; tail (male) 127-137, (female, one) 128. Weight no data.

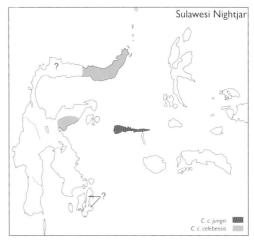

Sulawesi Nightjar

C. c. jungei
C. c. celebensis

DISTRIBUTION AND MOVEMENTS Occurs in N and CE Sulawesi, and on the Sula Islands. Recently reported from Buton Island, SE Sulawesi (see below).

   C. c. celebensis Recorded from the northern peninsula of Sulawesi (Lembeh Island, Koeandang, Gorontalo, Sumalata, Rurukan, Mogondo, and Tangkoko-Batuangus Nature Reserve) and CE Sulawesi (Morowali area). Sedentary.

C. c. jungei Sula Islands, known only from Taliabu and Mangole but possibly on other islands. Sedentary. The identification and status of this species on Buton Island, SE Sulawesi requires further study.

STATUS Locally common in parts of Sulawesi, reasonably common on Taliabu and uncommon on Mangole.

REFERENCES Catterall (1997), Coates & Bishop (1997), Mees (1977, 1985), Rozendaal (1990), Watling (1983).

---

91 DONALDSON-SMITH'S NIGHTJAR
Caprimulgus donaldsoni   Plate 26

Caprimulgus donaldsoni Sharpe, 1895, *Bull. Brit. Orn. Club* 4, p.29 (Hargeisa, Somalia)

IDENTIFICATION Length 18cm. A small, richly coloured Afrotropical nightjar of dry bush and scrub country. Sexually dimorphic. **At rest** Upperparts and wing-coverts generally rather chestnut or rufous, but occasionally variable in colour with some individuals greyer or, more rarely, browner. Broad rufous, tawny and buff collar on hindneck. Underparts chestnut or rufous, heavily spotted buff, becoming dark buff barred brown on belly. **In flight** The male has a white spot towards the wing-tip on the four outer primaries (innerweb only of outermost) and fairly broad white tips to the two outer tail feathers. The female has smaller spots on the four outer primaries and narrower white tips to the two outer tail feathers. **Similar species** None. Nubian Nightjar (85) is slightly larger, more round-winged and greyer, heavily spotted tawny and buff, or sandier-brown; both sexes have much larger white spots on the four outer primaries and broader white tips to the two outer tail feathers. Slender-tailed Nightjar (110) is generally greyer or browner with a gradated tail; the male has a white trailing edge to the inner wing, a whitish line across the closed forewing and white edges to the outer tail feathers (white replaced with buffish on the female).

VOICE The song is a series of short, melodious whistles, *tu-wee tiu*, repeated for up to 30 seconds or more, with only a very brief pause between each whistle. Comprising 4-5 notes, each whistle first rises (*tu-wee*) then descends (*tiu*) in pitch. Sings from the ground. May be heard mostly at dusk and dawn.

HABITAT Prefers arid and semi-arid scrub and bush country. Also occurs in wooded wadis. 0–1,700m.

HABITS Crepuscular and nocturnal. Roosts on the ground. Roost-sites are usually in the shade of a low bush and often in small clearings in impenetrable thorn scrub. Occasionally occurs in loose flocks of up to c. 40 birds, presumably outside the breeding season, e.g. at Tsavo in southern Kenya. Feeds at dusk and perhaps during the night by hunting low over the ground. Flight is rapid and erratic, with bird frequently twisting, turning and rising into the air. Also hunts over water, and may take food from the ground. No further information available.

FOOD Ants, grasshoppers, moths, beetles (including Staphilinidae, Scarabaeidae, Curculionidae and Cerambycidae) and caterpillars. No further data available.

BREEDING Breeding season May–June in Somalia and August–October? in Kenya.

No nest is constructed; the eggs are usually laid on sandy ground. Nest-sites are generally situated beneath a small bush. Clutch 2. Eggs ovate, dullish ivory heavily marbled greyish-brown on patches of violet-grey, 24.3-25.2 x 18.2-20.1mm. No further information available.

DESCRIPTION Adult male Forehead, crown and nape greyish-white, finely streaked and speckled light brown. Central feathers, except on nape, broadly streaked dark brown, edged brick-red and occasionally tipped buff. Broad collar on hindneck often a mixture of brick-red, tawny and buff. Mantle, back, rump and uppertail-coverts generally greyish-white, streaked and finely speckled light brown. Wing-coverts brick-red barred brown, with a thin dark brown streak in centres and broadly tipped buff, buffish-white or white. Scapulars generally brick-red, broadly edged buff, with a dark brown line between the two colours and along the feather-shaft. Primaries brown; white spot, towards feather-tip, on innerweb of P10, inner- or both webs of P9 and both webs of P8-P7. Rest of primaries and outer secondaries very broadly barred pale tawny or buff. Inner secondaries and tertials similar but tinged brick-red and tipped buff. Tail brown, R5 and R4 spotted tawny along edge of outerwebs and tipped white (15-25mm), central pair (R1) greyish, flecked and indistinctly barred brown. Lores and ear-coverts brick-red, with prominent white or buff sub-moustachial stripe. Chin buff, throat brick-red. White patch across lower throat, lower feathers of which have buff subterminal band with dark brown tips. Breast brick-red, heavily spotted buff. Belly, flanks and undertail-coverts buff barred brown. Underwing-coverts buff. **Adult female** Similar to the male but the spots on the outer four pri-maries are smaller and edged buff, and the white tips to the two outer tail feathers are slightly smaller (13-23mm), often washed pale buff on outerwebs. **Immature** and **Juvenile** Similar to the adult female but rather rufous. **Chick** Not known. **Bare parts** Iris, bill, legs and feet dark brown.

MEASUREMENTS Wing (male) 124-146, (female) 122-138; tail (male) 88-105, (female) 88-109; bill (male) 12.6?-17.0, (female) 15.1-15.6; tarsus (male) 16-21, (female) 16-21. Weight (male) 21-36g, (female) 26.5-36g.

MOULT The primaries are moulted descendantly. The tail moult is apparently variable with no obvious consistent pattern. No further data available.

GEOGRAPHICAL VARIATION Monotypic. Can be variable in general coloration, with some birds greyer or more rarely browner than described above, but not greatly so, the differences probably related to local soil colours.

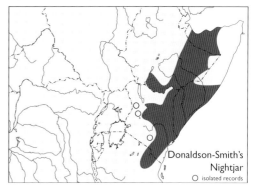

Donaldson-Smith's Nightjar
○ isolated records

DISTRIBUTION AND MOVEMENTS East Africa, mainly east of the Rift Valley, in NW and S Somalia, S and SE Ethiopia, S Sudan (possibly a seasonal visitor only, e.g. common in the Ilemi Triangle in February and June), NW, C and E Kenya and NE Tanzania. Sedentary.

STATUS Locally abundant at altitudes up to 1,400m throughout range, less common between 1,400 and 1,700m.

REFERENCES Archer & Godman (1961), Fry *et al.* (1988), Nikolaus (1989).

---

92   BLACK-SHOULDERED NIGHTJAR
Caprimulgus nigriscapularis   Plate 27

Caprimulgus nigriscapularis Reichenow, 1893, *Orn. Monatsb.* 1, p.31 (Songa, west of Lake Albert)

Forms a superspecies with Fiery-necked (which some authorities consider to be conspecific), Abyssinian and Montane Nightjars.

IDENTIFICATION Length 23-25cm. A small to medium-sized, variegated, brown or rufescent Afrotropical nightjar of lowland woods and forest edges. Sexually dimorphic. **At rest** Upperparts generally dark brown tinged rufous. Broad collar on hindneck, usually tawny-buff but sometimes paler. Lesser coverts blackish-brown contrasting with rest of wing-coverts to give distinct 'dark-shouldered' appearance. White throat-patch. Underparts rufescent-brown on breast, becoming tawny-buff on belly. **In flight** The male has a small white spot towards the wing-tip on the four outer primaries (innerweb only on outermost) and broad white tips to the two outer tail feathers. The female has slightly smaller white spots on the four outer primaries and narrower white tips to the two outer tail feathers. **Similar species** Fiery-necked Nightjar (93) is browner, less rufescent, the wing-coverts are more uniform with the lesser coverts not showing as distinct dark shoulders, and the hindneck collar is buffish rather than tawny-buff. Both sexes have larger white spots on the four outer primaries. Abyssinian (94) and Montane Nightjars (95) both have confusingly similar vocalisations, but are generally darker and browner, with far more white on the two outer tail feathers, and found at higher altitudes.

VOICE The song is an evenly pitched, double-noted whistle *peeeuo piririri* or *peeeuo pererere*, the second note being trilled. The song is often preceded by a rapid series of *werp* notes, repeated continuously for up to 13 seconds. These notes are shorter and faster than similar notes given by Fiery-necked Nightjar. Usually sings from branches in trees, but also from other perches, e.g. elephant-grass stalks. May be heard mainly at dusk and dawn, but also throughout moonlit nights. Calls, often given in flight, include 2-3 soft *chuck* or *tuc* notes uttered in quick succession, or up to 10 or more double *tuc-tuc* notes.

HABITAT Prefers lowland forest edges. Occurs in thick woods, gallery forest, secondary growth in rainforest and sparsely wooded, grassy slopes. In W Kenya, also inhabits mossy thickets with small trees. In Zaire it has also been recorded on stony hillsides. Found at all altitudes up to c. 2,000m.

HABITS Crepuscular and probably nocturnal. Roosts on the ground, occasionally in thick cover. If flushed from its roost, it re-alights on the ground or on low branches in trees. Forages at night, up to 20m above ground, amongst trees, in clearings, over neighbouring open spaces and on hillsides. No further information available.

FOOD Moths and beetles. No further data available.

BREEDING Breeding seasons poorly known. Possibly May in Gambia; April–May in Ivory Coast; August–December (chicks found September and December) in W Zaire; April–August in N Zaire; January–February in NE Zaire; March in Uganda; July–March (singing males) in S Nigeria.

No nest is constructed; the eggs are laid on the ground, usually on leaf-litter. Nest-sites are usually in woodland clearings. Clutch 1-2. Eggs elliptical, pale or creamy pink speckled reddish-brown and grey, markings usually concentrated in band around blunt end, 21.0-30.1 x 18.0-21.4mm. Incubation period not known. If flushed from its nest after the eggs have hatched, the female gives an injury-feigning distraction display by flying a short distance, alighting and fluttering about on the ground. Fledging period not known. No further information available.

DESCRIPTION Adult male Forehead, crown and nape greyish-brown tinged rufous, central feathers broadly streaked dark brown, except on nape. Broad to narrow tawny-buff collar on hindneck. Mantle, back, rump and uppertail-coverts brown streaked dark brown, becoming more rufous towards tail. Lesser coverts blackish-brown, finely speckled rufous or chestnut. Primary coverts brown, plain or with a few small buff spots on tips and edges. Rest of wing-coverts dark brown, outerwebs with buff spots on tips, innerwebs light brown speckled brownish-white. Scapulars largely dark brown with broad buff band on outerwebs, pattern variable. Primaries and secondaries dark brown; small white spot, towards the feather-tip, on innerweb of P10 and both webs of P9-P7; rest of primaries and all secondaries faintly barred buff. Tertials brown, tipped and speckled greyish-brown. Tail dark brown with buff or tawny spotting along edges of outerwebs R5-R2; R5 and R4 broadly (36-45mm) tipped white, outerwebs sometimes smudged brown or buff; R3 and R2 faintly barred greyish-brown, rufous, tawny or buff; central pair (R1) with broad bars or chevrons, speckled greyish-brown or rufous. Lores and ear-coverts rufous or rufous-buff, minutely speckled dark brown. Chin and throat rufous, finely barred brown. White patch on either side of lower throat or large white patch across whole of lower throat, lower feathers of which are broadly tipped blackish-brown with a buff subterminal band. Breast brown, finely barred light brown, often tinged rufous. Belly and flanks rufous-buff, narrowly barred brown. Undertail-coverts buff barred brown. Underwing-coverts mostly tawny-buff. **Adult female** Similar to the male. Generally has lighter head and narrower collar on hindneck. White spots on outer four primaries smaller and white tips to outer tow tail feathers also smaller (15-26mm). **Immature** and **Juvenile** Similar to the adults but rather more rufous. **Chick** At hatching, covered in pale greyish-buff down. **Bare parts** Iris dark brown; bill blackish; legs and feet dark brown.

MEASUREMENTS Wing (male) 145-159, (female) 147-165; tail (male) 115-126, (female) 110-124; bill (male) 12.3-13.6, (female) 11.1-13.0; tarsus (male) 15-16, (female) 15-16. Weight (male, two) 48-50g, (female) no data.

MOULT No published data available.

GEOGRAPHICAL VARIATION Monotypic. Colour variation is not common but does occur, e.g. a female (museum specimen) from Kinshasa, SW Zaire, is entirely rufous. A very pale bird (museum specimen) has been recorded from Burundi.

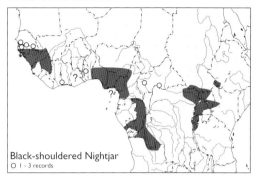

Black-shouldered Nightjar
○ 1 - 3 records

DISTRIBUTION AND MOVEMENTS W and C Africa, in Guinea Bissau, Guinea, W Sierra Leone, Ivory Coast (Marahoué National Park and Comoé National Park), Ghana?, S Nigeria, W Cameroon, Congo, SW and NE Zaire, Rwanda, Burundi, W and S Uganda, W Kenya and SW and extreme SE Sudan. Also 1-3 records from Senegal, The Gambia, Togo and Central African Republic. The records from Bioko Island are questionable, as the identification of birds seen has not been confirmed. Possibly sedentary.

STATUS Widespread and probably more so than current knowledge indicates. Frequent to common in many of the countries where it is found.

REFERENCES Cleere (1995), Fry *et al.* (1988), Louette (1990b), Salewski (1997).

93   FIERY-NECKED NIGHTJAR
Caprimulgus pectoralis   Plate 27

Caprimulgus pectoralis Cuvier, 1817, *Règne Anim.* 1, p.376 (Africa, based on Levaillant, p.149 = George, southern Cape)
Caprimulgus pectoralis shelleyi Bocage, 1879, *J. Acad. Sci. Lisboa* 24, p.266 (Caconda, northern Huila, Angola)

Caprimulgus pectoralis fervidus Sharpe, 1875, Layard's *Bds. So. Afr.* new ed., p.86 (Damaraland)
Caprimulgus pectoralis crepusculans Clancey, 1994, *Bull. Brit. Orn. Club* 114, p.51 (near Hlabisa, Lake St Lucia, eastern Zululand)

Forms a superspecies with Black-shouldered (which some authorities consider to be conspecific), Abyssinian and Montane Nightjars.

IDENTIFICATION Length 23-25cm. A small to medium-sized, brown or greyish-brown Afrotropical nightjar of lowland woods and forest edges. Sexually dimorphic. **At rest** Upperparts and wing-coverts dark brown, highly variegated greyish-brown and brownish-white. Broad collar on hindneck varying from pale buff to rich tawny-buff. Shows two or three distinctive rows of pale spots across the closed wing. White submoustachial stripe. Large white throat-patch. Underparts brown, speckled and barred brownish-white and buff. **In flight** Appears rather round-winged and short-tailed. The male has a large white spot towards the wing-tip on the four outer primaries (innerweb only on outermost) and broad white tips to the two outer tail feathers. The female has smaller (either white tinged and edged buff or entirely buff) spots on the four outer primaries, and smaller white tips to the two outer tail feathers, often smudged buff or brown on the underwebs. **Similar species** Black-shouldered Nightjar (92) is very similar to all races except nominate, differing in being generally more rufescent-brown, especially on the underparts, and having a tawnier collar on the hindneck; the lesser coverts are dark brown finely speckled rufous, giving it a distinctly dark-shouldered appearance at rest, and both sexes have smaller white spots on the four outer primaries. Abyssinian (94) and Montane Nightjars (95) both have confusingly similar vocalisations but are usually found at higher altitudes, are generally darker and browner, and have far more white on the two outer tail feathers. Sombre Nightjar (80) is extremely similar to the nominate but has a 'churring' song and prefers more open habitat. Occurs only in East Africa.

VOICE The song is a melodious, rather variable, double-noted whistle, *peeo-u-oh piriririri* or *peeo-u-oh pererererre*, occasionally *peeo-u-oh peeorererere*, and sometimes a faster *peeo-u-ohrerere*. The first note is rather undulating, the second an even-pitched trill, the two notes usually repeated once every 4-5 seconds. The song is often preceded by a series of *wherp* notes, lasting up to 22 seconds or more; these are slower, more drawn-out, than similar notes given by Black-shouldered Nightjar. Usually sings from branches 5-6m up in trees and often sits across boughs rather than lengthways. Occasionally sings from other perches such as fence-posts. May be heard chiefly at dusk and dawn but will also sing throughout moonlit nights. As with other nightjar species, tends to sing less once breeding has commenced. Persistent singing during the breeding season is probably by unmated individuals. Apparently has a single-noted contact call, although apparently this is, as yet, undescribed. Alarm call, given by both sexes, *woot woot woot*. When disturbed at the nest, adults give quiet *chuck* notes. During distraction displays, females utter a soft churring call. During threat/defence displays, utters a throaty hiss, also given when a bird is handled.

HABITAT Prefers *Brachystegia* (miombo) woodland savanna but also occurs in mopane and other deciduous woodlands. Also found in scrubland, especially with acacia, eucalyptus plantations, riparian forest, gardens and thickets. Avoids thick forest but will occur along forest edges. 0–1,500m.

HABITS Crepuscular and probably nocturnal. Roosts on the ground or occasionally in trees, and often wing-claps when flushed. Sits on roads and tracks at night. Drinks in flight by flying low over still water (including swimming pools) and dipping its bill into the surface. Hawks for food by 'flycatching' from perches. Also forages around animals and humans, feeding on insects disturbed from the ground or from low vegetation. No further information available.

FOOD Mantises, spiders, moths, grasshoppers and beetles (including Scarabaeidae, Cerambycidae, Carabidae and Elateridae). No further data available.

BREEDING Breeding season generally August–September in Angola; September–November in Zambia and Malawi; August–December in Botswana and Zimbabwe; and

August–November in South Africa. Breeding commences September in East Africa. Breeding season in all countries possibly longer than the periods given and tends to commence towards the end of the dry season, at the beginning of the rains.

Monogamous, usually pairing for life, and territorial. Breeding territories may be up to 6ha in size. Males defend their territory, and may dispute song-posts at the boundaries of adjoining territories by trying to dislodge each other with their wings; such disputes are often followed by aerial pursuits. No nest is constructed; the eggs are laid on leaf-litter on the ground. Nests are usually in full or partial shade but may occasionally be in full sun. Nest-sites are usually beneath trees inside woodland, in copses and under tree belts on well-drained soils. Also nests in thickets and beneath stands of acacia. Avoids arable land. Clutch 1-2, usually 2, laid on successive days. Eggs elliptical, glossy ivory-white to pale or creamy pink, either plain or with evenly distributed small reddish-brown and grey spots or darker pink blotches, 21.0-30.1 x 18.0-21.4mm. Double-brooded. A second clutch may be laid as early as 33 days after the first clutch hatches. Replacement clutches are often laid as a result of desertion, destruction (e.g. by fire) or predation, e.g. by snakes, mongooses or baboons. The adult may move, or attempt to move, the eggs away from a fire, although there is no direct evidence for this. Incubation commences when the first egg is laid and is usually by the female during the day. Whilst incubating, she sits upright, often with her eyes open. In hot weather the incubating bird often gular-flutters with its bill open. If disturbed at the nest, it flattens itself with its eyes closed. Males roost close to the nest-site early in breeding season but as the season progresses they use one of several favoured sites 50-120m away. The male incubates for much of the night, with the changeover occurring at, or just after, dusk. The incubation period is about 18 days, the eggs usually hatching asynchronously but once recorded synchronously at night. The eggshells are removed from the nest-site by the adult.

If flushed from the nest after the eggs have hatched, the female gives a distraction display by fluttering along the ground, irregularly flapping her outstretched wings and calling (see Voice). Whilst protecting its chicks from fire, an adult may flick its wings to clear away surrounding leaf-litter, although such behaviour may be rare. The semi-precocial young are able to walk within four hours of hatching. When 1-10 days old, they can move up to 10m towards the calling parent. The young are usually brooded by the female during the day and by the male on dark nights. Adults brood the young, which usually sit side-by-side and face forward, by tucking themselves against the chicks' backs. Both parents feed and brood the young at dusk and during moonlit nights. The young can remain at the nest-site for 9-13 days, after which they are brooded by the female at increasing distances away from it, but they apparently return to the nest-site to be fed. When threatened, chicks perform a defence display by spreading their wings, gaping and lunging towards the intruder. The chicks fledge at about 18 days but are still brooded by the female, near the nest-site, for up to 42 days; they can remain in the breeding area for up to 62 days, or even 145 days.

DESCRIPTION *C. p. pectoralis* Adult male Forehead, crown and nape brownish-grey, finely speckled and streaked brown, central feathers broadly streaked blackish-brown, except on nape. Narrow collar on hindneck varying from pale buff to rich tawny-buff. Mantle, back, rump and uppertail-coverts brown or dark brown, streaked brown and speckled greyish-brown or greyish-white. Primary coverts brown spotted tawny, rest of wing-coverts brown finely speckled greyish-white, many broadly tipped brownish-white tinged buff, vermiculated brown. Scapulars largely blackish-brown, especially centres, with buff on outerwebs and light brown innerwebs, speckled brown. Primaries dark brown; large white spot towards the feather-tip on innerweb of P10 and both webs of P9-P7; rest of primaries and all secondaries dark brown with some tawny barring and greyish-brown tips. Tertials brown, tipped and speckled greyish-brown. Tail dark brown with buff or tawny spotting along edges of outerwebs R5-R2; R5 and R4 very broadly (31-52mm, generally c. 50mm) tipped white; white on innerweb of R5 greater than on outerweb; white on R4 even across both webs, R3 and R2 with indistinct lighter brown barring over entire feather; central pair with broad speckled grey-brown bars or chevrons. Lores and ear-coverts rufous or rufous-buff, minutely speckled dark brown. White submoustachial stripe. Chin and throat dark brown, barred buff. White patch on either side of lower throat or large white patch across whole of lower throat, lower feathers of which are broadly tipped blackish-brown with buff subterminal band. Breast dark brown, barred and speckled brownish-white. Belly and flanks dark brown, barred buff. Undertail-coverts pale buff, plain or sparsely barred brown. Underwing-coverts mostly tawny-buff. **Adult female** Similar to the male but the white spots on the outer four primaries are smaller, edged and/or washed buff. The white tips to the two outer tail feathers are also smaller, usually c. 25mm but up to c. 38mm, and tinged buff and/or brown. **Immature** and **Juvenile** Similar to the adults but often paler and more rufous. **Chick** At hatching, covered with brown and grey down. **Bare parts** Iris brown; bill blackish; legs and feet brown.

MEASUREMENTS Wing (male) 158-174.5, (female) 156-170; tail (male) 110.5-132, (female) 104-134; bill (male) 19.0-23.5, (female) 19-23; tarsus (male) 12-16.6, (female) 11-16. Weight (both sexes) 43-66g.

MOULT No data available.

GEOGRAPHICAL VARIATION Individual variation is quite extensive within this species, but four races are currently recognised on the basis of general coloration, size and colour of hindneck collar, and amount of barring on the belly, flanks and undertail-coverts. Birds in the east of the range are often shorter-tailed.

C. p. pectoralis The darkest and least variegated race. Described above.

C. p. shelleyi Similar to the nominate but hindneck collar broader and more reddish, with broader pale buff streaking; ear-coverts, malar stripes, sides of throat and breast paler, browner and less dusky; underparts barred brown on the lower breast only; belly, flanks and undertail-coverts plain buff. Wing (male) 157-177, (female) 157-177; tail (male) 115-136, (female) 115-136. Weight (both sexes) 42-63g.

C. p. fervidus Similar to *crepusculans* but paler, especially on sides of crown and on scapulars and tertials; crown coarsely streaked black (streaks edged bright tawny); hindneck collar broader, paler and more orange-tawny; mantle, back and rump washed tawny, which gradually blends into the uppertail-coverts and wings; ear-coverts, malar stripes, sides of throat and upper breast generally tawny or rufous; underparts lightly barred brown. Rufous morphs occur (see below). Wing (male) 158-171.5, (female) 159-172; tail (male) 115-127, (female) 119-127. Weight unsexed (one) 55g.

C. p. crepusculans Paler than the nominate, with narrower black streaking on crown and a redder, rather broad hindneck collar streaked dark buff; small black markings on scapulars tipped buff; wings more reddish-buff, lesser coverts less blackish; ear-coverts, malar stripes, sides of throat and breast paler and browner; rest of underparts paler buff with finer brown barring, plainer over flanks and undertail-coverts; tail often more coarsely barred and vermiculated blackish-brown, and tends to be shorter. Wing (male) 152-172, (female) 153-163; tail (male) 110-130.5, (female) 110-121. Weight (male, one) 41.5g, (female, one) 38.6g.

Rufous morphs occur in at least one of these races and probably in the others.

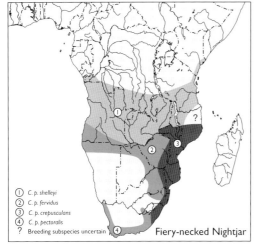

① *C. p. shelleyi*
② *C. p. fervidus*
③ *C. p. crepusculans*
④ *C. p. pectoralis*
? Breeding subspecies uncertain

Fiery-necked Nightjar

DISTRIBUTION AND MOVEMENTS SE and S Africa.

C. p. pectoralis S South Africa (W, S and E Cape Province, W Transkei and SW Orange Free State). Sedentary and partially migratory. After breeding, wanders north and north-east during April/May, to at least SE Zimbabwe, and there is one record from Barotse Province, Zambia, in July. Return movements commence approximately early September.

C. p. shelleyi Angola, W (Bas Zaire) and S Zaire, Zambia, N Malawi, SW and C? and NE? Tanzania and SE Kenya? Sedentary and partially migratory? Post-breeding movements poorly understood, but are possibly southward to N Namibia, N Botswana and NW Zimbabwe.

C. p. fervidus SW and S Angola, N Namibia (including Caprivi Strip), N and E Botswana, Zimbabwe and NE South Africa (NW and N Transvaal). Migratory. Post-breeding movements poorly understood but are probably northward to N Zambia, SE Zaire and Tanzania. Birds (museum specimens) resembling this race have also been recorded from Rwanda and Burundi.

C. p. crepusculans E South Africa (C and E Transkei, Natal, Zululand and E Transvaal), E Swaziland, SE

Zimbabwe, Mozambique and S Malawi? Northern limit of range unclear but possibly includes SE Tanzania. Mainly sedentary.

The post-breeding movements of all races are variable, with birds being common in some regions one year and absent in others.

STATUS Widely distributed and generally quite common throughout most of its range.

REFERENCES Clancey (1994), Cleere (1995), Fry *et al.* (1988), Harwin (1982), Jackson (1985a), Langley (1984), Louette (1990), Masterson (1994), Vernon & Dean (1988).

---

94   ABYSSINIAN NIGHTJAR
Caprimulgus poliocephalus   Plate 27

Other name: Mountain Nightjar

Caprimulgus poliocephalus Rüppell, 1840, *Neue Wirbelth.*, *Vögel* p.106 (Kulla, Ethiopia)

Forms a superspecies with Montane Nightjar, which some authorities consider to be conspecific, Fiery-necked and Black-shouldered Nightjars.

IDENTIFICATION Length 22-24cm. A medium-sized, greyish-brown Afrotropical nightjar of highland woods and forest edges. Sexually dimorphic. **At rest** Upperparts greyish-brown, streaked blackish-brown; broadly so on central crown. Broad buff or tawny-buff collar around the hindneck. Wing-coverts greyish-brown, speckled greyish-white and spotted pale buff. Scapulars blackish-brown, broadly edged buff. Has a whitish submoustachial stripe, and a white throat-patch often restricted to either side of the lower throat. Underparts greyish-brown, speckled and spotted buff, greyish-white and cinnamon, becoming buff barred brown on the belly and flanks. The female is generally darker than the male, with the white throat-patch smaller or absent. **In flight** Small-bodied. The male has a large white spot towards the wing-tip on the four outer primaries (innerweb only on outermost), and the two outer tail feathers are largely white. The female has smaller white spots, edged or washed buff, on the four outer primaries, and the two outer tail feathers are white distally, often on the innerwebs only. **Similar species** Montane Nightjar (95) is darker, with smaller white spots on the four outer primaries and less white on the two outer tail feathers. Fiery-necked Nightjar (93) is generally paler, greyer-brown, and has less white on the two outer tail feathers. Black-shouldered Nightjar (92) is paler, more rufescent, with smaller white spots on the four outer primaries and less white on the two outer tail feathers. Fiery-necked and Black-shouldered Nightjars are usually found at lower altitudes.

VOICE The song is a double-noted whistle *peuu-eee pe-uu-uu-uu*, or *pee-you pe-uu-uu-uu*, the first note undulating, the second trilled and descending slightly in pitch. Sings for several minutes at a time, with pauses of up to 10 seconds between each set of notes. Sings from branches in trees, up to 6m above ground, from houses and flat roofs c. 2m up, from overhead wires and occasionally from rocks. May be heard throughout the night, but mostly at dusk and dawn. **In flight**, often utters a series of deep *kah kah kah* notes, which may be given by one male to another during territorial disputes, or perhaps by both sexes during courtship.

HABITAT Prefers montane woods and forests. Occurs along the edges of all types of woodland, including olive, pine, juniper and bamboo. Also inhabits large suburban gardens (e.g. Nairobi, Kenya), steep, rocky hillsides with scattered eucalyptus (e.g. Addis Ababa, Ethiopia) and more open, wooded areas. In Saudi Arabia, it occurs in juniper forest interspersed with rocky outcrops. 1,000–3,350m.

HABITS Crepuscular and nocturnal. Roosts on the ground, usually on leaf-litter. Roost-sites are usually at the base of a tree or bush, and are occasionally beneath or within slightly denser cover. In Saudi Arabia, also roosts on rockier terrain, partly shaded by dense vegetation.

Often sits on roads, tracks and paths at night. Occasionally hovers with body held vertically (see Breeding). Forages over open ground, fields and pastures, in open wooded country and in wooded, suburban gardens. When hunting, flies rapidly around the edges of bushes and trees, up to c. 5m above ground. Also flycatches from perches high up in trees. When flycatching, flies with shallow, fluttering wingbeats and extremely agile twists and turns, often returning to the same perch. Also feeds on insects attracted to lights on buildings, or to campfires. No further information available.

FOOD Moths, beetles (including Scarabaeidae) and grasshoppers. No further data available.

BREEDING Breeding season March?–May? in Saudia Arabia; February?–May in Ethiopia; and September–January in Sudan, N Uganda, Kenya (also March–April) and N Tanzania.

Probably monogamous. No nest is constructed; the eggs are laid on bare ground or leaf-litter. Nest-sites are usually at or near the bases of trees or bushes, occasionally within hedgerows. Clutch usually 2. Eggs elliptical, creamy pink to pinkish-buff, spotted and blotched pale brown or reddish-brown, markings heavier around the blunt end, 24.2-27.0 x 18.4-19.5mm. Incubation is mainly by the female, the male relieving her for short periods during the night. Inquisitive, often hovering close to and above intruders, including humans, in its territory (see also Habits). Both adults feed the chicks. No further information available.

DESCRIPTION Adult male Forehead, crown and nape greyish-brown, finely speckled and streaked brown; central feathers broadly streaked blackish-brown. Broad buff or tawny-buff collar around the hindneck. Mantle, back, rump and uppertail-coverts greyish-brown, streaked and speckled brown. Lesser coverts brown, finely speckled rufous; primary coverts brown, spotted or barred tawny. Rest of wing-coverts greyish-brown, speckled and spotted brown and pale buff. Primaries brown; P10-P8 distally spotted tawny along outerwebs; large white spot towards the feather-tip on innerweb of P10 and across both webs of P9-P7; P6-P1 and secondaries brown broadly barred tawny, faintly tipped greyish-brown. Tertials greyish-brown mottled brown and buff. Tail brown, except outer two pairs (R5 and R4) white, broadly edged brown or buff along the outerwebs; R3 and R2 faintly and indistinctly barred with greyish-brown mottling; central pair (R1) greyish-brown, mottled and barred brown. Lores and ear-coverts brown speckled buff; submoustachial stripe white. Chin

and throat cinnamon barred brown. Lower throat white, or white patch on either side of lower throat. Breast greyish-brown, speckled brown and cinnamon, speckled and spotted buff. Belly, flanks, undertail- and underwing-coverts buff barred brown. **Adult female** Darker than the male, with the white throat-patch smaller or absent. The white spots on the four outer primaries are smaller, edged or washed buffish. Less white on the two outer tail feathers: R5 white on the distal half or two thirds of the innerweb, brown spotted tawny on the outerweb, R4 with less white on the innerweb, the outerweb brown, tawny and buff. **Immature** and **Juvenile** Paler than the adults and often rather rufous, the females more so than the males. The spots on the four outer primaries are heavily washed buff, and there is much less white on the two outer tail feathers. **Chick** Not described. **Bare parts** Iris dark brown; bill blackish; legs and feet darkish brown.

MEASUREMENTS Wing (male) 152-162, (female) 150-159; tail (male) 108-120, (female) 101-119; bill (male) 8-15, (female) 8-15; tarsus (male) 10-19, (female) 10-19. Weight (both sexes) 42-50g.

MOULT Possibly moults June–September. The primaries are moulted descendantly. No further data available.

GEOGRAPHICAL VARIATION Monotypic, although the newly discovered population in Saudi Arabia may be worthy of subspecific recognition after further study.

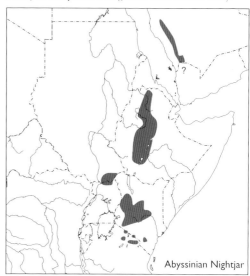

Abyssinian Nightjar

DISTRIBUTION AND MOVEMENTS Widely distributed in suitable habitat in Saudi Arabia and East Africa, ranging from SW Saudi Arabia (western slopes of Asir mountains), Yemen?, W and C Ethiopia, S Sudan and N Uganda (Imatong and Didinga Mountains), E Uganda? (Mt Elgon) into W, C and CS Kenya and N Tanzania (Mt Kilimanjaro and Arusha). Sedentary, although Saudi Arabian birds may move to lower altitudes in winter.

STATUS Locally common throughout its range.

REFERENCES Cleere (1995), Fry *et al.* (1988), Symens *et al.* (1994), Wilson & Wilson (1994).

Other name: Rwenzori Nightjar

Caprimulgus ruwenzorii Ogilvie-Grant, 1908, *Bull. Brit. Orn. Club* 23, p.94 (Mubuku Valley, Mt Ruwenzori)

Caprimulgus ruwenzorii guttifer Grote, 1921, *J. Orn.* 69, p.125 (Mlalo, Tanganyika Territory)

Forms a superspecies with Abyssinian Nightjar, which some authorities consider to be conspecific, Fiery-necked and Black-shouldered Nightjars.

IDENTIFICATION Length 22-24cm. A medium-sized, dark greyish-brown Afrotropical nightjar of highland woods and forest edges. Sexually dimorphic. **At rest** Upperparts dark greyish-brown streaked blackish-brown, broadly so on central crown. Broad buff or tawny-buff collar around the hindneck. Wing-coverts dark greyish-brown, speckled greyish-white and spotted pale buff. Scapulars blackish-brown, broadly edged buff on outer-webs. Has a whitish submoustachial stripe and a white throat-patch often restricted to either side of the lower throat. Underparts dark greyish-brown, speckled and spotted buff and pale buff, becoming buff barred brown on belly and flanks. **In flight** Small-bodied. The male has a small white spot towards the wing-tip on the four outer primaries (innerweb only on outermost) and white on the distal half of the two outer tail feathers. The female has the white spots on the four outer primaries tinged buffish, and less white on the two outer tail feathers. **Similar species** Abyssinian Nightjar (94) is paler, with larger white spots on the four outer primaries, and the two outer tail feathers are generally whitish. Fiery-necked Nightjar (93) is paler and greyer-brown, has larger white spots on the four outer primaries and less white on the two outer tail feathers. Black-shouldered Nightjar (92) is paler, more rufescent, and has less white on the two outer tail feathers.

VOICE The song is a double-noted whistle, *pee-eee pee-uuu*, the first note rather evenly pitched, the second slightly trilled. Sings for several minutes at a time, with a pause of 2-4 seconds between each set of notes, from branches in trees up to 10m above ground, from fences and posts, and from the ground. May chiefly be heard at dusk and dawn, and throughout moonlit nights. The flight call is a rapid series of soft *ka-ka-ka-kah* notes. Whilst perched, occasionally utters a soft *kweep*. When flushed, may give soft *yip yip* notes.

HABITAT Prefers the edges of montane woods and forests (including, in N Malawi at least, extensive tracts of coniferous *Pinus patula* woodland). Also occurs in clearings, open scrubland or woodland on mountain slopes, small, isolated woods on montane grasslands, on bracken-covered ridges, in bracken ferns and at the edges of bracken briars. 1,850–2,800m.

HABITS Crepuscular and nocturnal. Roosts on leaf-litter or pine needles on the ground, occasionally in slight hollows or depressions. Roost-sites can be fairly open or partly shaded by nearby vegetation, and may be inside woodland or on bracken- and scrub-covered hillsides. Roost-sites may be used for several days in succession, and are characterised by an accumulation of droppings and feathers. If flushed from its roost, occasionally calls (see Voice) and wing-claps. Flies only a short distance before re-alighting on the ground.

Often sits on roads and tracks at night. Forages along the edges of woods and forests, or over nearby grasslands and open areas. Also hunts amongst tree-tops, or flycatches from perches such as dead branches. No further information available.

FOOD Moths, beetles and termites. No further data available.

BREEDING Breeding season September–November in N Malawi and NE Zambia, and generally August/September–March throughout remainder of range.

No nest is constructed; the eggs are laid on bare ground. Nest-sites may be in burnt clearings, in bracken briars, beside boulders, on valley slopes or beneath trees, bushes or saplings. Clutch 1-2. Eggs elliptical, pale pinkish-cream to pale buff, speckled reddish-brown with markings denser around the blunt end, 26.0-27.3 x 19.0-20.0mm. No further information available.

DESCRIPTION *C. r. ruwenzorii* **Adult male** Forehead, crown and nape dark greyish-brown, finely streaked and speckled brown, central feathers broadly streaked blackish-brown. Broad buff or tawny-buff collar around hindneck. Mantle, back, rump and uppertail-coverts dark greyish-brown, streaked and speckled brown. Lesser coverts dark brown finely speckled rufous; primary coverts dark brown spotted tawny. Rest of wing-coverts dark greyish-brown, speckled and spotted pale buff. Scapulars blackish-brown, broadly edged buff on outerwebs. Primaries brown; P10-P8 distally spotted tawny along outerwebs; small white spot towards the feather-tip on innerweb of P10 and across both webs of P9-P7; P6-P1 and secondaries brown broadly barred tawny, faintly tipped greyish-brown. Tertials dark greyish-brown, mottled brown and buff. Tail brown, spotted tawny along edges of outerwebs of R5-R2; R5 and R4 very broadly (46-68mm) tipped white, edged brownish along outerwebs (on R5, amount of white is greater on innerweb, on R4 white is generally even across both webs); R3 and R2 faintly and indistinctly barred buffish; central pair (R1) dark greyish-brown, mottled and barred brown. Lores and ear-coverts brown speckled buff; submoustachial stripe white. Chin and throat cinnamon, finely barred brown. Lower throat white, or white patch on either side of lower throat. Breast dark greyish-brown, speckled and spotted buff and pale buff. Belly, flanks and undertail-coverts dark buff barred brown. Underwing-coverts generally tawny-buff. **Adult female** Similar to the male, but has the white spots on the four outer primaries tinged buffish, especially on P7, and narrower (21-33mm) white tips to the two outer tail feathers, with the outerwebs often brownish or buff. **Immature** and **Juvenile** Similar to the adults. **Chick** Not described. **Bare parts** Iris dark brown; bill blackish; legs and feet dark brown.

MEASUREMENTS Wing (male) 150-162, (female) 154-162; tail (male) 113-125, (female) 110-119; bill (male) 8-15, (female) 8-15; tarsus (male) 10.0-19.5, (female) 10.0-19.5. Weight (male) 43.8-55.0g, (female) 41.5-57.0g.

MOULT No data available.

GEOGRAPHICAL VARIATION Two races are currently recognised. A third race, *koesteri*, is here treated as a synonym of the nominate race.

  C. r. ruwenzorii Described above.
  C. r. guttifer Similar to the nominate, but has slightly

less white on the two outer tail feathers (38-42mm on males, 20-23mm on females). Wing (male) 156-162, (female) 152-160; tail (male) 111-120, (female) 110-124. Weight no data.

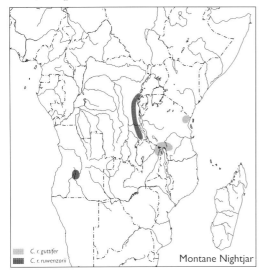

C. r. guttifer
C. r. ruwenzorii

Montane Nightjar

DISTRIBUTION AND MOVEMENTS There are four distinct populations in Africa.

C. r. ruwenzorii SW Uganda (Rwenzori Mountains and Bwindi Forest), W Rwanda and W Burundi (Mitumba Mountains) and E Zaire (Mitumba Mountains south to the Marungu Highlands). An isolated population occurs in W Angola (Sandula and Mt Moco). Sedentary.
C. r. guttifer SW Tanzania (highlands in the Tatanda region), N Malawi (Nyika Plateau, Viphya Mountains, Musisi and Misuku) and NE Zambia (Matinga Mountains and the western side of Nyika Plateau). An isolated population occurs in NE Tanzania (Usambara Mountains) and requires further study. Sedentary.

STATUS Little known, but locally common in suitable habitat.

REFERENCES Chapin (1939), Cleere (1995), Fry *et al.* (1988), Louette (1990).

---

96   INDIAN NIGHTJAR
Caprimulgus asiaticus   Plate 31

Caprimulgus asiaticus Latham, 1790, *Index. Orn.* 2, p.588 (India = Bombay)
Caprimulgus asiaticus eidos Peters, 1940, *Checklist of birds of the world* 4, p.211 (Vavuniya, northern Ceylon)
Caprimulgus asiaticus siamensis Meyer de Schauensee, 1934, *Proc. Acad. Nat. Sci. Phila.* 85, p.373 (Chieng Mai, Siam)

Possibly forms a superspecies with Madagascar Nightjar.

IDENTIFICATION Length 24cm. A medium-sized, greyish-brown, variegated Oriental nightjar. Sexually dimorphic. **At rest** Upperparts greyish-brown streaked blackish-brown, crown broadly streaked blackish-brown edged rufous. Broad buff or tawny collar around hindneck. Lesser coverts

greyish-brown speckled rufous, rest of wing-coverts greyish-brown boldly spotted buff. Scapulars broadly bordered buff with pointed blackish-brown centres. Whitish submoustachial stripe. Large white patch either side of lower throat. Underparts greyish-brown barred brown, boldly spotted buff, becoming buff barred brown on belly and flanks. **In flight** Slightly round-winged. The male has a white spot towards the wing-tip on the four outer primaries (innerweb only on outermost) and broad white tips to the two outer tail feathers. The female has smaller white spots, tinged or edged buff, on the four outer primaries, and narrower white tips to the two outer tail feathers. **Similar species** Jungle Nightjar (78) is slightly larger with an indistinct tawny-buff or pale buff hindneck collar; the male has larger white (the female buff) spots on the four outer primaries and white or white and brown (the female brownish-white or brownish-buff) tips to all but the central pair of tail feathers. Large-tailed Nightjar (87) is larger, with a less distinct hindneck collar, less boldly spotted wing-coverts and, in flight, more pointed-looking wings; the male has larger white (the female buffish) spots on the four outer primaries and broader white (the female buff or buffish-white) tips to the two outer tail feathers. Jerdon's Nightjar (88) is larger and pale-headed, with the crown boldly but sparsely streaked or spotted blackish-brown, a broad rufous hindneck collar merging onto the mantle, less boldly spotted wing-coverts and, in flight, more pointed-looking wings; the male has larger white (the female small buffish) spots on the four outer primaries and broader white (the female buff or buffish-white) tips to the two outer tail feathers. Savanna Nightjar (102) is generally plainer and less variegated, usually without a hindneck collar and with less spotting on the wing-coverts; the male often has larger white (the female buff) spots on the four outer primaries and two entirely whitish outer tail feathers. European Nightjar (79) occurs in the north-west of the Indian Nightjar's range in November–March, but is generally paler and greyer with no hindneck collar and a distinct buffish line across the forewing; the male has a white spot on the three outer primaries and white tips to the two outer tail feathers, while the female shows indistinct buffish spots on the three outer primaries.

VOICE The song, often likened to a 'ping-pong' ball bouncing to rest on a hard surface, is a distinctive *chuk-chuk-chuk-chuk-k-k-k-roo*. Each song phrase last 2-3 seconds and begins with 2-4 evenly pitched *chuk* notes. The final note of the song occasionally rises slightly in pitch. Sings, with short pauses, for hours on end. Sings from perches such as fence-posts, milestones, stakes, stones, boulders, occasionally also the ground, but not, apparently, from trees. When singing, the whole bird seems to vibrate. May mainly be heard at dawn and dusk, and throughout moonlit nights. In flight, the male possibly utters a short, sharp *quit-quit* or *chúk-chúk* call.

HABITAT Found in a wide variety of habitats and occurs from plains to foothills in thin scrub jungle, fallow land with euphorbia hedges and thickets, stony nullahs near cultivation, young forestry plantations (including teak), rambling overgrown gardens and thin bamboo jungle. In south-west Pakistan, occurs in low hill country with sparsely scattered thorn scrub, in low stony hills and in flat saline areas with tamarisk bushes. In Sri Lanka, found in scrublands (including waste ground), lowland tracts of sandy jungle, open wooded country and cinnamon plantations. 0–1,500m.

HABITS Crepuscular and nocturnal. Roosts on the ground, or on rocks. Roost-sites are often on bare earth near shrubs. When flushed from its roost, flies only a short distance, often weaving low amongst bushes, before re-alighting on the ground. When active, frequently perches on fence-posts and milestones, calling (see Voice). Often perches on dead branches at the tops of trees. Commonly sits on roads and tracks at night and, in Sri Lanka, also does so late on dull afternoons. Wing-claps (perhaps during courtship only). Often occurs in pairs or loose family parties. Few details on foraging behaviour have been described, but it may feed with other species, e.g. Indian Rollers *Coracias benghalensis*, on insects around mercury vapour lamps in populated areas. Also hunts in and around verandas and occasionally forages on the ground. No further information available.

FOOD Moths, beetles (including Scarabaeidae, Dysticidae and Elateridae), grasshoppers (including Acrididae), crickets and bugs. In winter, also takes the flowers of *Euphorbia caducifolia* and small mammals (e.g. *Mus cervicolor*)!

BREEDING Breeding season April–? in Pakistan; February–September (mainly April–May?) in India; January–October (mainly March–May and again in September) in Sri Lanka; and mid-March–? in Thailand. No data available from other regions.

No nest is constructed; the eggs are laid on leaf-litter or bare earth. Nest-sites may be shaded or unsheltered, and are usually close to bushes or stumps, beneath trees or saplings, at the base of walls, in dry, pebbly nullahs or in stony fields. Clutch 2. Eggs elliptical, cream or pale salmon-pink, spotted and smeared reddish-brown and purple, 24.6-29.2 x 18.3-21.3mm. Both sexes incubate. Possibly double-brooded. No further information available.

DESCRIPTION *C. a. asiaticus* **Adult male** Forehead, crown and nape greyish-brown speckled brown, central feathers broadly streaked blackish-brown edged rufous. Broad buff or tawny collar around hindneck. Mantle, back, rump and uppertail-coverts greyish-brown, speckled and barred brown, thinly streaked blackish-brown. Lesser coverts brownish, speckled rufous, feathers with dark brown dagger-shaped centres. Median coverts greyish-brown, broadly tipped buff. Rest of wing-coverts greyish-brown, boldly spotted buff on tips of outerwebs, buff spots smudged brown along outer edge. Scapulars broadly edged buff with blackish-brown pointed centres. Primaries brown; outerweb of P10 edged and spotted buff or pale buff; outerweb of P9 faintly spotted buff near tip; white spot towards the feather-tip on innerweb of P10 and across both webs of P9-P7, the outerwebs of which are often faintly washed pale buff; inner six primaries and secondaries brown regularly barred tawny, and all flight feathers tipped with light brown mottling. Tertials greyish-brown mottled brown, streaked blackish-brown along feather-shafts. Tail dark brown, faintly and indistinctly barred tawny; R5 and R4 broadly (29-40mm) tipped white, tip of outerweb on R5 (and occasionally on R4) washed brown; edge of outerweb of R5, above white tip, buff or buffish-white along entire length; central pair (R1) greyish-brown, mottled and barred brown. Lores and ear-coverts rufous speckled or barred brown; submoustachial stripe whitish. Chin buff, throat buff barred or vermiculated brown. Large white patch on either side of lower throat, the lower feathers of which are broadly tipped blackish-

brown with a buff subterminal band. Upper breast greyish-brown, occasionally washed buff or rufous, barred light brown, lower breast greyish-brown boldly spotted buff. Belly and flanks buff, irregularly barred brown. Undertail-coverts buff or whitish, unmarked. Underwing-coverts buff barred brown. **Adult female** Similar to the male; white spots on the four outer primaries generally smaller, tinged or edged buff; white tips to the two outer tail feathers narrower. **Immature** Similar to the adults but the outer primaries are broadly tipped buff. **Juvenile** Paler and plainer than the adults. Streaking on the upperparts restricted to the rear of the crown and nape; scapulars with rufous edging to blackish-brown centres. **Chick** At hatching, covered in rufous? down. **Bare parts** Iris dark brown; bill blackish; legs and feet brownish.

MEASUREMENTS Wing (male) 144-156, (female) 140-156; tail (male) 96-120, (female) 96-119; bill (male) 17-19, (female) 17-19; tarsus (male) 19-22, (female) 19-22. Weight (male, one) 46g, (female) no data, unsexed (one) 50.0g.

MOULT No published data available.

GEOGRAPHICAL VARIATION Three races are currently recognised, although the morphological differences are not always clear.

C. a. asiaticus Described above. Extremely variable in colour with greyish-brown birds being commonest; sandy-buff, grey, brown or rufous birds have also been recorded.

C. a. eidos May average slightly smaller than the nominate but doubtfully distinct when compared to birds from southern India. Wing (male) 132-148, (female) 132-148; tail (male) 95-113, (female) 95-113. Weight no data.

C. a. siamensis Paler, more silvery-grey than the nominate, with a paler hindneck collar. Wing (male, one) 138, (female) no data; tail (male, one) 110, (female) no data. Weight no data.

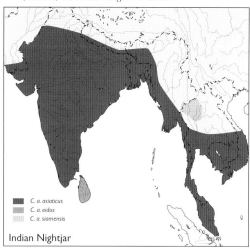

C. a. asiaticus
C. a. eidos
C. a. siamensis

Indian Nightjar

DISTRIBUTION AND MOVEMENTS Common and widely distributed throughout the Indian subcontinent and southern Indochina.

C. a. asiaticus SE Pakistan (S Sind), India, S Nepal, S Bhutan, Bangladesh, S Burma, S Thailand and S Indochina. Sedentary, also partially and locally migratory.

C. a. eidos Sri Lanka. Sedentary.

C. a. siamensis N Thailand. Sedentary.

STATUS Generally common and widespread throughout its range. In Sri Lanka common in suitable habitat in the Dry Zone, less common in the Wet Zone.

REFERENCES Ali & Ripley (1970), Bharos (1992), Legge (1880), Rana (1958), Roberts (1991).

---

97   MADAGASCAR NIGHTJAR
Caprimulgus madagascariensis Plate 29

Caprimulgus madagascariensis Sganzin, 1840, *Mém. Soc. Mus. Hist. Nat. Strasbourg* 3, p.28 (Sainte Marie, Madagascar)
Caprimulgus madagascariensis aldabrensis Ridgway, 1894, *Proc. U.S. Natn. Mus.* 17, p.373 (Aldabra Island)

Possibly forms a superspecies with Indian Nightjar.

IDENTIFICATION Length 21-23cm. A small to medium-sized, brownish, variegated nightjar, endemic to Madagascar and Aldabra Island. Sexually dimorphic. **At rest** Upperparts greyish-brown streaked blackish-brown. Generally no collar on hindneck, although some may have an indistinct tawny-buff collar. Lesser coverts greyish-brown speckled buffish and tawny, rest of wing-coverts greyish-brown, heavily spotted buff with brown centres. Scapulars blackish-brown bordered buff on outerwebs. Whitish submoustachial stripe. Small white patch on either side of lower throat. Underparts greyish-brown thinly barred greyish-white, becoming buff barred brown on belly and flanks. **In flight** Round-winged. The male has a white spot towards the wing-tip on the four outer primaries (innerweb only on outermost) and white tips to the two outer tail feathers. The female has smaller buff spots on the four outer primaries (innerweb only on outermost) and smaller white tips to the two outer tail feathers (often innerweb only on outermost). **Similar species** None within range. The only other species on Madagascar, Collared Nightjar (107), is darker with a scalier, less variegated appearance, a very broad, distinct hindneck collar pattern, no white markings on the wings and very narrow white tips to the two outer tail feathers.

VOICE The song is a distinctive, second-long *tuk-tr-tr-tr-tr*, repeated for minutes on end and occasionally preceded by a brief, muted *cop cop cop*, a soft cooing or a faint, quavering *huuu*. Sings from perches out in the open or from the ground. May be heard throughout the night. Tends to sing less often immediately after the breeding season. The call is a loud, liquid *wa-pit*, given in flight or whilst perched; this may be the same as the repeated whipcracking or *tyo* calls heard on Aldabra. Breeding birds on Aldabra utter muffled *chok* calls.

HABITAT Prefers open or lightly wooded country. Occurs in partially or totally degraded woodlands, forest edges and clearings, woods, savanna, heathland, scrubland, eucalyptus plantations and areas of afforestation. It is also found amongst cultivation, near urban areas and in gardens. Tends to avoid dense forest. On Aldabra it is found on open sandhills and in casuarina woods with little ground vegetation. 0–1,800m.

HABITS Crepuscular and nocturnal. Roosts on leaf-litter on the ground. Roost-sites may be anywhere in open forests, at the edge of thicker forests or in areas of secondary growth. In more open country, tends to roost in or near isolated areas of brush. When active, often perches on dead branches and frequently sits on roads and tracks at dusk. Forages in and around forest tree-tops, by fluttering over open country or by hawking low over land or water. Also feeds in a slow, gliding flight with its wings held in a V above its back. Usually occurs singly but flocks of up to c. 24 birds may congregate when fluttering about the tree-tops. On Aldabra hunts over dunes and around houses, and also feeds on beetles at piles of turtle bones. No further information available.

FOOD Grasshoppers, moths, cicadas and beetles (including Cerambycidae, Chrysomelidae, Alticinae, Curculionidae, Elateridae, Scarabaeidae and Hopliini). Plant seeds are possibly ingested accidentally. No further data available.

BREEDING Breeding season August–December in the south; October–November in the north; September–December on Aldabra Island.

No nest is constructed; the eggs are usually laid on the ground, often on leaf-litter. Apparently also nests on flat roofs. On Aldabra, the eggs are also laid on bare ground or on gravel. Nest-sites are usually in open forest or forest clearings. On Aldabra, nest-sites are often on open sandhills or beneath bushes by clearings or paths in thick scrub. Clutch 2. Eggs elliptical, glossy white, blotched and spotted brownish-grey or blackish-grey, 25.0-28.3 x 18.0-20.7mm. Incubation is probably by the female during the day, with the male often roosting close by. If danger approaches, the adult performs a threat/defence display by spreading and/or raising its wings, spreading its tail and gaping. Chicks are semi-precocial. No further information available.

DESCRIPTION *C. m. madagascariensis* **Adult male** Forehead, crown and nape greyish-brown or -white speckled brown, streaked blackish-brown, broadly so on crown. Generally no collar on hindneck although some may have very indistinct tawny-buff collar. Mantle, back, rump and uppertail-coverts greyish-brown or -white speckled and barred brown, streaked blackish-brown. Lesser coverts greyish-brown speckled buff and tawny. Rest of wing-coverts greyish-brown, boldly spotted buff with brown centres. Scapulars blackish-brown, broadly bordered pale buff on outerwebs. Primaries brown; white spot towards the feather-tip on innerweb of P10 and both webs P9-P7, spotted buff along edge of outerweb above white spot on P9-P7; inner six primaries and secondaries brown regularly spotted tawny. Tertials greyish-brown mottled brown, streaked blackish-brown. Tail brown, faintly and indistinctly barred tawny; R5 and R4 tipped white (28-40mm); central pair (R1) greyish-brown, mottled and barred brown. Lores and ear-coverts rufous or buffish, barred or speckled brown; submoustachial stripe whitish. Chin and throat rufous or buffish, barred brown. Small white patch on either side of lower throat. Breast greyish-brown, thinly barred greyish-white. Belly, flanks, undertail- and underwing-coverts buff barred brown. **Adult female** Similar to the male but perhaps browner and paler. The spots on P10-P7 are smaller and buff, the white tips to R5 (innerweb only) and R4 smaller and usually washed brown and buff. **Immature** and **Juvenile** Similar to the adult female? but R5-R2 more strongly barred tawny. **Chick** At hatching, covered in brown and buff down. **Bare parts** Iris dark brown; bill blackish; legs and feet dark brown.

MEASUREMENTS Wing (male) 147-163, (female) 149-166; tail (male) 96-112, (female) 96-113; bill (male) 12.3-14.6, (female) 11.9-13.5; tarsus (male) 17.4-19.4, (female) 15.9-19.0. Weight (male) 37-43g, (female) 45-51g.

MOULT Birds in wing and tail moult noted late December–February, suggesting a complete post-breeding moult strategy. No further data available.

GEOGRAPHICAL VARIATION Although two races are currently recognised, this species may well prove to be monotypic.

> **C. m. madagascariensis** Described above. Can be variable in colour, with darker or paler birds occurring throughout its range.
> **C. m. aldabrensis** Supposedly paler than the nominate on the crown and scapulars, but possibly not consistently; also described as having broader white tips to the two outer tail feathers, but this is only evident on a few museum specimens. White on R5 and R4 (male) 27-45mm. Wing (male) 153-162, (female) 150-159; tail (male) 110-115, (female) 105-112. Weight unsexed (two) 43.5-44.0g.

Aldabra Is. (C. m. aldabrensis)

Madagascar Nightjar

C. m. madagascariensis

DISTRIBUTION AND MOVEMENTS Confined to Madagascar and Aldabra Island.

> **C. m. madagascariensis** Occurs throughout Madagascar (including Nosy Boraha). Sedentary.
> **C. m. aldabrensis** Occurs throughout Aldabra. West Island (settlement and Bassin Cabri), Ile Polymnie (Palm Beach), Middle Island (Gionnet, Anse Malaban and west side of east channel), South Island (east side of east channel, Frigate Pool, Takamaka, Dune Jean-Louis and Dune d'Messe) and an island in the Passe Gionnet. Sedentary.

STATUS Common and widespread throughout Madagascar, especially in the east. Not uncommon on Aldabra.

REFERENCES Benson & Penny (1971), Dee (1986), Goodman *et al.* (1997), Langrand (1990), Rand (1936).

---

98   SWAMP NIGHTJAR
Caprimulgus natalensis   Plate 25

Other name: Natal Nightjar, African White-tailed Nightjar

Caprimulgus natalensis A. Smith, 1845, *Illustr. Zool. S. Afr., Aves* pl.99 and text: (Port Natal [=Durban], Natal)
Caprimulgus natalensis accrae Shelley, 1875, *Ibis* (3)5, p.379 (Accra, Gold Coast)

IDENTIFICATION Length 20-24cm. A medium-sized, short-tailed, spotted Afrotropical nightjar. Sexually dimorphic. **At rest** Upperparts brown or greyish-brown, heavily spotted with large, irregularly shaped dark brown marks on wing-coverts, scapulars and tertials. Indistinct collar on hindneck pale buff or buff barred brown. White throat-patch. Underparts brown heavily spotted buff or buffish-white, becoming buff barred brown on belly. **In flight** Male has a large white spot towards the wing-tip on the four outer primaries (innerweb only on outermost) and very broad white tips to the two outer tail feathers (outermost usually entirely white on outerweb). Female has buffish or pale tawny spots on the four outer primaries and narrow, buffish-white tips to the two outer tail feathers (outermost usually entirely buff on outerweb). **Similar species** None.

VOICE The song is a monotonous *chop chop chop chop*, either lasting up to 25 seconds or more without pause or delivered in groups of 6-24 notes with a slight pause between each set of notes. Occasionally sings at a faster rate. The song is sometimes preceded by a slow double *chop chop*. Sings from the ground amongst tall grass, termite mounds, low bushes or trees. When singing, the white throat-patch is extremely visible. May be heard predominantly at dusk and dawn and occasionally throughout the night. The flight call is a rapid *chip-chip-chip-chip* rising slightly in pitch. During courtship, pairs utter a *whip-whip-whip* call (which may be the same as above) or a melodious *wip hulululul*. Utters a soft *crup* when taking flight or alighting and a low *kik* when on the ground. Males may give a mewing call when flushed from the nest.

HABITAT Prefers wet lowland grasslands, damp meadows, edges of lagoons, swamps, marshes, bogs and dambos, marshy floodplains and vleis. In all habitats it likes areas interspersed with tufts or clumps of grasses and vegetation. Also occurs along the edges of woods and forests and in drier *Echinochloa* grassland. Tends to vacate areas after fires. In West Africa also occurs in damp grassy clearings in forests. In South Africa it is often found in areas with palms. 0–2,200m.

HABITS Crepuscular and nocturnal. Roosts on the ground, either in small open spaces or on flat stones. Roost-sites are often in marshy meadows or amongst ferns. When disturbed, often flies a short distance and re-alights within grassland, or flies to cover, e.g. trees or *Papyrus* beds. At night, often sits on roads and paths, or perches on posts. Usually occurs singly or in pairs, but up to eight can occur in small areas. Feeds by flying low over the ground or around termite hills, pastures and cowsheds. No further information available.

FOOD Moths, termites, bugs and beetles (including Geotrupidae). No further data available.

BREEDING Breeding season April–May in Nigeria; mid-August? to October? in SE Gabon; April–June in W Kenya;

March–May in NE Zaire; August–May in S Zaire; January–March, June–August and October in C and S Uganda; September–November in Zambia and Zimbabwe; and August–November in Angola, NW Zimbabwe and Natal, South Africa.

Monogamous. No nest is constructed; the eggs are laid on bare earth, usually close to grass. Nest-sites are often in long grass at the edges of marshes and airstrips or on sandy riverbanks. Clutch usually 2. Eggs elliptical, slightly glossy, whitish, pinkish or pale grey with faint lilac patches and indistinctly spotted grey and speckled brown, 25.5-29.7 (31.2?) x 19.2-22.2mm. Both sexes incubate, although the female probably incubates during the day and some of the night, with the male taking over at dusk and dawn. If flushed, an adult may accidentally knock the eggs a short distance away from the nest site, although they are possibly gathered back when the bird returns. After flushing from the nest, an adult may perform an injury-feigning distraction display, by flapping about across the grass or ground. The incubation period is c. 20 days, and egg shells are not removed from the site. After hatching, the chicks may be brooded for the first few days, after which they often hide in nearby grasses, with one or both parents roosting close by. No further information available.

DESCRIPTION *C. n. natalensis* **Adult male** Forehead, crown and nape blackish-brown, feathers edged buff, pale tawny-buff or cinnamon-buff. Sides of forehead and sides and rear of crown buff, greyish-brown or greyish-white, minutely speckled brown. Indistinct collar on hindneck pale buff or buff, occasionally barred brown. Mantle, back, rump and uppertail-coverts brown or greyish-brown, narrowly barred pale tawny, cinnamon or buff. Wing-coverts variegated buff, greyish-white and tawny, and heavily spotted with large, blackish-brown, irregularly shaped marks. Scapulars with large irregularly shaped blackish-brown centres, tips edged and spotted pale buff, buff and cinnamon-buff. Primaries brown; large white spot towards tip of feather on innerweb of P10 and both webs P9-P7, spots occasionally (perhaps indicating younger birds) washed buff or pale tawny; vestigial white mark occasionally on P6; outer primaries also very narrowly tipped pale buff, often on outerweb only; rest of primaries and all secondaries barred tawny and narrowly tipped pale buff. Tertials brown, mottled and barred pale tawny or buff, boldly spotted black. Tail brown; R5 and R4 broadly (42-63mm) tipped white, usually more so on outerwebs (white tips often thinly edged dirty buff); R3 and R2 indistinctly barred pale tawny; central pair (R1) densely mottled with greyish-buff or -brown bars or chevrons. Lores and ear-coverts dark brown, occasionally spotted pale buff or pale tawny on ear-coverts. Chin and throat buff, barred or spotted dark brown. Large white patch on either side of lower throat or entirely white across whole of lower throat, lower feathers of which have buff subterminal bar, broadly tipped dark brown. Breast brown heavily spotted buff, pale buff or buffish-white. Belly and flanks buff barred brown. Undertail-coverts buff, generally unmarked. Underwing-coverts buff, occasionally with some brown barring. **Adult female** Similar to the male but the white spots on the four outer primaries are often washed buff. The outer two tail feathers are brown barred pale tawny-buff, narrowly tipped buffish-white. R5 also narrowly edged pale tawny-buff on outerweb. **Immature** and **Juvenile** Similar to the adults but more spotted on the upperparts. **Chick** At hatching, covered in whitish down, dark grey on

rump. **Bare parts** Iris brown; bill dark brown; legs and feet pinkish-brown.

MEASUREMENTS Wing (male) 142-166, (female) 152-162; tail (male) 96-109, (female) 95-100; bill (male) 15.2-17.2, (female) 14.9-15.6; tarsus (male) 20-24, (female) 20-24. Weight (male, one) 86.7g, (female, one) 65g.

MOULT No published data available.

GEOGRAPHICAL VARIATION Two races are currently recognised.
  C. n. natalensis Described above. Can be quite variable in general coloration, the commonest forms being brown, greyish-brown and buffish-brown. Birds from the White Nile, Sudan (exact locality not known), appear darker than usual, with males having larger white spots on the four outer primaries and a broader white tip to the outermost tail feather.
  C. n. accrae Considered to be generally darker, duller and smaller than the nominate, but upperparts appear more uniform greyish-brown with fewer but larger blackish-brown spots on crown, wing-coverts and scapulars. Wing (male) 150-155, (female) 147-155; tail (male) 92-107, (female, one) 95. Weight no data.

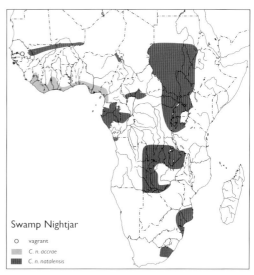

Swamp Nightjar

○ vagrant
▨ C. n. accrae
▩ C. n. natalensis

DISTRIBUTION AND MOVEMENTS Occurs discontinuously throughout West, Central and southern Africa.
  C. n. natalensis E Gambia (Prubru), C and S Mali (Anderamboukane, Payona, Kara, Bamako), Nigeria, shores of Lake Chad, S Central African Republic (Lobaye), C and S Sudan, Uganda, W Kenya (east to Lake Baringo and Narok region), Rwanda, Burundi, NW Tanzania, NW, NE and S Zaire, Gabon, E and extreme NW Angola, C Congo, W and N Zambia, NE Namibia (Caprivi), N Botswana, W Zimbabwe (Kazungula), S Mozambique and E South Africa (Kruger National Park, SE and NE Natal coasts and E Cape). Also recorded in W Ethiopia and E Tanzania. Probably sedentary throughout much of its range, but see below. One museum specimen (male, probably this race) taken from S Nigeria (no date).
  C. n. accrae Liberia, Ivory Coast (Toumodi, N'Douci, Dabou, Grand Lahou), coastal Ghana (Quaminfio, Christianborg, Labadi, Shai Hills), coastal Togo and

Benin, S Nigeria and W Cameroon. Probably sedentary, but see below.

Local movements of both races may be triggered by the flooding of its habitat after the rains or by habitat destruction, e.g. by fire, or trampling by animals.

STATUS Locally rare to fairly common in many parts of its range and often absent from many regions where there is apparently suitable habitat, although possibly underrecorded.

REFERENCES Chapin (1939), Evans & Balmford (1992), Fry *et al.* (1988), Harwin (1983), Hustler & Carson (1996), Hustler & Mitchell (1997), Jackson (1987), Lewis & Pomeroy (1989).

99   NECHISAR NIGHTJAR
Caprimulgus solala   Not illustrated

Caprimulgus solala Safford, Ash, Duckworth, Telfer and Zewdie, 1995, *Ibis* 137, p.301 (Nechisar Plains, North Omo region, Ethiopia)

Wing of Nechisar Nightjar

IDENTIFICATION Probably a large, reddish-brown Afrotropical nightjar. Known only from a single, unsexed road casualty, from which only the left wing was salvaged. **At rest** Unknown. **In flight** Round-winged. Broad buffish-white band, almost midway along the outerwing, across the four outer primaries (innerweb only on outermost), and white tips to the two outer tail feathers. **Similar species** No data available.

VOICE Unknown.

HABITAT The single specimen was discovered in an area of treeless grassland. 1,200m.

HABITS No information.

FOOD No information.

BREEDING No information.

DESCRIPTION (Left wing only) Lesser coverts dark brown, speckled reddish-brown and buff. Alula and primary coverts dark brown, broadly barred tawny. Rest of wing-coverts dark brown, speckled buff, reddish-brown and greyish-brown, boldly spotted buff. Primaries brown; P10-P7 with 2-4 indistinct greyish-brown bars towards feather-tips, becoming buffish on outerwebs of P10 and P9; very broad whitish band, almost midway along feather, angled across innerweb of P10 and across both webs of P9-P7; white band edged and lightly tinged tawny-buff on P10-P8, heavily and entirely washed tawny-buff on P7; inner six primaries regularly barred tawny and tipped greyish-brown speckled tawny. Secondaries dark brown, regularly barred tawny and tipped greyish-brown.

MEASUREMENTS Wing 189mm.

MOULT Unknown.

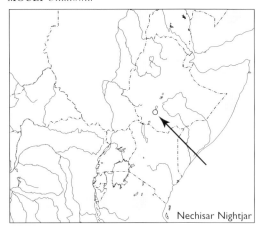

Nechisar Nightjar

GEOGRAPHICAL VARIATION Monotypic.

DISTRIBUTION AND MOVEMENTS The only known specimen was discovered at 6°00'N 37°47'E on the Nechisar Plains, North Omo region, southern Ethiopia, on 3 September 1990.

STATUS Known only from the type specimen.

REFERENCES Safford *et al.* (1995).

100   PLAIN NIGHTJAR
Caprimulgus inornatus   Plate 26

Caprimulgus inornatus Heuglin, 1869, *Orn. Nordost Afr.* 1, p.129 (Bogosland)

Possibly forms a superspecies with Star-spotted Nightjar.

IDENTIFICATION Length 22-23cm. A small to medium-sized, rather plain Afrotropical nightjar. Sexually dimorphic. **At rest** Upperparts and wing-coverts extremely variable in colour, ranging from blackish-brown, brown or greyish-brown to deep vinaceous, pale tawny-buff and sandy-buff. Rather uniform, with blackish-brown streaking and spotting generally restricted to head and scapulars. Occasionally shows lines of buffish spots across the wing-coverts. No collar on hindneck. Lacks noticeable white patch on throat. Underparts brownish or buff, barred brown. **In flight** The male has a white spot towards the wing-tip on the four outer primaries (innerweb only on outermost) and broad white tips to the two outer tail feathers. The female has tawny spots on the four outer primaries and lacks white tips to the two outer tail feathers. **Similar species** Star-spotted Nightjar (101) is extremely similar, but shorter-tailed and less variable in colour (generally dark greyish-brown) with a white throat-patch and narrower white tips to the two outer tail feathers; both sexes have white spots on the four outer primaries and white tips to the two outer tail feathers.

VOICE The song is a prolonged churr of constant pitch, often lasting for up to two minutes without pause. It sometimes commences with up to 65 short, deep *cuk* notes, interspersed with very short churrs. The *cuk* notes increase in speed until they merge into the churred song. May be heard predominantly at dusk and dawn. The flight call is a soft chuckling. On the ground, often utters low *chuck* notes. During threat/defence displays gives a throaty hiss, also given when the bird is handled.

HABITAT Prefers savannas with trees and bushes, subdesert steppe, open areas in lush savanna woodland and grassy clearings in forest. Winters mainly in wooded savannas, as far south as the edge of the forest zone. In Saudi Arabia it is generally found in rather barren habitats inland of the Asir mountains, but also occurs in rocky places at higher altitudes. In Yemen, it occurs in juniper forest on Jabal Iraf and on highly arid wadi slopes within the wadi Hadramawt region. 0–1,800m.

HABITS Crepuscular and nocturnal. Roosts on the ground, usually on leaf-litter, although sometimes on bare earth. Roost-sites are often in the shade of vegetation, in woodland clearings or on stony ground. In Mauritania it also roosts in rocky places and crevices. When flushed from its roost it usually flies a short distance, less than c. 20m, before alighting on the ground or occasionally in trees. Sometimes wing-claps twice when flushed. Double wing-claps are also given in flight, often repeated several times. Commonly sits on roads, paths and in clearings, especially at dusk, whence it often feeds by flycatching for insects. Also hunts by flitting about in buoyant flight, c. 5-7m above ground. Often hovers (see Breeding). No further information available.

FOOD Moths, termites, ants, grasshoppers, antlions, crickets, mantises and beetles (including Scarabaeidae, Carabidae, Elateridae and Anthicidae). No further data available.

BREEDING Breeding season usually April–June in Mali; May–June in Niger; March–June in Ethiopia; late April to mid-June in Somalia; and May–August in NW Kenya, although a nestling was noted on Mt Elgon in September. Also March–May in Nigeria and possibly May–June in Liberia, although two juveniles have been noted in December and January! No data available from Arabia or Yemen.

Possibly monogamous. No nest is constructed; the eggs are laid on bare ground, usually beneath low bushes. Clutch usually 2. Eggs elliptical ovate, glossy ivory-white or creamy, spotted and speckled varying shades of reddish-brown and lilac, 23.5-28.7 x 19.1-20.8mm. Often hovers when investigating an intruder in its territory. No further information available.

DESCRIPTION Adult male Forehead, crown and nape greyish-brown, finely speckled pale buff and off-white, central crown feathers streaked or spotted dark brown. Generally no collar on hindneck, although occasionally some individuals may have distinct broad buff collar. Mantle, back, rump and uppertail-coverts greyish-brown, finely speckled pale buff and sparsely streaked dark brown. Lesser coverts dark greyish-brown, often tinged rufous. Rest of wing-coverts greyish-brown, intricately patterned and speckled buff, occasionally with large buff spots on feather-tips, giving birds distinctly spotted appearance (occasionally these spots appear as distinct buff lines across closed wing). Marginal upperwing-coverts occasionally buff or pale buff. Scapulars greyish-brown, streaked or spotted blackish-brown, spots occasionally rather spidery or star-shaped; size and density of markings varies from individual to individual. Primaries brown, tips mottled

greyish-brown; white spot towards the feather-tip on innerweb of P10 and across both webs of P9-P7, occasionally suffused buffish on P7; outer four primaries also barred tawny or buff, usually above white spot; inner primaries broadly barred tawny. Secondaries brown broadly barred tawny, barring becoming more frequent towards inner wing. Tertials greyish-brown, mottled brown and buff. Tail brown, barred and mottled tawny and buff; R5 and R4 broadly (43-55mm) tipped white; central pair (R1) greyish-brown barred dark brown. Lores and ear-coverts greyish-brown finely speckled pale buff. Chin and throat buffish-white barred brown. No white on lower throat. Breast greyish-brown, barred and speckled brown. Belly, flanks and undertail- and underwing-coverts buff barred brown. **Adult female** Similar to the male but has tawny, not white, spots on the four outer primaries. Outer two tail feathers pale tawny, barred and mottled brown, with no white on tips. **Immature** and **Juvenile** Similar to the adults, but more densely barred tawny on primaries. **Chick** At hatching, covered with very pale buff down. **Bare parts** Iris dark brown; bill brown with black tip; legs and feet pale brown.

MEASUREMENTS Wing (male) 149-174, (female) 152-173; tail (male) 105-134, (female) 105-127; bill (male) 16-21, (female) 16-21; tarsus (male) 14-18, (female) 14-18. Weight (male) 33-61g, (female) 32-57g.

MOULT In E Africa (Kenya and Tanzania), birds in active moult December–March. The primaries are generally moulted descendantly, although occasionally they may be moulted in a serially descendant sequence. The secondaries are usually moulted ascendantly. The tail moult is extremely variable, with no obvious consistent pattern. No further data available.

GEOGRAPHICAL VARIATION Monotypic. Extremely variable in colour, birds ranging from blackish-brown, greyish-brown (described above) or brown to vinaceous, pale tawny-buff or sandy-buff. Colour variation is evident throughout the entire range and may bear relationship to local soil colour, but birds of all colour types occur together whilst on migration.

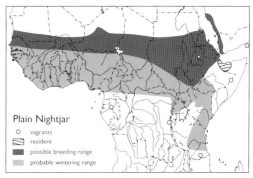

Plain Nightjar
○ vagrants
▨ resident
▩ possible breeding range
░ probable wintering range

DISTRIBUTION AND MOVEMENTS Africa and SW Arabia.

In Africa, a breeding visitor (April–November) to the Sahelian savannas, from S Mauritania and N Senegal, through S Mali, N Burkina Faso, S Niger (north of Air mountains), NW Nigeria and S Chad (north to Ennedi mountains) to central and SE Sudan, NW Kenya (Turkana and Elgon to Eldama Ravine and Marsabit), Eritrea?, N and W Ethiopia and Djibouti. Resident in NW Somalia. Outside the breeding season, moves south and winters mainly in wooded savannas. Occurs from Senegal to Liberia, east to NE Zaire, SW Sudan and SW Ethiopia? and south through Uganda, Kenya and N Tanzania to SC Tanzania (Iringa highlands) and E Tanzania (Usaramo). As a passage migrant, it is common in N Nigeria May–June and November–December. In Kenya, it is a regular migrant through the north and east during October–December, and return movements occur during March–April. In NE Zaire it is mainly a non-breeding visitor November–April. Occasionally birds stay and breed within the wintering range, e.g. Enugu (Nigeria) and Mt Nimba (Liberia). Birds present all year at Lagos, Nigeria. Vagrants recorded in Gabon, February and July.

An apparent breeding summer visitor along the Tihama, from the Asir mountains in SW Saudi Arabia, south into Yemen. A vagrant, presumably from this population, was recorded on board a ship off the Kuria Muria Islands, near the Oman coast, in November 1987.

STATUS Generally rather common throughout most of its African range. In Saudi Arabia, thought to be a summer visitor in small numbers, but possibly under-recorded. Locally common in Yemen.

REFERENCES Fry *et al.* (1988), Jennings (1995), Porter & Martins (1993), Short *et al.* (1990), Symens *et al.* (1994), Zimmerman *et al.* (1996).

---

101   STAR-SPOTTED NIGHTJAR
Caprimulgus stellatus   Plate 26

Caprimulgus stellatus Blundell and Lovat, 1899, *Bull. Brit. Orn. Club* 10, p.21 (Kassim River, southern Ethiopia)

Possibly forms a superspecies with Plain Nightjar.

IDENTIFICATION Length 21-23cm. A small to medium-sized, large-headed Afrotropical nightjar. Sexes similar. **At rest** Upperparts and wing-coverts rather uniform, generally dark greyish-brown, minutely speckled dark brown. Crown and scapulars with sparse dark brown streaks or spidery star-shaped spots. No collar on hindneck. Small white patch on either side of lower throat. Underparts paler, often brownish or buff barred brown. **In flight** Both sexes have a white spot towards the wing-tip on the four outer primaries (innerweb only on outermost) and narrow white tips to the two outer tail feathers. **Similar species** Plain Nightjar (100) is very similar but lacks white on the throat and can be extremely variable in colour; the male has much broader white tips to the two outer tail feathers, the female lacks white markings on the wings and tail.

VOICE The song is a rather weak, wheezy, yelping *pweu pweu pweu pweu* or *pwe-eh pwe-eh pwe-eh*, delivered at a rate of c. 13 notes per 10 seconds, with each note rising slightly in pitch at the end. Sings from the ground. May be heard chiefly at dusk and dawn. Also thought to utter a guttural *churr-krrk*, which may possibly be a flight call.

HABITAT Prefers dry, open bush and bushy grassland, stony semi-desert and black laval fields with densely scattered volcanic boulders, rocks and stones. Found at all altitudes up to 1,980m?

HABITS Probably crepuscular and nocturnal. Roosts on the ground, usually on leaf-litter. Very little appears to be known about this species.

FOOD Moths, mantises, beetles and grasshoppers. No further data available.

BREEDING Breeding season possibly January–March (probably longer?) in both Ethiopia and N Kenya. Birds singing strongly in Marsabit area, N Kenya, 20-22 January 1989, and museum specimens in breeding condition taken in same general area, 20-26 February 1956 (two males, three females), with immatures on 17 June 1970 and 31 July 1923. No further information available.

DESCRIPTION Adult male Forehead, crown and nape dark greyish-brown, often with vinaceous tinge, minutely speckled dark brown. Central feathers streaked or star-spotted dark brown, except on nape. No collar on hindneck. Mantle, back, rump and uppertail-coverts dark greyish-brown, generally unmarked. Wing-coverts, except lesser coverts, dark greyish-brown, finely speckled vinaceous-brown. Lesser coverts darker than rest of coverts, often with rufous tinge. Scapulars vinaceous grey-brown, with dark brown spidery, star-shaped spots. Primaries brown with mottled buffish tips; white spot with tawny edging, towards the feather-tip, on innerweb of P10 and both webs of P9-P7, P10 also spotted or barred tawny along outerweb above white spot; rest of primaries regularly barred tawny, P4-P1 tipped buffish. Secondaries brown, regularly barred tawny and tipped buffish. Tertials greyish-brown. Tail generally brown, barred and finely speckled tawny; R5 and R4 narrowly (20-26mm) tipped white; central pair greyish-brown with indistinct bars mottled tawny. Lores and ear-coverts greyish-brown, finely speckled pale buff or brown. Chin and throat pale greyish-buff. Small white spot on either side of lower throat. Breast greyish-brown barred brown. Belly and flanks buff, regularly and thinly barred brown. Undertail- and underwing-coverts buff barred brown. **Adult female** Similar to the male but perhaps paler, with heavy buff spotting on the upper wing-coverts. White spot on P7 washed tawny and white tips to R5 and R4 smaller (11-20mm), suffused tawny or buff. **Immature** and **Juvenile** Similar to the adults but upperparts more uniform, or rather rufous spotted dark brown, markings generally not star-shaped. White tips to the two outer tail feathers indistinct. **Chick** Not known. **Bare parts** Iris dark brown; bill blackish; legs and feet flesh brown.

MEASUREMENTS Wing (male) 149-164, (female) 151-159; tail (male) 95-112, (female) 96-102; bill (male) 13.3-16.3, (female) 12.2-16.3; tarsus (male) 17.9-22.4, (female) 18-22. Weight (male) 54-64g, (female) 50-69g.

MOULT No data available.

GEOGRAPHICAL VARIATION Monotypic. Slight colour variation noted with individuals ranging from greyish- or vinaceous-brown to paler, sandy-brown. The validity of race *simplex*, originally described from Lake Zwai, Ethiopia, in 1907, is questionable and not accepted here. It has also been suggested that Kenyan birds are on average more buffish than Ethiopian birds, but museum specimens do not appear to support this view.

DISTRIBUTION AND MOVEMENTS East Africa in Ethiopia (mainly Awash Valley, but also Artu and Nechisar National Park), N Kenya (Dida Galgalla, Chalbi and Koroli deserts; Marsabit and around southern half of Lake Turkana), NW Kenya (Lokitaung), C Kenya (Colcheccio, Kapedo and El Karama), NW Somalia (Dadab), Djibouti and SE Sudan. A record from SE Kenya (Voi) is possibly erroneous.

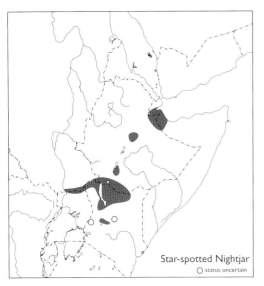

Star-spotted Nightjar
○ status uncertain

STATUS Locally common in Ethiopia, also in N and NW Kenya. Probably rare elsewhere, with only 1-3 records from most other localities where it has been recorded.

REFERENCES Fry *et al.* (1988).

---

102 SAVANNA NIGHTJAR
Caprimulgus affinis　　　　　Plate 31

Other name: Allied Nightjar

Caprimulgus affinis Horsfield, 1821, *Trans. Linn. Soc. London* 13, pt. 1, p.142 (Java)
Caprimulgus affinis kasuidori Hachisuka, 1932, *Bull. Brit. Orn. Club* 52, p.81 (Savu, Lesser Sunda Islands)
Caprimulgus affinis undulatus Mayr, 1944, *Bull. Amer. Mus. Nat. Hist.* 83, p.152 (Flores, Lesser Sunda Islands)
Caprimulgus affinis timorensis Mayr, 1944, *Bull. Amer. Mus. Nat. Hist.* 83, p.152 (Noilmina, Timor Island)
Caprimulgus affinis griseatus Walden, 1875, *Trans. Zool. Soc. London* 9, pt. 2, p.160 (Philippine Islands)
Caprimulgus affinis mindanensis Mearns, 1905, *Proc. Biol. Soc. Wash.* 18, p.85 (Malabang, Mindanao)
Caprimulgus affinis propinquus Riley, 1918, *Proc. Biol. Soc. Wash.* 31, p.155 (Parigi, Celebes)
Caprimulgus affinis monticolus Franklin, 1831, *Proc. Comm. Zool. Soc. London* p.116 (Ganges between Calcutta and Benares)
Caprimulgus affinis amoyensis Stuart Baker, 1931, *Bull. Brit. Orn. Club* 51, p.102 (Amoy, China)
Caprimulgus affinis stictomus Swinhoe, 1863, *Ibis* (1)5, p.250 (Ape's Hill, Formosa)

IDENTIFICATION Length 20-26cm. A small to medium-sized, generally greyish and rather uniform Oriental nightjar. The northern populations are larger and browner. Sexually dimorphic. **At rest** Upperparts brown speckled whitish or cinnamon, streaked blackish-brown. Very indistinct pale buffish, cinnamon or whitish collar around hindneck. Lesser coverts brown speckled pale buff. Rest of wing-coverts paler, boldly spotted pale buff.

Scapulars blackish-brown, broadly edged buff or whitish on outerwebs. Buffish submoustachial stripe. Small white patch on either side of lower throat. Underparts brown, barred, speckled and spotted buff and cinnamon, becoming buff barred brown on belly and flanks. **In flight** The male has a large white spot towards the wing-tip on the four outer primaries (innerweb only on outermost), and the two outer tail feathers are generally white, tipped or edged brownish (but see Geographical Variation). The female has buffish spots on the four outer primaries and lacks white on the tail. **Similar species** Indian Nightjar (96) is more variegated, with a broad buff or tawny-buff hindneck collar and heavier spotting on the wing-coverts; in flight the male often shows smaller white spots on the four outer primaries and the broad white tips to the two outer tail feathers, while the female has buff spots on the four outer primaries and white tips to the two outer tail feathers. Jungle Nightjar (78) is slightly larger and more heavily spotted on the wing-coverts, the male having white tips, distally washed brown, to all but the central pair of tail feathers, the female brownish-white or -buff tips. Large-tailed Nightjar (87) is slightly larger, browner and more variegated, the male with white tips to the two outer tail feathers, the female with buffish or buffish-white tips. Philippine (89) and Sulawesi Nightjars (90) are slightly larger, with a more spotted appearance, both sexes having a white spot on the second, third and fourth outer primaries and white tips to the two outer tail feathers.

VOICE The song (perhaps call) is a loud, grating *chwip* or *chweep*, repeated constantly for 30 minutes or more. Sings/calls mainly in flight. In Sumatra it also calls from flat roofs. In India and Pakistan the northern race *monticolus* also calls from the tops of trees and from telephone wires. May be heard throughout the night, from just before dusk until just after dawn. When flushed, gives a low chuckle or a soft screech.

HABITAT Prefers grasslands, grassy plains, open woodland and light forest with scrub or rocky outcrops. Also occurs on bare arable land, open stony and sparsely vegetated hillsides, barren ridges, edges of swamps and mangroves, sandy or shingle beaches, bare sand or riverbanks, along dry stony stream beds with scrub and grass, and coastal scrub and urban habitats, including cities. 0–1,500 (2,000?)m.

HABITS Crepuscular and nocturnal. Roosts on the ground, often amongst stones. Occasionally roosts in trees, perching lengthways along branches, or on flat rooftops of tall buildings in cities. When active, frequently perches on tree tops, fence-posts, large stones, telephone wires and rooftops. Occasionally spreads its tail and shuffles from side to side before settling. Often sits on roads and tracks at night. Can be quite gregarious, with feeding or passage flocks of up to 100 birds occurring together. When hunting, hawks or flies in wide circles, up to c. 20-50m above ground, or glides in a more direct flight, occasionally alighting on perches or on the ground. Forages over forests, cultivation, human settlements including open urban areas such as airports and golf courses, around city lights, lighted buildings and harbour floodlights. Drinks regularly, especially at forest pools, by flying low over the surface and dipping its bill into the water. No further information available.

FOOD Moths, mantises, beetles (including Elateridae and Lucanidae), termites and flying ants. No further data available.

BREEDING Breeding season June–July in NW Pakistan; April–August in India and the Himalayas; May–March? in the Philippines; March–December in Java; and April–January in Sumatra. No information available from other countries.

During courtship displays, flies with rather slow, jerky wingbeats. No nest is constructed; the eggs are laid on the ground, often amongst stones. Nest-sites may be out in the open or amongst scrub, beneath bushes or tufts of grass, or at the base of a tree. Nests in bare stony country, in ravines, on stony hillsides with scattered vegetation and on stony ridges. Clutch 1-2. Eggs elliptical, salmon-pink or pale buffish, spotted and blotched reddish-brown and deep red, 25.8-33.2 x 19.0-23.2mm. Both sexes incubate. When visiting the nest-site, an adult either alights directly onto the nest or lands a short distance away and approaches in a series of short walks, waddles or runs, interspersed with brief pauses. When running, the wings are occasionally held up almost vertically. If flushed from the nest, the adult performs an injury-feigning distraction display. Chicks nidicolous. Prior to fledging, the chicks can run short distances, often with their wings held up above their backs. No further information available.

DESCRIPTION *C. a. affinis* **Adult male** Forehead and sides of crown brown, heavily speckled whitish or cinnamon. Central crown and nape darker brown, lightly speckled white. Very indistinct buff or pale buff collar around hindneck. Mantle, back, rump and uppertail-coverts brown, thinly streaked blackish-brown. Lesser coverts dark brown, densely speckled pale buff. Rest of wing-coverts brown heavily spotted pale buff, spots occasionally with brown centres. Scapulars brown with blackish-brown centres, speckled pale buff on innerwebs and upper half of outerwebs, broadly edged pale buff on outerwebs. Primaries brown, tipped with pale greyish-brown mottling; large white spot towards the feather-tip on innerweb of P10 and across both webs of P9-P7; inner six primaries regularly spotted and barred tawny. Secondaries brown tipped with pale greyish-brown mottling, regularly spotted and barred tawny, markings becoming buffier on the inner secondaries. Tertials brown, densely mottled greyish-white or greyish-brown, tipped pale buff on outerwebs. R5 and R4 generally white, edged and/or tipped light brown, the amount of white on the innerweb of R4 often restricted to the distal portion; R3 and R2 brown, indistinctly barred tawny; central pair (R1) greyish-white, speckled and broadly barred brown. Lores and ear-coverts brown speckled greyish-white, buff or rufous. Chin and throat pale buff barred brown. Small white spot on either side of lower throat. Breast brown faintly barred and speckled buff, spotted pale buff and cinnamon. Belly, flanks and underwing-coverts buff barred brown. Undertail-coverts pale buff, almost whitish. **Adult female** Similar to the male. The spots on P10-P7 are smaller and buffish or tawny-buff. Generally lacks white on the tail, although R5 and R4 are narrowly tipped brownish-white or -buff. Very occasionally, has small whitish patch towards tip of innerweb of R5. **Immature** and **Juvenile** Similar to the adult female but paler, greyer-brown. **Chick** Not described. **Bare parts** Iris dark brown; bill blackish; legs and feet brown.

MEASUREMENTS Wing (male) 150-172, (female) 152-170; tail (male) 91-103, (female) 85-102; bill (male) c. 14, (female) c. 14; tarsus (male) c. 19, (female) c. 19. Weight no data.

MOULT In Java, moults from late December, suggesting

a post-breeding moult strategy. The primaries are moulted descendantly. No further data available.

GEOGRAPHICAL VARIATION Eleven races are currently recognised in two distinct groups. Southern populations occurring throughout Indonesia and the Philippines are split into seven small, greyish subspecies that form the nominate *affinis* group. The three northern races constitute the *monticolus* group and were formerly considered a distinct species, Franklin's Nightjar. They are generally larger and browner than the southern forms.

(a) *affinis* **group**

C. a. affinis Described above.

C. a. kasuidori Greyer and slightly paler than the nominate, with breast and upper flanks more coarsely barred, spots on the four outer primaries on average slightly larger (both sexes), the male having less white on the two outer tail feathers, R5 being broadly edged and tipped brown and R4 with only a vestigial white mark. Wing (male) 163-169, (female) 162-165; tail (male) 95-97, (female) 95-98. Weight no data.

C. a. undulatus Similar to the nominate, but with paler, more evenly coloured and more finely vermiculated upperparts, more closely and extensively barred underparts. Wing (male) 162-168, (female) 159-166; tail (male) 95-100, (female) 89-99. Weight no data.

C. a. timorensis Similar to *kasuidori* but less greyish, markings buffier. Slightly paler than the nominate, the male with less white on the two outer tail feathers, which are broadly edged and tipped brown, and R4 white on the innerweb of the distal half only. One female (museum specimen) has an incomplete white hindneck collar. Wing (male) 160-164, (female) 157-162; tail (male) 94-102, (female) 94-102. Weight no data.

C. a. griseatus Paler and greyer than the nominate with cinnamon markings and larger white patches on the lower throat; the male has white on the two outer tail feathers restricted to the distal half. One female (museum specimen) is paler and sandier. Wing (male) 163-164, (female, one) 169; tail (male) 93-96, (female, one) 94. Weight (male, one) 54.5g, (female) no data.

C. a. mindanensis Greyer and paler than the nominate with whiter markings, especially on the hindneck and scapulars. The male generally has larger white spots on the four outer primaries but less white on R4, which is merely broadly tipped white. Wing (male, one) 164, (female, one) 158; tail (male, one) 93, (female, one) 93. Weight no data.

C. a. propinquus Similar to the nominate but paler, with smaller blackish markings on the crown and scapulars, and narrower brown bars on the central tail feathers. The underparts are barred on the upper belly only. Wing (male, one) 170, (female, one) 164; tail (male) 101, (female, one) 96. Weight no data. One male (museum specimen) from southern Sulawesi suggests that birds from this region may represent an as yet undescribed form: the upperparts are as dark as the nominate but with tawnier markings, the crown is blacker, the brown bars on the central tail feathers are broader and the underparts are more rufous-buff.

(b) *monticolus* **group**

C. a. monticolus (Franklin's Nightjar) Larger and browner than the nominate, with larger spots on the four outer primaries. Variable in colour, ranging from darkish brown to buffish-brown, and often tinged rufous. Wing (male) 181-206, (female) 180-208; tail (male) 105-125, (female) 107-122. Weight no data.

C. a. amoyensis Generally rufous, although greyer-brown birds do occur. Wing (male) 199-208, (female) 183-200; tail (male) 115-123, (female) 100-116. Weight no data.

C. a. stictomus Generally greyish-brown, although the type specimen (a female) has buffish-brown upperparts and cinnamon-tinged underparts; two males (museum specimens) are also very buffish. Wing (male) 188-198, (female) 177-193; tail (male) 107-123, (female) 105-121. Weight (male) 71-86g, (female) 75-110g.

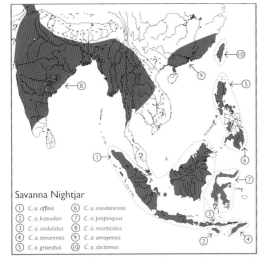

Savanna Nightjar

① C. a. affinis   ⑥ C. a. mindanensis
② C. a. kasuidori   ⑦ C. a. propinquus
③ C. a. undulatus   ⑧ C. a. monticolus
④ C. a. timorensis   ⑨ C. a. amoyensis
⑤ C. a. griseatus   ⑩ C. a. stictomus

DISTRIBUTION AND MOVEMENTS A widespread Oriental species, occurring from India to central Indonesia.

C. a. affinis S Sulawesi?, Sumatra, Nias, Riau Archipelago, Lingga Archipelago, Bangka, Belitung (Billiton), Borneo, Java, Bali, Karimon Java Islands and Lombok. Sedentary.

C. a. kasuidori Savu and Sumba in the Lesser Sundas. Sedentary.

C. a. undulatus Sumbawa, Komodo and Flores in the Lesser Sundas. Sedentary.

C. a. timorensis Alor, Timor, Roti and Kisar. Sedentary.

C. a. griseatus The Philippines on Luzon, Catanduanes, Mindoro, Sibuyan, Negros and Cebu. Sedentary.

C. a. mindanensis The Philippines on Mindanao only. Sedentary.

C. a. propinquus Sulawesi, except the Macassar region on the southern Peninsula? (see Geographical Variation). Sedentary.

C. a. monticolus NE Pakistan, India (south to Kerala and Madras), Bangladesh, Burma and Thailand. Sedentary and locally migratory. In NE Pakistan, appears to be a summer breeding visitor only, arriving in March–April and departing in October–November, probably migrating through the Punjab plains.

C. a. amoyensis SE China (SE Yunnan east to Fujian). Presumably sedentary.

C. a. stictomus Taiwan. Presumably sedentary. Some birds are said to move south-west and winter in Laos and SE Thailand, but this requires further examination.

A vagrant, possibly of the race *C. a. affinis*, recorded on Christmas Island on 30 May 1994, and again in October 1994. Possibly also recorded here in November 1996.

STATUS Locally common or abundant in many parts of its range.

REFERENCES Ali & Ripley (1970), Coates & Bishop (1997), Dickinson *et al.* (1991), Harvey (1976), Higgins (in press), Mayr (1944), Roberts (1991).

103   FRECKLED NIGHTJAR
Caprimulgus tristigma   Plate 25

Other name: Rock Nightjar

Caprimulgus tristigma Rüppell, 1840, *Neue Wirbelth., Vög.* p.105 (Gondar, Ethiopia)
Caprimulgus tristigma sharpei Alexander, 1901, *Bull. Brit. Orn. Club* 12, p.29 (Gambaga, Gold Coast)
Caprimulgus tristigma pallidogriseus Parker and Benson, 1971, *Bull. Brit. Orn. Club* 91, p.113 (Upper Ogun Estate, north of Iseyin, western Nigeria)
Caprimulgus tristigma lentiginosus A. Smith, 1845, *Illustr. Zool. S. Afr., Aves* pl.101 and text (Great Namaqualand)
Caprimulgus tristigma granosus Clancey, 1965, *Durban Mus. Novit.* 7, p.345 (near Bulawayo, Zimbabwe)

IDENTIFICATION Length 26-28cm. A large, greyish-black or blackish Afrotropical nightjar, occurring in, or near, rocky places. Sexually dimorphic. **At rest** Upperparts and wing-coverts blackish-brown, profusely spotted and speckled white, pale buff and cinnamon. No collar on hindneck. White throat-patch. Underparts dark brown barred whitish and cinnamon, becoming buff barred brown on belly. **In flight** Appears rather deep-chested and flies with deep slow wingbeats. The male has a small white spot towards the wing-tip on the four outer primaries and broad white tips to the two outer tail feathers. The female has smaller white spots on the four (sometimes only three) outer primaries and has no white on the tail. **Similar species** None.

VOICE The song can be quite variable but is usually given as a double-noted *whow-whow* or a treble-noted *whow-whow-whow*, although occasionally 4-5 notes may be delivered in quick succession. The song may be repeated for 30 seconds or more at a time, with only a very slight pause between each set of notes. A common variation of the song is given as *ow-whow ow-whow*. (Presumably singing) birds may also give up to 26 ringing *wha* notes, or 2-9 *wa* sounds. Sings from rocks, occasionally from roofs of buildings. May be heard mainly at dusk and dawn but will also sing throughout the night.

The flight calls include 2-5 *kheh-kheh-kheh* notes. The contact call is a double *wockwock* or treble *wockwockwock*, given in flight or when approaching the nest. When disturbed (flushed?), birds utter *kluk-kluk-kluk* notes. In response to the playback of its song, the male may give a long series of *whoot-whoot* notes; these notes are presumably also given during territorial disputes with neighbouring or intruding males. The alarm call is a yelping 'gobble'. During distraction displays, adults give soft, grumbling *grok-grok* calls. Chicks utter a soft, mewing *wee-oo wee-oo* at the nest.

HABITAT Prefers rocky places with vegetation, such as outcrops, rocky or boulder-strewn hills, kopjes, inselbergs, ravines and wooded slopes on escarpments. Also occurs on bare hills in forests, on rocks along rapids and, more recently, in built-up areas. Will vacate recently burnt areas. Outside the breeding season, birds may sometimes occur far from rocky habitats. 600–2,000m.

HABITS Crepuscular and nocturnal. Roosts on bare or lichen-covered rocks. Roost-sites are either in the open or amongst vegetation. Often sits on roads and tracks at night. Usually occurs singly or in pairs, sometimes in small groups. Generally feeds over rocks, rocky hillsides with vegetation, broken ground and cattle pastures. Also hawks for insects around tree-tops, e.g. *Diospyros mespiliformis*, and frequently perches atop vertical branches during forays. No further information available.

FOOD Moths, winged termites and beetles (including Scarabaeidae, Geotrupidae and Melolonthinae). No further data available.

BREEDING Breeding season January–May? in Nigeria; May–June in Ethiopia, Kenya and NE Zaire (chick found in May in Garamba); late August–November in Rwanda, Burundi, Tanzania, Zambia and Malawi; August–December in Zimbabwe; and September–November in S Mozambique? and South Africa.

Monogamous and territorial. No nest is constructed; the eggs are usually laid on vegetation or leaf-litter in depressions and shallow hollows on rocks. Also breeds on granite outcrops and boulders, and more recently on flat rooftops (e.g. in Durban, South Africa). Nest-sites are often near patches of lichen and either in full sun or partly shaded. Often uses the same nest-site in successive years. Clutch usually 2, the eggs being laid on successive days. Eggs elliptical, streaked whitish, speckled and blotched black, grey or light brown on underlying pale lilac, markings often concentrated near blunt end, 26.8-33.3 x 20.0-22.6mm. Possibly double-brooded, laying a second clutch shortly after the fledging of the first brood. Incubation of clutch commences when the first egg is laid and is by female during the day and apparently by the male at night. Changeover probably occurs just after dusk. In hot weather, the female gular-flutters with her bill open. If disturbed when on the nest, she adopts a flattened posture and closes her eyes. The incubation period is about 17-19 days. Eggshells are not removed by the adult after hatching and remain at the nest-site. If flushed after the eggs have hatched, the female gives a distraction display by fluttering around with her wings and tail spread. Distraction displays occur on rocks or in cover, c. 10m from nest. The semi-precocial young often shuffle about the nest-site soon after hatching. The female broods the young, which sit side-by-side and face forward, by tucking herself against the chicks' backs. Whilst brooding, she usually keeps her back to the sun. The chicks are first fed just after dusk. The adult raises its head slightly, then lowers its bill which is grasped by the chick. Food is probably carried in a ball in the adult's throat and the chicks are fed by regurgitation, every 10-15 minutes. Adults brood the young until they are c. 12 days old. Chicks can remain at the nest-site for 12-14 days, after which they may be found a short distance away. The chicks apparently return to the nest-site to be fed. Chicks (and adults?) defecate at the edge of the nest, causing a ring of droppings around the nest-site. If threatened, well-grown

chicks perform a threat/defence display by spreading their wings, gaping and lunging towards the intruder. Chicks fledge at about 20 days.

DESCRIPTION *C. t. tristigma* **Adult male** Forehead, crown, nape, mantle, back, rump and uppertail-coverts blackish-brown or black, profusely spotted and speckled whitish, pale buff and cinnamon. No collar on hind-neck. Wing-coverts blackish-brown or black, profusely speckled and spotted whitish, true cinnamon and pale buff. Scapulars similar but also irregularly blotched buff. Primaries brown, tipped with pale brown, pale tawny or greyish-white speckling, very broadly so on P10-P7; small white spot almost midway along feather on innerwebs of P10-P7, spot on P7 often washed buff or pale tawny; tawny spotting or barring along edge of outerweb of P10 and on outerwebs, above white spot, of P9 and P8; rest with tawny barring across both webs. Secondaries dark brown, broadly barred tawny. Tertials blackish, profusely speckled whitish and cinnamon. Tail dark brown, mottled and barred greyish-brown; R5 and R4 barred tawny along edge of outerwebs, and broadly (35-45mm) tipped white on both webs; white patch on R5 often edged tawny and tipped brown on outerweb; central pair (R1) darker than rest and more heavily mottled and barred greyish-brown. Lores and ear-coverts brown, finely speckled greyish-white. Chin and throat blackish, often tinged cinnamon, and indistinctly barred whitish, pale buff and brown. Small white patch on either side of lower throat or large white patch across entire lower throat, lower feathers of which have buff subterminal bar and dark brown tips. Breast blackish-brown barred whitish and true cinnamon. Belly, flanks, underwing- and undertail-coverts buff barred brown. **Adult female** Similar to the male, but the white spots on the outer four primaries are smaller, occasionally absent altogether on P7, with no white on the outer two tail feathers. **Immature** and **Juvenile** Similar to the adults. **Chick** At hatching, covered in mottled dark grey and off-white down. **Bare parts** Iris dark brown; bill blackish; legs and feet blackish.

MEASUREMENTS Wing (male) 170-186, (female) 171-186; tail (male) 117-133, (female) 112-122; bill (male) 17.2-19.0, (female) 17.4-17.8; tarsus (male) 12-18, (female) 12-18. Weight unsexed (one) 87g.

MOULT No published data available.

GEOGRAPHICAL VARIATION Five races are currently recognised.

C. t. tristigma Described above.

C. t. sharpei Darker and perhaps slightly smaller than the nominate, with darker and blacker upperparts, a darker breast and the belly darker buff. Wing (male) 171-177 (184?), (female) 165-180; tail (male) 107-120 (137?), (female) 122-125. Weight no data.

C. t. pallidogriseus Paler than the nominate with whiter speckling on the upperparts. Wing (male, one) 185, (female) 179-185; tail (male, one) 134, (female, one) 122. Weight (male, one) 100 g?, (female, one) 69g.

C. t. lentiginosus Similar to the nominate but slightly larger and paler, with upperparts speckled and spotted true cinnamon and buff rather than whitish. Wing (male, 177?) 191-193, (female, 177?) 183-191; tail (male) 129-141, (female) 127-135. Weight no data.

C. t. granosus Darker and larger than the nominate, with darker and blacker upperparts and a browner breast. Wing (male) 184-196, (female) 183-195; tail (male) 122-140, (female) 123-140. Weight (male) 70.3-88.8g, (female) 69-91g.

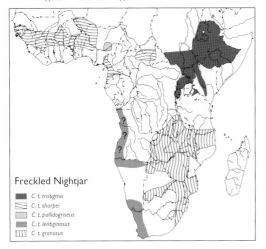

Freckled Nightjar

- ▨ *C. t. tristigma*
- ◫ *C. t. sharpei*
- ▦ *C. t. pallidogriseus*
- ▨ *C. t. lentiginosus*
- ▥ *C. t. granosus*

DISTRIBUTION AND MOVEMENTS West, East and southern Africa, although distribution is discontinuous.

C. t. tristigma Ethiopia, S Sudan, Uganda, Rwanda, Burundi, NW and WC Kenya and N Tanzania. Sedentary.
C. t. sharpei Guinea, N Sierra Leone, S Mali, SW Niger, SW and W Burkina Faso, N Ivory Coast, N Ghana, N Togo, C Benin, W and C? Nigeria, parts of W and S Cameroon, N Equatorial Guinea and C Central African Republic. Sedentary.
C. t. pallidogriseus Nigeria (Jos Plateau?). Exact distribution unclear, especially with regard to range of *sharpei*, which also occurs in Nigeria. Sedentary.
C. t. lentiginosus W? Angola, N and S Namibia and W South Africa. Sedentary.
C. t. granosus S Tanzania, SE Zaire, Zambia, Malawi, N and S Mozambique, Zimbabwe, N and S Botswana and NE and E South Africa. Sedentary.

Although all races are mainly sedentary, they may undertake some local movements in cold winters (e.g. at Matopos, Zimbabwe). Possibly migratory in Nigeria.

STATUS Fairly common throughout most of its range and locally abundant in some regions (e.g. Ethiopia). Possibly more widespread than currently known.

REFERENCES Elgood *et al.* (1994), Fry *et al.* (1988), Masterson (1992), Parker & Benson (1971), Steyn (1971).

---

104 BONAPARTE'S NIGHTJAR
Caprimulgus concretus   Plate 33

Caprimulgus concretus Bonaparte, 1850, *Consp. Av.* 1, p.60 (Ashanti, error = Borneo)

IDENTIFICATION Length 21-22cm. A small to medium-sized, brown forest nightjar, confined to Sumatra and Borneo. Sexually dimorphic. **At rest** Upperparts brown spotted chestnut. No obvious collar on hindneck. Wing-coverts brown spotted chestnut and cinnamon. Scapulars blackish-brown tipped chestnut, broadly bordered pale buff on outerwebs. White submoustachial stripe and large white throat-patch. Underparts brown barred chestnut,

becoming buff barred brown on belly and flanks. **In flight** Both sexes lack white on the wings, which are generally brown and unmarked. The male has white tips to the two outer tail feathers (innerweb only on outermost), the female lacks white or has the two outer tail feathers very narrowly tipped white. **Similar species** Salvadori's Nightjar (105) is darker, more heavily spotted. The male has small, irregularly shaped white marks on the four outer primaries and white tips (both webs) to the two outer tail feathers. The female has much smaller, buffier marks on the outer primaries and narrow buff or brownish-white tips to the two outer tail feathers. Malaysian Eared-nightjar (45) is larger with a distinct buffish collar around the hindneck. Both sexes lack white markings on the wings and tail.

VOICE The song is a low, mournful, double-noted *wa-ouuuu*, the second note descending in pitch. Sings only once or twice per minute. May be heard predominantly at dusk and dawn and throughout moonlit nights.

HABITAT Prefers lowland forests. Occurs in clearings and along the edges of dipterocarp forest, heath forest and secondary growth. 0–500m.

HABITS Crepuscular and nocturnal. When active, often alights on branches, perching with a rather vertical stance. Forages in short sallies from branches, often returning to the same perch. Often hunts from branches overhanging rivers. No further information available.

FOOD No data available.

BREEDING No information available.

DESCRIPTION Adult male Forehead, crown, nape, mantle, back, rump, lesser wing-coverts and uppertail-coverts brown spotted chestnut, with lower nape feathers brown tipped chestnut but not showing as a hindneck collar. Rest of wing-coverts brown spotted chestnut and cinnamon. Scapulars blackish-brown tipped chestnut, broadly bordered pale buff on outerwebs. Primaries brown, unmarked. Secondaries brown edged with small rufous-buff spots. Tertials brown mottled buff and tawny. Tail brown, indistinctly barred chestnut or tawny; R5 and R4 tipped white (c. 20mm) on innerweb of R5, both webs of R4. Lores and ear-coverts dark brown speckled rufous. White submoustachial stripe. Chin brown barred pale buff. Throat white. Breast brown barred chestnut. Lower breast and upper belly buffish-white barred brown. Belly, flanks, undertail- and underwing-coverts buff barred brown. **Adult female** Similar to the male, perhaps fractionally paler. Lacks white on the two outer tail feathers or has extremely narrow (c. 4mm) whitish tips. **Immature** and **Juvenile** Not known. **Chick** Not known. **Bare parts** Iris dark brown; bill brownish; legs and feet brown.

MEASUREMENTS Wing (male) 158-174, (female) 166-175; tail (male) 95-110, (female) 104-112; bill (male) 12.6-14.4, (female) 11.1-13.9; tarsus (male) 19.4-21.0, (female) 15.6-18.4. Weight no data.

MOULT The primaries are moulted descendantly. Tail moult has not been documented, but may occasionally commence with the outermost (R5). No further data available.

GEOGRAPHICAL VARIATION Monotypic.

DISTRIBUTION AND MOVEMENTS Confined to Sumatra, Belitung (Billiton) and Borneo. Sedentary.

273

Bonaparte's Nightjar

STATUS Widely distributed, but rare throughout its range.

REFERENCES MacKinnon & Phillipps (1993), Mann (in prep.), van Marle & Voous (1988), Parrott & Andrew (1996), Smythies (1981).

105 SALVADORI'S NIGHTJAR
Caprimulgus pulchellus   Plate 33

Caprimulgus pulchellus Salvadori, 1879, *Ann. Mus. Civ. Genova* 14, p.195 (Mt Singalan, Sumatra)
Caprimulgus pulchellus bartelsi Finsch, 1902, *Notes Leyden Mus.* 23, p.148 (Pasir Datar, western Java)

IDENTIFICATION Length 19-21.5cm. A small, darkish Indonesian nightjar, occurring only on Sumatra and Java. Only the male is known from Sumatra; the Javan population is sexually dimorphic. **At rest** Upperparts and wing-coverts dark brown, spotted and barred tawny, cinnamon and buff, crown and nape paler, greyer-brown, central feathers broadly streaked blackish. Indistinct tawny-buff collar around hindneck. Tawny submoustachial stripe and large white patch on either side of lower throat. Underparts tawny, buff and greyish-white, barred brown, becoming buff barred brown on lower belly, flanks and undertail-coverts. **In flight** The male has a small white spot or bar towards the wing-tip on the second to fifth outermost primaries, and a white spot on the tips of the two outermost tail feathers. Females (currently known only for race *bartelsi*) sometimes have a small tawny spot on the second and third outer primaries, and have white or buff tips to the two outer tail feathers. **Similar species** See Bonaparte's Nightjar (104).

VOICE The song/call (this species?) is a short irregular series of up to five *tock* notes. May be heard mainly at dusk. No further information available.

HABITAT Prefers montane and submontane forests. Often occurs near cliffs and occasionally inhabits small, marshy areas (this species?). 800–2,100m.

HABITS Crepuscular and nocturnal. Roosts in trees or on the ground. Roost-sites may include grassy areas in small marshes. If flushed from its roost, it may fly a short distance and re-alight on a horizontal branch. Occasionally occurs in small flocks of up to five birds. Often sits on cliff faces during the night and also perches in trees, often high above ground, and on tree-stumps. Forages over forest clearings or near cliffs, flying with slow, flapping wingbeats interspersed with short glides with wings held in a V above its back. Also flycatches in short sallies from cliff faces, or takes prey from cliff surfaces. No further information available.

FOOD Insects. No further data available.

BREEDING Breeding season late March–May on Java. No data available from Sumatra.

No nest is constructed; the eggs are laid on leaf-litter on the ground. Nest-sites may be beneath shrubs or bushes. Clutch 1-2. Eggs elliptical, glossy white and unmarked, 29.0 x 21.5mm. No further information available.

DESCRIPTION *C. p. pulchellus* **Adult male** Forehead, crown and nape greyish-brown, speckled greyish-white and thinly streaked blackish, central feathers boldly streaked blackish. Indistinct collar around hindneck tawny-buff, barred brown. Mantle, back and rump dark brown barred tawny and cinnamon, uppertail-coverts dark brown, broadly barred and ocellated tawny. Lesser coverts dark brown, thinly barred tawny; primary coverts and median coverts dark brown, boldly spotted tawny along edges of outerwebs and on tips. Rest of wing-coverts brown, spotted buff and pale buff, barred greyish-white. Scapulars blackish, thinly edged buff along outerwebs. Primaries brown; small white spot almost midway along feather on innerweb of P9; white bar separated by dark feather-shafts (c. 5mm) across P8 and P7, and white bar on outerweb of P6. Secondaries brown, outer feathers boldly spotted tawny along outerwebs, inner feathers spotted tawny-buff with brown speckling. Tertials brown, speckled greyish-white and spotted pale buff on tip of outerweb. Tail brown, vermiculated and speckled tawny, the central pair of feathers (R1) densely so; small white spot on tips of innerwebs of R5 (c. 17mm) and R4 (c. 14mm), the spots extending to the inner 2-4mm of the outerwebs. Lores and ear-coverts chestnut barred brown. Tawny feathers barred brown along submoustachial stripe. Chin and throat brown, speckled and thinly barred buffish. Large white patch on either side of lower throat, the lower feathers of which are broadly tipped blackish, with a very thin, pale buff subterminal band. Breast tawny, buff and greyish-white, thinly barred brown. Belly and flanks boldly spotted with buff and greyish-white 'arrow-head' marks, barred brown, the bars further apart than on breast. Undertail-coverts pale buff, thickly barred brown. Under-wing-coverts brown barred tawny. **Adult female** Unknown. **Immature** and **Juvenile** Unknown. **Chick** Unknown. **Bare parts** Iris brown; bill blackish; tarsus brownish.

MEASUREMENTS (two males only) Wing 153-160; tail 92-97; bill 14-17; tarsus 14-17. Weight no data.

MOULT The type specimen of the nominate race, a male taken in July, had just begun to moult its central tail feathers. No further data available.

GEOGRAPHICAL VARIATION Two races are currently recognised; *bartelsi* is considered a distinct species by some authorities, but until more data become available, including more specimens of the Sumatran form, its taxonomic status remains unclear.

    C. p. pulchellus Described above.
    C. p. bartelsi Similar to the nominate but fractionally smaller. The male is lightly spotted cinnamon-buff on the head, with no hindneck collar, a small white spot

on the innerweb of P10 and both webs of P9 and a narrow white band across P8 and P7 and half-way across the innerweb of P7, white tips (c. 19mm) to both webs of R5 and R4, a white patch across the whole of the lower throat, and whiter undertail-coverts. The female is paler, more cinnamon or rufous, on upperparts and breast, lacking white marks on the outer primaries but sometimes with small tawny spots on P9 and P8; R5 and R4 are tipped whitish or buffish, washed brown (c. 10mm). Wing (male, five) 148-152, (female, five) 148-156; tail (male, five) 96-101, (female, five) 95-100. Weight no data.

Salvadori's Nightjar
▨ *C. p. bartelsi*
▦ *C. p. pulchellus*

DISTRIBUTION AND MOVEMENTS A little-known Indonesian species, endemic to Sumatra and Java.

    C. p. pulchellus Sumatra. The type specimen, a male, was taken on Mount Singgalang in the Padang Highlands, W Sumatra, on 11 July 1878 and a second male was taken on Gunung Dempo, on 15 July 1936. Also reported from Mamas Valley in the Gunung Leuser National Park, Aceh, from Deleng Singut, Berastagi and Sikulikap waterfall, N Sumatra and at Muara Senami, Jambi. Sedentary.

    C. p. bartelsi Java. Occurs in suitable habitat in western and central Java, and in the Tengger Highlands in eastern Java. Presumably sedentary.

STATUS Little data available and probaly under-recorded, although records suggest that it is possibly uncommon in both Sumatra and Java.

REFERENCES Andrew (1985), Finsch (1902), Hellebrekers & Hoogerwerf (1967), Holmes (1996), MacKinnon & Phillipps (1993).

---

106 PRIGOGINE'S NIGHTJAR
Caprimulgus prigoginei   Plate 25

Other name: Itombwe Nightjar

Caprimulgus prigoginei Louette, 1990, *Ibis* 132, p.349 (Malenge, Itombwe, Kivu province, Zaire).

IDENTIFICATION Length 19cm. A small, spotted and rather darkish Afrotropical nightjar with a short tail and fairly large head. Known only from a single female specimen. **At rest** Upperparts and wing-coverts brown, speckled and spotted dark brown, tawny and buff. No collar on hindneck. Underparts brown on breast, spotted and barred tawny and buff. Belly paler, barred brown. **In**

flight Small tawny spot towards the wing-tip on innerwebs of second and third outermost primaries and both webs of fourth outermost. Narrow whitish tips to outermost tail feathers, narrower buffish or tawny tips to remainder. **Similar species** None.

VOICE Unknown. An unidentified, 'churring' nightjar, possibly this species, was heard in the Itombwe mountain forests near Lake Lungwe, in February 1952. A rapid 'knocking' sound, similar to the song of Swamp Nightjar (98), recently recorded in the Itombwe forest and at Ndoki, Congo, might also be the song of this species. Calls may include *rak rak* or *rek rek* notes.

HABITAT Unknown, but possibly a forest species. The single specimen is from 1,280m.

HABITS No information available.

FOOD No data available.

BREEDING No information available.

DESCRIPTION Adult male Unknown. **Adult female** Forehead and crown brown, thickly blotched blackish-brown, spotted and speckled tawny and buff. Sides of crown, above eyes, paler. Nape similar to crown although sides much lighter, giving large pale patch behind eye. No collar on hindneck, but two pure white feathers situated at the rear of left side of nape and one partially white one on right. Mantle, back, rump and uppertail-coverts brown blotched blackish-brown, speckled and spotted tawny and buff. Wing-coverts brown. Lesser coverts with tawny barring, rest of coverts heavily spotted tawny and darkish buff. Scapulars distally blackish-brown with small buff spot on tip of innerweb and tawny spots on tip and edge of outerweb, rest of feather buff. Primaries dark brown, P10 with small tawny spots along edge of outerweb; small tawny spot roughly midway between centre and tip of feather on innerwebs of P9 and P8, and both webs of P7. Inner six primaries and all secondaries with larger and more regular tawny spotting, becoming more barred towards inner secondaries. Tertials as scapulars but browner and paler. Underwing-coverts brown, barred tawny. Tail brown; R5 regularly barred tawny-buff and tipped whitish (c. 14mm) on both webs; R4 similar, but white tips suffused in parts with buff or light brown; R3 and R2 with less distinct barring and tawny spots on tips of both webs; central pair (R1) irregularly patterned buff and tawny, with buff tips to outer portions of both webs. Lores and ear-coverts buff, barred brown. Chin and throat tawny, barred brownish-buff. Small buffish-white spot on either side of lower throat, with some whitish feathers in centre. Breast brown, spotted and heavily barred tawny and buff. Belly and underwing-coverts buff barred brown. Undertail-coverts buff with brown barring. **Immature** and **Juvenile** Not known. **Chick** Not known. **Bare parts** Iris not known; bill blackish; legs and feet reddish-brown.

MEASUREMENTS (one female) Wing 166, tail 89, bill 20.5, tarsus 14.0. Weight no data.

MOULT No data available.

GEOGRAPHICAL VARIATION Monotypic.

DISTRIBUTION AND MOVEMENTS The only known specimen was taken at 3°26'S 28°30'E near Malenge, Itombwe, Kivu province, eastern Zaire, on 11 August 1955.

STATUS Known only from the type specimen.

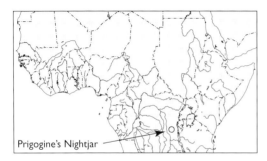

Prigogine's Nightjar

REFERENCES Curry-Lindahl (1960), Louette (1990).

107 COLLARED NIGHTJAR
Caprimulgus enarratus   Plate 29

Caprimulgus enarratus G. R. Gray, 1871, *Ann. Mag. Nat. Hist.* (4)8, p.428 (Madagascar)

IDENTIFICATION Length 24cm. A medium-sized, brown forest nightjar, endemic to Madagascar. Sexes similar. **At rest** Large-headed. Upperparts greyish-brown boldly spotted blackish-brown, spots with chestnut edges. Very broad rufous collar around hindneck, above which is a thin, well-defined buff band. Wing-coverts greyish-brown boldly spotted blackish-brown, spots broadly bordered chestnut or pale buff. Scapulars greyish-brown, very broadly spotted blackish-brown with chestnut edges. Tawny-buff band around lower throat. Underparts generally brownish, boldly spotted blackish-brown with broad chestnut edges, becoming less spotted and more streaked on the belly and flanks. **In flight** Both sexes lack white markings on the wings, which are brown regularly spotted tawny, and have narrow white tips to the outer one or two tail feathers. **Similar species** None. Madagascar Nightjar (97) is paler and more variegated, generally lacking or has only a very indistinct tawny-buff hindneck collar; the male has a white spot towards the wing-tip on the four outer primaries, and broader white tips to the two outer tail feathers; the female has buff spots on the four outer primaries and brownish- or buffish-white tips to the two outer tail feathers.

VOICE The song is unknown. If danger approaches the nest-site, the adult repeatedly gives soft, liquid *kow* or *keeow* notes. During threat/defence displays, the adults make throaty hissing sounds. Nestlings and juveniles utter soft *chic* notes.

HABITAT Prefers dense, humid, evergreen forest and primary lowland forest. Also occurs in adjacent second growth and sometimes in dry deciduous forest. It has recently been recorded in brush forest and mangroves in the Morondava area, western Madagascar. 0–1,880m.

HABITS Crepuscular, nocturnal and secretive. Roosts on leaf-litter on the ground, often amongst roots or beneath rocky outcrops. Also roosts on logs or pandan leaves just above ground. Roost-sites are usually inside closed-canopy forest and may be used for several days in succession. Often roosts in pairs. If flushed from its roost, it occasionally flies to a low branch. At dusk, it leaves its roost quietly. Often feeds beneath the canopy within forests but also

hawks for food above the canopy. No further information available.

FOOD Beetles (including Scarabaeidae, Melolonthinae and Tenebrionidae) and other insects. No further data available.

BREEDING Breeding season late September to early December (mainly October–November).

No nest is constructed; the eggs are possibly laid on leaf-litter on the ground. It also nests on epiphytic ferns *Asplenium* on tree-trunks and in the crowns of free-standing ferns, so far always within 2m of the ground. Nest-sites are usually at the edge of forest trails and clearings. Clutch 2. Eggs glossy white often lightly washed pinkish-brown, 25.9-26.1 x 19.1-19.4mm. Incubating adults sit very tightly. If danger approaches, the adult performs a threat/defence display by gaping and hissing (see Voice); if danger persists it may lift its wings above its body. If flushed from its chicks, the adult performs an injury-feigning distraction display by fluttering about on the ground for 30 seconds or more. If flushed from the ground, feathered chicks may flutter up onto a low branch. No further information available.

DESCRIPTION Adult male Forehead, crown and nape greyish-brown, central feathers boldly spotted blackish-brown, edged tawny at tips. Sides of crown above the eyes paler, feathers tipped greyish-white. Thin, well-defined buff collar around upper nape. Nape and upper mantle rufous. Lower mantle, back, rump and uppertail-coverts greyish-brown with large, blackish-brown 'spear-head' or 'star-shaped' spots, edged chestnut. Wing-coverts greyish-brown, boldly spotted blackish-brown edged chestnut or pale buff. Scapular pattern complex: upper half buff on outerweb, blackish-brown on innerweb, lower half boldly spotted blackish-brown (one or both webs) edged chestnut. Primaries brown regularly spotted pale tawny along outerwebs, faintly tipped greyish-brown. Secondaries brown, regularly barred pale tawny, faintly tipped greyish-brown. Tertials greyish-brown, boldly spotted blackish-brown edged buff or chestnut. Tail brown indistinctly barred tawny; R5 narrowly (c. 10mm) tipped white, R4 narrowly (5mm or less) and indistinctly tipped whitish, occasionally on outerweb only; central pair (R1) greyish-brown tinged pale chestnut, mottled and barred brown. Lores and ear-coverts rufous, almost chestnut. Chin and throat light greyish-brown, feathers tipped buff. Broad tawny-buff band around lower throat. Breast greyish-brown, occasionally washed chestnut, boldly spotted blackish-brown edged buff or chestnut. Belly and flanks greyish-brown streaked blackish-brown, feathers narrowly tipped buff. Undertail-coverts buff barred brown. Underwing-coverts dark brown, lightly barred brownish-buff. **Adult female** Similar to the male. **Immature** Not known. **Juvenile** Paler and buffier than the adults, with a dark sooty collar around the hindneck and a row of large blackish spots across the wing-coverts. **Chick** Not described. **Bare parts** Iris dark brown; bill blackish or pinkish-grey with a black tip; legs and feet dark brown or pinkish-grey.

MEASUREMENTS Wing (male) 139-159, (female) 143-154; tail (male) 100-116, (female) 102-114; bill (male) 14.0-16.6, (female) 14.0-18.1; tarsus (male) c. 21, (female) c. 21. Weight (male) no data, (female, one) 54.0g.

MOULT No data available.

GEOGRAPHICAL VARIATION Monotypic. Very little colour variation has been noted within this species.

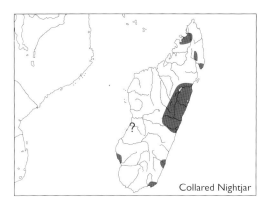

Collared Nightjar

DISTRIBUTION AND MOVEMENTS Endemic to Madagascar, where it is found mainly in the north-eastern and central-eastern parts of the country, at Antananarivo, Analamazaotra, Ranomafana, eastern Imerina, Fanovana, Fito, Perinet, Sihanaka Forest, between Nosibey and Foule Point, Cap Masoala, Tsaratanana, Maroantsetra, Andapa, Sambirano, Anaborano, Mt d'Ambre and Ankarana. It also occurs, or has occurred, further to the south and south-west, at Manombo, Morondava?, Baly Bay and Fort Dauphin. In the past, it was also occasionally encountered in the western parts of the south-central plateau and was common in Bara country further to the west. Sedentary.

STATUS Generally rather rare, but it may be locally common in some localities.

REFERENCES Dee (1986), Dhondt (1976), Goodman *et al.* (1997), Langrand (1990), Rand (1936).

---

108 BATES'S NIGHTJAR
Caprimulgus batesi   Plate 25

Caprimulgus batesi Sharpe, 1906, *Bull. Brit. Orn. Club* 19, p.18 (River Ja, Cameroon)

IDENTIFICATION Length 29-31cm. A large, very dark, Afrotropical nightjar, occurring in rainforests. Sexually dimorphic. **At rest** Large-headed and long-tailed. Upperparts and wing-coverts dark brown, broadly streaked, spotted and speckled blackish-brown, buff and tawny. Generally indistinct buff or tawny collar on hindneck, but sometimes very pronounced, sometimes almost invisible. White throat-patch. Underparts blackish-brown speckled buff on breast, becoming buff barred brown on belly. **In flight** The male has a very small white spot towards the wing-tip on the four outer primaries (edge of innerweb only on two outermost) and white tips to the two outer tail feathers. The female is paler and lacks white markings on the wings and tail, although a few have a buff spot on the outerwebs of two or three outer primaries (never the outermost). **Similar species** None. The other African rainforest species, Brown Nightjar (76), is smaller, paler and less variegated; both sexes lack white markings on the wings and tail.

VOICE The song is a loud *whow whowhowhowhow*. After the first note there is a slight pause, then the notes are repeated rapidly 2-12 (usually four) times. Sings from trees, at all levels up to the canopy, and occasionally from the ground. May be heard predominantly at dusk, but also sings throughout the night. The flight call is a low *wuh-wuh*.

HABITAT Prefers lowland primary rainforest, inhabiting clearings and edges. Also occurs in thick secondary forest, and plantations along forest edges. It is often common near water, especially in and along the edges of flooded forests.

HABITS Crepuscular and nocturnal. Roosts on the ground in forest clearings and on paths, or perched on lianas several metres above ground. When flushed, either re-alights on the ground, flies up onto a branch in a tree c. 2-3m above ground, or disappears into thick cover. When active, may perch across branches, 10-15m above ground. Forages above and amongst the canopy, or along the edges of riverine forest and grassy plains. No further information available.

FOOD Mantises, crickets, grasshoppers, beetles, moths and ants. No further data available.

BREEDING Breeding season December–January in Gabon; February–March (possibly November–July) in Cameroon; and possibly all year in Zaire (Haut Zaire egg in July, chicks in April, September and October; Lukokela, egg in October; Barumba, chick in July; Evenaar, juvenile in October).

Breeding territory c. 16-20ha? No nest is constructed; the egg is laid on bare earth or leaf-litter. Nest-sites may be on paths or trails, on ground with sparse vegetation or along the edges of thick forest, plantations or gardens. Clutch one. Egg elliptical; rather glossy white or pale pink, heavily blotched and mottled brown and lavender-grey, 31-35 x 23-25mm.

If flushed from its young, the adult flies around the intruder and alights on a branch or liana, 3-4m above ground. No further information available.

DESCRIPTION Adult male Forehead, crown and nape brown, speckled greyish-white and occasionally tinged rufous. Central feathers broadly streaked dark brown. Indistinct collar on hindneck barred brown and buff or tawny; very pronounced on some individuals, almost non-existent on others. Mantle, back, rump and uppertail-coverts dark brown, speckled greyish-white, buff and tawny. Wing-coverts brown, speckled greyish-white and buff and heavily blotched dark brown. Scapulars generally buff or pale buff barred dark brown on upper two-thirds, and dark brown speckled and tipped buff on lower third. Primaries dark brown; P10 and P9 have a very small dirty white or buffish spot on the edge of the innerweb, P8 and P7 have a small white spot across both webs, spots situated towards the feather-tip; rest of primaries and all secondaries dark brown, thinly barred tawny and/or pale buff. Tertials dark brown, heavily speckled tawny, buff and greyish-white. Tail dark brown with broad bars of greyish-white and buff speckling; R5 and R1 plainer, sprinkled with small tawny bars or spots and narrowly (21-27mm) tipped white (tips often edged brown). Lores and ear-coverts dark brown, narrowly barred tawny. Chin and throat dark brown, mottled tawny. Lower throat either entirely white or with large white patch on either side. Breast variable, ranging from dark brown, finely or heavily speckled tawny and pale buff, to brown tinged rufous and streaked and speckled dark brown. Belly and flanks buff, barred brown on lower belly. Undertail-coverts buff barred brown. Underwing-coverts dark buff barred dark brown. **Adult female** Similar to the male, but generally paler and more variable in colour, e.g. some appear rather pale-headed and some have entire upperparts and breast tinged rufous. No white spot on the four outer primaries, but some have small pale buff or tawny spot on outerwebs of P7 and P8, occasionally on P9 also. Lacks white tips to two outer tail feathers. **Immature** and **Juvenile** Similar to the adults but paler and more buffish. **Chick** At hatching, covered in plain, yellowish-buff down. **Bare parts** Iris, bill, legs and feet dark brown.

MEASUREMENTS Wing (male) 180-204, (female) 182-198; tail (male) 139-158, (female) 132-158; bill (male) 10-14.1, (female) 10-14.5; tarsus (male) 16-20, (female) 16-20. Weight (both sexes) 89-112g.

MOULT No published data available.

GEOGRAPHICAL VARIATION Monotypic.

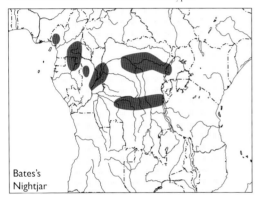

Bates's Nightjar

DISTRIBUTION AND MOVEMENTS West and Central Africa. Extremely fragmented distribution in rainforest belt. S Cameroon, W Cameroon (Korup National Park), Gabon, S Central African Republic, NE and W Congo, W, N and C Zaire and W Uganda (Bwamba Forest). Sedentary.

STATUS Possibly locally common throughout range.

REFERENCES Brosset & Erard (1986), Dowsett & Dowsett-Lemaire (1991), Fry *et al.* (1988).

---

109 LONG-TAILED NIGHTJAR
Caprimulgus climacurus   Plate 28

Caprimulgus climacurus Vieillot, 1825, *Gal. Ois.* 1, p.195 (Senegal)
Caprimulgus climacurus nigricans (Salvadori 1868), *Atti Soc. Ital. Soc. Nat. Milano* 11, p.449 (Fiume Bianco = White Nile)
Caprimulgus climacurus sclateri (Bates 1927), *Ibis* (12)3, p.20 (Ngaundere, northern Cameroon)

Forms a superspecies with Slender-tailed and Mozambique Nightjars.

IDENTIFICATION Length 28-43cm. A small-bodied, very long-tailed, greyish-brown Afrotropical nightjar. Sexually dimorphic. **At rest** Upperparts and wing-coverts generally greyish-brown, finely streaked brown. The male has a white line across the forewing, the female a buff or buffish-white line. Broad tawny or buff collar on hindneck. White throat-patch. Underparts pale brown speckled and barred pale buff, becoming buff thinly barred brown on belly and flanks. **In flight** The male has a broad white band towards the wing-tip across the five outer primaries (innerweb only on outermost) and a white trailing edge to the inner wing. Tail gradated, with the central pair of feathers much longer than the outer pair. Outer tail feathers generally tipped white on innerweb and entirely white on outerweb. Second outermost tail feathers generally tipped white on outerweb. The shorter-tailed female has the white band across the outer primaries washed buff on the outerwebs and a buff or buffish-white trailing edge to the inner wing. Outer tail feather tipped buff on innerweb and entirely buff on outerweb. Second outermost tail feather tipped buff on outerweb. **Similar species** Slender-tailed Nightjar (110) is extremely similar but much shorter-tailed, although some female Long-tailed Nightjars approach male Slender-tailed Nightjars in tail length. Mozambique Nightjar (111) is generally darker and shorter-tailed.

VOICE The song is a constant, even-pitched churr, lasting up to five minutes or so without pause, usually ending with 2-9 *chong* or *chiow* notes. Usually sings from branches in trees, but also from the ground, at dusk and often more strongly at dawn, also occasionally in the middle of the day when cloudy. Sometimes calls without singing, giving up to 23 *chong* notes in succession. The flight call is a short *chong-chong*, which is also given when flushed. Other calls include 2-4 *chack* notes, possibly given when alarmed. During threat/defence displays, utters a throaty hiss, also given when the bird is handled.

HABITAT Found in a variety of habitats, from rather arid semi-deserts to woods, forests and forest clearings. Also occurs quite commonly in all types of grassland and in cultivated areas. Outside the breeding season it is also found on stony hillsides and in papyrus swamps.

HABITS Crepuscular and nocturnal. Roosts on the ground, usually in shade, on leaf-litter, bare earth or flat stones. Roost-sites are often in woodland, grassland, copses or under thornbushes. When flushed, flies low for up to 50m before re-alighting on ground. If repeatedly flushed, will fly up into a tree or onto the roof of hut, but will return to the ground as soon as danger has passed. In trees or bushes, tends to perch across rather than along branches. Outside the breeding season, often roosts in loose flocks of up to 100 birds. At the beginning of the breeding season, 2-3 birds may fly almost vertically up to a height of c. 20-30m above ground, hover for 1-2 seconds, then dive down again before levelling off just above the ground and alighting. This behaviour, throughout which the birds are silent, may be repeated 5-6 times over 15-20 minutes, although it is not known if these are feeding flights or a courtship display. At night, feeds fairly low down near and amongst trees, and over cultivated areas. Often sits on roads and paths, especially at and just after dusk. In W Eritrea, often sits beneath street lights in small towns at night. Drinks in flight by hovering slowly above the water, then dropping to the surface (sometimes in stages) and dipping its bill in the water, before flying off; birds may occasionally catch their wings in the water, causing them to land briefly on the surface.

FOOD Beetles, moths, mantises, bugs, ants, winged termites and grasshoppers. No further data available.

BREEDING Breeding season March–September in N Senegal (and Gambia?); March–August in Mali and N Nigeria; January–October? in S Nigeria (Lagos); January–

December in Ghana; February?–August? in Togo; April–July in Uganda; March–June in NE Zaire; and August–November in S Zaire (Kwilu district).

Probably monogamous. No nest is constructed; the eggs are laid on leaf-litter or bare earth. Nest-sites are on or alongside paths, in copses or in cultivated fields. Clutch usually two. Eggs elliptical, creamy white, buff or pinkish, heavily blotched grey or greyish-purple and stained umber, 22.7-26.4 x 17.3-19.8mm. No further information available.

DESCRIPTION *C. c. climacurus* **Adult male** Forehead, crown and nape grey-brown, finely peppered brown, central feathers broadly streaked dark brown, except on nape. Broad collar on hindneck varying from buff to tawny-buff. Mantle and back greyish-brown, finely streaked brown. Rump and uppertail-coverts greyish-brown, speckled, streaked and barred brown. Lesser coverts brown tinged rufous. Median coverts brown or grey-brown, broadly tipped white forming a white line across forewing. Rest of coverts brown or grey-brown with large buff spot on outerweb of tips. Scapulars dark brown with buff borders, very broad on outerwebs, narrower on innerwebs. Primaries brown; white spot towards the feather-tip on innerweb of P10 and broad white bar across P9-P6; P5 has narrow, tawny-white band across both webs; inner primaries heavily spotted, almost barred, tawny. Secondaries brown, heavily spotted tawny and broadly tipped white. Tertials brown or grey-brown, speckled dark brown and tipped buff or buffish-white. Tail brown or grey-brown; R5 has innerweb barred or spotted white or buffy-white and broadly tipped white, outerweb entirely white or buffy-white; R4 tipped white on outerweb only; central pair (R1) brown or grey-brown, thinly barred dark brown. Tail very long and strongly gradated. Lores and ear-coverts rufous, finely speckled dark brown. Chin and throat buff vermiculated brown. White triangular patch across lower throat, lower feathers of which have buff subterminal bar and dark brown or blackish tips. Breast pale brown, speckled and barred pale buff. Belly and flanks buff, regularly and thinly barred brown. Undertail-coverts buff, generally unmarked. Underwing-coverts buff barred brown. **Adult female** Similar to the male but shorter-tailed. Tips to median-coverts and secondaries buff. White band across P10-P6 often heavily tinged buff, usually so on outerwebs and restricted to small spot on innerwebs of P10 and P9. Tail less gradated, R5 tipped buff and, occasionally, entirely buff on outerweb, R4 sometimes tipped buff. **Immature** and **Juvenile** Similar to the adult female but paler. **Chick** Not described. **Bare parts** Iris brown; bill brown; legs and feet brownish.

MEASUREMENTS Wing (male) 129-160, (female) 131-157; tail (male) 135-303, (female) 107-256; bill (male) 13.7-15.0, (female) 13-14.2; tarsus (male) 14-21.4, (female) 14-19.1. Weight (male) 39-58g, (female) 35-61g.

MOULT Generally undertakes a complete post-breeding moult on the wintering grounds. The primaries are moulted descendantly. The secondaries are moulted aberrantly in two units, an inner one commencing around S9 and proceeding descendantly (and ascendantly through tertials) and an outer one commencing at the outermost (S1) and proceeding ascendantly. The moult converges on the fifth secondary. The tail moult appears to be variable, without a consistent pattern. Some birds may arrest their moult during the cycle, but it is not known when they resume. No further data available.

GEOGRAPHICAL VARIATION Three races are currently recognised.

C. c. climacurus Described above. Extremely variable in colour, ranging from pale brown, brown and greyish-brown to sandy-buff.

C. c. nigricans Upperparts blackish or very dark grey, finely peppered white or greyish-white. Males are often longer-tailed than the nominate. Wing (male) 147-151, (female) 139-150; tail (male) 221-335, (female) 179-195. Weight no data.

C. c. sclateri Slightly darker and more rufous than the nominate. Variable in colour, ranging from dark brown and rufescent-brown to extremely rufous. Wing (male) 138-149, (female, one) 145; tail (male) 206-275 (female, one) 177. Weight no data. Birds from Ndop Plain, Cameroon, are extremely rufous, rather small and short-tailed. Wing (male) 138-145, (female) no data tail (male) 122-130, (female) no data. Weight no data.

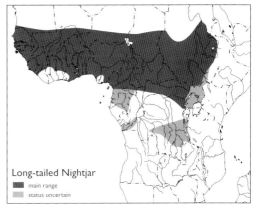

Long-tailed Nightjar
- main range
- status uncertain

DISTRIBUTION AND MOVEMENTS West, Central and parts of East Africa. Breeds from S Mauritania, Senegal and Gambia east through S Mali, Burkina Faso, S Niger and S Chad to C and S (but not SE) Sudan and E Ethiopia and south to Liberia, Guinea Bissau, Guinea, Sierra Leone, N Ivory Coast, Ghana, Togo, Benin, Nigeria, much of Cameroon, N Congo; Central African Republic, W and S Uganda and N and SE Zaire (but not Shaba district in extreme SE). Outside breeding season, also occurs in S Cameroon, Equatorial Guinea, S Ivory Coast, Gabon, SE Congo (lower Congo river valley), NE Angola (1 record Luaco), SE Sudan, SW Ethiopia, W Kenya (sporadic in Turkana and Pokot region) and E Uganda.

C. c. climacurus Breeds in semi-arid country in the northern part of the range. Migratory and partially sedentary, some populations moving south after the breeding season.

C. c. sclateri Breeds in the savanna and forest zone in the southern part of the range. Possibly sedentary and partially migratory.

C. c. nigricans Apparently only along the White Nile in Sudan, from Kosti south to Shambe and Lake Nyubor. Also occurs along the Bahr el Zeraf and Sobat river. Sedentary.

STATUS Common and locally abundant, although perhaps less common in forest clearings in the more southerly parts of its range.

REFERENCES Fry *et al.* (1988), Herremans & Stevens (1983), Louette (1990b), Short *et al.* (1990), Tye (1984).

110 SLENDER-TAILED NIGHTJAR
Caprimulgus clarus   Plate 28

Caprimulgus clarus Reichenow, 1892, *J. Orn.* 40, p.29
(Bukoba, Tanzania)

Forms a superspecies with Mozambique Nightjar, with
which it was formerly considered conspecific, and Long-
tailed Nightjar.

IDENTIFICATION Length 28cm. A small, greyish-brown
East African nightjar. Sexually dimorphic. **At rest** Upperparts and wing-coverts generally greyish-brown streaked
dark brown. The male has a white line across the forewing,
the female a buff line. The central tail feathers are thinly
barred brown. Broad tawny or buff collar on hindneck.
White throat-patch. Underparts light brown, speckled and
barred pale buff, becoming buff thinly barred brown on
belly and flanks. **In flight** The male has a broad white band
towards the wing-tip across the six outer primaries and a
white trailing edge to the inner wing. Tail gradated and
wedge-shaped, with the central pair slightly longer than
the outer pair. The outer tail feathers are broadly tipped
white on the innerweb and entirely white on the outerweb.
The female has a narrower white band across the outer
primaries, washed buff or tawny on the outerwebs, and a
buff or buffish-white trailing edge to the inner wing. Tail
less gradated with outer tail feathers tipped buff on
innerwebs and entirely buff on outerwebs. **Similar species**
Long-tailed Nightjar (109) is extremely similar but much
longer-tailed (although some male Slender-tailed Nightjars can approach female Long-tailed Nightjars in tail
length), more widely distributed and more variable in
colour. Mozambique Nightjar (111) is also extremely
similar but darker, browner, more heavily streaked on the
crown and more thickly barred dark brown on the (un-
gradated) tail. See also Nubian Nightjar (85) and
Donaldson-Smith's Nightjar (91).

VOICE The song is a rapid series of *wa-wa-wa-wa-wa* notes
lasting 30 seconds or more without pause, occasionally
interspersed with higher-pitched *weet* notes. Song phrases
occasionally end with a double-noted *chor-chor* or, more
rarely, a 'bubbling' series of notes that descend in pitch.
The song is occasionally delivered as a slow churr, e.g.
when notes are extremely close together. Sings from the
ground, occasionally from trees or telegraph wires. May
be heard predominantly at dusk and dawn. The flight call
is a treble-noted *whit-whit-whit.*

HABITAT Prefers thorny bush country, lightly wooded or
bushy grassland and sparse woodland. 0–2,000m.

HABITS Crepuscular and probably nocturnal. Roosts on
the ground. Outside the breeding season, up to six birds
may roost semi-colonially. Often sits on roads, tracks and
paths at night, and frequently alights on bare ground,
rocks and fallen trees. Forages low over open ground,
grassland or rocky slopes. Also feeds on insects attracted
to building lights. No further information available.

FOOD Moths, flies, beetles (including Carabidae,
Erotylidae, Curculionidae and Scarabaeidae), ants, bugs
(including Pentatomidae) and Orthoptera (including
Tettigoniidae). No further data available.

BREEDING Breeding season February–May in Ethiopia;
April–June? and November in Kenya and NE Tanzania;

April–August? in Somalia; and May–August in Uganda.
No data available from other regions.

Possibly monogamous. No nest is constructed; the eggs
are laid on bare ground. Nest-sites are usually near or
under a small bush, sometimes close to rocks and stones.
Clutch usually 2. Eggs elliptical creamy or pinkish,
blotched brown and faintly marked greyish-lilac, 22.8-27.8
x 17.3-19.0mm. If flushed from the chicks, the adult
performs an injury-feigning distraction display by flapping
along the ground with one or both wings outstretched.
No further information available.

DESCRIPTION Adult male Forehead and crown grey-
brown, broadly streaked dark brown. Nape, mantle, back,
rump and uppertail-coverts greyish-brown streaked dark
brown. Broad collar on hindneck varying from buff to
tawny-buff. Lesser-coverts brown tinged rufous. Median
coverts grey-brown broadly tipped white, which shows as
white line across forewing. Rest of coverts grey-brown with
large buff spot on outerweb of tips. Scapulars dark brown
with buff borders which are very broad on outerwebs and
narrow on innerwebs. Primaries brown; broad white bar,
midway along feather, across innerweb of P10 and both
webs of P9-P5, occasionally on P4 also; P10 often has white
edge or small white bar on outerweb; inner primaries
brown heavily spotted, almost barred, tawny. Secondaries
brown, heavily spotted tawny and broadly tipped white.
Tertials brown, strongly speckled dark brown and tipped
buff or buffish-white. Tail brown; R5 broadly tipped white
on innerweb and entirely white, edged buff, on outerweb;
central pair (R1) grey-brown, flecked and thinly barred
dark brown. Tail gradated with R5 up to 32mm shorter
than R1. Lores and ear-coverts dark brown, finely speckled
rufous. Chin and throat buff vermiculated brown. White
triangular patch across lower throat, lower feathers of
which have buff subterminal bar and dark brown or blackish
tips. Breast pale brown, speckled and barred pale
buff. Belly and flanks buff, regularly and thinly barred
brown. Undertail-coverts buff, generally unmarked.
Underwing-coverts buff barred brown. **Adult female**
Similar to the male but tips to median coverts buff and
tips to secondaries buff or buffish-white. White band across
P10-P6 only, narrower and often buff or tawny on some or
all of outerwebs. R5 narrowly tipped brownish-buff on
innerweb and entirely buff or pale tawny on outerweb.
Tail less gradated. **Immature** and **Juvenile** Similar to the
adult female but paler. **Chick** Not known. **Bare parts** Iris
brown; bill brown with black tip; legs and feet brownish.

MEASUREMENTS Wing (male) 133-159, (female) 134-
157; tail (male) 100-151, (female) 103-132; bill (male) 13.3-
15.5, (female) 12.7-15.2; tarsus (male) 14.5-20.6, (female)
19.4-22.6. Weight (male) 36-49g, (female) 34-53g.

MOULT The primaries are moulted descendantly. No
further data available.

GEOGRAPHICAL VARIATION Monotypic. Slight colour
variation noted, with some individuals being very buff,
dark brown or blackish. Birds from the north of the range
(Ethiopia, SE Sudan, Somalia and N Kenya) are thought
to be longer-tailed than birds from the south and are
considered a distinct race *apatelius* by some authorities.
However, museum specimens do not always support this
view, and the subspecies is not recognised here.

DISTRIBUTION AND MOVEMENTS East Africa, in
Djibouti, Ethiopia (see below), SE Sudan, Uganda (except

NW and SW?), NE Zaire?, much of Kenya (although absent in north-central and many south-central regions), NW and SW Somalia and Tanzania (south to the Wembere region, Dodoma, Morogoro and Bajamoyo). In Ethiopia, occurs across the centre of the country from NE to SW, but is possibly more widespread than records suggest. Possibly sedentary throughout entire range, although in Somalia birds may move locally according to the rains.

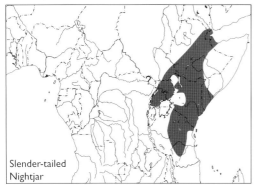

Slender-tailed
Nightjar

STATUS Common to locally abundant throughout its range.

REFERENCES Archer & Godman (1961), Fry *et al.* (1988), Peters & Loveridge (1936), Short *et al.* (1990), van Someren (1956), Wilson & Wilson (1994).

---

111 MOZAMBIQUE NIGHTJAR
Caprimulgus fossii   Plate 28

Other names: Gabon Nightjar, Square-tailed Nightjar

Caprimulgus fossii Hartlaub, 1857, *Syst. Orn. Westafr.* p.23 (Gaboon)
Caprimulgus fossii welwitschii Bocage, 1867, *J. Sci. Math. Phys. Nat. Lisboa* 1 No.2, p.133 (between Penedo and Cacuaco, Luanda, Angola)
Caprimulgus fossii griseoplurus Clancey, 1965, *Durban Mus. Novit.* 3, p.4 (27km east of Murwamusa Pan, Kalahari, Botswana)

Forms a superspecies with Slender-tailed Nightjar, with which it was formerly considered conspecific, and Long-tailed Nightjar.

IDENTIFICATION Length 23-24cm. A small, dark, rather spotted Afrotropical nightjar. Sexually dimorphic. **At rest** Upperparts generally dark greyish-brown, heavily speckled greyish-white. Broad buff or tawny-buff collar around the hindneck. Wing-coverts dark greyish-brown, speckled and spotted greyish-white and pale buff. The male has a white, sometimes buffish, band across the forewing, the female a buff band. Scapulars blackish-brown, broadly edged buff on outerwebs. The central tail feathers are thickly barred brown. Has a prominent buffish-white submoustachial stripe and a white throat-patch. Underparts dark greyish-brown, speckled and spotted buffish-white or buff, becoming buff barred brown on belly and flanks. **In flight** Square-tailed. The male has a broad white band towards the wing-tip across the five outer primaries (innerweb only on outermost), a white trailing edge to the innerwing, and the outermost tail feather broadly edged (outerweb) and

tipped white. The female has a narrower whitish band across the five outer primaries, a buff trailing edge to the inner wing, and the outermost tail feather broadly edged (outerweb) and tipped buffish. **Similar species** Slender-tailed Nightjar (110) is paler, greyer-brown, and less heavily streaked on the crown; the tail is paler with thinner brown barring, and is gradated. Long-tailed Nightjar (109) is more variable in colour, and has a much longer, extremely gradated tail.

VOICE The song is a distinctive churring, with each churr lasting 4-7 seconds, rising in pitch before levelling off. Sings for minutes on end, with only a very slight pause between each churr. Song phrases occasionally end with a single *wow* note. Sings from the ground, and sometimes from trees. May mostly be heard at dusk and dawn. The flight call is a short series of *a-whoow* notes. Occasionally utters a *whit joe* call whilst perched. When alarmed, gives a rapid *shwip-ip-ip-ip-ip*. Males make throaty hissing or growling sounds on the ground or in flight, especially during aerial (presumably territorial) pursuits of other males. Similar sounds are also given by adults and chicks during threat/defence displays, or when they are handled.

HABITAT Prefers open scrubland and woodland, wooded grasslands and sandy country near water. Occurs in riverine forest, mopane woodland and scrub, open miombo woodland, woodland edges, wooded suburban gardens, wooded hillsides, thorn and bush country, and the edges of cultivated land. Also inhabits plantations, teak forest, stony hillsides with scattered vegetation, burnt vleis, treeless dambos, urban gardens, savannas, swamps, trampled reed beds beside water, and the lower slopes of kopjes. 0–1,850m.

HABITS Crepuscular and nocturnal. Roosts on leaf-litter on the ground, roost sites often being concealed by grass, or situated at the edge of thickets. If flushed from its roost, flies only a short distance before re-alighting. Outside the breeding season, occasionally roosts semi-colonially.

Commonly sits on roads and tracks at night. Seldom perches in trees, but then tends to sit along branches. Often rather gregarious during migrations. Forages low over the ground or water, and also makes short sallies from the ground or perch. Also hawks around camps and campfires. No further information available.

FOOD Moths (including Noctuidae), beetles (including Scarabaeidae), grasshoppers, winged termites, ants and bugs. No further data available.

BREEDING Breeding season June on Pemba Island; October on Zanzibar; September–December in S Burundi, S Tanzania and N Mozambique; August–November in Malawi and S Mozambique; September–November in Zambia and Zimbabwe; October–January in S Zaire; August–October in Angola; and September–December in Botswana and South Africa. No data available from other regions.

Monogamous and territorial. No nest is constructed; the eggs are laid on leaf-litter, bare ground, sand or fine gravel. Nest-sites are often amongst scattered clumps of grass or bushes, on burnt ground, at the edge of thickets, or near water. Also nests on the slopes of kopjes. Clutch 1-2. Eggs elliptical, matt or glossy, creamy-pink blotched and smeared brown, finely speckled grey and lilac-grey, markings denser around the blunt end, 23.4-31.1 x 17.7-21.5mm. Incubation is mainly by the female, with the male possibly relieving her for short periods during the night.

The incubation period is generally 14-17 days.

The semi-precocial young are extremely active within the first day. If flushed from the nest, the adults perform a distraction display, although details have yet to be provided. Possibly single-brooded, although lays a replacement clutch if the first is lost. The fledging period is undocumented, but chicks possibly become independent within 30-45 days. No further information available.

DESCRIPTION *C. f. fossii* **Adult male** Forehead, crown and nape greyish-brown speckled brown, buff and greyish-white; central feathers broadly streaked blackish-brown. Broad tawny, tawny-buff or buff collar around the hindneck. Mantle, back, rump and uppertail-coverts greyish-brown speckled brown and greyish-white. Lesser coverts brown, tipped buff or cinnamon, median coverts greyish-brown broadly tipped white or buff, showing as a band across the forewing. Primary coverts brown broadly barred tawny. Rest of wing-coverts greyish-brown, speckled and boldly spotted greyish-white, buff or pale buff. Scapulars blackish-brown, broadly edged buff on outerwebs. Primaries brown tipped greyish-brown; broad white band, midway along feather, on innerweb of P10 and across both webs of P9-P6, vestigial white mark occasionally on P5; inner five primaries broadly barred tawny. Secondaries brown barred tawny and broadly tipped white. Tertials greyish-brown, mottled blackish-brown, greyish-white and buff. Tail brown; R5 broadly edged (outerweb) and tipped white, partially suffused buffish; central pair (R1) greyish-brown, mottled and thickly barred brown. Tail generally not gradated, although central pair sometimes c. 15mm longer than outermost. Lores and ear-coverts rufous speckled brown. Prominent buffish-white submoustachial stripe. Chin and throat buff vermiculated brown. White patch across lower throat, the lower feathers of which are tipped blackish-brown, with a buff subterminal band. Breast greyish-brown tinged cinnamon, barred brown speckled and spotted buffish. Belly, flanks, undertail- and underwing-coverts buff barred brown. **Adult female** Similar to the male, but has narrower, buff tips to the median coverts, a narrower white band across P10-P6 (outerwebs washed tawny) and buff tips to the secondaries. R5 broadly edged (outerweb) and tipped buff. **Immature** and **Juvenile** Similar to the adult female, but paler and plainer. **Chick** At hatching, covered in dark brown and buffish down. **Bare parts** Iris brown; bill blackish; legs and feet fleshy-brown or blackish.

MEASUREMENTS Wing (male) 146-148, (female) 142-151; tail (male) 104-108, (female) 94-101; bill (male) 16.5-22.0, (female) 16.5-21.0; tarsus (male) 12-18, (female) 12-18. Weight no data.

MOULT Apparently undertakes a complete post-breeding moult (but see below), which commences on the breeding grounds, with adult males beginning slightly earlier than adult females. Immatures begin their moult at c. 50 days old. The primaries are moulted descendantly, the secondary moult centripetal, moulting descendantly from S12 and ascendantly from S1, the moult converging on S5. The secondary moult commences with S12 (S13), when the primary moult has reached P3, the ascendant sequence begins with S1, when the primary moult has reached P5 or P6. Some of the inner secondaries between S2 and S9, are occasionally replaced out of sequence. Tail moult is generally centifugal, following the sequence R1, R2, R3, R5, R4, although R2 is occasionally replaced out of

sequence. In southeastern populations, the moult period can be quite prolonged and can take up to c. 130 days to complete. Migratory populations occasionally suspend their moult during migration, and recommence on the wintering grounds. Some immature birds may retain one or two inner secondaries until after the following breeding season, although this may be rather uncommon.

GEOGRAPHICAL VARIATION Three races are currently recognised.

C. f. fossii Described above.

C. f. welwitschii Generally larger than the nominate, with heavier spotting on the wing-coverts, the female often with rufous spotting. Variable in colour, ranging from buffish- to blackish-brown. Wing (male) 146-175, (female) 145-169; tail (male) 103-139, (female) 102-130. Weight (male) 46.1-70.0g, (female) 47.3-77.4g.

C. f. griseoplurus Larger, greyer and paler than the nominate. Upperparts pale greyish, finely speckled blackish, breast darker with pale spotting reduced or absent. Wing (male) 157-166, (female) 158-163; tail (male) 120-132, (female) 116-129. Weight (unsexed, one) 64g.

Mozambique Nightjar

○ *vagrants*

▨ *C. f. fossii*

▨ *C. f. welwitschii resident*

▨ *C. f. welwitschii breeding visitor*

▥ *C. f. welwitschii non-breeding season visitor*

▨ *C. f. griseoplurus*

↘ *C. f. griseoplurus movements*

DISTRIBUTION AND MOVEMENTS Widely distributed throughout central and southern Africa.

C. f. fossii N and SW Gabon, and possibly SW Congo. Presumably sedentary.

C. f. welwitschii S Zaire, S Burundi, S Tanzania, Zanzibar and Pemba Islands, Angola, Zambia, Malawi, Mozambique, Zimbabwe (except central plateau), N Botswana?, N Namibia and E South Africa. Sedentary and partially migratory. In S Malawi and S Mozambique, probably sedentary in lowlands below 650m, possibly migratory at higher altitudes. Breeding visitor only to central plateau, Zimbabwe, and parts of NE South Africa. Non-breeding (winter) visitor to N Zaire, N Burundi, Rwanda, S and W Uganda, S Kenya and N Tanzania. Apparently vagrant to S Botswana and C South Africa.

C. f. griseoplurus W Botswana (Kalahari Desert) and extreme N South Africa (N Cape Province?). Sedentary and partially migratory. Non-breeding (winter) visitor to Zambia and Angola. Apparent vagrant to N Zimbabwe.

Vagrants of unidentified race have been recorded in N

Ivory Coast (Comoe and Korhogo) and S Ghana (Accra and Cape Coast).

STATUS Very common to locally abundant throughout

much of its range.

REFERENCES Clancey (1965), Fry *et al.* (1988), Hanmer (1996), Jackson (1987).

MACRODIPTERYX

Macrodipteryx Swainson, 1837, Bds. W. Afr., 2, p. 62. Type by monotypy, *Macrodipteryx africanus* Swainson 1837 = *Caprimulgus longipennis* Shaw 1796.

This genus contains two migratory, Afrotropical species. They have small heads and bills and rather weak vocalisations. Both species are polygamous and show sexual dimorphism. The breeding males of both species have extremely elongated second primaries which are displayed during their courtship rituals. Both species roost and breed on the ground, do not build nests and are aerial feeders.

Despite their obvious similarities, there are distinct differences between the two species, noticeably in their plumage, the shape of their wings and, in the breeding males, the structure of their second primaries. For these reasons, *Macrodipteryx vexillarius* was originally placed in a seperate genus, *Semeiophorus* Gould, 1838.

112 STANDARD-WINGED NIGHTJAR
Macrodipteryx longipennis   Plate 30

Caprimulgus longipennis Shaw, 1796, *Nat. Misc.* 8, pl.265 (Sierra Leone)

IDENTIFICATION Length 21-22cm. A medium-sized, greyish or greyish-brown Afrotropical nightjar. Sexually dimorphic, the breeding male being unmistakable. **At rest** Upperparts brown speckled greyish-white, crown also speckled buff or tawny and boldly spotted blackish-brown. Broad collar around hindneck, tawny or tawny-buff, spotted blackish-brown. Wing-coverts brown speckled greyish-white and pale tawny, heavily spotted buff. Scapulars blackish-brown, broadly but irregularly edged buff. Rather short supercilium buff, throat-patch buff barred brown. Underparts brown speckled greyish-white, speckled and spotted buff, becoming buff barred brown on belly and flanks. **In flight** Square-tailed. Both sexes lack white on wings and tail; wings are brown regularly barred tawny. Breeding males have 'standards' trailing upwards from the centre of the wing, the second innermost primaries having extremely elongated feather-shafts with large webs at the tips only, the innerweb being much broader than the outerweb. **Similar species** Female Pennant-winged Nightjar (113) similar (breeding male unmistakable: see that species) but slightly larger and darker with a tawnier, more defined hindneck collar, a longer buffish supercilium, white throat-patch, tawnier breast and more strongly barred underparts, with primaries and secondaries more broadly barred tawny.

VOICE The song is a rapid series of very soft, high-pitched *s* or *t* notes, repeated for up to 75 seconds or more without pause. Also gives a slower, harsher, double-noted *s-ch*. Sings from the ground, a low perch, or during display flights. During the male's display flight, a *trrp* sound is often made (see Breeding), and a quiet *chchchch* call may also be given. At display arenas, males occasionally give a soft *tsui-tsui*, usually from a perch, when other males approach. The flight call is a low *cuck* note.

HABITAT Prefers lightly wooded bush or thorn scrub savannas. Also occupies farmland, thickly wooded

savannas, grassy open country, stony hillsides with scattered trees and shrubs, coastal plains, sandy wastelands, pastures, lawns, paved areas, thorn thickets, clearings near villages and grassy inselbergs within the forest zone. 0–1,400m.

HABITS Crepuscular and nocturnal. Roosts on leaf-litter on the ground. Roost-sites are often under low bushes or in open woodland, and may be used for several days in succession. Favoured sites may be identified by an accumulation of droppings. If flushed from the roost, flies only a short distance before re-alighting, then often walks a short distance before finally settling.

At dusk, often sits on roads, tracks and paths. Also sits on top of low termite mounds and branches, especially during the rains when the ground may be wet. Occurs singly, in pairs or loose flocks, especially on the wintering grounds, when up to 40 birds may be found in a few hectares. Begins feeding late into dusk. Forages by hawking over open spaces and along roadsides. Also feeds at insect swarms and on insects disturbed by grass fires.

Males tend to leave the breeding grounds and migrate north before females and immatures. No further information available.

FOOD Beetles, moths, grasshoppers, cicadas, earwigs, bugs, leafhoppers, flies, winged ants, winged termites and mosquitoes. No further data available.

BREEDING Breeding season March–July in Senegal and Gambia; November–July in Mali; January–March in Ivory Coast; February?–May? in Togo; January–May in Ghana; January–June in Nigeria; September and February–April in N Uganda; and late January to early April in N Zaire. Breeding seasons may be longer than given here, and are possibly influenced by the rains. Southern populations breed earlier than in the north. No data available from other countries.

Polygamous and possibly non-territorial. Males and females gather at display arenas in open spaces, including paved areas and gravel paths. Up to six males and many more females may assemble at display sites. The males' display flights begin well into dusk. The male arrives at the display site, alights on the ground and often flicks his wings before folding them, the standards usually lying on the ground at an angle to to the body, occasionally even in front of the bird, the vanes resting on their outer edges The females then arrive, and perch within 3-10m of the male. The male then takes flight, often flicking his wings before doing so, and begins displaying up to c. 3m above ground. During the slow, undulating display flight, the male circles a female, vibrates his stiffly bent wings to produce a *trrp* sound, and calls (see Voice). Whilst displaying, the standards rise almost vertically (also see below). Display flights last c. 10 seconds and end abruptly when the male drops and alights on the ground or on a low perch, such as a termite mound, vegetation, small rock or stone. He may remain perched for 1-3 minutes before taking flight and repeating the display. Display flights may be repeated several times during each visit to the display arena. After the male has alighted following a display flight, a female may fly around him, quivering her wings and calling (see Voice), or may alight nearby.

If two males alight close to one another in a display arena, both birds may take it in turns to shuffle towards the other, but even though they may approach to within c. 50cm of each other, neither attempts to drive the other bird away (but see below). During this shuffling display, a male may often stop and call (see Voice), bill opening and closing whilst doing so. Occasionally, he may also call from a low perch, e.g. a rock or stone. The male often calls louder when another male is flying nearby.

Occasionally up to four males may display together, up to 8m above ground, slowly circling with their wings drooped and standards raised vertically. Dominant males may have the largest 'standards' (with longer feather-shafts and/or larger webs) and often swoop at other males perched in a display arena.

Nests solitarily or semi-colonially, e.g. up to three nests may be within 20m of each other. No nest is constructed; the eggs are laid on the ground or on bare, sandy soil. Nest-sites may be near tussocks of grass or clumps of stunted trees, or out in the open. Clutch 1-2. Eggs elliptical, slightly glossy, pinkish-buff, salmon-pink or reddish-chestnut, smeared and spotted brown and grey, markings denser around the blunt end, 23.1-28.2 x 18.1-20.1mm. The eggs are laid on successive days. Incubation begins when the first egg is laid and is mainly by the female, the male often roosting close to the nest-site. Incubating females may face the sun at dusk and dawn.

The semi-precocial young may move 1-2m away from the nest-site, to shelter at the base of a nearby bush. If flushed from the chicks, the female may perform an injury-feigning distraction display, by fluttering along the ground. No further information available.

DESCRIPTION Adult male (Breeding) Forehead, crown and nape brown speckled greyish-white, buff or pale tawny, central feathers boldly spotted blackish-brown. Broad collar around hindneck tawny or tawny-buff, spotted blackish-brown. Mantle, back, rump and uppertail-coverts brown faintly speckled greyish-white. Lesser coverts brown speckled pale tawny. Rest of wing-coverts brown speckled greyish-white and pale tawny, boldly spotted buff on tips of outerwebs. Scapulars blackish-brown, broadly and irregularly bordered buff on outerwebs. Primaries (except P2) and secondaries brown regularly barred tawny, and tipped greyish-brown; P2 forms the 'standard', in which the feather-shaft is extremely elongated (c. 450-535mm) and is unwebbed except at the tip; the webs are dark brown, broadly but faintly barred greyish-brown on the upper surface, 150-197mm long, and c. 50mm wide in

total, the innerweb being much broader than the outerweb. Tertials dark brown, speckled and mottled greyish-brown, tipped buff on outerwebs. Tail brown, R5-R2 broadly barred buff or pale tawny, mottled brownish; central pair (R1) greyish-brown tinged tawny, barred and mottled brown. Supercilium buff and rather shortish, lores and ear-coverts buff speckled dark brown. Chin and throat buff barred brown. Breast brown, speckled buff and greyish-white, spotted buff. Belly, flanks and underwing-coverts buff barred brown. Undertail-coverts buff. **Adult male** (Non-breeding) Similar, but lacks the standards. **Adult female** Similar to the non-breeding male (i.e. lacks the standards) and is often slightly paler. **Immature** and **Juvenile** Similar to the adult female. Males have P2 blackish or dark grey but not elongated, i.e. almost the same length as P1. **Chick** At hatching, covered in buffish down, mottled black on the upperparts. **Bare parts** Iris dark brown; bill blackish; legs and feet dark brown.

MEASUREMENTS Wing (male, excluding 'standards') 166-181, (female) 158-172; tail (male) 104-124, (female) 99-115; bill (male) 22-26, (female) 22-26; tarsus (male) 17-21.4, (female) 17-21.5. Weight (male) 32.2-65.0g, (female) 32.0-65.0g.

MOULT Adults probably undertake a complete post-breeding moult on the wintering grounds, e.g. in Sudan the male's 'standards' are dropped upon their arrival in July. The primaries are moulted descendantly, the secondaries ascendantly. In many areas, males arrive back on the breeding grounds in around October–December with their 'standards' still developing. They become fully grown by early to mid-January.

Immatures may also undertake a complete post-breeding moult, although males do not attain their 'standards' until the second complete moult (i.e. after the following breeding season). No further data available.

GEOGRAPHICAL VARIATION Monotypic, but variable in colour. Males are often darker and blacker, with whiter speckling, and this may be the commonest form in many regions. Females are often buffier or sandier, and some occasionally are pale straw-brown, giving a very bleached appearance.

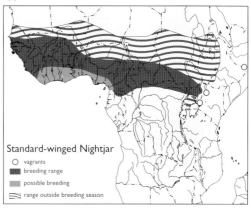

Standard-winged Nightjar

○ vagrants
▮ breeding range
▨ possible breeding
〰 range outside breeding season

DISTRIBUTION AND MOVEMENTS An intra-African migrant, breeding in the southern savannas of West and Central Africa.

Breeds S Senegal, Gambia, Guinea Bissau, Guinea, Sierra Leone and W Liberia, east through S Mali, N Ivory

Coast, Burkina Faso, N and C Ghana, Togo (north of 7°30'W), Benin, Nigeria (except N and S) and N and C Cameroon, to S Chad, Central African Republic, N Congo?, NE Zaire, SW Sudan, NW Uganda and NW Kenya ? (Lokichokio). Also present in the dry season in E Liberia, S Ivory Coast, S Ghana (Accra plains), coastal SW Nigeria and W Cameroon (Douala), and SE Uganda (December–February), but breeding not confirmed.

Migratory. Leaves the breeding grounds mid-April–August?, moving north to spend the wet season in the savannas of the Sahel and Sudan, eastern populations moving east or north-east from April. Movements rather protracted and possibly influenced by the rains, but not fully understood. Occurs August?–December? in N Senegal, S Mauritania, C Mali (north to c. 18°N), S Niger, N Nigeria and C Chad (north to Ennedi Mts). Also occurs in C and SE Sudan (mid-April?–September) and in W Ethiopia (recorded January), Uganda and W Kenya. Return movements are poorly documented. Birds (presumably vagrants) have also been recorded in W Kenya (Lake Baringo and Mumias District) and N Somalia.

STATUS Widespread and frequent to abundant throughout much of its breeding range. Outside the breeding season, widely distributed and locally common to fairly numerous in many regions, less common at limits of its range.

REFERENCES Archer & Godman (1961), Bannerman (1933), Chapin (1939), Cheke & Walsh (in press), Colston & Curry-Lindahl (1986), Dorst *et al.* (1975), Fry (1969), Fry *et al.* (1988), Stresemann & Stresemann (1966).

---

113 PENNANT-WINGED NIGHTJAR
Macrodipteryx vexillarius   Plate 30

Semeiophorus vexillarius Gould, 1838, *Icones Av.* pt. 2, pl.[13] and text (islands between Bourbon and Madagascar; numerous on the shores of the Red Sea and in the island of Scutra [i.e. Socotra], error = Sierra Leone?). The specific name is occasionally given as *vexillaria*, but is correct as originally named, *fide* Dowsett and Dowsett-Lemaire (1993).

IDENTIFICATION Length 24-28cm. A medium to large, brownish Afrotropical nightjar. Sexually dimorphic, the breeding male is unmistakable. **At rest** Upperparts brown speckled and barred greyish-brown, greyish-white and buff, crown also boldly spotted blackish-brown. Broad tawny collar around the hindneck, barred brown or speckled blackish. Wing-coverts brown speckled buff and greyish-white, and speckled and spotted tawny. Scapulars generally blackish-brown on innerwebs, buff on outerwebs. Supercilium buff and rather long, throat-patch white. Underparts brown, tinged and spotted tawny or tawny-buff, becoming white (male) or buff (female), barred brown, on the belly and flanks. **In flight** Broad-winged and slightly fork-tailed. The male has blackish wings, with narrow white tips to the four outer primaries, and a white trailing edge to the inner wing, also a broad bow-shaped white band towards the wing-tip across the eight outer primaries. The breeding male has unique wing-shape and 'pennants', the fifth to second innermost primaries being longer than the preceding feather, with the second innermost primary (the 'pennant') extremely elongated and generally whitish in colour. The female has brown wings, broadly barred tawny.

Both sexes lack white on the tail. **Similar species** Female Standard-winged Nightjar (112) is similar (breeding male unmistakable: see that species) but slightly smaller and paler, with a paler, softer-edged tawny hindneck collar, shorter, buffish supercilium, buff throat-patch, buffier breast and less strongly barred underparts; the primaries and secondaries are less broadly barred tawny.

VOICE The song is a very rapid series of soft, high-pitched *tseet* notes, repeated for up to 10 seconds or more without pause, often likened to the twittering sounds of a shrew, bat or insect. Sings in display flights or whilst perched on a stump, small rock or stone. The flight calls are querulous *wheeeo* or *chup* notes. During courtship, females often utter soft *schurr* notes prior to copulation.

HABITAT Prefers mature miombo or mopane woodland, but occurs in other types of woodland, part-burnt or -felled woodlands, wooded grasslands and bush country, wooded suburban areas, cultivated land, disused agricultural ground and gardens, river valleys, burnt open dambos and burnt vleis. Also inhabits teak forests, stony hillsides and sandy ground or open grassland within woodlands. Tends to avoid acacia bush and thornveld. On migration, is also found in clearings and natural openings within forests, and on the wintering grounds also occupies eucalyptus plantations. 0–2,800m.

HABITS Crepuscular, nocturnal and partially diurnal. Roosts on the ground or on low, flat stones. If flushed from its roost, often flies to a tree and settles lengthways along a branch. On the wintering grounds sometimes roosts communally, with up to 13 birds occurring together. Often sits on roads and tracks at night. When active, rarely settles in trees except during heavy showers or prolonged rain. Often flies into obstacles such as walls, windows or wires, in built-up areas. Flies freely during the day, often flying very high above ground.

Prior to migration, sizeable flocks may build up; often migrates in sexually segregated flocks, although pairs also migrate together, the female generally following the male.

Drinks in flight by dipping down to the surface of still water. At dusk, forages earlier than other nightjar species, often very high up, and will also feed during the day. Forages in flight, or hawks for food from roads and tracks. Often hunts in pairs, the female following the male, and on the wintering grounds flocks of 10-30 birds may feed together. No further information available.

FOOD Moths, beetles (including Carabidae, Tenebrionidae, Scarabaeidae, Erotylidae and Cerambycidae), winged termites and ants, crickets, grasshoppers, mantids, cockroaches, earwigs, shieldbugs, leafhoppers and cicadas.

BREEDING Breeding season August–October in Angola; late August–November in Zambia; August–March in S Tanzania; October–December in Malawi, Mozambique and Zimbabwe; and September–November (December?) in South Africa.

Males tend to arrive on the breeding grounds 2-3 weeks before females. Polygamous. Possibly territorial, although perhaps only with regards to courtship display arenas (see below). The male performs courtship display flights in the early evenings, by gliding about at treetop height, 'pennants' fluttering behind him, calling continuously (see Voice). Whilst displaying, the male is often followed by one or two females. The male also displays from regular perches such as large stones or termite mounds. If a female is nearby, the perched male spreads his wings in a shallow

V and rotates slowly, vibrating his pennants and calling continuously (see Voice). During such displays, he occasionally takes flight and circles the display arena c. 1m above ground or up to treetop height. Males appear to defend their display areas, and will chase away intruding males.

No nest is constructed; the eggs are laid on bare ground or on leaf-litter. Nest-sites may be in the shade of trees or out in the open, and are often on burnt ground. In some regions, breeding may be semi-colonial, with nests 6.3-19.5m apart. Clutch 1-2. Eggs elliptical, rounded or almost biconical, glossy, pale to deep salmon-pink, marbled, blotched and spotted dark pink, reddish-brown, violet and grey, 26.0-34.9 x 19.4-23.6mm. The eggs are laid 1-2 days apart, and the second egg is often larger and heavier than the first. Incubation begins when the first egg is laid, and is by the female. In the early stages of incubation the male often roosts close to the nest-site, sometimes within 2-3m. The female occasionally moves the eggs with her feet, although this is perhaps accidental. Females appear to sit less tightly than other nightjar species and are prone to desert their clutches more readily. The incubation period is 15-18 days. Single-brooded. No further information available.

DESCRIPTION Adult male (Breeding) Forehead, crown and nape brown speckled greyish-white, tawny and buff, central feathers boldly spotted blackish-brown. Broad, well-defined tawny collar around hindneck, barred brown and speckled blackish. Mantle, back, rump and uppertail-coverts brown, faintly barred and speckled greyish-brown and buff. Wing-coverts brown speckled buff, tawny and greyish-white, with many feathers boldly spotted tawny edged buff on tips of outerwebs. Scapulars blackish-brown on innerwebs, buff on outerwebs and tipped with tawny and buff speckling. Primaries (except P2) blackish-brown; P9-P6 narrowly (c. 5mm) tipped white or greyish-white; broad white band, almost midway along feather, across P10-P3; P5-P3 ascendantly longer than the preceding feather; P2 (the 'pennant') extremely elongated and either white, brownish-white or white, distally tinged brown. Secondaries blackish-brown, narrowly tipped white or greyish-white. Tertials brown speckled buff and tawny, with a large buff spot on the tips of the outerwebs. Tail brown; R5-R2 broadly barred with buffish speckling; central pair (R1) broadly barred with greyish-brown and buff mottling. Supercilium buff and rather long, lores and ear-coverts rufous or buff, speckled brown. Chin and sides of throat buff barred brown. Throat white, the lower feathers tipped blackish-brown with a buff subterminal band. Breast brown, barred and spotted buff and pale tawny. Belly and flanks white or greyish-white, barred brown. Undertail-coverts white. Underwing-coverts whitish or buffish-white, barred brown. **Adult male** (non-breeding) Similar, but lacks the pennants, which are either broken off or being renewed. **Adult female** Similar to the non-breeding male but has no white in the wings, which are brown broadly and regularly barred tawny, and has buff (not white) underparts barred brown. **Immature** and **Juvenile** Similar to the adult female but paler, with upperparts usually tinged rufous, and wings more broadly barred tawny. Males have more marked scapulars, and P1 and S1 dark brown, faintly barred on innerwebs, and slightly longer than adjacent feathers. **Chick** Not described. **Bare parts** Iris dark brown; bill blackish-brown; legs and feet pinkish-brown or greyish-brown.

MEASUREMENTS Wing (male, excluding pennants) 200-266, (female) 177-202; tail (male) 126-157, (female) 113.5-136; bill (male) 16.5-22.0, (female) 16.0-20.0; tarsus (male) 23.0-29.0, (female) 19.0-27.0. Weight (male) 59-85g, (female) 61-88g.

MOULT Towards the end of the breeding season, the male's pennants are often broken off (perhaps through wear) before they are dropped. Adults undertake a complete post-breeding moult (see below), which commences on the breeding grounds, is suspended prior to or during migration, and is completed on the wintering grounds.

Males replace the innermost primary (P1) on the breeding grounds. When the moult resumes on the wintering grounds, the remaining primaries are generally moulted descendantly, although P2 (the pennant) grows slowly and is often not fully grown by the time birds return to the breeding grounds. The secondaries are moulted ascendantly from S1 and descendantly from S12-S13, the moult converging on S7-S8. The inner one or two secondaries (S1 and S2) are moulted on the breeding grounds, the remainder on the wintering grounds. The tail moult is generally centrifugal, although the outermost tail feather, R5, is often moulted before R5, the sequence therefore being R1, R2, R3, R5, R4. The central pair (R1) and occasionally the next pair (R2) are moulted on the breeding grounds.

Females moult the inner three, four or five primaries on the breeding grounds. The remaining moult timings and sequences are similar to those of the adult male.

Immatures also undertake a complete post-breeding moult, commencing on the breeding grounds with the body feathers and the innermost primary (P1). No further data available.

GEOGRAPHICAL VARIATION Monotypic. Colour variation is minimal, although darker, blacker birds do occur.

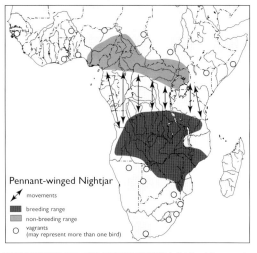

Pennant-winged Nightjar

↗ movements
▓ breeding range
░ non-breeding range
○ vagrants (may represent more than one bird)

DISTRIBUTION AND MOVEMENTS A fairly widespread, transequatorial migrant.

Breeds, generally late August to February (occasionally late August to early April), in C, NE and E Angola, S Zaire, SW Tanzania, Zambia, Malawi, Zimbabwe, NE Botswana, NE Namibia (Caprivi Strip), C Mozambique and extreme NE South Africa.

Migratory. Leaves the breeding grounds February–April, and moves north through Gabon (uncommon), S Cameroon, Congo, C Zaire, Burundi (uncommon),

Tanzania (occasionally eastwards to the coast) and SW Kenya. Generally 'winters' February/April–August/October in SE Nigeria, Cameroon (except the south), SW Chad (also a November record), Central African Republic (but possibly not the north-east), N and NE Zaire, S Sudan and Uganda. Return movements south occur during July–October. Migrations are rather protracted and not fully understood. At times, movements may be irruptive.

During the northward migration/non-breeding season period, has occurred as a presumed vagrant in Gambia (November), Guinea Bissau, S Ghana?, Togo, SW and NE Nigeria, SW Niger, SE Chad, W Sudan (possibly regular to frequent in Darfur), E Sudan (Blue Nile) and S Somalia. Although the type locality for this species is given as Sierra

Leone, recent authorities do not include it in that country's avifauna. The data accompanying the type specimen is ambiguous and require further investigation. Some West African records may possibly refer to misidentified Standard-winged Nightjars.

During the southward migration/breeding season period, has occurred as a presumed vagrant in N Namibia, W Botswana and South Africa (E and S Cape Province, and Natal).

STATUS Common to locally abundant throughout much of its breeding range.

REFERENCES Chapin (1939), Fry *et al.* (1988), Shaw (1993), Stresemann & Stresemann (1966).

HYDROPSALIS

Hydropsalis Wagler, 1832, Isis von Oken, col. 1222. Type by subsequent designation, *Caprimulgus furcifer* Vieillot 1817 (G. R. Gray, 1855, Cat. Gen. Subgen. Bds., p. 11).

Two Neotropical species. Both species within the genus have distinctive 'trident-shaped' tails, which are especially evident in the males. The two species differ from each other primarily in the hindneck collar, the markings on the wings and, in the males, the length of the outermost tail feathers. Both species show sexual dimorphism. Both species breed on the ground but do not construct nests. They generally roost on the ground and are aerial feeders.

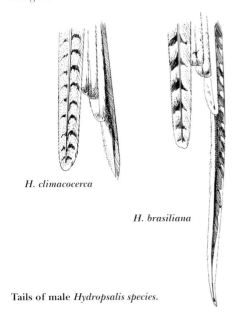

H. climacocerca

H. brasiliana

Tails of male *Hydropsalis* species.

114 LADDER-TAILED NIGHTJAR
Hydropsalis climacocerca   Plate 21

Caprimulgus climacocerca Tschudi, 1844, *Arch. f. Naturg.* 10, Bd. 1, p.269 (Peru)
Hydropsalis climacocerca schomburgki Sclater, 1866, *Proc. Zool. Soc. London* p.142 (British Guiana)
Hydropsalis climacocerca pallidior Todd, 1937, *Ann. Carnegie Mus.* 25, Novit. p.245 (Santarém, Brazil)
Hydropsalis climacocerca intercedens Todd, 1937, *Ann. Carnegie*

Mus. 25, Novit. p.245 (islands in the Amazon River, opposite Obidos, Brazil)
Hydropsalis climacocerca canescens Griscom and Greenway, 1937, *Bull. Mus. Comp. Zool.* 81, p.425 (Lago Grande, south bank of the Amazon, west of the Rio Tapajóz, Brazil)

IDENTIFICATION Length 24-26cm. A medium-sized, variegated Neotropical nightjar. Sexually dimorphic. **At rest** Upperparts greyish-brown or brownish, streaked blackish-brown. Buffish collar around the hindneck, often indistinct. Wing-coverts brown or greyish-brown, boldly spotted buffish. Scapulars blackish-brown, broadly edged buff on the outerwebs. White submoustachial stripe and white (male) or buffish (female) throat-patch. Underparts greyish-brown or brown, barred and spotted buff becoming buff barred brown on belly and flanks. **In flight** The male has a broad white band towards the wing-tip across the four outer primaries, and the almost trident-like or W-shaped tail is largely white except for the central tail feathers (details in Description). The female has a narrower white band, often edged or partly washed buffish, across the four outer primaries, and rarely shows white in the less strongly shaped tail (see Description). **Similar species** Scissor-tailed Nightjar (115) is slightly larger and darker, with a sharper, tawnier hindneck collar and no white band across the outer primaries, the brown wings being boldly spotted or barred buffish (both sexes); the male has longer but much less white outermost tail feathers; the female lacks white on the more strongly buff-barred tail.

VOICE The song (perhaps call) is a high-pitched *chip* note, monotonously repeated once every 1-1.5 seconds. If flushed, utters a soft, musical *chewit* or a snipe-like *cheeit*. No further information available.

HABITAT Prefers rainforest, open woodland, second

growth and riverine forest and grassland, occurring along riverbanks and on sandbars, stones and rocks in rivers. It may also be found in thickets. 0–500m.

HABITS Nocturnal and crepuscular? Roosts on the ground. Roost-sites may be in thickets or canes, or amongst piles of driftwood on sandbars, sandbanks or riverbanks. Occasionally roosts in loose groups of 3-4 birds. If flushed from its roost, it generally flies only a short distance before alighting. At night, it frequently perches on branches. Forages by making short sallies from low perches along the edges of rivers, or from sandbars. No further information available.

FOOD Insects. No further data available.

BREEDING Breeding season late July?–August? in Colombia and December–February in Brazil (NW Amazonas). No published data available from other regions.

No nest is constructed; the eggs are laid on sand or bare ground. Nest-sites may be on mudflats or sand and are usually shaded by vegetation. Nests may also be amongst pieces of driftwood. Clutch 2. Eggs elliptical, olive-drab speckled, spotted and scrawled grey and brown, 25.7-28.8 x 18.6-20.1mm. No further information available.

DESCRIPTION *H. c. climacocerca* **Adult male** Forehead, crown and nape greyish-brown or -white, speckled brown and streaked blackish-brown; central feathers very broadly streaked blackish-brown. Indistinct collar around hindneck tawny-buff barred brown. Mantle greyish-brown, barred, streaked and spotted dark brown. Back and rump similar but paler, often tinged buffish on lower rump. Uppertail-coverts pale greyish-brown barred dark brown. Lesser coverts brown speckled greyish-brown and buffish. Primary coverts brown, spotted white on innerwebs. Rest of wing-coverts brown speckled greyish-brown, buffish or cinnamon, boldly spotted buff, greyish-white or whitish on tips of outerwebs. Scapulars blackish-brown speckled greyish-brown and buff, broadly edged tawny, buff or pale buff on outerwebs. Primaries brown; broad white band, almost midway along feather, across P10-P7, with a vestigial white spot or band towards the tip of P6; P7-P1 with large white spots on the inner or both webs of the upper part of the feathers. Secondaries brown narrowly tipped pale buff or whitish, boldly spotted white on innerwebs. Tertials brown mottled greyish-brown. Tail shape and markings as follows: R5 longest with rather pointed tip, R4 40-50mm shorter, R3 and R2 square-ended and 20-25mm shorter than R4, central pair (R1) almost as long as R5; R5 brown broadly edged white, the white extending diagonally across and along the distal half of the innerweb, the rest of the feather barred whitish; R4-R2 largely whitish, broadly tipped brown and buff; central pair greyish-brown, mottled and barred brown. Lores and ear-coverts buffish speckled brown. Chin and throat white. Breast buffish, often tinged cinnamon or whitish, narrowly barred brown. Belly, flanks and undertail-coverts whitish. Underwing-coverts whitish, barred brown and spotted cinnamon and buffish. **Adult female** Similar to the male but with a buffish throat, narrower white band across P10 -P7, often tinged buffish, and buffier markings on the inner primaries and secondaries. Tail less strongly shaped, R4-R2 broadly edged white on proximal half of innerwebs, often extending to feather-shafts. **Immature** and **Juvenile** Similar to the adult female but with tawnier markings on the primaries and secondaries. **Chick** Not described. **Bare parts** Iris dark brown; bill blackish; legs and feet brownish.

MEASUREMENTS Wing (male) 153-173, (female) 152-156; tail (male) 149-169, (female) 131-135; bill (male) 10.7-14.5, (female) 13.6-15.3; tarsus (male) 16.0-18.9, (female) 17.3-19.0. Weight no data.

MOULT No published data available.

GEOGRAPHICAL VARIATION Five races are currently recognised, although three, *intercedens*, *canescens* and *pallidior*, occur along a c. 120km stretch of the lower Amazon between Obidos and Santarém, and their validity has been questioned by some authorities.

H. c. climacocerca Described above.

H. c. schomburgki Darker and browner than the nominate and averages slightly smaller. Wing (male) 151-164, (female) 147-163; tail (male) 130-158, (female) 119-136. Weight (male) 42-46g, (female) 45-52g.

H. c. pallidior Similar to *canescens* but paler with less distinct darkish markings, greyer upperparts and narrower barring on the tail. Males on average have more white on the wings and tail. Wing (male) 142?-157, (female) 147-155; tail (male) 147-182, (female) 118-145. Weight no data.

H. c. intercedens The male is darker than *canescens* and paler than *schomburgki*, also differing from *schomburgki* in having more white on the outer tail feathers (R5) and white (not black) bases to R3 and R2. The female closely resembles *canescens*. Wing (male, one) 145, (female) 145-151; tail (male, one) c. 140, (female) 130-139. Weight no data. Possibly intergrades with *schomburgki*.

H. c. canescens The male has paler, greyer upperparts, less buff and white underparts, and whiter-spotted wing-coverts than the nominate. The female has slightly paler underparts than the nominate and paler, greyer barring on all but the outermost pair of tail feathers. No biometrical data available.

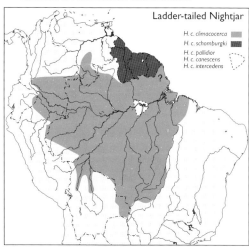

Ladder-tailed Nightjar

H. c. climacocerca
H. c. schomburgki
H. c. pallidior
H. c. canescens
H. c. intercedens

DISTRIBUTION AND MOVEMENTS Widely distributed throughout much of C South America.

H. c. climacocerca SE and E Colombia (Caquetá and Amazonas to E Guainía?), S Venezuela? (NW Bolívar and Amazonas), E Ecuador, E Peru, N and C Bolivia (Pando, Beni, La Paz, Cochabamba and Santa Cruz) and Amazonian Brazil (Amazonas east to W Pará and possibly Amapá south to Rondônia and Mato Grosso). Presumably sedentary.

H. c. schomburgki Extreme E Venezuela (E Bolívar), Guyana, Surinam and French Guiana. Presumably sedentary.

H. c. pallidior NC Brazil. Known only from the type locality at Santarém in W Pará. Presumably sedentary.

H. c. intercedens NC Brazil. Known only from the type locality at Obidos in W Pará. Presumably sedentary.

H. c. canescens NC Brazil. Known only from the lower Tapajós in W Pará. Presumably sedentary.

STATUS Generally quite common locally in many parts of its range.

REFERENCES Griscom & Greenway (1937), Haverschmidt & Mees (1994), Hilty & Brown (1986), Meyer de Schauensee & Phelps (1978), Peters (1940), Todd (1937).

---

115 SCISSOR-TAILED NIGHTJAR
Hydropsalis brasiliana   Plate 21

Caprimulgus brasilianus Gmelin, 1789, *Syst. Nat.* 1, pt. 2, p.1031 (Brazil)
Hydropsalis brasilianus furcifera (Vieillot, 1817), *Nouv. Dict. Hist. Nat.* 10. p.242 (Paraguay)

IDENTIFICATION Length 25-30cm, excluding the male's outer tail feathers. A medium-sized to large variegated Neotropical nightjar. Sexually dimorphic. **At rest** Upperparts brown streaked blackish-brown. Broad tawny or buff collar around the hindneck. Wing-coverts brown heavily spotted buff and greyish-white. Distinct buffish line along the scapulars. Thin whitish submoustachial stripe, throat pale but without an obvious white patch. Underparts brown, barred and spotted buff, becoming pale buff or buffish-white barred brown on belly and flanks. **In flight** Both sexes lack white markings on the wings, which are brown regularly barred or spotted buff, although the tips of the four outer primaries are plain. The male has an almost trident-like or W-shaped tail, with the outermost pair of feathers elongated and extending well beyond the central pair. The tips and innerwebs of the outermost tail feathers are largely brownish-white or greyish-white, the second to fourth outer tail feathers are broadly tipped greyish-cinnamon tinged whitish. The female's tail is less strongly shaped, with no white or elongated outer tail feathers. **Similar species** Ladder-tailed Nightjar (114) is slightly smaller and paler, and shows a buffier, less distinct hindneck collar, both sexes having a white band, almost midway along the outer wing, across the four outer primaries; the male has shorter but much whiter outermost tail feathers; the female may occasionally show some white in the tail (see that species). Long-trained Nightjar (118) is larger, darker and longer-winged, the male being longer-tailed with very long outermost tail feathers and a different tail structure (see that species). Lyre-tailed Nightjar (117) is slightly browner and paler, the male being much longer-tailed, with broader, darker and very long outermost tail feathers with white tips. Swallow-tailed Nightjar (116) is smaller and darker, heavily spotted tawny with no hind collar or obvious scapular pattern; both sexes have darker, plainer wings, the male being longer-tailed with darker, longer outermost tail feathers.

VOICE The song is a series of short *tsip* notes delivered at a rate of about one note per second. Sings for up to three minutes or more at a time, with only a brief pause between each burst of song, from perches such as branches and roofs, and occasionally in flight. May apparently be heard mainly at dusk. The flight call is a high-pitched *tsig*. No further information available.

HABITAT Prefers forest, woodland and cerrado. Also occurs in espinilho grassland with scattered vegetation, eucalyptus and acacia groves, campo sujo, and parkland in cities. Exact altitudinal range not documented, although it occurs at c. 500m.

HABITS Crepuscular and nocturnal. Roosts on the ground? If flushed from its roost, it usually flies off silently and alights 20-30m away behind trees or other vegetation, although it occasionally perches on low stumps or logs. Often sits on roads at dusk and dawn. Forages by flycatching from branches, roofs or other perches. No further information available.

FOOD Beetles (including Carabidae, Curculionidae, Dytiscidae, Hydrophilidae, Chrysomelidae, Elateridae, Scarabaeidae, Staphylinidae and Tenebrionidae), moths, flies, mayflies, bugs (including Belostomatidae and Fulgoridae), ants and Orthoptera (including Acrididae, Gryllotalpidae, Gryllidae and Tetrigidae).

BREEDING Breeding season November January in SE Brazil (Rio Grande do Sul). No data available from other regions.

Territorial. Males 'wing-clap' in flight when chasing off intruding males. In courtship display, the male alights in an open area on the ground, e.g. a dirt track, stretches his wings almost vertically and snaps them shut, producing a clap. This wing-snapping may be repeated up to five times, during which he may also stretch his head up and forward several times in quick succession. During this display, the male either remains fairly still, or lifts slightly off the ground. The display is often interrupted by short flights of a few metres, the bird wing-snapping as it re-alights, and the whole performance lasting for up to 20 minutes.

No nest is constructed; the eggs are laid on bare soil or granite. Nest-sites may be in scrub on rocky hillsides or amongst young plantings of acacia. Clutch 2. Eggs elliptical, light brown? creamy white or pinkish-buff, densely scrawled grey and brown, 24.6-30.8 x 17.9-22.6mm. No further information available.

DESCRIPTION *H. b. brasiliana* **Adult male** Forehead, crown and nape brown speckled greyish-white; central feathers broadly streaked blackish-brown and boldly ocellated or spotted tawny. Broad tawny collar around hindneck. Mantle, back and rump brown speckled greyish-white. Uppertail-coverts brown, boldly mottled greyish-brown. Lesser coverts brown speckled tawny. Primary coverts brown, edged or spotted buff. Rest of wing-coverts brown, speckled, spotted and ocellated tawny, buff and greyish-white. Scapulars blackish-brown ocellated tawny, broadly edged buff on outerwebs. Primaries brown, P10 edged buff on proximal half of outerweb, P9-P7 spotted buff along both webs, except towards tips; inner six primaries spotted buff, more so on innerwebs, and narrowly tipped greyish-buff. Secondaries brown, spotted buff along innerwebs and tipped buffish or pale buff. Tertials brown mottled greyish-brown. Tail shape unusual, with R5 elongated, R4 120-130mm shorter and R3 and R2 20-30mm shorter than R4, central pair (R1) 15-25mm longer than R4; R5 brown broadly tipped whitish, with white extending along distal edge of outerweb and diagonally across distal half of innerweb, rest of feather spotted buff along outerweb and barred whitish or buffish-white along innerweb; R4-R2 brown, boldly barred buffish-white and very broadly (c.40-50mm) tipped greyish-cinnamon speckled brown, often tinged whitish; central pair greyish-brown, speckled and broadly barred dark brown. Lores and ear-coverts brown speckled tawny or buff. Whitish submoustachial stripe. Chin buffish, throat pale buff or whitish, barred or spotted brown. Sides of lower throat often dark brown spotted tawny. Breast buff or pale buff, narrowly barred brown. Belly and flanks buff or pale buff broadly barred brown. Undertail-coverts buffish and generally unmarked. Underwing-coverts buff barred brown. **Adult female** Similar to the male but has tawnier markings on the wings, barred undertail-coverts and no white on the tail, R5-R2 being brown broadly barred buffish, R5 never elongated and only marginally longer than R4. **Immature** and **Juvenile** Not described. **Chick** Not described. **Bare parts** Iris dark brown; bill dark brown tipped black; legs and feet brownish.

MEASUREMENTS Wing (male) 168-170, (female) 151-165; tail (male, to tip of R5) 270-280, (female) 131-141; bill (male) 14.2-18.2, (female) 17.0-18.2; tarsus (male) 17.8-21.1, (female) 17.8-19.8. Weight no data.

MOULT No published data available.

GEOGRAPHICAL VARIATION Two races are currently recognised.

    H. b. brasiliana Described above.

    H. b. furcifera Larger (and perhaps generally paler) than the nominate, with usually a buffier hindneck collar. Wing (male) 169-192, (female) 161-180; tail (male, to tip of R5) 260-360, (female) 134-169. Weight (male) 47.5-52.3g, (female, two) 48.0-57.0g.

DISTRIBUTION AND MOVEMENTS Widely distributed throughout most of central South America.

    H. b. brasiliana S Surinam, EC Peru (Junín) and C and E Brazil (E Amazonas east to Alagoas, south to E Mato Grosso and São Paulo). Sedentary and partially migratory?

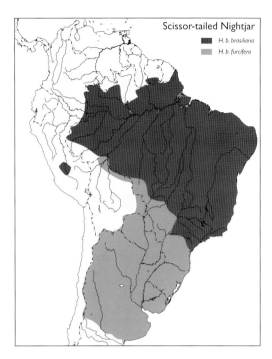

Scissor-tailed Nightjar
H. b. brasiliana
H. b. furcifera

H. b. furcifera N and E Bolivia, S Brazil (S Mato Grosso south to Rio Grande do Sul), Paraguay, N and C Argentina (south to Mendoza, La Pampa and Buenos Aires) and Uruguay. Sedentary? and partially migratory? e.g. disappears from many areas of Rio Grande do Sul, S Brazil, in winter.

STATUS Probably not particularly common throughout its range, but possibly under-recorded in some regions. The disjunct population in central Peru appears to be an isolated one.

REFERENCES Belton (1984), Haverschmidt & Mees (1994), de Urioste (1994).

UROPSALIS

Uropsalis W.Miller, 1915, Bull. Am. Mus. Nat. Hist., 34, p.516. Type by original designation, *Hydropsalis lyra* Bonaparte 1850.

Two Neotropical species. The males of both species have extremely elongated outermost tail feathers, that have narrow outerwebs and broad innerwebs. Differences between the two species include their overall plumages, their hindneck collars and the markings on their wings. Both species show sexual dimorphism. Both species breed on the ground but do not construct nests. They generally roost on the ground and are aerial feeders.

116 SWALLOW-TAILED NIGHTJAR
Uropsalis segmentata   Plate 21

Hydropsalis segmentatus Cassin, 1849, *Proc. Acad. Nat. Sci. Phila.* 4, p.238 (Bogotá)
Uropsalis segmentata kalinowskii (Berlepsch and Stolzmann, 1894), *Ibis* (6)6, p.399 (Pariayacu, near Maraynioc, Peru)

IDENTIFICATION Length 20-22cm, excluding the male's outer tail feathers. A small to medium-sized, dark, heavily

spotted Neotropical nightjar. Sexually dimorphic. **At rest** Upperparts dark brown heavily spotted tawny. No collar around hindneck. Wing-coverts dark brown, spotted and barred tawny and buff. No obvious scapular pattern, white submoustachial stripe or throat-patch. Underparts dark brown spotted tawny and buff, becoming tawny-buff barred brown on belly and flanks. **In flight** Both sexes lack white markings on the plain brown wings. The male has extremely elongated outer tail feathers with very narrow white outerwebs and very broad dark brown innerwebs. The female lacks white on the tail and elongated outer

290

tail feathers. **Similar species** Lyre-tailed Nightjar (117), found in lower, less open habitats, is larger, paler and more variegated, with a distinct tawny hindneck collar, a tawny or buff band around the lower throat and tawny spotting in the wings; the male is longer-tailed, the outermost tail feathers being longer, broader and darker, with white tips. Long-trained Nightjar (118) is larger, stockier and more variegated, with a buff line along the scapulars, a distinct tawny collar around the hindneck and broader wings, barred and spotted pale tawny and buff; the male shows more white in the tail (see that species). Scissor-tailed Nightjar (115) is larger, paler and more variegated, with a buffish line along the scapulars, a distinct tawny or buff hindneck collar, and buff-barred and -spotted buff wings except the wing-tips; the male is shorter-tailed with more white (see that species).

VOICE The song is a whistled *purrrrr-sweeeee* lasting 2.5-3 seconds, the first note rising in pitch, the second descending. Sings from the ground and may be heard predominantly at dusk? If flushed, utters a low churr. No further information available.

HABITAT Prefers forest edges, clearings and glades, often where there is bamboo, coarse grass or shrubby vegetation, and inhabits humid, elfin and cloud-forest. It also occurs in páramo, clearings along the treeline and open or shrubby slopes. 2,300–3,600m.

HABITS Crepuscular and nocturnal. Roosts on the ground or on low vines. Roost-sites are often beneath bushes and may be near or beside roads. Often sits on roads and tracks at night. Forages by making short sallies from the ground or a low perch. It also hunts low over open, grassy slopes and along forest edge. No further infor-mation available.

FOOD No data available.

BREEDING Breeding season August–September and January–February in Colombia. No data available from other countries.

During courtship displays, several males may circle and chase several females, although this behaviour does not appear to have been fully documented. Eggs elliptical, 27.5-28.4 x 20.2-20.5mm. No further information available.

DESCRIPTION *U. s. segmentata* **Adult male** Forehead, crown, nape, mantle and back dark brown, heavily spotted tawny, with no collar around hindneck. Rump and uppertail-coverts dark brown barred tawny. Wing-coverts dark brown, barred and spotted tawny and buff. Scapulars dark brown, barred and spotted tawny. Primaries brown, P10 edged buffish, almost midway along feather, on outerweb, P9 with a small buffish spot at the emargination on outerweb; rest of primaries unmarked. Secondaries brown narrowly tipped greyish-brown, inner secondaries spotted or barred tawny on outerwebs. Tertials brown, spotted and barred tawny. Tail brown; R5 elongated, with very narrow, whitish outerwebs proximally edged buffish, white feather-shafts and broad, dark brown innerwebs; R4-R1 barred and spotted tawny. Lores and ear-coverts dark brown, heavily spotted tawny. Chin and throat dark brown spotted buff, lower throat often buffish. Breast dark brown, spotted or scalloped tawny and buff. Belly, flanks, undertail- and underwing-coverts buff barred brown. **Adult female** Similar to the male, but often more densely spotted tawny and therefore appearing paler. Lacks the elongated outer tail feathers. **Immature** and **Juvenile** Similar to the adults but secondaries and inner primaries broadly tipped

tawny or buff. **Chick** Not described. **Bare parts** Iris brown; bill blackish; legs and feet brownish.

MEASUREMENTS Wing (male) 162-175, (female) 168-170; tail (male, to tip of R5) 500-540, (female) 117-126; bill (male) 15.6-18.5, (female) 17.2-19.7; tarsus (male) 15.1-17.5, (female) 15.0-17.1. Weight (male, one) 45g, (female, one) 50g.

MOULT No data available.

GEOGRAPHICAL VARIATION Two races are currently recognised.

U. s. segmentata Described above.

U. s. kalinowskii Males are shorter-tailed than the nominate, with the upper half of the innerweb of R5 barred whitish with irregular blackish spots, R4-R2 having a whitish subterminal band c. 10mm from the tip. Wing (male) 162-168, (female) 158-166; tail (male, to tip of R5) 407-468, (female) 119-(169?). Weight no data.

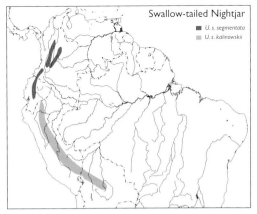

DISTRIBUTION AND MOVEMENTS A montane forest species, patchily distributed in the Andes of north-western and western-central South America.

U. s. segmentata Colombia (western slope of the Andes in S Nariño, central Andes in Antioquia, Caldas, E Cauca and W Huila, and eastern Andes in Norte de Santander, Boyacá, Cundinamarca and E Huila) and Ecuador (Imbabura, Pichincha? and E Chimborazo). Presumably sedentary.

U. s. kalinowskii C Peru (along the slopes of the eastern Andes) and W and C Bolivia (La Paz and Cochabamba). Presumably sedentary.

STATUS Locally uncommon to fairly common in suitable habitat throughout its limited range.

REFERENCES Fjeldså & Krabbe (1990), Hilty & Brown (1986).

---

117 LYRE-TAILED NIGHTJAR
Uropsalis lyra   Plate 22

Hydropsalis lyra 'Gould' Bonaparte, 1850, *Consp. Av. 1*, p.59 (Bogotá)
Uropsalis lyra peruana (Berlepsch and Stolzmann, 1906), *Ornis* 13, p.121 (Chontapunco, Marcapata, Peru)
Uropsalis lyra argentina Olrog, 1975, *Neotropica* 21, No. 66, p.148 (Perico, Jujuy, Argentina)

IDENTIFICATION Length 25-28cm, excluding the male's outer tail feathers. A medium-sized, variegated Neotropical nightjar. Sexually dimorphic. **At rest** Upperparts brown, spotted greyish-white, buff, tawny and cinnamon. Broad tawny or tawny-buff collar around the hindneck. Wing-coverts brown boldly spotted tawny and buff. No obvious scapular pattern. Lacks a white throat-patch but has a tawny or buff band around the lower throat. Underparts brown, spotted and barred tawny, buff and cinnamon, becoming buff barred brown on flanks and lower belly. **In flight** Both sexes lack white markings on the wings, which are brown spotted tawny. The male has extremely elongated outer tail feathers, very broad and dark, with white tips. The female lacks white on the tail and elongated outer tail feathers. **Similar species** Long-trained Nightjar (118) is larger-bodied, with a buff line along the scapulars, no tawny or buff band around the lower throat, and paler markings in the wings, which are brown, regularly barred and spotted buff or pale tawny; the male has, on average, a shorter, paler tail (see that species), the elongated outermost tail feathers being shorter, thinner and broadly edged whitish on the innerwebs. Swallow-tailed Nightjar (116), a bird of more open habitats at higher altitudes, is smaller, darker and heavily spotted tawny, plainer-winged, with no obvious scapular pattern, hindneck collar or tawny or buff band around the lower throat; the male is shorter-tailed, the outermost tail feathers being shorter and thinner, with thin white outerwebs. Scissor-tailed Nightjar (115) is slightly darker, the male much shorter- and paler-tailed (see that species).

VOICE The song is a series of 5-11 *wéeou-tee* notes, gradually rising in pitch. Sings from the ground or from perches, including fence-posts. May be heard mostly at dusk. During court- ship display flights, utters a rapid *weep-weep-weep-weepupup*. The call is a *weep-weep-weep* or *chip-chip-chip*, given in low fast flight or whilst perched. No further information available.

HABITAT Prefers forest edges, clearings and glades, and occurs in generally humid areas such as cloud- or rain-forest, where it may often be found near cliffs, rocky ravines or cave entrances. Also inhabits open woodland, usually close to water. In Argentina, possibly occurs in scrubland bordering alder forests. 800–3,500m.

HABITS Crepuscular and nocturnal. Occasionally roosts crossways on a low perch, e.g. on thin vines at cave entrances. At night, frequently perches on low branches, and often hovers in flight. Probably forages by making short sallies from the ground or a perch, along the edges of forest clearings. No further information available.

FOOD No data available.

BREEDING Breeding season June–August and December in Colombia. No data available from other countries.

Males perform courtship display flights at communal leks, calling (see Voice) and circling and chasing females. No further information available.

DESCRIPTION *U. l. lyra* **Adult male** Forehead, crown and nape brown densely spotted greyish-white, buff, tawny and cinnamon; central feathers broadly streaked or spotted blackish-brown. Broad tawny or tawny-buff collar around hindneck. Mantle and back brown spotted tawny and cinnamon. Rump and uppertail-coverts brown barred cinnamon or tawny. Lesser coverts brown, barred or spotted pale tawny. Rest of wing-coverts brown, boldly spotted tawny, buff and pale buff. Scapulars blackish-

brown, barred and spotted cinnamon, pale buff, buff or tawny. Primaries brown, P10 narrowly edged buff on proximal half of outerweb, P8-P5 spotted tawny along outerwebs, P4-P1 tipped buffish and spotted tawny along outerwebs. Secondaries brown tipped buffish, spotted or mottled tawny on both webs. Tertials brown, mottled tawny, buff and cinnamon. Tail brown; R5 extremely elongated with a very broad innerweb becoming much thinner towards the tip, and a very narrow outerweb; innerweb very narrowly edged greyish-brown speckled brown, both webs being very broadly (c. 100mm) tipped greyish-white or -brown, speckled brown; R4-R1 barred and mottled tawny and buff. Lores and ear-coverts brown speckled tawny or buff. Chin and throat tawny or buff, spotted and barred brown. Tawny or buff band around lower throat. Breast and upper belly brown, spotted and densely barred tawny, cinnamon and buff. Lower belly, flanks and undertail-coverts buff barred brown. Underwing-coverts tawny or buff, barred brown. **Adult female** Similar to the male, but lacks the elongated outer tail feathers. **Immature** and **Juvenile** Not described. **Chick** Not described. **Bare parts** Iris brown; bill blackish; legs and feet brownish.

MEASUREMENTS Wing (male) 171-185, (female) 165-181; tail (male, to tip of R5) 635-790, (female) 136-145; bill (male) 16.0-18.2, (female) 17.9-19.2; tarsus (male) 15.5-19.4, (female) 17.4-18.5. Weight (male, one) 68.5g, (female, two) 74.0-79.0g.

MOULT No data available.

GEOGRAPHICAL VARIATION Three races are currently recognised.

U. l. lyra Described above.

U. l. peruana Generally larger and more reddish than the nominate. Wing (male, one) 198, (female) no data; tail (male, one, to tip of R5) 800, (female) no data. Weight no data.

U. l. argentina Largest race, with whiter markings on breast and male's elongated outer tail feathers tipped greyish, not white. Wing (male, one) 207, (female) no data; tail (male, one, to tip of R5) c. 750?, (female) no data. Weight no data.

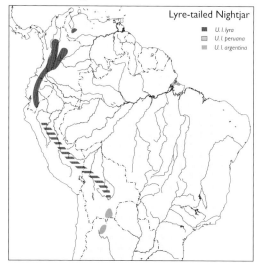

Lyre-tailed Nightjar
■ *U. l. lyra*
▦ *U. l. peruana*
▨ *U. l. argentina*

DISTRIBUTION AND MOVEMENTS An Andean species, locally distributed in western South America.

U. l. lyra W Venezuela (Mérida), W Colombia (Andes from N Antioquia south to Cauca/W Huila, from N Boyacá and W Santander south to E Huila, and recently reported from the western slope in S Nariño) and C Ecuador. Presumably sedentary.

U. l. peruana Peru (eastern slopes of the Andes) and, perhaps this race, W and C Bolivia (La Paz, Cochabamba and W Santa Cruz). Presumably sedentary.

U. l. argentina N Argentina (SE Jujuy) and, perhaps this race, S Bolivia (Tarija). Presumably sedentary.

STATUS Local and possibly not common anywhere within its range.

REFERENCES Fjeldså & Krabbe (1990), Hilty & Brown (1986), Meyer de Schauensee & Phelps (1978).

MACROPSALIS

Macropsalis Sclater, 1866, Proc. Zool. Soc. London, p. 141 (in key), p. 143. Type by subsequent designation, *Caprimulgus forcipatus* Nitzsch = *Hydropsalis creagra* Bonaparte 1850 (Hartert, 1892, Cat. Bds. Brit. Mus., 16, p. 601).

One Neotropical species. The male has the outermost pair of tail feathers extremely elongated and a distinctive tail structure that differentiates it from similar males in the Neotropical genus *Uropsalis*. The species shows sexual dimorphism. It breeds on the ground and does not construct a nest. It generally roosts on the ground and is an aerial feeder.

118 LONG-TRAINED NIGHTJAR
Macropsalis creagra   Plate 22

Hydropsalis creagra Bonaparte, 1850, *Consp. Av.* 1, p.58 (Brazil)

IDENTIFICATION Length 28-31cm, excluding the male's outer tail feathers. A medium-sized, variegated Neotropical nightjar. Sexually dimorphic. **At rest** Upperparts brown, spotted and barred greyish-brown, tawny, buff and cinnamon. Broad tawny or tawny-buff collar around the hindneck. Lesser coverts brown, barred or spotted tawny, rest of wing-coverts brown boldly spotted tawny and buff, with a buffish line along the scapulars. No white submoustachial stripe or throat-patch. Underparts brown, barred and scalloped tawny and buff, becoming buff barred brown on belly and flanks. **In flight** Both sexes lack white markings on the wings, which are brown spotted and barred buff and pale tawny. The male has elongated outer tail feathers, broadly edged brownish-white or whitish on the innerwebs. The second outermost tail feathers are also broadly edged brownish-white or whitish on the innerwebs and the inner three pairs are entirely greyish- or brownish-white on the innerwebs. The female lacks elongated outer tail feathers and white in the tail. **Similar species** Scissor-tailed Nightjar (115) is smaller, paler and shorter-winged, the male being shorter-tailed with a different tail structure (see that species). Lyre-tailed Nightjar (117) is smaller-bodied, lacks an obvious scapular pattern, shows a tawny or buff band around the lower throat and has darker, tawnier markings on the wings; the male has, on average, a longer, darker tail (see that species), the elongated outermost tail feathers being longer, broader and only tipped whitish. Swallow-tailed Nightjar (116) is smaller and heavily spotted tawny, plain-winged, with no obvious scapular pattern and or hindneck collar; the male shows less white in the tail (see that species).

VOICE The call (perhaps song) is a rapidly repeated, high-pitched *tsip-tsip-tsip-tsip*, given by both sexes, often in courtship flights. No further information available.

HABITAT Prefers forest edges, second growth and woodland, often close to water. In south-east Brazil (Paraná) it also inhabits dry, sandy areas, vegetated beaches and saline environments. In the more northerly parts of its range it tends to occur in more mountainous regions. 0–1,800m.

HABITS Crepuscular and nocturnal. Roosts on the ground. Roost-sites are often on patches of leaf-litter, lichen and moss. If flushed from its roost, it may fly a short distance and re-alight on a low branch, often perching across it rather than sitting lengthways. In cold, rainy weather, birds may become lethargic and semi-torpid. Forages in flight by taking insects from the leaves of trees and by hawking for insects attracted to lights. No further information available.

FOOD Insects. No further data available.

BREEDING Breeding season October–January? in S Brazil (Minas Gerais and Paraná). No data available from other regions.

During the courtship display, the male alights on an area of bare ground, e.g. a dirt track or road. The female flies over and hovers in front of the male, c. 80cm above ground, and he responds by puffing out his throat-patch and raising his tail at rightangles, forming a very conspicuous white V. After a few seconds she flies off, followed by the male. Alternatively, she may alight in front of the male, prompting him to fly up and hover around her, with tail spread out downwards; he may circle her several times, then alight on her back and copulation takes place. The male flaps his wings continuously during copulation and both sexes fly off afterwards. Courtship display areas may be used for up to two months. No nest is constructed; the eggs are laid on leaf-litter on the ground. Nest-sites may be in shaded areas, often amongst lichen and bushes. Eggs elliptical, pinkish-blue, speckled chestnut and buff, 24.9-31.5 x 18.7-22.6mm. Incubation is mainly by the female during the day. If flushed from the eggs, she may fly a short distance, alight on the ground and perform a distraction display by repeatedly flying up to c. 2m into the air. After several flights, she may then perform an injury-feigning distraction display along the ground, with wings outstretched. At dusk, the incubating female may leave the eggs unattended for short periods whilst she feeds in the vicinity of the nest. No further information available.

DESCRIPTION Adult male Forehead, crown and nape brown densely spotted greyish-brown, buff, tawny and cinnamon; central feathers boldly streaked or spotted blackish-brown. Broad tawny or tawny-buff collar around hindneck. Mantle, back and rump dark brown, spotted or barred tawny, buff or cinnamon. Uppertail-coverts brown, barred greyish-brown, tawny, buff or cinnamon. Lesser coverts brown, barred or spotted tawny. Rest of wing-coverts brown boldly spotted tawny and buff. Scapulars blackish-brown, spotted and ocellated tawny, cinnamon or buff, broadly edged buff on outerwebs. Primaries brown, P9-P1 spotted buff or pale tawny along outerwebs, barred buff or pale tawny along innerwebs. Secondaries brown narrowly tipped buffish or pale tawny, barred tawny along both webs. Tertials brown mottled buff, pale tawny and greyish-white. Tail brown, all feathers with pointed tips; R5 extremely elongated, with a very broad innerweb, broadly edged brownish-white or whitish, narrowing towards the tip, and a narrow outerweb, barred tawny or buff proximally; R4 similar to R5 but 300-400mm shorter; R3-R1 generally greyish-brown or -white on the innerwebs, and speckled brown; R3 c. 100mm shorter than R4, R2 30-40mm shorter than R3, the central pair (R1) c. 20mm shorter than R2. Lores and ear-coverts brown speckled tawny. Chin buffish, throat brown barred tawny, lower throat buffish. Breast brown, barred and boldly scalloped tawny, buff and pale buff. Belly, flanks and undertail-coverts buff barred brown. Underwing-coverts buff barred brown. **Adult female** Similar to the male but lacks the elongated outer tail feathers. Tail brown, barred tawny and mottled greyish-brown. **Immature** and **Juvenile** Not described. **Chick** At hatching, covered in greyish down, streaked buffish-chestnut and black. On the back, these markings have an 'eyes and mouth' mask-like formation. **Bare parts** Iris brown; bill blackish; legs and feet brown.

MEASUREMENTS Wing (male) 217-232, (female, one) 194; tail (male, to tip of R5) 480-680, (female, one) 172; bill (male) 15.2-18.9, (female, one) 15.3; tarsus (male) 16.1-19.8, (female, one) 18.0. Weight no data.

MOULT No data available.

GEOGRAPHICAL VARIATION Monotypic.

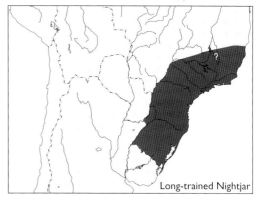

Long-trained Nightjar

DISTRIBUTION AND MOVEMENTS Currently known only from the south-eastern states of Brazil (Espírito Santo, Minas Gerais?, Rio de Janeiro, São Paulo, Paraná, Santa Catarina? and Rio Grande do Sul) and NE Argentina (Misiones). Presumably sedentary.

STATUS Within its restricted range, rare to locally common and possibly a threatened species.

REFERENCES Olmos & Rodrigues (1990), Santos Morães & Krul (1995), Sick (1993).

ELEOTHREPTUS

Eleothreptus G.R.Gray, 1840, List Gen. Bds., p. 7. New name for *Amblypterus* Gould, 1838. Type by original designation and monotypy, *E.anomalus* (Gould) = *Amblypterus anomalus* Gould 1837.

One small and very distinct Neotropical species (but see below). It has a unique wing shape which is especially evident in the male, a short, square tail, a broad bill, very long rictal bristles around the gape and partially feathered tarsi, i.e. feathering on upper frontal tarsi only. The species shows strong sexual dimorphism. It breeds on the ground but does not construct a nest. It generally roosts on the ground and is an aerial feeder.

The White-winged Nightjar *Caprimulgus candicans* may also prove to belong in this genus, as it appears to have many similar features, e.g. a pale cinnamon-tinged plumage, outer primaries that are slightly bent inwards, a short tail, a broad bill surrounded by long rictal bristles and partially feathered tarsi. It may also have similar habits, such as the male's use of wing sounds (other than wing clapping) during courtship displays. Both species generally inhabit South American grasslands.

119 SICKLE-WINGED NIGHTJAR
Eleothreptus anomalus Plate 19

Amblypterus anomalus Gould, 1837, *Proc. Zool. Soc. London* p.105 (Demerara, error = São Paulo, Brazil, by designation of Pinto, 1938, *Rev. Mus. Paulista* 32, p.237)

IDENTIFICATION Length 18-20cm. A small, pale, greyish-brown Neotropical nightjar. Sexually dimorphic.

At rest Large-headed and short-tailed. The male's outermost primaries often curve slightly upwards. Upperparts pale greyish-brown lightly spotted dark brown, boldly spotted blackish-brown on head. Occasionally shows an indistinct buffish collar on the hindneck. Wing-coverts generally pale greyish-brown, barred blackish-brown, streaked pale buff. Shows a distinct cinnamon patch, distally edged whitish, on the primary coverts. Scapulars pale greyish-brown, with blackish-brown centres shaped like inverted Christmas trees. Has a pale buffish-white stripe above the eye, but no noticeable submoustachial stripe and no white on the throat. Underparts darkish brown tinged cinnamon, barred brown, becoming pale buff indistinctly barred brown on lower belly and flanks. Females are browner. **In flight** Flies with slow, fluttering wingbeats which often gives the impression of an injured bird, or flaps and glides low over the ground. The male has a distinctive wing-shape and white tips to the five outermost primaries, but these features are generally not noticeable in the field. The broad buff bases to the primaries are also not generally seen in flight. All but the central pair of tail feathers are broadly tipped white or buffish-white. The female has paler, browner wings, indistinctly barred tawny, and all the tail feathers narrowly tipped buffish. **Similar species** (the following possibly only applies to females and immatures). White-winged Nightjar (68) is slightly paler and more heavily tinged cinnamon (females only), and lacks white spotting on the upperparts (immatures only). The underparts are less heavily spotted and barred brown, the primaries more thinly barred tawny and, at rest, the wing-tips often reach the tip of the tail.

VOICE The song (perhaps call) is a soft *chip, tchup* or *tchut*, repeated at a rate of c. 8 notes per second, for up to 2-3 minutes at a time. Sings/calls from the ground or in flight. Probably moves around its territory and calls from different locations. Perhaps heard chiefly at dusk and dawn. In flight, the female utters a harsh, nasal *gzee gzee*.

HABITAT Prefers gallery forest (occurring around the edges, along streams or on river banks), monte (chaco-type woodland) and transitional woodlands, plus (in northeast Argentina) periodically flooded grasslands with areas of 'chañar monte' (chaco-type woodland). Also occurs in or near savannas and grasslands, marshland, swamps, campo, lagoon edges with spiny scrub and along steams, pools and flooded palm groves.

HABITS Crepuscular and nocturnal. Roosts on the ground and possibly also on low branches. Roost-sites may be on small patches of bare earth or in hollow depressions, and are often amongst clumps of vegetation such as thistles or grasses. If flushed from its roost, tends to fly low, 2-4m above ground, for up to 40m before re-alighting on the ground amongst vegetation. Occasionally opens and closes its tail immediately before landing. Often sits on roads and tracks at night. If danger approaches, makes short jerking movements or jumps 10-20cm into the air. If danger persists, flies to nearby cover, but often returns to roads or tracks once danger has passed. Takes flight with very rapid wingbeats, but soon reverts to slow, fluttering flaps and glides when flying normally. Readily perches on low branches, bushes or wire fencing. Forages along the borders of open areas and grassy tracks, fluttering and gliding low over vegetation, occasionally rising suddenly after insects. Also makes short sallies from the ground. No further information available.

FOOD Beetles, moths and ants. No further data available.

BREEDING Breeding season August–January? in SE Brazil (August in Paraná, October–December in Minas Gerais, November to early January in São Paulo state) and September?– December? in NE Argentina. No data available from other localities.

Territorial. Males patrol their territories at heights of 10-40m above ground, during which they make distinctly audible flapping sounds with their wings. Bursts of 1-4 flaps

are given at a rate of 13 flaps per second, and up to 17 flaps may be given in a series, with a pause of 1-28 seconds between each set of flaps. In perfect weather conditions, these flapping sounds are audible for distances of up to 200m.

During courtship flights, the male flaps and glides low over his territory, 0.8-1.2m above ground, occasionally making muffled thudding sounds with his wings, e.g. *tuktuktuk*.

Eggs elliptical or ovate, pinkish-buff or pale buffish, spotted and scrawled brown and grey, 23.2-31.4 x 18.2-22.8mm. No further information available.

DESCRIPTION Adult male Forehead, crown and nape pale greyish-brown, central feathers boldly spotted blackish-brown with tawny edges. Some nape feathers occasionally tipped buff and showing as an indistinct collar on the hindneck. Mantle and back pale greyish-brown, lightly spotted dark brown. Rump and uppertail-coverts pale greyish-brown, lightly spotted dark brown and thinly barred brown. Lesser coverts greyish-brown barred brown. Primary coverts cinnamon-drab, speckled light brown, narrowly (c. 4mm) tipped whitish. Rest of wing-coverts pale greyish-brown, streaked pale buff and barred brown or blackish-brown, bars often V-shaped in centres. Scapular pale greyish-brown, with blackish-brown centres shape like inverted Christmas trees. Primaries buff on proxima half, dark brown on distal half; P10-P6 boldly tipped whit (c. 10mm), the extent generally being greater on th outerwebs, the white on the outerwebs also often edge buffish; the primaries curve inwards towards the body, P4 -P2 the longest, P1 the shortest. Secondaries (much shorte than the primaries) cinnamon-drab speckled light brown tipped whitish (c. 4mm). Tertials pale greyish-brown boldly marked with blackish-brown star-shaped spots. Tai brown, broadly barred cinnamon-buff; R5-R2 tippe whitish or buffish-white (c. 10mm); central pair (R1) pal greyish-brown, speckled and thinly barred brown. Lore and area around eyes rufous barred brown, ear-covert buffish-white barred brown. Supercilium pale buffish -white, barred brown. Submoustachial stripe greyish-whit tinged cinnamon. Chin buffish-white barred brown Throat brown tinged cinnamon, barred brown an streaked buffish. Lower throat and upper breast darkis brown, boldly spotted and streaked buff. Lower breast an upper belly greyish-buff speckled brown. Lower belly an flanks pale buff barred brown. Undertail-coverts pale buff Underwing-coverts buff, spotted and barred brown. **Adul female** Browner than the male and often longer-winge and -tailed, but without the distinctive wing-shape of th male. Primaries brown, regularly barred pale tawny an very narrowly tipped buffish-white, P9 the longest. Al secondaries very narrowly tipped buffish-white. All tai feathers narrowly (c. 5mm) tipped buff speckled brown **Immature** Not described. **Juvenile** Similar to the adul female, although the upperparts are tinged cinnamon especially on the wing-coverts, and speckled or spotte white. **Chick** Not known. **Bare parts** Iris dark brown; bil brownish or blackish; legs and feet brownish

MEASUREMENTS Wing (male) 127-136, (female) 128 -153; tail (male) 70-77, (female) 76-90; bill (male) 16.5 -18.0, (female) 16.0-20.0; tarsus (male) 20.0-22.0, (female 19.0-22.2. Weight (male, one) 43.7g, (female) no data.

MOULT No data available.

GEOGRAPHICAL VARIATION Monotypic.

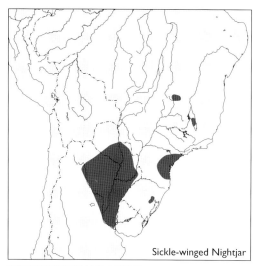

Sickle-winged Nightjar

DISTRIBUTION AND MOVEMENTS Widely, but never commonly, distributed in C, E and SE Brazil (Distrito Federal, Minas Gerais, São Paulo, Paraná, Santa Catarina and Rio Grande do Sul), E Paraguay (Concepción, Guairá, Cordillera, Central and Misiones) and NE Argentina (Misiones, Corrientes, Formosa, Chaco, Santiago del Estero, Córdoba, Santa Fé, Entre Ríos and Buenos Aires, with records from Catamarca and Salta possibly in error).

Sedentary and partially migratory, southern populations moving north to avoid the austral winters, April–August.

STATUS Very scarce and little known throughout its range.

REFERENCES Collar *et al.* (1992), Kirwan *et al.* (in prep.), Lowen *et al.* (1996b, 1997), Pearman & Abadie (1995), Straneck & Viñas (1994), Straube (1990).

BIBLIOGRAPHY

Aldrich, E. C. 1935. Nesting of the Dusky Poorwill. *Condor* 37: 49-55.

Aldridge, H. D. J. N. & Brigham R. M. 1991. Factors influencing foraging time in two aerial insectivores: the bird *Chordeiles minor* and the bat *Eptesicus fuscus. Can. J. Zool.* 69: 62-69.

Alexander, I. 1983. Chick growth rates of the nightjar (*Caprimulgus europaeus*) in southeast Dorset. *Stour Ringing Group Annual Report* 1982 (unpublished).

— 1984. An examination of nightjar movements in southeast Dorset. *Stour Ringing Group Annual Report* 1983 (unpublished): 28-37.

— 1985. Feeding techniques of the nightjar (*Caprimulgus europaeus*). *Stour Ringing Group Annual Report* 1984 (unpublished): 48-53.

— & Cresswell, B. 1990. Foraging by nightjars (*Caprimulgus europaeus*) away from their nesting areas. *Ibis* 132: 568-574.

Ali, S. & Ripley, S. D. 1970. *The Handbook of the Birds of India and Pakistan*, Vol. 4. Oxford University Press, Bombay.

Alvarez del Toro. 1949. A Guerrero Whip-poor-will impaled by an insect. *Condor* 51: 272.

Amadon, D. & Short, L. 1992. Taxonomy of lower catagories – suggested guidelines. *Bull. Brit. Orn. Club* 112A: 11-36.

American Ornithologists' Union 1983. *Check-list of North American birds.* 6th ed. American Ornithologists' Union, Lawrence, Kansas.

Andrew, P. 1985. An annotated checklist of the birds of the Cibodas-Gunung Gede Nature Reserve. *Kukila* 2(2): 10-28.

Angus, R. 1994. Observation of a Papuan Frogmouth at Cape York. *Australian Birds* 28(1): 10-11.

Aragonés, J. (in press). Risk taking and flushing distance: a way of parental investment in the Pauraque (*Nyctidromus albicollis*). *Etologia* 5.

— 1997. Influencia de la cripsis en el comportamiento del Chotacabras Pardo *Caprimulgus ruficollis.* Tesis Doctoral, Universidad de Córdoba, Córdoba, Spain (unpublished).

Archer, G. F. & Godman, E. M. 1961. *The Birds of British Somaliland and the Gulf of Aden* Vol. 3. Oliver & Boyd, Edinburgh and London.

Armstrong, J. T. 1965. Breeding home range in the nighthawk and other birds: its evolutionary and ecological significance. *Ecology* 46: 619-629.

Ash, J. S. & Miskell, J. E. 1983. A migration of (Eurasian) nightjars (*Caprimulgus europaeus*) at Cape Guardafui, Somalia. *Bull. Brit. Orn. Club* 103: 107-110.

Atherton, R. G., Mathew, P. A. & Winter, J. W. 1980. Notes on the crop contents and locality records of the Marbled Frogmouth *Podager ocellatus marmoratus* Gould, from Cape York Peninsula. *Sunbird* 11 (3/4): 71-72.

Austin, G. T. & Bradley, W. G. 1969. Additional responses of the Poorwill to low temperature. *Auk* 86: 717-725.

Baha el Din, M. 1995. Egyptian Nightjar on horseback. *Birding World* 8: 145.

Baicich P. J. & Harrison C. J. O. 1997 *A Guide to the Nests, Eggs and Nestlings of North American Birds.* 2nd Edition.
Academic Press, San Diego and London.

Baird, R. F. 1991. Holocene avian assemblage from Skull Cave (AU-8), south-western Western Australia. *Rec. West. Austral. Mus.* 15: 267-286.

— 1993. Pleistocene avian fossils from Pyramids Cave (M-89), eastern Victoria, Australia. *Alcheringa* 17: 383-404.

Baker, K. 1993. *Identification Guide to European Non-passerines.* B.T.O. Guide 24. British Trust for Ornithology, Thetford.

Balát, F. & González, H. 1982. Concrete data on the breeding of Cuban birds. *Acta. Sci. Nat. Brno* 16(8): 1-46.

Balouet, J. C. 1990. *Extinct Species of the World.* Charles Letts & Co.

— & Olson, S. L. 1989. Fossil birds from late quaternary deposits in New Caledonia. *Smithsonian Contrib. Zool.* 469.

Bannerman, D. A. 1933. *Birds of Tropical West Africa* Vol. 3. Oliver & Boyd, Edinburgh and London.

— 1953. *The Birds of West and Equatorial Africa* Vol. 1. Oliver & Boyd, Edinburgh and London.

Barker, R. D. & Vestjens, W. J. M. 1989. *The Food of Australian Birds 1. Non-passerines.* C.S.I.R.O. Melbourne.

Barnes, R., Bartrina, L., Butchart, S. H. M., Clay, R. P., Esquivel, E. Z., Etcheverry, N. I., Lowen, J. C. & Vincent, J. 1993. *Bird Surveys and Conservation in the Paraguayan Atlantic Forest.* Birdlife Study Report 57, BirdLife International, Cambridge, U.K.

Barrowclough, G. F., Lentino, R. M. & Sweet, P. R. 1997. New records of birds from Auyán-tepui, Estado Bolívar, Venezuela. *Bull. Brit. Orn. Club* 117: 194-198.

Bartels, M. 1938. Notizen über einige *Batrachostomus*-Arten. *J. Orn.* 86: 244-247.

Bartholomew, G. A., Hudson, J. W. & Howell, T. R. 1962. Body temperature, oxygen consumption, evaporative water loss and heart rate in Poorwill. *Condor* 64: 117-125.

Bates, G. L. 1908. Observations regarding the breeding seasons of the birds of southern Kamerun. *Ibis* (2)9: 558-570.

Bates, J. M., Garvin, M. C., Schmitt, D. C. & Schmitt, G. C. 1989. Notes on bird distribution in northeastern Dpto. Santa Cruz, Bolivia, with 15 species new to Bolivia. *Bull. Brit. Orn. Club* 109: 236-244.

— , Parker, T. A., Capparella, A. P. & Davis, T. J. 1992. Observations on the *campo, cerrado* and forest avifaunas of eastern Dpto. Santa Cruz, Bolivia, including 21 species new to the country. *Bull. Brit. Orn. Club* 112: 86-98.

Bayne, E. M. & Brigham, R. M. 1995. Prey selection and foraging constraints in Common Poorwills (*Phalaenoptilus nuttallii*: Aves: Caprimulgidae). *J. Zool. Lond.* 235: 1-8.

Beehler, B. M., Pratt, T. K. & Zimmerman, D. A. 1986. *Birds of New Guinea.* Princeton University Press, Princeton.

Bell, H. L. 1986. Occupation of urban habitats by birds in Papua New Guinea. *Proc. West. Found. Vert. Zool.* 3: 5-48.

de Bellard-Pietri, E. 1953. The Guacharo. *Prem. Congrès Int. de Spéléologie. Extrait des Publ. du Congrès* III.

Belton, W. 1984. Birds of Rio Grande do Sul. *Bull. Amer. Mus. Nat. Hist.* 178: 371-631.

Beltzer, A. H., Ríos de Salusso, M. L. & Bucher, E. H. 1988. Alimentación del ñacundá (*Podager nacunda*) en Paraná (Entre Ríos). *Hornero* 13: 47-52.

Benson, C. W. 1955. Nightjars on roads at night. *Ibis* 97: 370-371.

— & Benson, F. M. 1977. *The Birds of Malawi*. Montford Press, Limbe.

—, Brooke, R. K., Dowsett, R. J. & Irwin, M. P. S. 1971. *The Birds of Zambia*. Collins, London.

— & Colebrook-Robjent, J. F. R. 1977. Erythrism in Fiery-necked Nightjar *Caprimulgus pectoralis*. *Bull. Brit. Orn. Club* 97: 37-39.

— & Penny, M. J. 1971. The land birds of Aldabra. *Phil. Trans. Roy. Soc. London* 260B: 417-527.

Bent, A. C. 1940. Life histories of American woodpeckers, cuckoos and allies. *U.S. Natn. Mus. Bull.* 174.

van den Berk, V. & van der Winden, J. 1992. Diurnal migration of Nightjars at the Goksu Delta, Turkey. *OSME Bull.* 28: 20-21.

Berry, R. 1979. Nightjar habitats and breeding in East Anglia. *Brit. Birds* 72: 207-218.

— & Bibby, C. J. 1981. A breeding study of nightjars. *Brit. Birds* 74: 161-169.

Beruldsen, G. 1980. *Fieldguide to Nests and Eggs of Australian birds*. Rigby Publishers. Sydney.

— 1991. Large-tailed Nightjar in southeastern Queensland. *Bird Observer* 709: 58.

— 1993. The undescribed *oom-oom-oom* call of the Marbled Frogmouth. *Sunbird* 23(4): 93-94.

— 1997. Notes on Vocal Behaviour and Breeding of the Plumed Frogmouth *Podargus ocellatus plumiferus*. *Aust. Bird Watcher* 17 (4): 192-197.

Beven, G. 1973. Studies of less familiar birds, 171: Red-necked Nightjar. *Brit. Birds* 66: 390-396.

Bharos, A. M. K. 1992. Feeding by Common Nightjar *Caprimulgus asiaticus* and Indian Roller *Coracias benghalensis* in the light of mercury vapour lamps. *J. Bombay Nat. Hist. Soc.* 89: 124.

Binford, L. C. 1989. *A distributional survey of the birds of the Mexican state of Oaxaca*. A.O.U. Ornithological Monograph No. 43.

Bishop, K. D. 1987. Interesting bird observations in Papua New Guinea. *Muruk* 2(2): 52-57.

— & Diamond, J. M. 1997. Rediscovery of Heinrich's Nightjar *Eurostopodus diabolicus*. *Kukila* 9: 71-73.

Bjorklund, R. & Bjorklund, E. 1983. Notes on the behaviour and nesting of caprimulgids in the Sand Ridge State Forest. *Illinois Audubon Bull.* 207: 21-28.

Blackford, J. L. 1953. Breeding haunts of the Stephen's Whip-poor-will. *Condor* 55: 281-286.

Blake, E. R. 1949. Distribution and variation of *Caprimulgus maculicaudus*. *Fieldiana Zool.* 31: 207-212.

Blakers, M., Davies, S. J. J. F. & Reilly, P. N. 1984. *The Atlas of Australian Birds*. Royal Australasian Ornithologists' Union, Victoria.

Blem, R. 1972. Stomach capacity in the Common Nighthawk. *Wilson Bull.* 84: 492-493.

Bond, J. 1928a. The distribution and habits of the birds of the Republic of Haiti. *Proc. Acad. Nat. Sci. Philadelphia* 80: 483-521.

— 1928b. A remarkable West Indian goatsucker. *Auk* 45: 471-474.

— 1934. The Cuban Nightjar (*Antrostomus c. cubanensis*) in the Isle of Pines. *Auk* 51: 523.

Bornschein, M. R., Reinert, B. L. & Bóçon, R. 1996. A new record of the Sickle-winged Nightjar *Eleothreptus anomalus* for southern Brazil. *Bull. Brit. Orn. Club* 116: 125-126.

Borrero, J. I. 1974. Notes on the structure of the upper eyelid of potoos (*Nyctibius*). *Condor* 76: 210-211.

Borrett, R. P. & Jackson, H. D. 1970. The winter quarters of *Caprimulgus europaeus plumipes* Przhevalski. *Bull. Brit. Orn. Club* 90: 25-26.

Bosque, C. & de Parra, O. 1992. Digestive efficiency and rate of food passage in Oilbird nestlings. *Condor* 94: 557-570.

— & Ramirez, R. 1988. Post breeding migration of Oilbirds. *Wilson Bull.* 100: 675-677.

—, — & Ramirez, D. 1995. The diet of the Oilbird in Venezuela. *Ornitología Neotropical* 6: 67-80.

Bowden, C. G. R. & Green, R. E. 1994. The ecology of Nightjars on pine plantations in Thetford Forest. R.S.P.B. Research Report, Sandy, U.K.

Bowers, R. K. Jr. & Dunning, J. B. Jr. 1997. *Buff-collared Nightjar* (*Caprimulgus ridgwayi*). In *The Birds of North America*. No 267 (A. Poole & F. Gill eds.). The Academy of Natural Sciences, Philadelphia, and The American Ornithologists' Union, Washington, D.C.

Brauner, J. 1952. Reactions of Poorwills to light and temperature. *Condor* 54: 152-159.

— 1953. Observations on the behaviour of a captive Poorwill. *Condor* 55: 68-74.

Brazil, M. A. 1991. *The Birds of Japan*. Christopher Helm, London.

Brigham, R. M. 1989. Roost and nest sites of Common Nighthawks: are gravel roofs important? *Condor* 91: 722-724.

— 1990. Prey selection by big brown bats and Common Nighthawks. *Amer. Midl. Nat.* 124: 73-80.

— 1991. Apparent drinking by the Common Poorwill (*Phalaenoptilus nuttallii*). *Northwest Naturalist* 72(2): 82-84.

— 1992. Daily torpor in a free-ranging goatsucker, the Common Poorwill (*Phalaenoptilus nuttallii*). *Physiol. Zool.* 65: 457-472.

— 1994. Goatsuckers: just feathered bats? *Cordillera* 1(2): 12-17.

— & Barclay, R. M. R. 1992. Lunar influence on foraging and nesting activity of Common Poorwills (*Phalaenoptilus nuttallii*). *Auk* 109: 315-320.

— & — 1995. Prey detection by Common Nighthawks: does vision impose a constraint? *Ecoscience* 2: 276-279.

— & Fenton, M. B. 1991. Convergence in foraging strategies by two morphologically and phylogenetically distinct nocturnal aerial insectivores. *J. Zool.* 223: 475-489.

— & Geiser, F. 1997. Breeding biology of Australian Owlet-nightjars *Aegotheles cristatus* in eucalypt woodland. *Emu* 97: 316-321.

—, Morgan, K. H. & James, P. C. 1995. Evidence that free-ranging Common Nighthawks may enter torpor. *Northwest Naturalist* 76: 149-150.

— & Trayhorn, P. 1994. Brown fat in birds? A test for the 'mammalian' bat-specific mitochondrial uncoupling protein in Common Poorwills. *Condor* 96: 208-211.

—, Tremont, S. M., Ford, H. A. & Debus, S. J. S. 1997. Re-use of nest stumps and re-nesting by Australian Owlet-nightjars. *Austral. Bird Watcher* 17: 107-108.

Britton, P. L. 1969. Weights of the Pennant-winged Nightjar. *Bull. Brit. Orn. Club* 89: 21-24.

Brodkorb, P. 1971. Catalogue of fossil birds: part 4 (Columbiformes through Piciformes). *Bull. Florida State Mus. Biol. Sci.* 15: 163-266.

Brosset, A. & Erard, C. 1986. *Les oiseaux des régions forestières du nord-est du Gabon.* Vol. 1. Société Nationale de Protection de la Nature, Paris.

Brouwer, J. 1992. Road kills of three nightjar species near Niamey, Niger. *Malimbus* 14: 16-18.

— & Mullié, W. C. 1992. Range extensions of two nightjar species in Niger, with a note on prey. *Malimbus* 14: 11-14.

Brown, L. H. 1979. Encounters with nightjars. *Wildlife* 21(6): 40-43.

Bühler, P. 1970. Schädelmorphologie und Kiefermechanik der Caprimulgidae (Aves). *Z. Morph. Tiere* 66: 337-399.

— 1987. Zur Strategie des Beutefangs der Nachtschwalben (Caprimulgidae). *J. Orn.* 128: 488-491.

Burns, B. G. 1992. Tawny tableaux. *Bird Observer* 718: 12.

Bustamante, P. F. S. & Simon, J. E. 1996. Reprodução de *Lurocalis semitorquatus* (Gmelin, 1788) (Caprimulgidae) em Viçosa, MG. *V Congresso Brasileiro de Ornitologia* ?: 16.

Caccamise, D. F. 1994. Competitive relationships of the Common and Lesser Nighthawks. *Condor* 76: 1-20.

Cadbury, C. J. 1981. Nightjar census methods. *Bird Study* 28: 1-4.

Carroll, R. W. & Fry, C. H. 1987. A range extension and probable breeding record of the Brown Nightjar (*Caprimulgus binotatus* Bonaparte) in southwestern Central African Republic. *Malimbus* 9: 125.

Carter, C. & Colebrook-Robjent, J. F. R. 1983. Nest of Bates' Nightjar *Caprimulgus batesi* in Zaire. *Bull. Orn. Club* 103: 76.

Catterall, M. 1997. Results of the 1996 bird survey of Buton Island, Sulawesi, Indonesia. Ecosurveys, Spilsby, U.K.

Chafer, C. J. 1992. Observations of the Powerful Owl *Ninox strenua* in the Illawarra and Shoalhaven regions of New South Wales. *Austral. Birdwatcher* 14: 289-300.

Chapin, J. P. 1916. The Pennant-winged Nightjar of Africa and its migration. *Bull. Amer. Mus. Nat. Hist.* 35: 73-81.

— 1939. The Birds of the Belgian Congo, II. *Bull. Amer. Mus. Nat. Hist.* 75: 1-632.

Chapin, R. T. 1978. Brief accounts of some Central African birds based on the journals of James Chapin. *Rev. Zool. Afr.* 92: 805-836.

Chapman, F. M. 1923. Descriptions of proposed new birds from Panama, Venezuela, Ecuador, Peru and Bolivia. *Amer. Mus. Novit.* 67.

— 1929. New birds from Mt Roraima. *Amer. Mus. Novit.* 341.

— 1931. The upper zonal bird-life of Mts Roraima and Duida. *Bull. Amer. Mus. Nat. Hist.* 63: 1-135.

Chappuis, C. 1981. Illustration sonore de problèmes bioacoustiques posés par les oiseaux de la zone Ethiopienne. Disque No. 12. *Alauda* 49: 35-58.

Charlton, M. 1993. Nighthawk on the golf course. *Blue Jay* 51: 153-154.

Chebez, J. C., Heinonen, S. & Bosso, A. 1988. Nidificación del atajacaminos oscuro (*Caprimulgus sericocaudatus*) en Misiones, Argentina. *Hornero* 13: 90-91.

Cheke, R. A. & Walsh, J. F. 1996. *The birds of Togo.* B.O.U. Check-list No. 14, Tring, U.K.

— & — (in press). Behaviour of Standard-wing Nightjars in Togo. *Ostrich.*

Chenaux-Repond, R. 1971. Observations on nightjars. *Honeyguide* 67: 15-16.

— 1980. Fiery-necked Nightjar. *Honeyguide* 101: 31.

— 1981. A diurnal nightjar. *Honeyguide* 106: 31.

Cheng Tso-Hsin 1987. *A Synopsis of the Avifauna of China.* Paul Parey, Hamburg and Berlin, and Science Press, Peking.

Chubb, C. 1910. On the birds of Paraguay. *Ibis* 9(4): 53-78.

Claffey, P. M. 1995. Notes on the avifauna of the Bétérou area, Borgou Province, Republic of Benin. *Malimbus* 17(2): 63-84.

Clancey, P. A. 1965. Miscellaneous taxonomic notes on African birds 23: the austral races of the nightjar *Caprimulgus fossii* Hartlaub. *Durban Mus. Novit.* 8: 1-9.

— 1966. Racial variation in the southern populations of *Caprimulgus rufigena* Smith. *Bull. Brit. Orn. Club* 86: 6-7.

— (ed.) 1980. *S.A.O.S. Checklist of Southern African birds.* Southern African Orn. Soc., Johannesburg.

— 1994. The austral races of the Afrotropical Fiery-necked Nightjar *Caprimulgus pectoralis* Cuvier 1816. *Bull. Brit. Orn. Club* 114: 48-55.

— & Mendelsohn, J. M. 1979. The races of the Nightjar *Caprimulgus europaeus* Linnaeus wintering in southern Africa. *Durban Mus. Novit.* 12: 83-86.

Clark, A. N. 1985. *Longman Dictionary of Geography: human and physical.* Longman, Harlow.

Clarke, S. 1912. Examples of two new African birds. *Bull. Brit. Orn. Club* 31: 108.

Cleere, N. 1991a. Woodcock mobbing nightjar. *Brit. Birds* 84: 60.

— 1991b. Nightjar giving contact call after alighting on perch. *Brit. Birds* 84: 61.

— 1995. The identification, taxonomy and distribution of the Mountain Nightjar *Caprimulgus poliocephalus*/ Fiery-necked Nightjar *Caprimulgus pectoralis* complex. *Bull. Afr. Bird Club* 2: 86-97.

Coates, B. J. 1985. *The Birds of Papua New Guinea, 1. Non-passerines.* Dove Publications, Alderley, Queensland.

— & Bishop, K. D. 1997. *A Guide to the Birds of Wallacea: Sulawesi, the Moluccas and Lesser Sunda Islands, Indonesia.* Dove Publications, Alderley, Queensland.

Cohn-Haft, M. 1993. Rediscovery of the White-winged Potoo (*Nyctibius leucopterus*). *Auk* 110: 391-394.

Colebrook-Robjent, J. F. R. 1979. The nightjars of Zambia. *Black Lechwe* 13: 20-28.

— 1984. Nests and eggs of some African nightjars. *Ostrich* 55: 5-11.

Collar, N. J., Crosby, M. J. & Stattersfield, A. J. 1994. *Birds to Watch 2: the World List of Threatened Birds.* BirdLife Conservation Series No. 4, Cambridge, U.K.

—, Gonzaga, L. P., Krabbe, N., Madroño Nieto, A., Naranjo, L. G., Parker, T. A. & Wege, D. C. 1992. *Threatened birds of the Americas: the ICPB/IUCN Red Data Book.* International Council for Bird Preservation, Cambridge, U.K.

— & Stuart, S. N. 1988. *Key forests for Threatened Birds in Africa.* ICPB Monograph No. 3. International Council for Bird Preservation, Cambridge, U.K.

Colston P. & Curry-Lindahl K. 1986. *The Birds of Mount Nimba, Liberia.* British Museum (Natural History), London.

Condon, H. T. 1975. *Checklist of the Birds of Australia: Part 1, Non-passerines.* R.A.O.U. Melbourne.

Conule, L. E. 1987. White-throated Nightjar *Caprimulgus mystacalis* roosting in tree hollow. *Austral. Birdwatcher* 12: 33.

Coomans de Ruiter L. 1931. Nesten en Eieren van de Javaansche Hoornzwaluw (*Batrachostomus javensis* [Horsf.]). *De Tropische Natuur* 20: 21-24.

Cooper, R. J. 1981. Relative abundance of Georgia caprimulgids based on call counts. *Wilson Bull.* 93: 363-371.

Copete, J. L. & Gustamante, L. 1992. Agonistic interaction between a Nightjar *Caprimulgus europaeus* and a Red-necked Nightjar *Caprimulgus ruficollis*. *Butll. G.C.A.* 9: 47-48.

Cory, C. B. 1917. Notes on little known species of South American birds with descriptions of new subspecies. *Field Mus. Nat. Hist. Zool.* 12: 3-7.

— 1918. Catalogue of the birds of the Americas. *Field Mus. Nat. Hist. Ser.* 13 (Publ. 197).

Cowan, P. J. 1982. Birds in west central Libya 1980-1981. *Bull. Brit. Orn. Club* 102: 32-35.

Cowles, G. S. 1967. The palate of the Red-necked Nightjar, with a description of a new feature. *Ibis* 109: 260-265.

Cowles, R. B. & Dawson, W. R. 1951. Cooling mechanism of Texas Nighthawk. *Condor* 53: 19-22.

Cramp, S. (ed.) 1985. *The Birds of the Western Palearctic.* Vol. 4. Oxford University Press, Oxford.

Cresswell, B. 1986. The Nightjar project. Some results of the radio-tracking work. *Stour Ringing Group Annual Report* 1985: 52-55.

— 1987. Nightjars. A preview of some early results from analysis of 1986 data. *Stour Ringing Group Annual Report* 1986: 30-31.

— 1990. The effects of moonlight and temperature on nightjar foraging. *Stour Ringing Group Annual Report* 1989: 38-39.

— 1992. Nightjars and the moon. *Stour Ringing Group Annual Report* 1991: 36-37.

— 1993. Site and habitat preferences of nesting and roosting Nightjars. *Stour Ringing Group Annual Report* 1992: 33-35.

— 1996. Nightjars: some aspects of their behaviour and conservation. *British Wildlife* 7: 297-304.

— & Alexander, I. 1990. A case of mate-switching between broods in the Nightjar. *Ringing and Migration* 11: 73-75.

— & — 1992. Activity patterns of foraging Nightjars (*Caprimulgus europaeus*). In Priede I. G. and Swift S. M. (eds.) *Wildlife Telemetry* 7, Ellis Horwood Series in Environmental Management, Science and Technology.

Croxall, J. P. 1969. Bird notes from Sarawak, September-October 1968. *Sarawak Mus. J.* 17: 391-398.

Csada, R. D. & Brigham, R. M. 1992. Common Poorwill. *The Birds of North America*, No. 32 (A. Poole, P. Stettenheim and F. Gill, eds.) Academy of Natural Sciences,

Philadelphia, and American Ornithologists' Union, Washington, D.C.

— & — 1994a. Breeding biology of the Common Poorwill at the northern edge of its distribution. *J. Field Orn.* 65: 186-193.

— & — 1994b. Reproduction constrains the use of daily torpor by free-ranging Common Poorwills (*Phalaenoptilus nuttallii*) (Aves: Caprimulgidae). *J. Zool.* 234: 209-216.

—, — & Pittendrigh, B. R. 1992. Prey selection in relation to insect availability by the Common Poorwill (*Phalaenoptilus nuttallii*). *Can. J. Zool.* 70: 1299-1303.

Cuadrado, M. & Domínguez, F. 1996. Phenology and breeding success of Red-necked Nightjar *Caprimulgus ruficollis* in southern Spain. *J. Orn.* 137: 249-253.

Culbertson, A. E. 1946. Occurrences of Poorwills in the Sierran foothills in winter. *Condor* 48: 158-159.

Curry-Lindahl, K. 1960. Ecological studies on mammals, birds, reptiles and amphibians in the eastern Belgian Congo, Part II. *Ann. Mus. Royal Congo Belge.* 87: 136-139.

Danielsen, F. & Heegaard, M. 1995. The birds of Bukit Tigapuluh, southern Riau, Sumatra. *Kukila* 7: 99-120.

Davis, J. 1959. A new race of the Mexican Potoo from western Mexico. *Condor* 61: 300-301.

Davis, L. I. 1962. Acoustic evidence of relationship in *Caprimulgus. Texas J. Sci.* 14: 72-106.

— 1978. Acoustic evidence of relationship in *Caprimulgus. Pan. Amer. Studies* 1(1): 4-21.

Davis, S. E., Rocha O., O., Sarmiento, J. & Hanagarth, W. 1994. New departmental records and notes for some Bolivian birds. *Bull. Brit. Orn. Club* 114: 73-85.

— & Flores, E. 1994. First record of White-winged Nightjar *Caprimulgus candicans* for Bolivia. *Bull. Brit. Orn. Club* 114: 127-128.

Davis, W. E. & Beehler, B. M. 1993. Dual singing between an adult and fledgling Marbled Frogmouth. *Corella* 17: 111-113.

Davison G. W. H. 1997. Bird Observations in the Muratus Mountains, Kalimantan Selatan. *Kukila* 9: 114-121.

Dawson, W. R. & Fisher, C. D. 1969. Responses to temperature by the Spotted Nightjar (*Eurostopodus guttatus*). *Condor* 71: 49-53.

Day, R. H., Knudtson, E. P., Woolington, D. W. & Schulmeister, R. P. 1979. *Caprimulgus indicus, Eurynorhynchus pygmeus, Otus scops* and *Limicola falcinellus* in the Aleutian Islands, Alaska. *Auk* 96: 189-190.

De Bellard-Pietri E. 1953. The Guacharo. *Prem. Congrès Int. De Spéléologie. Extrait des Publ. de Congrès* III: 265-274.

Dee, T. J. 1986. *The Endemic birds of Madagascar.* International Council for Bird Preservation, Cambridge, U.K.

Deignan, H. G. 1945. The Birds of Northern Thailand. *U.S. Natn. Mus. Bull.* 186.

— 1950. Two new races of the Spotted Nightjar *Eurostopodus guttatus* (Vigors and Horsfield). *Emu* 50: 21-23.

— 1951. A new frogmouth from Groote Eylandt, Gulf of Carpentaria. *Emu* 51: 71-73.

Dementiev G. P. & Gladkov N. A. Eds. 1996. *Birds of the Soviet Union* Vol. 1. Israel Program for Scientific Translation.

Demey, R. & Fishpool, L. D. C. 1991. Additions and annotations to the avifauna of Côte D'Ivoire. *Malimbus* 12: 61-86.

Dexter, R. W. 1952. Banding and nesting studies of the Eastern Nighthawk. *Bird-Banding* 23: 109-114.

— 1956. Further banding and nesting studies of the Eastern Nighthawk. *Bird-Banding* 27: 9-16.

— 1961. Further studies on nesting of the Common Nighthawk. *Bird-Banding* 32: 79-85.

Dhondt, A. 1976. Une nidification de l'Engoulevent à collier *Caprimulgus enarratus. Oiseau et R.F.O.* 46: 173-174.

Diamond, J. M. 1967. New subspecies and records of birds from the Karimui Basin, New Guinea. *Amer. Mus. Novit.* 2284.

— 1969. Preliminary results of an ornithological exploration of the north coastal range, New Guinea. *Amer. Mus. Novit.* 2362.

— 1972. Avifauna of the eastern highlands of New Guinea. *Publ. Nuttall Orn. Club* 12.

— 1994. Stinking Birds and Burning Books. *Natural History* 2: 4-12.

— & LeCroy, M. 1979. Birds of Karkar and Bagabag Islands, New Guinea. *Bull. Amer. Mus. Nat. Hist.* 164: 471-531.

Dickerman, R. W. 1975. New subspecies of *Caprimulgus sericocaudatus* from the Amazon River Basin. *Bull. Brit. Orn. Club* 95: 18-19.

— 1981. Geographic variation in the juvenal plumage of the Lesser Nighthawk (*Chordeiles acutipennis*). *Auk* 98: 619-621.

— 1982. Further notes on the juvenal plumage of the Lesser Nighthawk. *Auk* 99: 764.

— 1985. Taxonomy of the Lesser Nighthawks (*Chordeiles acutipennis*) of North and Central America. Pp. 356-359 in P. A. Buckley *et al.*, eds. *Neotropical ornithology.* Ornithological Monograph No. 36, American Ornithologists' Union.

— 1986. Possible breeding of Lesser Nighthawk in Tulsa County, Oklahoma. *Bull. Oklahoma Orn. Soc.* 19: 1-2.

— 1988. A review of the Least Nighthawk *Chordeiles pusillus. Bull. Brit. Orn. Club* 108: 120-125.

— 1990. Geographic variation in the juvenal plumage of the Common Nighthawk (*Chordeiles minor*) in North America. *Auk* 107: 610-613.

— & Phelps, W. H. 1982. An annotated list of the birds of Cerro Urutaní on the border of Estado Bolívar, Venezuela and Territoria Roraima, Brazil. *Amer. Mus. Novit.* 2732.

Dickey, D. R. 1928. A new poorwill from the Colorado river valley. *Condor* 30: 152-153.

— & van Rossem, A. J. 1928. Further descriptions of new birds from El Salvador. *Proc. Biol. Soc. Wash.* 41: 129-132.

Dickinson, E. C., Kennedy, R. S. & Parkes, K. C. 1991. *The Birds of the Philippines.* B.O.U. Check-list No. 12, Tring, U.K.

Dod, A. S. 1979. The Least Pauraque in the Dominican Republic. *Amer. Birds* 33: 826-827.

Dorst, J., Dorst, E. & Plouchard, J.-L. 1975. Notes sur le comportement de l'engoulevent à balanciers. *Oiseau et R.F.O.* 45: 1-6.

Dowsett, R. J. & Dowsett-Lemaire, F. 1991. Flora and fauna of the Kouilou Basin (Congo) and their exploitation. *Tauraco Research Report* No. 4.

— & — 1993. A contribution to the distribution and taxonomy of Afrotropical and Malagasy birds. *Tauraco Research Report* No. 5.

— & — 1997. Flora and fauna of the Odzala National Park, Congo. *Tauraco Research Report* No. 6.

—, Lemaire, F. & Stjernstedt, R. 1977. The voice of the courser *Rhinoptilus cinctus. Bull. Brit. Orn. Club* 97: 73-75.

Dowsett-Lemaire, F. & Dowsett, R. J. 1998. Vocal and other peculiarities of Brown Nightjar *Caprimulgus binotatus. Bull. Afr. Bird Club.* 5: 35-38.

Dutson, G. & Branscombe, J. 1990. Rainforest birds in south-west Ghana. *ICPB Study Report* No. 46, Cambridge, U.K.

Edwards, E. P. 1989. *Fieldguide to the Birds of Mexico.* E. P. Edwards, Virginia.

Eisenmann, E. 1962. Notes on nighthawks of the genus *Chordeiles* in southern Middle America and a description of a new race of *Chordeiles minor* breeding in Panama. *Amer. Mus. Novit.* 2094.

Elgood, J. H. 1972. The breeding season of *Caprimulgus tristigma* in Nigeria. *Bull. Brit. Orn. Club* 92: 33-34.

—, Heigham, J. B., Moore, A. M., Nason, A. M., Sharland, R. E. & Skiner, N. J. 1994. *The Birds of Nigeria.* B.O.U. Check-list No. 4, (2nd edition) Tring, U.K.

Elliot, A. J. 1935. Notes on the White-throated Nightjar. *Emu* 35: 129-132.

Evans, M. & Balmford, A. 1992. Birds in the Ishasha sector of Queen Elizabeth National Park, Uganda. *Scopus* 16: 34-49.

Evans, M. I. 1993. Nest sites of Brown Nightjar *Caprimulgus binotatus* and Collared Nightjar *Caprimulgus enarratus. Malimbus* 15: 49-50.

Evans, R. N. 1967. Nest site movements of a Poorwill. *Wilson Bull.* 79: 453.

Evison, S. & Daly, G. 1995. Do White-throated Nightjars *Eurostopodus mystacalis* (Caprimulgidae) make scrapes for their egg sites? *Austral. Birdwatcher* 16: 165-166.

Fears, O. T. 1975. Observations on the aerial drinking performance of a Poorwill. *Wilson Bull.* 87: 284.

Feduccia, A. 1996. *The Origin and Evolution of Birds.* Yale University Press, New Haven and London.

Ferguson, D. E. 1967. A possible case of egg transport by a Chuck-wills-widow. *Wilson Bull.* 79: 452-453.

ffrench, R. & O'Neill, J. P. 1991. *Guide to the Birds of Trinidad and Tobago.* Christopher Helm, London.

Ficken, R. W., Ficken, M. S. & Hadaway, E. S. 1967. Mobbing of a Chuck-wills-widow by small passerines. *Auk* 84: 266-267.

Finsch, O. 1902. Ueber zwei neue Vogelarten von Java. *Notes Leyden Mus.* 23: 147-152.

Firman, M. C., Brigham, R. M. & Barclay, M. R. 1993. Do free-ranging Common Nighthawks enter torpor? *Condor* 95: 157-162.

Fitzpatrick, J. W. & Willard, D. E. 1982. Twenty-one bird species new to or little known from the republic of Colombia. *Bull. Brit. Orn. Club* 102: 153-158.

Fjeldså, J. & Krabbe, N. 1990. *Birds of the High Andes.* Zoological Museum, University of Copenhagen, and Apollo Books, Svendborg.

Ford, J. 1986. Avian hybridization and allopatry in the region of the Einasleigh uplands and Burdekin-Lynd divide, north-eastern Queensland. *Emu* 86: 87-110.

Forero, M. G., Tella, J. L. & Garciá, L. 1995. Age-related evolution of sexual dimorphism in the Red-necked Nightjar *Caprimulgus ruficollis*. *J. Orn.* 136: 447-451.

— & — 1997. Sexual dimorphism, plumage variability and species determination in nightjars: the need for further examination of the Nechisar Nightjar *Caprimulgus solala*. *Ibis* 139: 407-409.

Foster, M. S. & Johnson, N. K. 1974. Notes on birds of Costa Rica. *Wilson Bull.* 86: 58-63.

Fowle, C. D. & Fowle, A. M. 1954. Observations at a Whip-poor-will's nest. *Can. Field Nat.* 68: 37-39.

Friedman, H. 1945. The genus *Nyctiprogne. Proc. Biol. Soc. Wash.* 58: 117-120.

Fry, C. H. 1969. Structural and functional adaptation to display in the Standard-winged Nightjar *Macrodipteryx longipennis. J. Zool.* 157: 19-24.

— 1988a. Skulls, songs and systematics of African nightjars. *Proc. VI Pan-African Orn. Congr.*: 105-131.

— 1988b. Brown Nightjar. *Malimbus* 10: 222.

—, Keith, S. & Urban, E. K. 1988. *The Birds of Africa*, Vol. 3. Academic Press, London.

Fuller, R. 1995. Territory, organisation and singing activity in the Red-necked Nightjar *Caprimulgus ruficollis*: the search for the optimum survey method. Unpublished.

Garcia, G. A. 1985. Observaciones sobre nidificación y conducta en un Guabairo *Caprimulgus cubanensis cubanensis* (Lawrence) (Aves: Caprimulgiformes, Caprimulgidae). *Ciencias Biológicas* 13: 90-95.

Gargallo, G. 1994. Flight feather moult in the Red-necked Nightjar *Caprimulgus ruficollis. J. Avian Biol.* 25: 119-124.

Garrido, O. H. 1983. A new subspecies of *Caprimulgus cubanensis* (Aves: Caprimulgidae) from the Isle of Pines, Cuba. *Auk* 100: 988-991.

— & Reynard, G. B. 1994. The Greater Antillean Nightjar: is it one species? *El Pitirre* 7(1): 5.

Gauntlett, F. M. 1995. What is the range of Jerdon's Nightjar? *Oriental Bird Club Bull.* 22: 55.

Giai, A. G. 1950. Notas de viajes. *Hornero* 9: 130-131.

Gibbs, D. 1996. Mountain Eared Nightjar in Arfak Mountains, Irian Jaya: range extension and first description of nest and egg. *Dutch Birding* 18: 246-247.

Gibson, R. M. & Bacon, P. J. 1985. Nightjars drinking in flight. *Brit. Birds* 78: 596.

Gilliard, E. T. & LeCroy, M. 1961. Birds of the Victor Emanuel and Hindenburg Mountains, New Guinea. *Bull. Amer. Mus. Nat. Hist.* 123: 1-86.

Ginn, H. B. & Melville, D. S. 1983. *Moult in Birds*. B.T.O. Guide No. 19. Tring.

Ginn, P. J. 1969. Some notes on nightjars and their eggs. *Honeyguide* 60: 24-25.

Giraudoux, P., Degauquier, R., Jones, P. J., Weigel, J. & Isenmann, P. 1988. Avifauna du Niger. *Malimbus* 10: 1-140.

González-García, F. 1993. Avifauna de la Reserva de la Biosfera "Montes Azules", Selva Lacandona, Chiapas, México. *Acta Zool. Mexicana* n.s. 55: 38-39.

Goodman, S. M., Pidgeon, M., Hawkins, A. F. A. & Schulenberg, T. S. 1997. The Birds of southeastern Madagascar. *Fieldiana: Zoology New Series* 87: 1-132.

Gore, M. E. J. 1990. *The Birds of The Gambia*. B.O.U. Checklist No. 3, Tring, U.K.

Gramza, A. F. 1967. Responses of brooding Nighthawks to disturbance stimulus. *Auk* 84: 72-86.

Grant, C. H. B. & Mackworth-Praed, C. W. 1946. Notes on East African birds. *Bull. Brit. Orn. Club* 67: 10-13.

Green, R. H. 1993. *The Birds of Tasmania*. Potoroo Publishing. Launceston.

Greene, E. R. 1943. Cuban Nighthawk breeding on Lower Florida Keys. *Auk* 60: 105.

Greenway, J. C. 1978. Type specimens of birds in the American Museum of Natural History, part 2. *Bull. Amer. Mus. Nat. Hist.* 161: 1-305.

Gribble, F. C. 1983. Nightjars in Britain and Ireland in 1981. *Bird Study* 30: 165-176.

Griffin, D. R. 1953. Acoustic orientation in the Oilbird, *Steatornis. Proc. Natn. Acad. Sci.* 39: 884-893.

Grimes, L. G. 1987. *The Birds of Ghana*. B.O.U. Check-list No. 9, Tring, U.K.

Grinnell, J. 1928. Notes on the systematics of west American birds II. *Condor* 30: 153-154.

Griscom, L. & Greenway, J. C. 1937. Critical notes on new Neotropical birds. *Bull. Mus. Comp. Zool.* 81: 416-437.

Griswold, J. A. 1936. A new subspecies of *Lurocalis* from Panama. *Proc. New England Zool. Club* 15: 101-103.

Groom, M. J. 1992. Sand-colored Nighthawks parasitize the antipredator behavior of three nesting bird species. *Ecology* 73: 785-793.

Hagemeijer, E. G. M. & Blair, M. J. (Eds.) 1997. *The EBCC Atlas of European Breeding Birds: Their Distribution and Abundance*. T. & A. D. Poyser, London.

Hall, B. P. 1960. The ecology and taxonomy of some Angolan birds. *Bull. Brit. Mus. (Nat. Hist.) Zool.* 6: 370-453.

Hamilton, R. D. 1948. The correct name for the "Pauraque". *Auk* 65: 129-130.

Hanmer, D. B. 1996. Measurements and moult of four species of nightjar from Mozambique and Malawi. *Honeyguide* 42(2): 75-95.

Hannecart, F. & Letocart, Y. 1983. *Oiseaux de Nouvelle Calédonie et des Loyautés.* Vol. 2. Editions Cardinalis, Nouméa.

Hardy, J. W., Reynard, G. B. & Coffey, B. B. 1989. *Voices of the New World nightjars and their allies.* ARA Records, Gainesville, Florida.

— & Straneck, R. 1989. The Silky-tailed Nightjar and other Neotropical caprimulgids: unravelling some mysteries. *Condor* 91: 193-197.

Hartert, E. 1892. *Catalogue of the birds in the British Museum.* Vol 16. British Museum, London.

— & Venturi, S. 1909. Notes sur les oiseaux de la République Argentine. *Novit. Zool.* 16: 159-267.

Harvey, W. G. 1976. *Caprimulgus affinis* as an urban species in Indonesia. *Bull. Brit. Orn. Club* 96: 122-123.

Harwin, R. M. 1982. On the breeding biology of the Fiery-necked Nightjar. *Honeyguide* 65: 111-112.

— 1983. Reappraisal of variation in the nightjar *Caprimulgus natalensis* Smith. *Bull. Brit. Orn. Club* 103: 140-144.

— 1984. African nightjar noises. *Honeyguide* 30: 69-71.

— 1994. The Pennant- and Standard-winged Nightjars. *Honeyguide* 40: 26.

Haverschmidt, F. 1948. Observations on *Nyctibius grandis* in Surinam. *Auk* 65: 30-33.

— 1955a. Nightjars on roads at night. *Ibis* 97: 371-372.

— 1955b. Notes on some Surinam breeding birds. *Ardea* 43: 137-144.

— 1958. Notes on *Nyctibius griseus* in Surinam. *Ardea* 46: 144-148.

— & Mees, G. F. 1994. *The Birds of Suriname*. VACO Uitgeversmaatschappij, Paramaribo.

Hayes, F. E. 1995. Definitions for migrant birds. What is a Neotropical migrant? *Auk* 112: 521-523.

— , Scharf, P. A. & Ridgely, R. S. 1994. Austral bird migrants in Paraguay. *Condor* 96: 83-97.

Hellebrekers, W. P. J. & Hoogerwerf, A. 1967. A further contribution to our oological knowledge of the island of Java (Indonesia). *Zool. Ver.* 88: 3-164.

Hellmayr, C. E. 1929. A contribution to the ornithology of northeastern Brazil. *Field Mus. Nat. Hist. Publ. Zool. Ser.* 12, no. 18 (Publ. 255).

— 1932. The birds of Chile. *Field Mus. Nat. Hist. Publ. Zool. Ser.* 19 (Publ. 308).

Helme, N. A. 1996. New departmental records for Dpto. La Paz, Bolivia, from the Pampas del Heath. *Bull. Brit. Orn. Club* 116: 175-177.

Herremans, M. & Stevens, J. 1983. Moult of the Long-tailed Nightjar *Caprimulgus climacurus* Vieillot. *Malimbus* 5: 5-16.

Hickey, M. B. C. 1993. Thermoregulation in free-ranging Whip-poor-wills. *Condor* 95: 744-747.

Hicks, R. 1992. Recent observations in Papua New Guinea. *Muruk* 5: 94-96.

Higgins P. Ed. (in press). *Handbook of Australian, New Zealand and Antarctic Birds* Vol. 4. Oxford University Press, Melbourne.

Hilty, S. L. & Brown, W. L. 1986. *A Guide to the Birds of Colombia*. Princeton University Press, Princeton.

Holden, F. M. 1964. Observations of a Chuck-wills-widow flycatching. *Cornell Lab. Orn. Newsletter* 32: 9.

Hollands, D. 1991. *Birds of the Night*. Reed, Melbourne.

Holmes, D. A. 1996. Sumatra Bird Report. *Kukila* 8: 9-56.

— 1997. Kalimantan Bird Report 2. *Kukila* 9: 141-169.

— & Burton, K. 1987. Recent notes on the avifauna of Kalimantan. *Kukila* 3: 2-32.

Holmes, G. 1981. Field identification of the Marbled Frogmouth. *Austral. Birds* (15)4: 74-75.

Holmes, P. & Wood, H. 1980. *The Reort of the Ornithological Expedition to Sulawesi, 1979*. Ruislip, Middlesex, England; privately printed.

Hoogerwerf, A. 1962. Some ornithological notes on the smaller islands around Java. *Ardea* 50: 180-206.

Howard, R. & Moore, A. 1980. *A Complete Checklist of the Birds of the World*. Second edition. Academic Press, London.

Howell, T. R. & Bartholomew, G. A. 1959. Further experiments on torpidity in the Poorwill. *Condor* 61: 180-185.

Howell, S. N. G., Dowell, B. A., James, D. A., Behrstock, A. & Robbins, C. S. 1992. New and noteworthy bird records from Belize. *Bull. Brit. Orn. Club* 112: 235-244.

— & Webb, S. 1994. Additional information on the birds of Guerrero, Mexico. *Bull. Brit. Orn. Club* 114: 232-243.

— & — 1995. *A Guide to the Birds of Mexico and Northern Central America*. Oxford University Press, Oxford.

Hoyt, S. F. 1953. Incubation and nesting behaviour of the Chuck-will's-widow. *Wilson Bull.* 65: 204-205.

Huber, W. 1923. Two new birds from Nicaragua. *Auk* 40: 300-302.

Humphrey, P. S. & Parkes, K. C. 1959. An approach to the study of molts and plumages. *Auk* 76: 1-31.

Hunter, M. L. 1980. Vocalization during inhalation in a nightjar. *Condor* 82: 101-103.

Hustler, K. & Carson, D. 1996. Status of the Swamp Nightjar in Zimbabwe. *Honeyguide* 42: 96-100.

— & Mitchell, B. 1997. The first breeding record and further comments on the status of the Swamp Nightjar in Zimbabwe. *Honeyguide* 43(3): 147-152.

Ingels, J. 1975. Notes on the Pauraque *Nyctidromus albicollis* in French Guiana. *Bull. Brit. Orn. Club* 95: 115-116.

— 1988. A review of the Neotropical *Caprimulgus* species *maculosus*, *nigrescens* and *whitelyi*. Unpublished.

— & Ribot, J.-H. 1982. Variation in the white markings of the Blackish Nightjar *Caprimulgus nigrescens*. *Bull. Brit. Orn. Club* 102: 119-122.

— & — 1983. The Blackish Nightjar *Caprimulgus nigrescens* in Surinam. *Gerfaut* 73: 127-146.

— , — & de Jong, B. H. J. 1984. Vulnerability of eggs and young of the Blackish Nightjar (*Caprimulgus nigrescens*) in Suriname. *Auk* 101: 388-391.

Ingram, C. 1958. Notes on the habits and structure of the Guacharo *Steatornis caripensis*. *Ibis* 100: 113-119.

Jackson, F. J. 1938. *The Birds of Kenya Colony and the Uganda Protectorate*. Gurney and Jackson, London.

Jackson, H. D. 1970. Further records of *Caprimulgus europaeus plumipes* Przhevalski in southwestern Africa. *Bull. Brit. Orn. Club* 90: 135.

— 1971. Ornithological results of the 1970 National Museums of Rhodesia expedition to Malawi. *Arnoldia Rhod.* 5(12): 1-10.

— 1973. Faunal notes from the Chimanimani Mountains, based on a collection of birds and mammals from the Mucrera River, Moçambique. *Durban Mus. Novit.* 10: 23-42.

— 1975. The distribution of nightjars in Rhodesia (Aves: Caprimulgidae). *Arnoldia Rhod.* 7(19): 1-18.

— 1978. Nightjar distribution in Rhodesia (Aves: Caprimulgidae). *Arnoldia Rhod.* 8(28): 1-29.

— 1984a. Key to the nightjar species of Africa and its islands (Aves: Caprimulgidae). *Smithersia* 4: 1-55.

— 1984b. Capture/recapture data on the nightjars of Ranelia Farm, Zimbabwe. *Safring News* 13(2): 43-50.

— 1984c. Variations in body mass of the Fiery-necked Nightjar (Aves: Caprimulgidae). *Arnoldia Zimbabwe* 9(14): 223-230.

— 1984d. Finding and trapping nightjars. *Bokmakierie* 36: 86-89.

— 1985a. Aspects of the breeding biology of the Fiery-necked Nightjar. *Ostrich* 56: 263-276.

— 1985b. Mouth size in the *Macrodipteryx* and other African nightjars. *Bull. Brit. Orn. Club* 105: 51-54.

— 1985c. Commentary and observations on the alleged transportation of eggs and young by caprimulgids. *Wilson Bull.* 97: 381-385.

— 1986. Identifying nightjars in southern Africa. *Bokmakierie* 38: 41-44.

— 1987. Nightjar notes from the Katombora and Kazungula development areas of Zimbabwe. *Ostrich* 58: 141-143.

— 1993. The English names of the Afrotropical nightjars (Caprimulgidae). *Ostrich* 64: 148-159.

Jaeger, E. C. 1948. Does the Poorwill hibernate? *Condor* 50: 45-46.

— 1949. Further observations on the hibernation of the Poorwill. *Condor* 51: 105-109.

Jany, E. 1956. Zur Verbreitung von *Caprimulgus pulchellus* Salvadori. *J. Orn.* 97: 239.

Jenkinson, M. A. & Mengel, R. M. 1970. Ingestion of stones by goatsuckers (Caprimulgidae). *Condor* 72: 236-237.

Jennings, M. C. 1995. *An Interim Atlas of the Breeding Birds of Arabia*. NCWCD, Saudi Arabia.

Johnson, A. W. 1967. *The Birds of Chile and Adjacent Regions of Argentina, Bolivia and Peru*. Vol 2. Platt Establicimientos Gráficos, Buenos Aires.

Johnston, R. F. & Hardy, J. W. 1959. The Ridgway's Whippoor-will and its associated avifauna in southwestern New Mexico. *Condor* 61: 206-209.

Junge, G. C. A. 1936. Fauna simalurensis – Aves. *Temminckia* 1: 1-74.

Kannan, R. 1993. Recent sightings of the Ceylon Frogmouth in India. *Oriental Bird Club Bull.* 17: 37-38.

— 1994. Are frogmouths 'living flytraps'? *Oriental Bird Club Bull.* 19: 57.

Kenyon, P. E. (in press). A study of upland Nightjars on Nercwys Mountain. *Welsh Birds*.

Kepler, C. B. & Kepler, A. K. 1973. The distribution and ecology of the Puerto Rican Nightjar, an endangered species. *Living Bird* 11: 207-299.

Kiff, L. F. 1975. Notes on southwestern Costa Rican birds. *Condor* 77: 101-103.

— , Marin, M. A., Sibley, F. C., Matheus, J. C. & Schmitt, N. J. 1989. Notes on some nests and eggs of some Ecuadorian birds. *Bull. Brit. Orn. Club* 109: 25-31.

Kilgore, D. L. Jr., Bernstein, M. H. & Hudson, D. M. 1976. Brain temperatures in birds. *J. Comp. Physiol.* B 110: 209-215.

Kilham, L. 1957. Egg carrying by the Whip-poor-will. *Wilson Bull.* 69: 113.

King, B. 1994. A possible sighting of Diabolical Eared-Nightjar *Eurostopodus diabolicus* in Sulawesi. *Oriental Bird Club Bull.* 19: 56-57.

Kirwan, G. M., Martuscelli, P., Silveira, L. F. & Williams, R. S. R. (in prep). Further records of the Sickle-winged Nightjar *Eleotreptus anomalus* in south-east Brazil.

Kissner, K. J. & Brigham, R. M. 1993. Evidence for the use of torpor by incubating and brooding Common Poorwills *Phalaenoptilus nuttallii*. *Ornis Scand.* 24: 333-334.

Komar, O. & Rodríguez, F. 1997. Nesting of Lesser Nighthawks on beaches in El Salvador. *Wilson Bull.* 109: 167-168.

Konishi, M. & Knudsen, E. I. 1979. The Oilbird: hearing and echolocation. *Science* 204: 425-427.

Krabbe, N. 1992. Notes on distribution and natural history of some poorly known Ecuadorian birds. *Bull. Brit. Orn. Club* 112: 169-174.

— , Poulsen, B. O., Frølander, A. & Barahona, O. R. 1997. Range extensions of cloud forest birds from the high Andes of Ecuador: new sites for rare or little-recorded species. *Bull. Brit. Orn. Club* 117 (4): 248-256.

Lack, D. 1929. Some diurnal observations of the Nightjar. *London Naturalist*: 47-55.

— 1930a. Double-brooding of the Nightjar. *Brit. Birds* 23: 242-244.

— 1930b. A further note on double-brooding of the Nightjar. *Brit. Birds* 24: 130-131.

— 1932. Some breeding habits of the European Nightjar. *Ibis* 74: 266-284.

— 1957. Notes on nesting nightjars. *Brit. Birds* 50: 273-277.

Lambert, F. R. 1994. Notes on the avifauna of Bacan, Kasiruta and Obi, North Moluccas. *Kukila* 7: 1-9.

Lambert, F. & Yong, D. 1989. Some recent bird observations from Halmahera. *Kukila* 4: 30-33.

Land, H. C. 1970. *Birds of Guatemala*. Livingston Publishing Company, Wynnewood, Pennsylvania.

— & Schultz, W. L. 1963. A proposed subspecies of the Great Potoo *Nyctibius grandis* (Gmelin). *Auk* 80: 195-196.

Langley, C. H. 1984. Observations on two nests of the Fiery-necked Nightjar. *Ostrich* 55: 1-4.

Langrand, O. 1990. *Guide to the Birds of Madagascar*. Yale University Press, New Haven and London.

Langridge, H. P. 1996. Probable Common Poorwill *Phalaenoptilus nuttallii* at Dry Tortugas National Park. *Florida Field Nat.* 24: 16-17.

Lasiewski, R. C. & Bartholomew, G. A. 1966. Evaporative cooling in the Poorwill and the Tawny Frogmouth. *Condor* 68: 253-262.

— & Dawson, W. R. 1964. Physiological responses to temperature in the Common Nighthawk. *Condor* 66: 477-490.

— , — & Bartholomew, G. A. 1970. Temperature regulation in Little Papuan Frogmouth *Podargus ocellatus*. *Condor* 72: 332-338.

Latta, S. C. & Baltz, M. E. 1997. *Lesser Nighthawk (Chordeiles acutipennis)*. In *The Birds of North America*, No. 314 (A. Poole & F. Gill eds.). The Academy of Natural Sciences, Philadelphia, and The American Ornithologists' Union, Washington, D.C.

Layard, E. L. & Layard, E. L. C. 1881. Notes on the avifauna of New Caledonia and the New Hebrides. *Ibis* (4)5: 132-139.

Legge, V. 1880. *A History of the Birds of Ceylon*. Vol. 2. Reissued in 1983. Tisara Prakasakayo, Dehiwala.

Lencioni-Neto, F. 1994. Une nouvelle espèce de *Chordeiles* (Aves, Caprimulgidae) de Bahia (Brazil). *Alauda* 62: 241-245.

Lewis, A. & Pomeroy, D. 1989. *A Bird Atlas of Kenya*. A. A. Balkema, Rotterdam.

Ligon, J. D. 1970. Still more responses of the Poorwill to low temperatures. *Condor* 72: 496-498.

Lincoln, R. J. & Boxshall, G. A. 1987. *The Cambridge Illustrated Dictionary of Natural History*. Cambridge University Press, Cambridge.

Lönnberg, E. 1929. A new nightjar from Haiti. *Arkiv Zool.* 20B(6): 1-3.

Louette, M. 1990a. A Brown Nightjar (*Caprimulgus binotatus*) nestling from Liberia. *Malimbus* 11: 148-149.

— 1990b. The nightjars of Zaire. *Bull. Brit. Orn. Club* 110: 71-77.

— 1990c. A new species of nightjar from Zaire. *Ibis* 132: 349-353.

Lowen, J. C., Bartrina, L., Brooks, T. M., Clay, R. P. & Tobias, J. A. 1996a. Project Yacutinga '95: bird surveys and conservation priorities in eastern Paraguay. *Cotinga* 5: 14-17.

—, —, Clay, R. P. & Tobias, J. A. 1996b. Biological surveys and conservation priorities in eastern Paraguay. CSB Conservation Publications, Cambridge, U.K.

—, Clay, R. P., Barnett, J. M., Madroño, N. A., Pearman, M., Lanús, B. L., Tobias, J. A., Liley, D. C., Brooks, T. M., Esquivel, E. Z. & Reid, J. M. 1997. New and noteworthy observations on the Paraguayan avifauna. *Bull. Brit. Orn. Club* 117 (4): 275-293.

López Lanús, B., Clay, R. P. & Lowen, J. C. (in prep). A new plumage of the White-winged Nightjar *Caprimulgus candicans* (Aves: Caprimulgidae).

Lowther, E. H. N. 1939. Notes on some Indian birds. *J. Bombay Nat. Hist. Soc.* 39: 543-551.

— 1949. *A Bird Photographer in India*. Oxford University Press, Oxford.

Lydekker, R. 1891. *Catalogue of Fossil Birds in the British Museum (Natural History)*. Trustees of the British Museum, London.

MacKinnon, J. 1988. *Field Guide to the Birds of Java and Bali*. Gadjah Mada University Press, Yogyakarta.

— & Phillipps, K. 1993. *A Field Guide to the Birds of Borneo, Sumatra, Java and Bali*. Oxford University Press, Oxford.

Mackworth-Praed, C. W. & Grant, C. H. B. 1952. *Birds of Eastern and North Eastern Africa*. Vol. 1. Longman, London and New York.

— & — 1962. *Birds of the Southern Third of Africa*. Vol. 1. Longman, London and New York.

— & — 1970. *Birds of West Central and Western Africa*. Vol. 1. Longman, London and New York.

Maclean, G. L. 1985. *Roberts' Birds of Southern Africa*. John Voelcker Bird Book Fund, Cape Town.

Madoc, G.C. 1936. On the nidification of some Malayan Birds. *Bull. Raffles Mus.* 12: 124-133.

Madroño N., A. & Esquivel, E. Z. 1997. Noteworthy records and range extensions of some birds from the Reserva Natural del Bosque Mbaracayú (Mbaracayú Forest Nature Reserve), Departmento de Canindeyú, Paraguay. *Bull. Brit. Orn. Club* 117: 166-176.

Mann, C. 1991. Sunda Frogmouth *Batrachostomus cornutus* carrying its young. *Forktail* 6: 77-78.

— (in prep). *The Birds of Borneo*. B.O.U. Check-list, Tring, U.K.

Marchant, S. 1987. Nesting of the White-throated Nightjar *Caprimulgus mystacalis*. *Austral. Birds* 21: 44-50.

Mariaux, J. & Braun, M. J. 1996. A molecular phylogenetic survey of the nightjars and allies (Caprimulgiformes) with special emphasis on the potoos (Nyctibiidae). *Molecular Phylogenetics and Evolution* 6: 228-244.

Marin, M. A. & Schmitt, N. J. 1991. Nests and eggs of some Costa Rican birds. *Wilson Bull.* 103: 506-509.

—, Kiff, L. F. & Luis Pena, G. 1989. Notes on Chilean birds with descriptions of two new subspecies. *Bull. Brit. Orn. Club* 109: 66-82.

van Marle, J. G. & Voous, K. H. 1988. *The Birds of Sumatra*. B.O.U. Check-list No. 10, Tring, U.K.

Marshall, J. T. 1955. Hibernation in captive goatsuckers. *Condor* 57: 129-134.

— 1978. *Systematics of Smaller Asian Nightbirds Based on Voice*. Ornithological Monograph 25, American Ornithologists' Union.

Martin, G. 1990. *Birds by Night*. T. and A. D. Poyser, Calton.

Masterson, A. N. B. 1992. Freckled Nightjars perching in trees. *Honeyguide* 38: 126-127.

— 1994. Fire and the Fiery-necked Nightjar. *Honeyguide* 40: 179-180.

Mayr, E. 1937. Birds of the Whitney Expedition, 35: notes on New Guinea birds. *Amer. Mus. Novit.* 939.

— 1941. Birds of the Whitney Expedition, 47: a new nightjar from New Caledonia. *Amer. Mus. Novit.* 1152.

— 1944. The birds of Timor and Sumba. *Bull. Amer. Mus. Nat. Hist.* 83: 129-194.

— & Rand, A. L. 1935. Results of the Archbold Expedition, No. 6: twenty-four apparently undescribed birds from New Guinea and the D'Entrecasteaux Archipelago. *Amer. Mus. Novit.* 814.

— & — 1936. Neue Unterarten von Vögeln aus Neu-Guinea. *Mitt. Zool. Mus. Berlin* 21: 241-248.

— & — 1937. Results of the Archbold Expeditions, 14: birds of the 1933-1934 Papuan Expedition. *Bull. Amer. Mus. Nat. Hist.* 73: 1-248.

Mazar Barnett, J. & Pearman, M. (in press). *Annotated Checklist of the Birds of Argentina*. Worldwide Publications, Belper, U.K.

McAllan, I. A. W. 1995. Southern record of the Plumed Frogmouth *Podargus ocellatus plumiferus*. *Austral. Birdwatcher* 16: 43-45.

McAtee, W. L. 1948. Confusion of eastern Caprimulgidae. *Auk* 65: 128-129.

McGowan, K. J. & Woolfenden, G. E. 1986. Aerial rain bathing by Common Nighthawks. *Wilson Bull.* 98: 612-613.

McLean, J. A. 1983. Notes on the nesting of the Large-tailed Nightjar *Caprimulgus macrurus*. *Sunbird* 13: 72-73.

Medway, Lord & Wells, D. R. 1976. *The Birds of the Malay Peninsula*. Vol. 5. H. F. & G. Witherby, London.

Mees, G. F. 1977. Geographical variation of *Caprimulgus macrurus* (Aves: Caprimulgidae). *Zool. Verh.* 155.

— 1982. Birds from the lowlands of southern New Guinea (Merauke and Koembe). *Zool. Verh.* 191.

— 1985. *Caprimulgus macrurus* Horsfield and related forms, a re-evaluation (Aves: Caprimulgidae). *Pr. K. Ned. Akad. Wet.* 88: 419-428.

Meggs, T. 1993. The distribution, abundance and habitat preference of the Marbled Frogmouth in the Northern Rivers region. Thesis, Southern Cross University (unpublished).

Meller, N. H. 1954. A winter active Poorwill. *Condor* 57: 120.

Mengel, R. M. 1976. Rapid tail moult and temporarily impaired flight in the Chuck-will's-widow. *Wilson Bull.* 88: 351-353.

— & Jenkinson, M. A. 1971. Vocalisations of the Chuck-will's-widow and some related behaviour. *Living Bird* 10: 171-184.

—, Sharpe, R. S. & Woolfenden, G. E. 1972. Wing clapping in territorial and courtship behaviour of Chuckwills-widow and Poorwill. *Auk* 89: 440-444.

Meyer de Schauensee, R. 1933. A new race of *Caprimulgus asiaticus* from north Siam. *Proc. Acad. Nat. Sci. Philadelphia* 85: 373.

— 1970. *A Guide to the Birds of South America.* Livingston Publishing Company, Wynnewood, Pennsylvania.

— 1984. *The Birds of China.* Oxford University Press, Oxford.

— & Phelps, W. H. 1978. *A Guide to the Birds of Venezuela.* Princeton University Press, Princeton.

Miller, A. H. 1925. The boom flight of the Pacific Nighthawk. *Condor* 27: 141-143.

— 1937. The nuptial flight of the Texas Nighthawk. *Condor* 39: 42-43.

— 1948. A new subspecies of Eared-Poorwill from Guerrero, Mexico. *Condor* 50: 224-225.

— 1950. Temperatures of Poorwills in the summer season. *Condor* 52: 41-42.

— 1959. A new race of Nighthawk from the Upper Magdalena Valley of Colombia. *Proc. Biol. Soc. Wash.* 72: 155-158.

Miller, W. de W. & Griscom, L. 1925. Descriptions of new birds from Nicaragua. *Amer. Mus. Novit.* 159.

Mills, A. M. 1986. Influence of moonlight on behaviour of goatsuckers (Caprimulgidae). *Auk* 103: 370-378.

— 1987. Wooing Whip-poor-wills. *Canadian Geographic* 107(2): 32-37.

Mitchell, P. 1994. Bird reports 107 (Pt. 1). *Bird Observer* 746: 15.

Monroe, B. L. 1968. *A Distributional Survey of the Birds of Honduras.* Ornithological Monograph 7, American Ornithologists' Union.

Morel, G. J. & Morel, M.-Y. 1990. *Les Oiseaux de Sénégambie.* Editions de L'ORSTOM, Paris.

Morgan, F. J. 1960. White-throated Nightjar nesting at Glasshouse Mountains, Queensland. *Austral. Birdwatcher* 1(4): 117-118.

Morris, A., Burgess, D., Fuller, R. J., Evans, A. D. & Smith, K. W. 1994. The status and distribution of Nightjars *Caprimulgus europaeus* in Britain in 1992. A report to the British Trust for Ornithology.

Mourer-Chauviré, C. 1980. The Archaeotrogonidae of the Eocene and Oligocene phosphorites du Quercy (France). *Contrib. Sci. Nat. Hist. Mus. Los Angeles County* 330: 17-31.

— 1988. Le gisement du Bretou (phosphorites du Quercy, Tarn-et-Garonne, France) et sa faune de vertébrés de l'Eocène supérieur. II Oiseaux. *Palaeontographica* A, 205: 34-36.

— 1989. Les Caprimulgiformes et les Coraciiformes de l'Eocène de l'Oligocène des phosphorites du Quercy et description de deux genres nouveaux de Podargidae et Nyctibiidae. *Acta XIX Congress Inter. Orn.:* 2047-2055.

— 1995. Dynamics of the avifauna during the Paleogene and the early Neogene of France. Settling of the recent fauna. *Acta. Zool. Cracov.* 38: 325-342.

Narosky, T. & Yzurieta, D. 1987. *Birds of Argentina and Uruguay: a field guide.* Vasque Mazzini Editores, Buenos Aires.

Nash, S. V. & Nash, A. D. 1985. A checklist of the forest and forest edge birds of the Padang-Sugihan Wildlife Reserve, South Sumatra. *Kukila* 2(3): 51-63.

Newman, K. 1983. *Newman's Birds of Southern Africa.* Macmillan, Johannesburg.

Newton, S. F. 1992. Ornithological research at the National Wildlife Research Centre, Taif, Saudi Arabia. *OSME Bull.* 29: 1-5.

Nikolaus, G. 1989. Birds of South Sudan. *Scopus Special Supplement* No. 3: 1-124.

Noble, R. E. 1988. Singing in the Puerto Rican Nightjar. *Carib. J. Sci.* 24: 82-83.

—, Vilella, F. J. & Zwank, P. J. 1986a. Status of the endangered Puerto Rican Nightjar in 1985. *Carib. J. Sci.* 22: 137-143.

—, — & — 1986b. Research note. Apuntes sobre el anidamiento del Guabairo. *Carib. J. Sci.* 22: 223.

Nores, M. & Yzurieta, D. 1984. Consideraciones acerca de la taxonomía y distribución de *Caprimulgus sericocaudatus saltarius* Olrog 1979. *Assoc. Orn. del Plata V Reunión de Orn.* 16.

North, M. E. W. 1963. An investigation of the songs of the nightjars of East, Central and South Africa. Unpublished.

Oates, E. W. (ed.) 1890. *Hume's Nests and Eggs of Indian Birds.* Vol. 3. R. H. Porter, London.

Oberholser, H. C. 1914. A monograph of the genus *Chordeiles* Swainson, type of a new family of goatsuckers. *U.S. Natn. Mus. Bull.* 86.

Ogilvie-Grant, W. R. 1894. The birds of the Philippine Islands. *Ibis* (6)6: 501-522.

— 1908. New species obtained by the Ruwenzori expedition. *Bull. Brit. Orn. Club* 23: 94.

Olmos, F. 1993. Birds of Serra da Capivara National Park in the 'caatinga' of north-eastern Brazil. *Bird Conserv. Internatn.* 3: 21-36.

— & Rodrigues, M. 1990. Courtship display of the Long-trained Nightjar *Macropsalis creagra. Bull. Brit. Orn. Club* 110: 203-205.

Olrog, C. C. 1962. Notas ornitológicas sobre la colección del Instituto Miguel Lilloana. *Acta. Zool. Lilloana* 28: 111-120.

— 1975. *Uropsalis lyra* nueva para la fauna Argentina (Aves: Caprimulgidae). *Neotropica* 21(66): 147-148.

— 1978. Nueva lista de la avifauna Argentina. *Opera Lilloana* 27: 5-324.

— 1979. Notas ornitológicas XI. Sobre la colección del Instituto Miguel Lillo. *Acta Zool. Lilloana* 33(2): 1-7.

Olson, J. & Hayes, G. 1994. White-throated Nightjar: a breeding record for the Australian Capital Territory. *Austral. Birdwatcher* 15(5): 229.

Olson, S. L. 1985. A new species of *Siphonorhis* from quaternary cave deposits in Cuba (Aves: Caprimulgidae). *Proc. Biol. Soc. Wash.* 98: 526-532.

— 1987. An early eocene Oilbird from the Green River formation of Wyoming (Caprimulgiformes: Steatornithidae). *Doc. Lab. Géol. Lyon* 99: 57-69.

—, Balouet, J. C. & Fisher, C. T. 1987. The owlet-nightjar of New Caledonia *Aegotheles savesi*, with comments on the systematics of the Aegothelidae. *Gerfaut* 77: 341-352.

— & Steadman, D. W. 1977. A new genus of flightless

ibis (Threskiornithidae) and other fossil birds from cave deposits in Jamaica. *Proc. Biol. Soc. Wash.* 90: 447-457.

Orians, G. H. & Paulson, D. R. 1969. Notes on Costa Rican birds. *Condor* 71: 426-431.

Orr, R. T. 1948. Nesting behaviour of the Poorwill. *Auk* 65: 46-54.

Ovngi, J. 1995. Breeding records. *Kenyan Birds* 4: 23-26.

Parker, R. H. & Benson, C. W. 1971. Variation in *Caprimulgus tristigma* Rüppell especially in West Africa. *Bull. Brit. Orn. Club* 91: 113-116, 117-119.

Parker, T. A., Castillo U., A., Gell-Mann, M. & Rocha O., O. 1991. Records of new and unusual birds from northern Bolivia. *Bull. Brit. Orn. Club* 111: 120-138.

— , Foster, R. B., Emmons, L. H., Freed, P., Forsyth, A. B., Hoffman, B. & Gill, B. D. 1993. *A biological assessment of the Kanuku Mountain region of southwestern Guyana.* Conservation International (RAP Working Papers 5), Washington, D.C.

— & Rowlett, R. A. 1984. Some noteworthy records of birds from Bolivia. *Bull. Brit. Orn. Club* 104: 110-113.

Parrott, S. & Andrew, P. 1996. An annotated checklist of the birds of Way Kambas National Park, Sumatra. *Kukila* 8: 57-85.

Paynter, R. A. 1955. The ornithogeography of the Yucatán Peninsula. *Peabody Mus. Nat. Hist. Bull.* 9: 3-347.

Pearce-Higgins, J., Thompson, A., Hall, S., Kealy, I. & Kemp, P. 1994. A survey of mammals and birds in the Parque Nacional Noel Kempff Mercado. Nottingham University Bolivia Project 1994.

Pearman, M. & Abadie, E. I. 1995. Field identification, ecology and status of the Sickle-winged Nightjar *Eleothreptus anomalus*. *Cotinga* 3: 12-14.

— & — in press. Mesopotamia grassland and wetland survey: conservation of threatened birds and habitat in northwestern Argentina 1991-1993. Final Report.

Peiponen, V. A. 1965. On hypothermia and torpidity in the Nightjar (*Caprimulgus europaeus* L.). *Ann. Acad. Sci. Fenn.* A. IV. 87: 3-15.

— 1966. The diurnal heterothermy of the Nightjar (*Caprimulgus europaeus* L.). *Ann. Acad. Sci. Fenn.* A. IV. 101: 3-35.

— 1970. Body temperature fluctuations in the Nightjar (*Caprimulgus e. europaeus* L.) in light conditions of southern Finland. *Ann. Zool. Fennici* 7: 239-250.

— & Bosley, A. 1964. Torpidity in a captive European Nightjar (*Caprimulgus europaeus* L.). *Ornis Fennica* 41: 40-42.

Penry, H. 1994. *Bird Atlas of Botswana.* University of Natal Press, Pietermaritzburg.

Pereyra, J. A. 1939. Miscelanea ornitológica. *Hornero* 7: 234-243.

— 1950. Avifauna Argentina. *Hornero* 9: 178-241.

Pérez del Val, J., Castroviejo, J. & Purroy, F. J. 1997. Species rejected from and added to the avifauna of Bioko Island (Equatorial Guinea). *Malimbus* 19: 19-31.

Perry, D. R. 1979. The Great Potoo in Costa Rica. *Condor* 81: 320-321.

Peters, J. L. 1940. *Check-list of Birds of the World.* Vol. 4. Museum of Comparative Zoology, Cambridge, Massachusetts.

— & Loveridge, A. 1936. Scientific results of an expedi-

tion to rainforest regions in eastern Africa. *Bull. Mus. Comp. Zool.* 79: 129-205.

Pettet, A. 1982. Nightjar taking water in flight. *Brit. Birds* 75: 37.

Phelps, W. H. 1938. The geographical status of the birds collected at Mount Roraima. *Bol. Soc. Venez. Cien. Nat.* 36: 83-95.

— & Phelps, W. H. 1952. Nine new subspecies of birds from Venezuela. *Proc. Biol. Soc. Wash.* 65: 39-54.

Phillips, W. W. A. 1947. A note on the nesting of the Ceylon Frogmouth, *Batrachostomus moniliger* Blyth. *Ibis* 89: 515-516.

Phillipps, S. 1981-1982. Bird notes from Sabah 1981-1982. *Sabah Soc. J.* 7: 153-154.

Pickwell, G. & Smith, E. 1938. The Texas Nighthawk in its summer home. *Condor* 40: 193-215.

Pierson, J. 1986. Notes on the vocalisations of the Yucatan Poorwill (*Nyctiphrynus yucatanicus*) and Tawny-collared Nightjar (*Caprimulgus salvini*). *MBA 'Bulletin Board'* 1 (86-1): 3-4.

Pinchon, R. 1963. Une sous-espèce nouvelle d'engoulevent à la Martinique. *Oiseau et R.F.O.* 33: 107-110.

Pinto, A. A. da Rosa 1983. *Ornitologia de Angola.* Vol. 1 (non-passerines). Instituto de Investigação Científica Tropical, Lisboa.

Pinto, O. M. de O. & de Camargo, E. A. 1952. Nova contribuição à ornitologia do Rio das Mortes. *Pap. Avuls. Dep. Zool. São Paulo* 10(11): 213-234.

Porter, R. & Martins, R. 1993. OSME in Southern Yemen and Socotra. *OSME Bull.* 31: 1-4.

Poulin, R. G., Grindal, S. D. & Brigham, R. M. 1996. Common Nighthawk (*Chordeiles minor*). *The Birds of North America* No. 213 (A. Poole and F. Gill, eds.). Academy of Natural Sciences, Philadelphia, and American Ornithologists' Union, Washington D.C.

Priest, C. D. 1934. *The Birds of Southern Rhodesia.* Vol. 2. William Clowes, London and Beccles.

Rana, B. D. 1988. A note on winter food of Indian Nightjar *Caprimulgus asiaticus* under desert environment. *Pavo* 26: 67-68.

Rand, A. L. 1936. Distribution and habits of Madagascar birds. *Bull. Amer. Mus. Nat. Hist.* 72: 142-499.

— & Gilliard, E. T. 1967. *The Handbook of New Guinean birds.* Weidenfeld and Nicolson, London.

Rangel-Salazar, J. L. & Vega-Rivera, J. H. 1989. Two new records of birds for southern Mexico. *Condor* 91: 214-215.

— , Tercero, R. & Enriquez, P. L. 1991. The Great Potoo (*Nyctibius grandis*) as a probable resident in southern Mexico. *Ornitología Neotropical* 2: 38-39.

Rajathurai, S. 1996. The birds of Batam and Bintan Islands, Riau Archipelago. *Kukila* 8: 86-113.

Rasmussen, J. F., Rahbek, C., Poulsen, B. O., Poulsen, M. K. & Bloch, H. 1996. Distributional records and natural history notes on threatened and little known birds of southern Ecuador. *Bull. Brit. Orn. Club* 116: 26-46.

Ravenscroft, N. O. M. 1989. The status and habitat of the Nightjar *Caprimulgus europaeus* in coastal Suffolk. *Bird Study* 36: 161-169.

Raynor, G. S. 1941. The nesting habits of the Whip-poorwill. *Bird Banding* 12: 98-104.

Reynard, G. B. 1962. Rediscovery of the Puerto Rican

Whip-poor-will. *Living Bird* 1: 51-59.

Ribon, R. 1995. Nova subspécie de *Caprimulgus* (Linnaeus) (Aves, Caprimulgidae) do Espírito Santo, Brasil. *Revta. Bras. Zool.* 12: 333-337.

Rich, P. V. & McEvey, A. 1977. A new owlet-nightjar from the early to mid-Miocene of eastern New South Wales. *Mem. Nat. Mus. Victoria* 38: 247-253.

— & Scarlett, R. J. 1977. Another look at *Megaegotheles*, a large owlet-nightjar from New Zealand. *Emu* 77: 1-8.

Ridgely, R. S. & Gwynne, J. A. 1989. *A Field Guide to the Birds of Panama (with Costa Rica, Nicaragua and Honduras)*. Second edition. Princeton University Press, Princeton.

Ripley, S. D. 1945. A new race of nightjar from Ceylon. *Bull. Brit. Orn. Club* 65: 40-41.

— 1964. A systematic and ecological study of New Guinea birds. *Peabody Mus. Nat. Hist. Bull.* 19.

— & Beehler, B. M. 1987. New evidence for sympatry in the sibling species *Caprimulgus atripennis* Jerdon and *Caprimulgus macrurus* Horsfield. *Bull. Brit. Orn. Club* 107: 47-49.

— & Rabor, D. S. 1958. Notes on a collection of birds from Mindoro Island, Philippines. *Peabody Mus. Nat. Hist. Bull.* 13: 1-83.

Robbins, M. B. & Parker, T. A. 1997. Voice and taxonomy of *Caprimulgus (rufus) otiosus* (Caprimulgidae), with a reevaluation of *Caprimulgus rufus* subspecies. Pp.601-607 in J. V. Remsen, ed. *Studies in Neotropical Ornithology Honoring Ted Parker*. Ornithological Monographs no. 48, American Ornithologists' Union, Washington, D.C.

— & Ridgely, R. S. 1992. Taxonomy and natural history of *Nytiphrynus rosenbergi* (Caprimulgidae). *Condor* 94: 984-987.

—, — & Cardiff, S. W. 1994. Voice, plumage and natural history of Anthony's Nightjar (*Caprimulgus anthonyi*). *Condor* 96: 224-228.

Roberts, G. J. & Ingram, G. J. 1978. Marbled Frogmouth in the Conondale Range, south-eastern Queensland. *Emu* 78: 41-42.

Roberts, T. J. 1991. *The Birds of Pakistan*. Vol. 1. Oxford University Press, Oxford.

Robertson, I. 1992. New information on birds in Cameroon. *Bull. Brit. Orn. Club* 112: 36-42.

Robin, P. 1969. L'engoulevent du Sahara (*Caprimulgus aegyptius saharae*) dans le sud Marocain. *Oiseau et R.F.O.* 39: 1-7.

Robinson, L. N. & Whitbourn, E. J. 1961. The nesting of two species of nightjars. *Austral. Birdwatcher* 1(5): 130-135.

Roca, R. L. 1994. Oilbirds of Venezuela: ecology and conservation. *Publ. Nutt. Orn. Club* 24.

Rockingham-Gill, D. V. 1982. Nightjars drinking. *Honeyguide* 111/112: 66.

Rodewald, P. G., Dejaifve, P. A. & Green, A. A. 1994. The birds of Korup National Park and Korup Project Area, Southwest Province, Cameroon. *Bird Conserv. Internatn.* 4: 1-68.

Rodriguez-Teijeiro, J. D., Cordero-Tapia, P. J., Gallego, S. & Salaet, M. A. 1986. Dark non orientation in some Apodidae and Caprimulgidae of the Palearctic region. *Orientation in space* (G. Beugnon, ed.) Privat I.E.C. Toulouse: 29-32.

Rohwer, S. A. 1971. Molt and the annual cycle of the Chuck-will's-widow *Caprimulgus carolinensis*. *Auk* 88: 485-519.

Rose, A. B. 1976. Mass of wild birds of the order Caprimulgiformes. *Austral. Bird Bander* 14: 50-51.

— 1997. Notes on the diet of nightjars in New South Wales. *Austral. Bird Watcher* 17: 105-106.

— & Eldridge, R. H. 1997. Diet of the Tawny Frogmouth *Podargus strigoides* in eastern New South Wales. *Austral. Bird Watcher* 17: 25-33.

Roth, P. 1985. Breeding biology of the Blackish Nightjar *Caprimulgus nigrescens* in western Brazil. *Gerfaut* 75: 253-264.

Rothschild, N. C. & Wollaston, F. R. 1902. Birds from Shendi, Sudan. *Ibis* 2 (5): 1-33.

Rowland, P. 1995a. A specimen of Mountain Nightjar *Eurostopodus archboldi* from the Hindenburg Ranges. *Muruk* 7: 41.

— 1995b. Birds collected in southern Sandaun Province, Papua New Guinea. *Muruk* 7: 60-69.

Rowland, R. 1994. Mountain Nightjar *Eurostopodus archboldi* breeding at Ambua. *Muruk* 6: 11.

Rozendaal, F. 1990. Vocalisations and taxonomic status of *Caprimulgus celebensis*. *Dutch Birding* 12: 79-81.

Rust, H. J. 1947. Migration and nesting of nighthawks in northern Idaho. *Condor* 49: 177-188.

Ryan, P. G. 1989. Common Nighthawk *Chordeiles minor* and new records of seabirds from Tristan da Cunha and Gough Islands. *Bull. Brit. Orn. Club* 109: 147-149.

Safford, R. J., Duckworth, J. W., Evans, M. I., Telfer, M. G., Timmins, R. J. & Zewdie, C. 1993. The birds of Nechisar National Park, Ethiopia. *Scopus* 16: 61-80.

—, Ash, J. S., Duckworth, J. W., Telfer, M. G. & Zewdie, C. 1995. A new species of nightjar from Ethiopia. *Ibis* 137: 301-307.

Salaman, P. (ed.) 1994. Surveys and conservation of biodiversity in the Chocó, south-west Colombia. *BirdLife Study Report* No. 61, Cambridge, U.K.

Salewski, V. 1997. Notes on some bird species from Comoé National Park, Ivory Coast. *Malimbus* 19: 61-67.

Salvin, O. 1885. A list of the birds obtained by Mr Henry Whitely in British Guiana. *Ibis* 3: 195-219.

Santos Morães, V. D. & Krul, R. 1995. Ocorrência e nidificação de *Macropsalis creagra* na Ilha do Mel, Paraná, Brasil (Caprimulgiformes: Caprimulgidae). *Ararajuba* 3: 79-80.

Scarlett, R. J. 1968. An owlet-nightjar from New Zealand. *Notornis* 15: 254-266.

Schaldach, W. J. & Phillips, A. R. 1961. The Eared Poorwill. *Auk* 78: 567-572.

Schlegel, R. 1967. Die Ernährung des Ziegenmelkers *Caprimulgus europaeus*, seine wirtschaftliche Bedeutung und seine Siedlungsdichte in einem oberlausitzer Kiefernrevier. *Beitr. Vogelk.* 13: 145-190.

— 1969. *Der Ziegenmelker (Caprimulgus europaeus L.)*. Neue Brehm Bücherei (406), Wittenburg Lutherstadt.

Schmitt, C. G. & Schmitt, D. C. 1990. First record of the White-tailed Nightjar *Caprimulgus cayennensis* in Ecuador. *Bull. Brit. Orn. Club* 110: 139-140.

Schodde, R. 1977. *Survey of the birds of southern Bougainville Island, Papua New Guinea*. CSIRO, Australia.

— & Hitchcock, W. B. 1968. Contributions to Papuasian

ornithology 1. Report on the birds of the Lake Kutubu area, Territory of Papua and New Guinea. Division of Wildlife Research Techn. Paper No. 13. CSIRO. Australia.

— & Mason, I. J. 1981. *Nocturnal Birds of Australia.* Lansdowne, Melbourne.

— & — 1997. Aves (Columbidae to Coraciidae). In Houston, W. W. K. & Wells, A. (eds.) *Zoological Catalogue of Australia* Vol. 37.2. CSIRO, Australia.

Schönwetter, M. 1964. *Handbuch der Oologie* (ed. W. Meise) Lieferung 10: 631-640. Akademie-verlag, Berlin.

— 1966. *Handbuch der Oologie* (ed. W. Meise) Lieferung 11: 641-651. Akademie-verlag, Berlin.

Schulenberg, T. S., Allen, S. E., Stotz, D. F. & Wiedenfeld, D. A. 1984. Distributional records from the Cordillera Yanachaga, central Peru. *Gerfaut* 74: 57-70.

— & Remsen, J. V. 1982. Eleven bird species new to Bolivia. *Bull. Brit. Orn. Club* 102: 52-57.

Schwartz, P. 1968. Notes on two Neotropical nightjars *Caprimulgus anthonyi* and *Caprimulgus parvulus*. *Condor* 70: 223-227.

Sclater, P. L. 1861. List of a collection of birds made by the late Mr W. Osburn in Jamaica, with notes. *Proc. Zool. Soc. London* 1861: 69-82.

— 1866. Notes upon the American Caprimulgidae. *Proc. Zool. Soc. London* 1866: 123-145.

Selander, R. K. 1954. A systematic review of the Booming Nighthawks of western North America. *Condor* 56: 57-82.

— & Alvarez del Toro, M. 1955. A new race of Booming Nighthawk from southern Mexico. *Condor* 57: 144-147.

Serventy, D. L. 1936. Feeding methods of *Podargus*. *Emu* 36: 74-90.

Seutin, G. & Letzer, M. 1995. The Short-tailed Nighthawk is a tree nester. *J. Field Orn.* 66: 30-36.

Shaw, J. R. 1993. Are Pennant-winged Nightjars polygamous? *Honeyguide* 39: 56-59.

— 1997. More on nightjars drinking. *Honeyguide* 43: 106-107.

Shields, W. M. & Bildstein, K. L. 1979. Birds versus bats: behavioural interactions at a localized food source. *Ecology* 60: 468-474.

Shirihai, H. 1996. *The Birds of Israel.* Academic Press, London.

Short, L. L. 1975. A zoogeographic analysis of the South American chaco avifauna. *Bull. Amer. Mus. Nat. Hist.* 154: 165-352.

—, Horne, J. F. M. & Muringo-Gichuki, C. 1990. Annotated check-list of the birds of East Africa. *Proc. West. Found. Vert. Zool.* 4: 61-246.

Sibley, C. G. & Ahlquist, J. E. 1990. *Phylogeny and Classification of Birds: A Study in Molecular Evolution.* Yale University Press, New Haven and London.

—, & Monroe, B. L. 1988. A classification of the living birds of the world based on DNA-DNA hybridization studies. *Auk* 105: 409-423.

— & Monroe, B. L. 1990. *Distribution and Taxonomy of Birds of the World.* Yale University Press, New Haven and London.

— & — 1993. *A Supplement to Distribution and Taxonomy of Birds of the World.* Yale University Press, New Haven and London.

Sick, H. 1950. Contribuição ao conhecimento da ecologia de *Chordeiles rupestris*. *Revta. Bras. Biol.* 10: 295-306.

— 1953. The voice of the Grand Potoo. *Wilson Bull.* 65: 203.

— 1979. Notes on some Brazilian birds. *Bull. Brit. Orn. Club* 99: 115-120.

— 1985. *Ornitologia brasileira, uma introdução.* Editora Universidade de Brasília, Brasília.

— 1993. *Birds in Brazil – a natural history.* Princeton University Press, Princeton.

da Silva, J. M. C. 1995. Biogeographic analysis of the South American cerrado avifauna. *Steenstrupia* 21: 49-67.

Skutch, A. F. 1970. Life history of the Common Potoo. *Living Bird* 9: 265-280.

— 1972. Studies of tropical American birds. *Publ. Nutt. Orn. Club* 10.

— 1983. *Birds of Tropical America.* University of Texas Press, Austin.

Slud, P. 1960. The birds of Finca 'La Selva', Costa Rica: a tropical wet forest locality. *Bull. Amer. Mus. Nat. Hist.* 121: 53-148.

— 1964. The birds of Costa Rica: distribution and ecology. *Bull. Amer. Mus. Nat. Hist.* 128: 1-430.

— 1979. Calls of the Great Potoo. *Condor* 81: 322.

Smith, G. C., Hamley, B. J., Park, K. M. & Kehl, J. C. 1993. Home range of Plumed Frogmouths *Podargus ocellatus plumiferus* during the non-breeding season as shown by radio-tracking. *Emu* 94: 134-137.

—, de Baar, M., Kehl, J., Milledge, D. & Schodde, R. 1994. Notes on the foods of the Plumed Frogmouth *Podargus ocellatus plumiferus*. *Sunbird* 24: 91-93.

Smithe, F. B. 1975. *Naturalist's Color Guide.* American Museum of Natural History, New York.

Smythies, B. E. 1981. *The Birds of Borneo.* Third edition. Sabah Society and Malayan Nature Society, Kuala Lumpur.

Snow, B. K. 1979. The oilbirds of Los Tayos. *Wilson Bull.* 91: 457-461.

Snow, D. W. 1961. Natural history of the Oilbird in Trinidad, West Indies. Part 1. *Zoologica* 46: 27-50.

— 1962. Natural history of the Oilbird in Trinidad, West Indies. Part 2. *Zoologica* 47: 199-221.

— (ed.) 1978. *An Atlas of Speciation in African Non-passerine Birds.* British Museum (Natural History), London.

— & Perrins, C. M. (eds.) 1998. *The Birds of the Western Palearctic Conise Edition* Vol 1. Oxford University Press, Oxford.

Stafford, J. 1962. Nightjar enquiry 1957-1958. *Bird Study* 9: 104-115.

Stagg, A. 1992. Mountain Nightjar: a new breeding bird for Arabia. *Phoenix* 9: 5.

Stebbins, R. C. 1957. A further observation on torpidity in the Poorwill. *Condor* 59: 212.

Stephens, F. 1913. Nighthawk drinking. *Condor* 15: 184.

Stevenson, H. M., Eisenmann, E., Winegarner, C. & Karlin, A. 1983. Notes on Common and Antillean Nighthawks of the Florida Keys. *Auk* 100: 983-988.

Steyn, P. 1971. Notes on the breeding biology of the Freckled Nightjar. *Ostrich* 9 (Suppl.): 179-188.

— & Myburgh, N. J. 1975. Notes at a Fiery-necked Nightjar's nest. *Ostrich* 46: 265-266.

Stiles, F. G. 1988. Notes on the distribution and status of certain birds in Costa Rica. *Condor* 90: 931-933.

— & Skutch, A. F. 1989. *A Guide to the Birds of Costa Rica.* Cornell, New York.

Stjenstedt, R. 1976. Nightjars: two further contributions. *Zambian Orn. Soc. Newsletter* 6: 128.

Storer, R. W. 1989. Notes on Paraguayan birds. *Occ. Pap. Mus. Zool. Univ. Mich.* 719: 1-21.

Straneck, R. & Johnson, A. 1990. *Nyctibius aethereus* (Wied 1820) nueva especie para la Republica Argentina (Aves, Nyctibiidae). *Nótulas Faunisticas* 23: 1-3.

—, Ridgely, R., Rumboll, M. & Herrera, J. 1987. El nido del Atajacaminos castaño *Lurocalis nattereri* (Temminck) (Aves, Caprimulgidae). *Mus. Arg. Cien. Nat. Bernardino Rivadavia* 4(17): 133-136.

— & Viñas, M. J. 1994. Some comments on the habits and the acoustic behaviour of the Sickle-winged Nightjar *Eleothreptus anomalus* (Gould 1838) (Aves, Caprimulgidae). *Nótulas Faunisticas* 67: 1-4.

Straube, F. C. 1990. Notas sobre a distribuicão de *Eleothreptus anomalus* (Gould 1837) e *Caprimulgus longirostris longirostris* (Bonaparte 1825) no Brazil (Aves: Caprimulgidae). *Acta. Biol. Leopoldensia* 12: 301-312.

Stresemann, E. 1931. Vorläufiges über die ornithologischen Ergebnisse der Expedition Heinrich 1930-1931. *Orn. Monatsber.* 39: 102-105.

— 1937. Die Gattung *Batrachostomus. Mitt. Zool. Mus. Berlin* 22: 304-329.

— & Stresemann, V. 1966. Die Mauser der Vögel. *J. Orn.* 107 (sonderheft).

Stuart-Rowley, J. 1984. Breeding records of land birds in Oaxaca, Mexico. *Proc. West. Found. Vert. Zool.* 2: 76-221.

Sugathan, R. 1981. A survey of the Ceylon Frogmouth (*Batrachostomus moniliger*) habitat in the Western Ghats of India. *J. Bombay Nat. Hist. Soc.* 78: 309-315.

Sutherland, C. A. 1963. Notes on the behaviour of Common Nighthawks in Florida. The *Living Bird* 2: 31-38.

Sutton, G. M. 1941. The plumages and molt of the young Eastern Whip-poor-will. *Occ. Pap. Mus. Zool. Univ. Mich.* 446: 1-6.

Swash, A. & Cleere, N. 1989. Identification of Egyptian and Nubian Nightjars. *Birding World* 2: 163-166.

Swenson, J. E. & Hendricks, P. 1983. Chick movements in Common Poorwills. *Wilson Bull.* 95: 309-310.

Symens, P., Newton, S. F., Winkler, H. & Stagg, A. J. 1994. Mountain Nightjar *Caprimulgus poliocephalus* in Arabia: identification, status and distribution. *Sandgrouse* 14: 81-92.

Tano, J. 1996. More new records from Ambua, and a further sighting of a mystery bird. *Muruk* 8: 37.

Tarr, H. E. 1985. Notes on nesting Tawny Frogmouths *Podargus strigoides. Austral. Birdwatcher* 11: 62-63.

Tate, D. P. 1994. Observations on nesting behaviour of the Common Potoo in Venezuela. *J. Field Orn.* 65: 447-452.

Teixeira, D. M., Nacinovic, J. B. & Tavares, M. S. 1986. Notes on some birds of northeastern Brazil. *Bull. Brit. Orn. Club* 106: 70-74.

Thewlis, R. M., Duckworth, J. W., Anderson, G. Q. A., Dvorak, M., Evans, T. D., Nemeth, E., Timmins, R. J. & Wilkinson, R. J. 1995. Ornithological records from Laos 1992-1993. *Forktail* 11: 47-100.

Thomas, D. W., Brigham, R. M. & Lapierre, H. 1996. Field metabolic rates and body mass changes in Common Poorwills (*Phalaenoptilus nuttallii*: Caprimulgidae).

Ecoscience 3: 70-74.

Thompson, P. M., Harvey, W. G., Johnson, D. L., Millin, D. J., Rashid, S. M. A., Scott, D. A., Stanford, C. & Woolner, J. D. 1993. Recent notable bird records from Bangladesh. *Forktail* 9: 12-44.

Thomson, A. L. (ed.) 1964. *A New Dictionary of Birds.* British Ornithologists' Union, London.

Thornburg, F. 1953. Another hibernating Poorwill. *Condor* 55: 274.

Thurber, W. A. & Serrano, J. F. 1987. Status of uncommon and previously unreported birds of El Salvador. *Proc. West. Found. Vert. Zool.* 3: 109-293.

Todd, L.D., Poulin, R. G. & Brigham, R. M. 1998. Diet of Common Nighthawks (*Chordeiles minor*: Caprimulgidae) relative to prey abundance. *Am. Midl. Nat.* 139: 20-28.

Todd, W. E. C. 1920. Descriptions of apparently new South American birds. *Proc. Biol. Soc. Wash.* 33: 71-75.

— 1937. New South American birds. *Ann. Carnegie Mus.* 25: 243-255.

— & Carriker, M. A. 1922. The birds of the Santa Marta region of Colombia. *Ann. Carnegie Mus.* 14: 3-611.

Tolhurst, L. P. 1993. Nesting observations on Papuan Frogmouth *Podargus papuensis. Muruk* 6: 6-9.

Tomas, F. J. 1991. Reactivation of interrupted moult by a Red-necked Nightjar *Caprimulgus ruficollis* in Catalonia (N E Spain). *Butll. G.C.A.* 8: 29-31.

Tomkins, I. R. 1942. The "injury-feigning" behaviour of the Florida Nighthawk. *Wilson Bull.* 54: 43-49.

Tostain, O., Dujardin, J-L., Érard, C. & Thiollay, J.-M. 1992. *Oiseaux de Guyane.* Société d'Etudes Ornithologiques, Muséum National d'Histoire Naturelle, Brunoy, France.

Traylor, M. A. 1958. Birds of northeastern Peru. *Fieldiana Zool.* 35: 87-141.

Tree, A. J. 1992. Pallid western race of the Mozambique Nightjar at Lake Manyame. *Honeyguide* 38: 125-126.

Tucker, G. M. & Heath, M. F. 1994. *Birds in Europe: their Conservation Status.* BirdLife International (BirdLife Conservation Series No.3), Cambridge.

Turner, D. A., Pearson, D. J. & Zimmerman, D. A. 1991. Taxonomic notes on some East African birds. Part 1. Non-passerines. *Scopus* 14: 84-91.

Tye, A. 1984. Long-tailed Nightjar drinking in flight. *Malimbus* 6: 4.

Tyler, D. 1992. Rufous-cheeked Nightjar in Robertson. *Promerops* 203: 14.

Tyndale-Biscoe, R. M. 1981. Nightjar on table. *Honeyguide* 106: 31.

de Urioste, R. J. 1994. Estudio de la ecología y las interacciones competitivas entre *Caprimulgus* y con los quiropteros insectivoros de vuela rapido en Espiritu, Beni-Bolivia. Thesis, Universidad Mayor de San Andrés.

Vanderwerf, E. A. 1988. Observations on the nesting of the Great Potoo (*Nyctibius grandis*) in central Venezuela. *Condor* 90: 948-950.

van Someren, V. G. L. 1956. Days with birds: studies of habits of some East African birds. *Fieldiana Zool.* 38: 5-520.

van Tyne, J. 1935. The birds of northern Petén, Guatemala. *Univ. Mich. Mus. Zool. Misc. Publ.* 27: 6-46.

Vaurie, C. 1960a. Systematic notes on Palearctic birds, no. 39: Caprimulgidae: a new species of *Caprimulgus. Amer. Mus. Novit.* 1985.

— 1960b. Systematic notes on Palearctic birds, no. 40: Caprimulgidae. *Amer. Mus. Novit.* 1997.

Vernon, C. J. & Dean, W. R. J. 1988. Further African bird-mammal feeding associations. *Ostrich* 59: 38-39.

Vilella, F. J. 1989. The reproductive ecology and population biology of the Puerto Rican Nightjar. Ph.D. dissertation, Louisiana State University.

— 1995. Reproductive ecology and behaviour of the Puerto Rican Nightjar *Caprimulgus noctitherus. Bird Conserv. Internatn.* 5: 349-366.

— & Zwank, P. J. 1987. Density and distribution of the Puerto Rican Nightjar in the Guayanilla Hills. *Carib. J. Sci.* 23: 238-242.

— & — 1988. Red data bird: Puerto Rican Nightjar. *World Birdwatch* 10: 9.

— & — 1993a. Ecology of the Small Indian Mongoose in a coastal dry forest of Puerto Rico where sympatric with the Puerto Rican Nightjar. *Carib. J. Sci.* 29: 24-29.

— & — 1993b. Geographic distribution and abundance of the Puerto Rican Nightjar. *J. Field Orn.* 64: 223-238.

Voous, K. H. 1961. Birds collected by Carl Lumholtz in eastern and central Borneo. *Nytt Mag. Zool.* 10: 127-180.

— 1965. Checklist of the birds of Aruba, Curaçao and Bonaire. *Ardea* 53: 14-234.

Wahlberg, N. 1990. Barred Owlet-nightjar *Aegotheles cristatus* at The King Bird Tree. *Muruk* 4: 111.

Walker, T. 1969. Nightjar calls. *Honeyguide* 60: 27.

Wang, K., Kalcounis, M. C., Bender, D. J., Gummer, D. L. & Brigham, R. M. 1995. Predation on free-ranging Common Poorwills in Saskatchewan. *J. Field Orn.* 66: 400-403.

— & Brigham, R. M. 1997. Roost-site characteristics of Common Poorwills *Phalaenoptilus nuttalli,* in Saskatchewan. *Canadian Field-Naturalist.* 111 (4): 543-547.

Watling, D. 1983. Ornithological notes from Sulawesi. *Emu* 83: 247-261.

Webb, G. A. 1989. A note on the diet of the Australian Owlet-nightjar *Aegotheles cristatus. Corella* 13: 90-91.

Wedgewood, J. 1992. Common Nighthawks in Saskatoon. *Blue Jay* 50: 211-217.

Weller, M. W. 1958. Observations on the incubation behaviour of a Common Nighthawk. *Auk* 75: 48-59.

Wells, D. R. & Medway, Lord 1976. Taxonomic and faunistic notes on birds of the Malay Peninsula. *Bull. Brit. Orn. Club* 96: 20-34.

Welsh, C. W. 1933. Eggs of the Plumed Frogmouth. *Emu* 32: 193.

Westoll, T. S. & Stoddart, D. R. 1971. A discussion on the results of the Royal Society expedition to Aldabra 1967-1968. *Phil. Trans. Royal Soc. London* 226 (836): 472-475.

Wetmore, A. 1919. Description of a new Whip-poor-will from Puerto Rico. *Proc. Biol. Soc. Wash.* 32: 235-238.

— 1968. The birds of the Republic of Panama. *Smithsonian Misc. Coll.* 150(2).

— & Phelps, W. H. 1953. Notes on Rufous Goatsuckers of Venezuela. *Proc. Biol. Soc. Wash.* 60: 15-20.

— & Swales, B. H. 1931. The birds of Haiti and the Dominican Republic. *U.S. Natn. Mus. Bull.* 155.

Whistler, H. 1921. The call of Franklin's Nightjar (*Caprimulgus monticola*) Frankl. *J. Bombay Nat. Hist. Soc.* 24: 284.

— & Kinnear, N. B. 1935. The Vernay scientific survey of the Eastern Ghats (ornithological section) Part II. *J. Bombay Nat. Hist. Soc.* 38: 26-40.

White, C. M. N. & Bruce, M. D. 1986. *Birds of Wallacea (Sulawesi, the Moluccas and Lesser Sunda Islands).* B.O.U. Check-list No. 7, Tring, U.K.

Wilkinson, R., Dutson, G. & Sheldon, B. 1990. The avifauna of Barito Ulu, central Borneo. *ICBP Study Report* No. 48, International Council for Bird Preservation, Cambridge, U.K.

Wilson, N. & Wilson, V. G. 1994. Avifauna of the southern Kerio Valley with emphasis on the area around the Kenya Fluorspar Mine site, August 1989–July 1993. *Scopus* 18: 65-115.

Withers, P. C. 1977. Respiration, metabolism and heat exchange of euthermic and torpid poorwills and hummingbirds. *Physiol. Zool.* 50: 43-52.

Wood, K. A. 1995. A foraging observation of the White-throated Nightjar. *Wingspan* 5(4): 36-37.

Woods, R. S. 1924. Notes on the life history of the Texas Nighthawk. *Condor* 26: 3-6.

Woodell, S. R. J. & Newton, L. E. 1975. A Standard-winged Nightjar breeding in the forest zone of Ghana. *Nigerian Field* 40(4): 169-171.

Wright, J. A. 1984. Nightjars copulating on elevated perch. *Brit. Birds* 77: 568.

Zimmerman, D. A. 1957. Spotted-tailed Nightjar nesting in Veracruz, Mexico. *Condor* 59: 124-127.

— , Turner, D. A. & Pearson, D. J. 1996. *Birds of Kenya and Northern Tanzania.* Christopher Helm, London.

Zurowski, K. L. & Brigham, R. M. 1994. Does use of doubly labeled water in metabolic studies alter activity levels of Common Poorwills? *Wilson Bull.* 106: 412-414.

INDEX

Species are listed by their vernacular name (e.g. European Nightjar) and by their scientific name. Specific scientific names are followed by the generic name as used in the book (e.g. *europaeus, Caprimulgus*) and subspecific names are followed by both the specific and generic names (e.g. *unwini, Caprimulgus europaeus*). Numbers in *italic* type refer to the first page of the relevant systematic entry. Numbers in **bold** type refer to the colour plate numbers.

313

A Sound Guide to Nightjars and Related Nightbirds

Compiled by Richard Ranft

The British Library National Sound Archive

Consultant Nigel Cleere

A CD has been produced to complement
NIGHTJARS: A Guide to Nightjars and Related Nightbirds
by Nigel Cleere and Dave Nurney.

It contains the voices of 108 species of caprimulgids
– over 90% of all the known species, including many
published for the first time.

Available from leading booksellers and audio suppliers.

In case of difficulty in obtaining copies in the U.K. apply to Pica Press,
The Banks, Mountfield, Nr. Robertsbridge, East Sussex TN32 5JY

in the U.S.A. to Yale University Press,
P.O. Box 209040, New Haven, CT 06520-9040